13s

Certificate Mathematics 1

a course for standard grade and GCSE

Units M1 – M12

Modular Mathematics Organization

Heinemann Educational Books

Heinemann Educational Books Ltd
22 Bedford Square, London WC1B 3HH

LONDON EDINBURGH MELBOURNE AUCKLAND
HONG KONG SINGAPORE KUALA LUMPUR NEW DELHI
IBADAN NAIROBI JOHANNESBURG
PORTSMOUTH (NH) KINGSTON PORT OF SPAIN

ISBN 0 435 50933 0

First published 1979
Reprinted 1982, 1984, 1985

British Library Cataloguing in Publication Data

Modular Mathematics Organization
Certificate Mathematics Units M1–M12.
1. Mathematics – 1961–
I. Title
510 QA39.2

ISBN 0 435 50933 0

Photoset and printed in Malta
by Interprint Limited.

Acknowledgements

Acknowledgement is due to the following for permission to reproduce photographs on the pages indicated:

Barnabys Picture Library, pp. 99 (left) 190, 265; British Airways, p. 189; Bryant & May, p. 5; Chris Gilbert, pp. 32, 235, 271, 275, 321; Crown Copyright, National Railway Museum, York, p. 6; Lotus Cars Ltd., p. 19; P & O Steam Navigation Co., p. 135; Popperfoto, p. 30, Rainer Drechsler/David Redfern p. 3; Scottish Tourist Board, p. 99 (right)

PREFACE

Certificate Mathematics Book 1 is the second of three books which together form a comprehensive and highly adaptable bank of materials ideally suited for 14–16 year old students taking GCSE, Scottish Standard Grade, or other similar exams. The detailed contents of the course are listed on the back cover.

This book, like the others, is organized in the following way:

1. It is made up of self-contained *Units*. These are available in textbook form, as here, or as individual booklets.
2. Each Unit is divided into sections. The first sections are at *Basic Level* — these provide a core course suitable for the majority of students. The later sections are at *Continuation Level* and are suitable for those students taking courses such as GCSE or Standard Grade General and Credit Level.

The overall course is divided into *Certificate Arithmetic* and *Certificate Mathematics Books 1 and 2*. More able students would be expected to cope with all the Units and the Arithmetic and Mathematics books would run in parallel. An average student would certainly cover all the Arithmetic Units but might omit some of the more advanced Mathematics Units. Weaker students should attempt all the Arithmetic Units but might only tackle a limited number of Mathematics Units. The choice of topics in each case would depend on pupil ability and on the specific syllabus being followed.

This textbook includes answers to the Exercises and Progress Checks which occur within each Unit — these answers are not included in the individual Unit booklets.

To accompany the geometry material in Units M1, M2, M3, M5, M8, M9 and M12 there is a book of photocopiable worksheet masters — *Certificate Mathematics Worksheet Masters*.

There is also a companion volume of further questions to accompany this textbook — *Exercises for Certificate Mathematics Book 1*.

The members of the Modular Mathematics Organization responsible for writing these Units were A. A. Crawford, J. B. Elliot, J. G. Ferguson, J. K. Fergusson, H. S. Flockhart, J. N. Gillam, J. L. MacLachlan, D. Smart, D. M. Smith, and L. Stevenson.

CONTENTS

PREFACE iii

UNIT M1 Similarity

Basic Level A Similar figures — B Enlargement — C Reduction — D Drawing similar figures — E Similar triangles — F Unknown sides — G Different positions — H Progress check 1

Continuation Level I Practical problems — J Sides in proportion — K Areas — L Volume — M Progress check 21

Worksheets M1/1, M1/2, M1/3

UNIT M2 Vectors

Basic Level A Moving a triangle — B Describing translations — C Components — D A component game — E Negative components F Using negative components — G Another component game — H Arrow heads — I Labelling vectors — J Length of a vector — by measurement — K Length of a vector — by calculation — L 'Adding' vectors — M The sum of two vectors — N Negative of a vector — O Multiplication by a number — P Multiplication by a negative number Q Progress check 33

Continuation Level R Order of addition — S Adding three vectors — T Multiplication by a fraction — U Use of brackets — V Subtraction of vectors — W Vectors—without a grid — X Directed line segments — Y Vectors applied to geometry — Z Progress check 54

Worksheets M2/1, M2/2, M2/3

UNIT M3 Simple Equations and Inequations

Basic Level A True replacements — B Equation dominoes — C Solving equations — D Dividing both sides of an equation — E Multiplying both sides of an equation — F Two step equations — G More equations — H Equations with brackets — I Progress check 69

Continuation Level J Inequations — K Showing solutions on the number line — L Comparisons — M Solving inequations — N Beware of the minus — O (In)equations with fractions — P Setting up (in)equations — Q Changing the subject of a formula — R Progress check 84

Worksheet M3/1

UNIT M4 Solution of Right-angled Triangles

Basic Level A Similar triangles — B Height and shadow — C Tangent — D Tangent by drawing — E Tangent from tables — F Calculating angle sizes — G Calculating lengths of sides — H Sine — I Sine by drawing and from tables — J Sine from tables

— K Calculating sides — L Calculating angles — M Sine or tangent? — N Cosine — O Use of cosine — P Cosine used to find angles — Q Sine, cosine, or tangent? — R Progress check 99
Continuation Level S The hypotenuse — T Some problems — U Isosceles triangles — V Bearings — W Progress check 129

UNIT M5 Simple Functions and Their Graphs

Basic Level A The function machine — B Naming a function — C Applying the rule — D The *f*(*x*) notation — E Domain and range — F Progress check 139
Continuation Level G Real numbers — H Graphs of functions — I Finding the input — J Domain values — K Other names for functions — L Find the function — M The function game — N Progress check 147
Worksheets M5/1, M5/2, M5/3, M5/4, M5/5, M5/6

UNIT M6 Periodicity and the Sine Function

Basic Level A Repeating patterns — B Patterns in nature — C Going round in a circle — D How high? — E Round and round and round — F Sine graph — G Sines to angles — H Angles to sines — I Progress check 157
Continuation Level J Rotating arms — K Sign of the sine — L Extending the graph — M Related graphs — N Progress check 176

UNIT M7 Equations of Straight Lines

Basic Level A Gradient — B Finding gradients — C Negative gradients — D Parallel lines — E Drawing lines of given gradient — F Drawing lines on the coordinate plane — G Gradient of the sides of parallelograms and trapeziums — H Graph of $y = mx$ — I Graph of $y = mx + c$ — J Finding equations of straight lines — K Distance–time graphs — L More distance–time graphs — M Progress check 189
Continuation Level N Gradient formula — O Gradients of lines parallel to the axes — P Distance formula — Q The equation $y = mx + c$ — R The equation $ax + by = c$ — S Drawing the graph of $ax + by = c$ — T Drawing the graph of $y = mx + c$ — U Progress check 216

UNIT M8 Quadratic Functions and Their Graphs

Basic Level A Functions — B Sets of numbers — C Straight line graphs — D Tables of values — E Curves — F The parabola — G $y = x^2 + k$ — H $y = -x^2 + k$ — I More tables of values — J Turning points — K $y = kx^2$ — L $y = x^2 + ax + b$ — M Progress check 229
Continuation Level N Calculating turning values — O Recognizing quadratic functions — P Solving quadratic equations graphically — Q Approximate solutions — R Problems — S Progress check 252

UNIT M9 Transformations

Basic Level A Translations — B Vector components — C Drawing images — D Translations using instruments — E Reflections — F Overlapping images — G Image in an axis — H Reflections using instruments — I Rotations — J Image under rotation — K Rotations using instruments — L Enlargement — M Dilation — N Scale factors less than 1 — O Dilations with centres other than the origin — P Dilatations using instruments 261

Continuation Level Q Translation: images using components — R Translations: the straight line — S Reflections: points reflected in the axis — T Lines reflected in the axis — U Points reflected in other lines — V Rotations—coordinates — W Halfturns—coordinates — X Dilatations: negative scale factor — Y Dilatations: negative scale factor using instruments — Z The centre of a dilatations — & Progress check 280

Worksheets M9/1, M9/2, M9/3, M9/4, M9/5, M9/6, M9/7, M9/8, M9/9, M9/10

UNIT M10 Simultaneous Equations and Inequations

Basic Level A Straight lines — B Testing for solutions — C Simultaneous equations—graphical solution — D Solving simultaneous equations — E The disappearing terms — F Eliminating the *x*s or the *y*s — G Different coefficients—opposite signs — H Different coefficients—same signs — I Progress check 297

Continuation Level J Regions of the plane — K Intersections — L Dividing the plane — M Shading a region — N Intersecting sets — O Solution regions — P Progress check 309

UNIT M11 Circles

Basic Level A Isosceles triangles in circles — B Angles at centre and circumference — C Angles at the circumference — D Angles in the same segment — E Angles in a semi-circle — F Cyclic quadrilaterals — G Symmetry in a circle — H Circumcircles — I Tangents — J Progress check 321

Continuation Level K Common tangents — L Tangent and chord — M Tangent kite — N In-circles — O Sectors of the circle — P The equation of a circle — Q Progress check 339

UNIT M12 The Cosine and Tangent Functions

Basic Level A Sine Function — B Cosine function — C Cosine of angles — D Find the angle — E Negative angles — F Tangent function — G Tangents of angles — H Angles greater than 360° — I Summary — J Progress check 353

Continuation Level K Combining graphs — L Graphical solutions of trigonometrical equations — M Progress check 373

Worksheets M12/1

ANSWERS

UNIT M1
Similarity

A Similar figures

Figures which have the **same shape** are said to be **similar**. (The figures do not need to be the same size.)

Here are four similar figures:

Figure 1 Figure 2 Figure 3 Figure 4

Masks

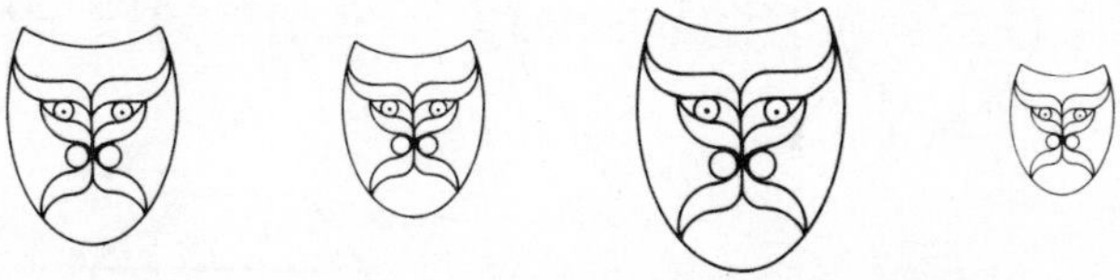

All four masks are **similar** to each other since they have the **same shape**.

See if you can decide which of the following masks is *not* similar to the others:

Figure 1 Figure 2 Figure 3 Figure 4

Masks

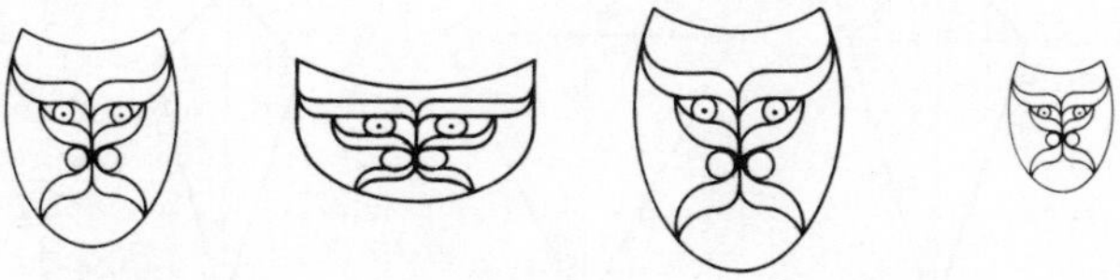

Of course, Figure 2 is the odd one out. It is **not similar** to the other masks since it has a **different shape**. All its features are out of proportion.

Exercise

'Odd One Out'

In each case, decide which of the figures is *not similar* to the others.

Figure 1 Figure 2 Figure 3 Figure 4

1 Coins

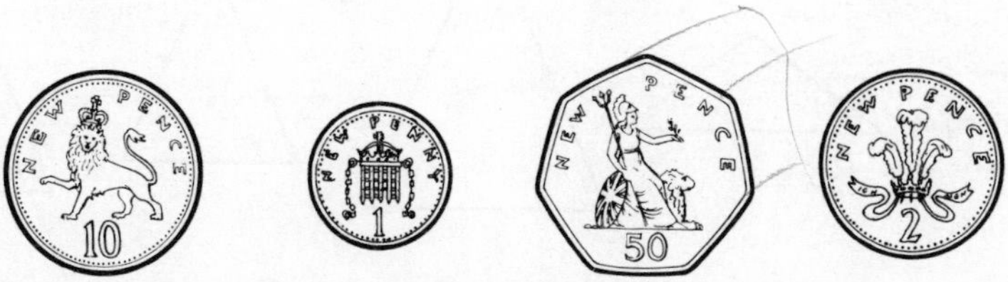

2 Candles

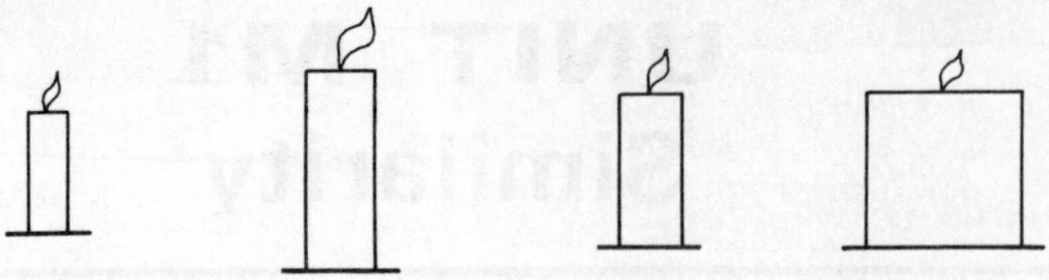

3 Clocks

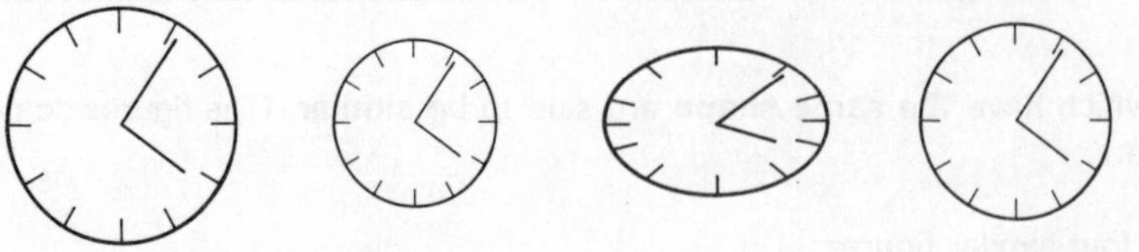

4 Balloons

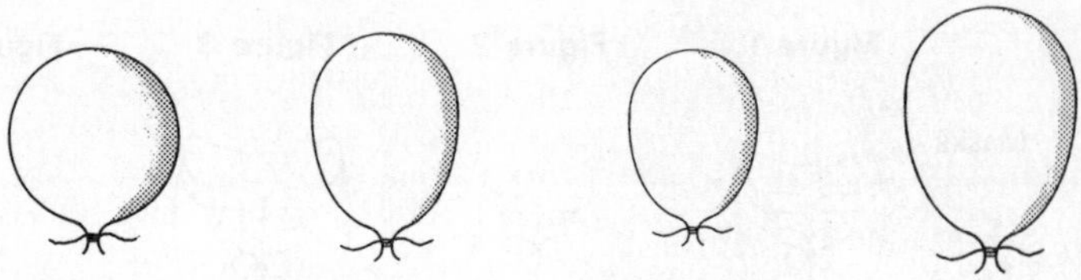

5 Houses

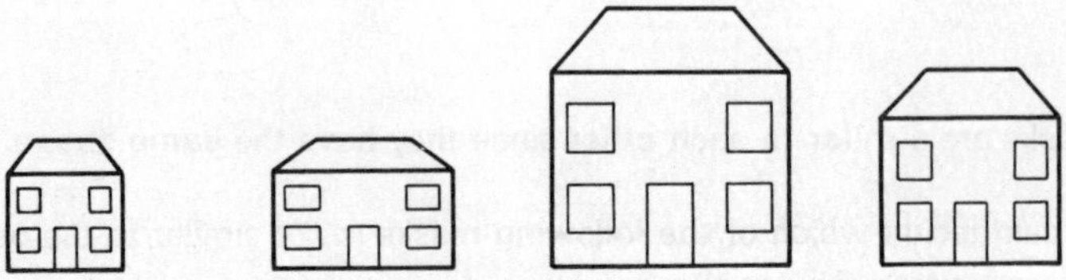

6 Kites

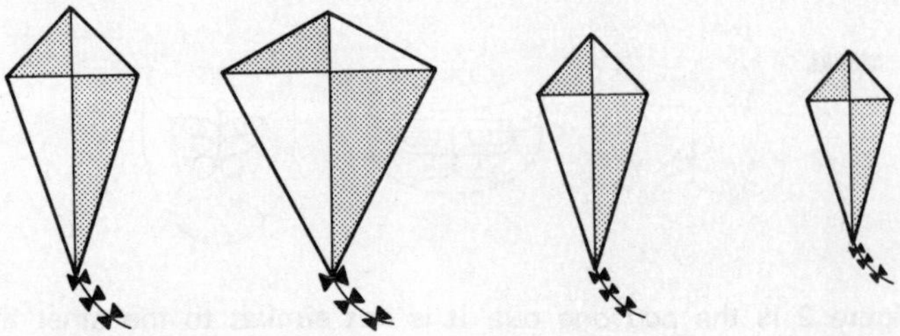

7 Letters

8 Triangles

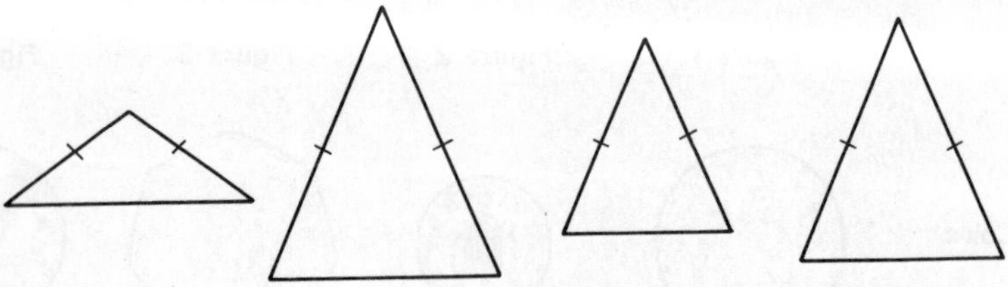

Figure 1 **Figure 2** **Figure 3** **Figure 4**

9 Cars

10 Rectangles

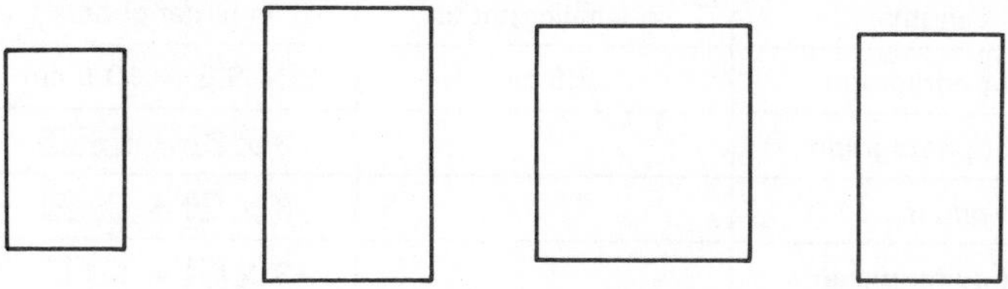

Continue with Section B

B Enlargement

Look at the two photographs.

The larger one is a **3 to 1 enlargement** (we write this as 3 : 1).

Every length in the larger photograph is *three times* the corresponding length in the smaller photograph. Check this for yourself.

Exercise

1 Copy and complete the following table:

Length	Measured distance in smaller photo	Calculated distance in larger photo	Measured distance in larger photo
Length of photograph	3.5 cm	$3 \times 3.5 = 10.5$ cm	10.5 cm
Breadth of photograph		$3 \times$ ▢ = ▢	
Length of guitar		$3 \times$ ▢ = ▢	
Height of guitar player		$3 \times$ ▢ = ▢	
Diameter of drum		$3 \times$ ▢ = ▢	

This enlargement number is usually called the **scale factor** and is denoted by the letter k.
In this example $k = 3$.

2 A photographer wishes to make a 3 : 1 enlargement of this picture.

Measure the length and breadth in centimetres.

Copy and complete the following sentences:

(a) The length of the picture is ▢ cm.

(b) The breadth of the picture is ▢ cm.
The scale factor $k = 3$.

(c) The length of the enlargement is

$3 \times$ ▢ = ▢ cm.

(d) The breadth of the enlargement is

▢ $\times$ ▢ = ▢ cm.

3 The dimensions of this kite have to be enlarged by a scale factor of 30 to give the size of the actual kite.
Measure the lengths of the cross pieces AB and CD and calculate their actual length.

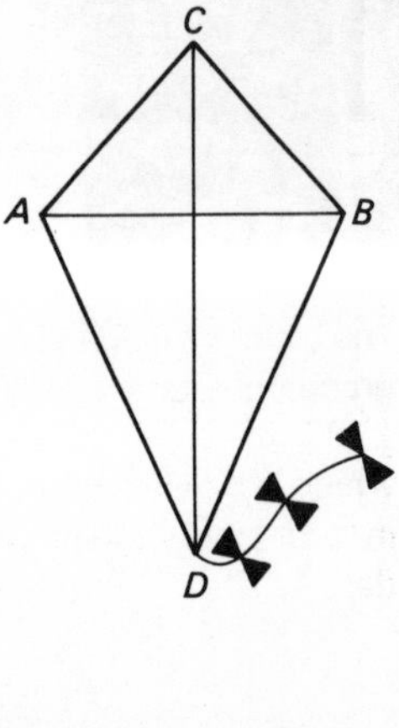

Copy and complete:

(a) Length of AB = ▢ cm.

(b) Length of CD = ▢ cm.
Scale factor $k = 30$

(c) Actual length of $AB = 30 \times$ ▢ cm.
= ▢ cm.

(d) Actual length of CD = ▢ $\times$ ▢ cm.
= ▢ cm.

4 The scale of this house plan is 1 : 150. Measure the diagram and calculate the actual dimensions of
(a) the lounge,
(b) the dining room,
(c) the kitchen.

PLAN OF GROUND FLOOR

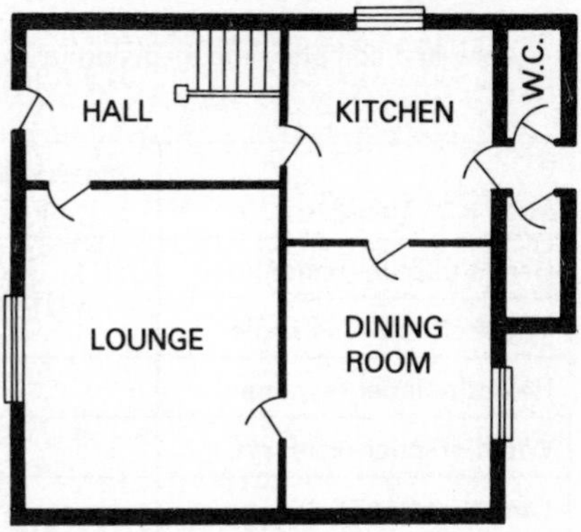

Note: In an **enlargement**, the scale factor k is always **greater** than 1.

Continue with Section C

C Reduction

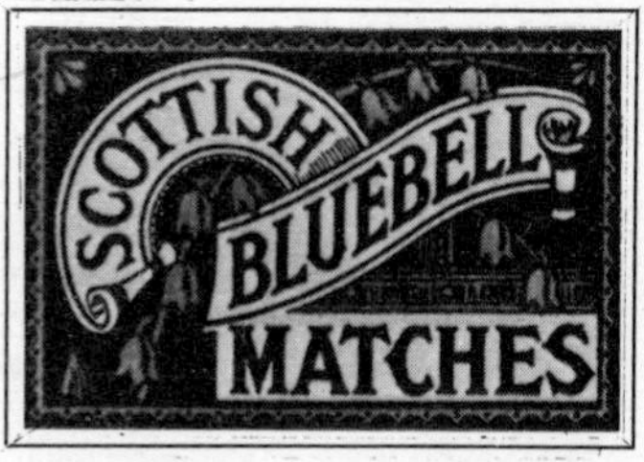

The artist's design above has been reduced by a photographic process in the ratio of 1 : 2 (scale factor $k = \frac{1}{2} = 0.5$). In this way a matchbox label has been made which is similar to the design but smaller. Every length in the label is half the corresponding length in the design. Check this for yourself.

Exercise

1 Copy and complete the following table:

Length	Measured distance on design	Calculated distance on label	Measured distance on label
Height of outer rectangle	6 cm	$0.5 \times 6 = 3$ cm	3 cm
Width of outer rectangle		$0.5 \times$ □ = □	
Height of inner rectangle		$0.5 \times$ □ = □	
Width of inner rectangle		$0.5 \times$ □ = □	
Length of 'MATCHES'		$0.5 \times$ □ = □	

2 Under a microscope which magnifies 10:1, an insect appears as shown in the picture.

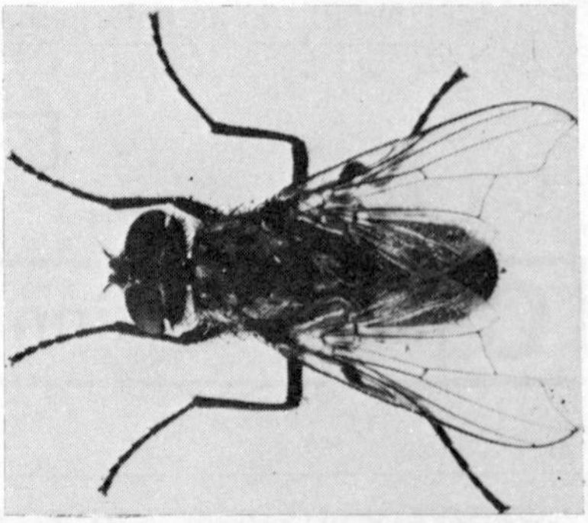

To find the actual wingspread and length, copy and complete the following:

Scale factor $k = \frac{1}{10} = 0.1$

Actual wingspread $= 0.1 \times 2.6 = 0.26$ cm $= 2.6$ mm

Actual length = □ × □ = □ cm = □ mm

3 A locomotive is 23 m long, 3 m wide, and 5 m high.

A model is to be made to the scale 1:200.

To find the size of the model, copy and complete the following:

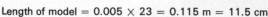

Scale factor $k = \frac{1}{200} = 0.005$

Length of model $= 0.005 \times 23 = 0.115$ m $= 11.5$ cm

Width of model = □ × □ = □ m = □ cm

Height of model = □ × □ = □ m = □ cm

4 (a) The lounge of a house is 18 m long and 12 m wide. A plan is drawn to a scale of 1:500.

To find the length and breadth of the lounge on the plan copy and complete the following:

Scale factor $k = \frac{1}{500} = 0.002$

Length on the plan = □ × □ = □ m = □ cm

Breadth on the plan = □ × □ = □ m = □ cm

(b) Find the length and breadth of the garage on the plan if its actual length and breadth are 8 metres and 4.5 metres respectively.

Note: In a **reduction**, the scale factor *k* is always **less** than 1.

Continue with Section D

D Drawing similar figures

Example

Enlarge the rectangle in the ratio 3:2. In an enlargement, $k > 1$.

Scale factor $k = \frac{3}{2} = 1.5$.

Length of enlargement $= 1.5 \times 8 = 12$ units.

Breadth of enlargement $= 1.5 \times 4 = 6$ units.

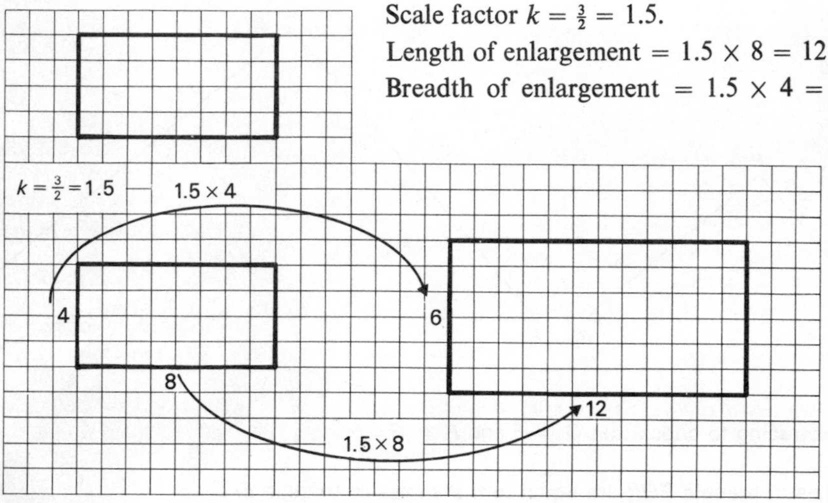

Example

Enlarge the house in the ratio 2:1. In an enlargement, $k > 1$.
Scale factor $k = \frac{2}{1} = 2$. Notice how the sloping line is enlarged.

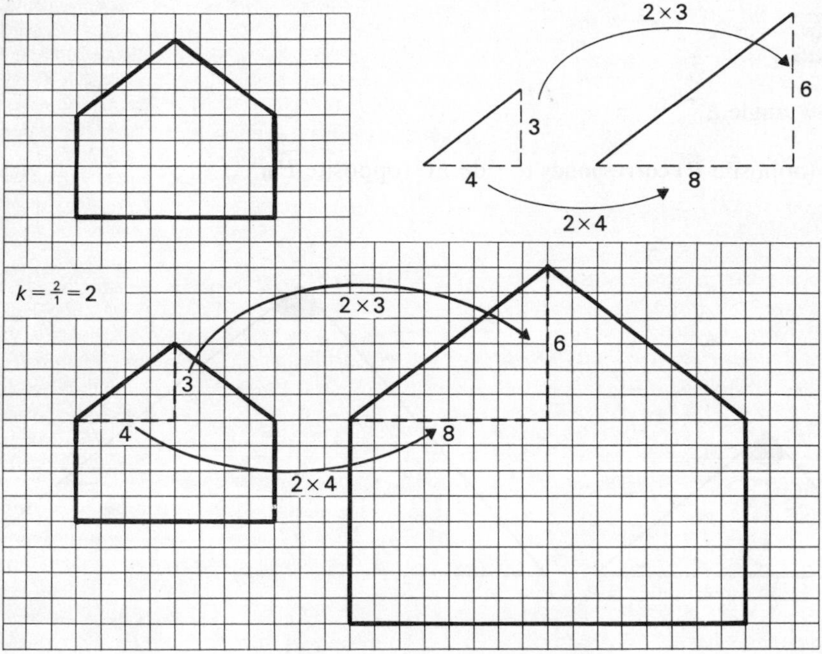

Continue with Sheet M1/1

E Similar triangles

Trace triangle *PQR* and find which of the angles is equal to $\hat{E}$ in triangle *EFG*.

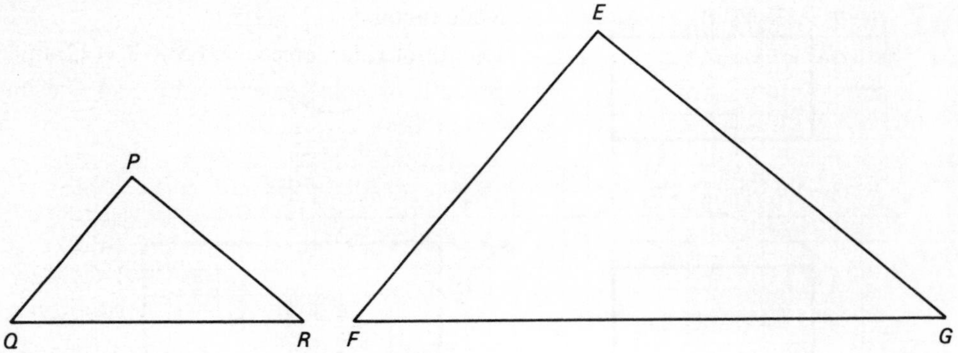

Use your tracing to check that $\hat{Q} = \hat{F}$ and $\hat{R} = \hat{G}$.

The angles of triangle *PQR* are equal to the angles of triangle *EFG*.

We say that the triangles are **equiangular**.

The sides opposite the equal angles are called **corresponding** sides.

Example

Angle P = angle E.

Side QR (opposite $\widehat{P}$) **corresponds** to side FG (opposite $\widehat{E}$).

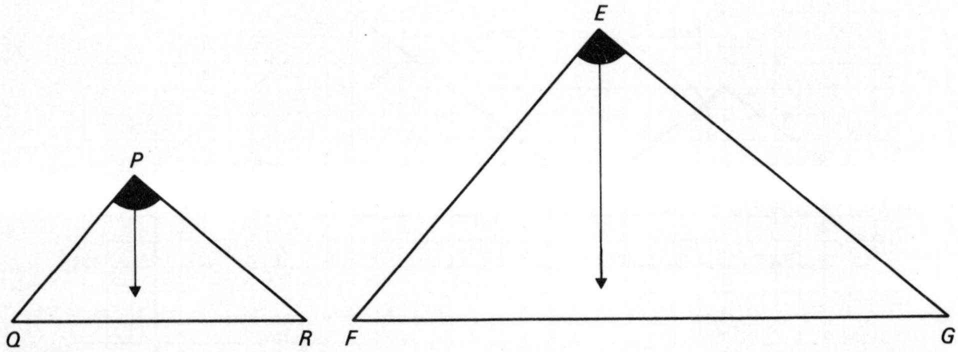

Exercise

1 Copy and complete:

Triangles *PQR* and *EFG* are similar.

(a) Angle Q = angle F.

Side *PR* (opposite $\widehat{Q}$) corresponds to side □ (opposite $\widehat{\square}$).

(b) Angle R = angle G.

Side *PQ* (opposite $\widehat{R}$) corresponds to side □ (opposite $\widehat{\square}$).

Measure the sides of triangles *PQR* and *EFG* in centimetres. Copy and complete the following table:

Triangle *PQR*	Triangle *EFG*	Ratio of corresponding sides
QR = 4 cm	*FG* = 8 cm	$\frac{FG}{QR} = \frac{8}{4} = 2$
PR = □ cm	*EG* = □ cm	$\frac{EG}{PR} = \frac{\square}{\square} = \square$
PQ = □ cm	*EF* = □ cm	$\frac{EF}{PQ} = \frac{\square}{\square} = \square$

Each side of triangle *EFG* is **twice** the length of the corresponding side of triangle *PQR*.

The scale factor is **2**.

Triangles *EFG* and *PQR* are **similar.**

2 Trace triangle *ABC* and check that triangles *ABC* and *LMN* are **equiangular.**

Copy and complete the following:

In triangles *ABC* and *LMN*

$\widehat{A} = \widehat{L}$

$\widehat{B} = \widehat{\square}$

$\widehat{C} = \widehat{\square}$

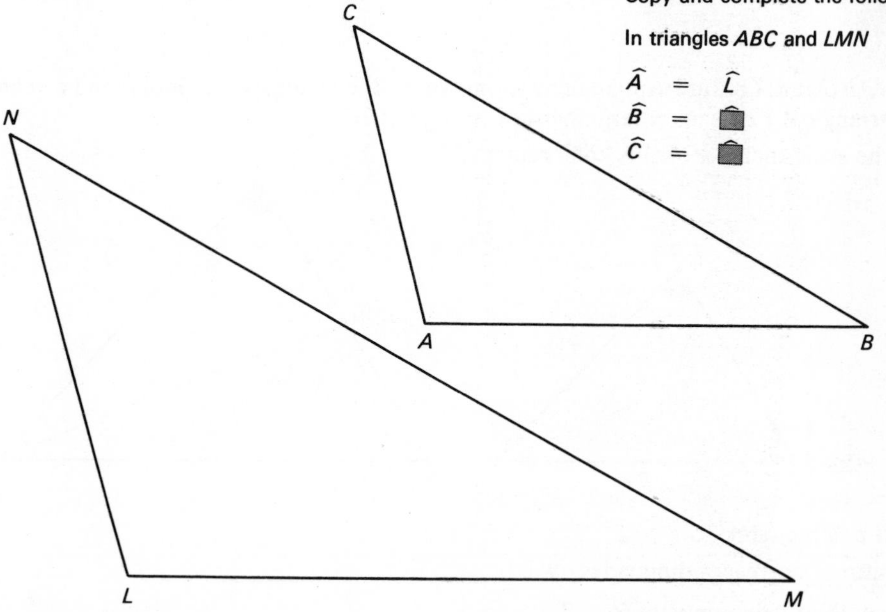

Side BC (opposite $\widehat{A}$) corresponds to side MN (opposite □).
Side □ (opposite $\widehat{B}$) corresponds to side □ (opposite □).
Side □ (opposite $\widehat{C}$) corresponds to side □ (opposite □).

Measure the lengths of the sides of the triangles ABC and LMN.
Copy and complete the following table:

Triangle ABC	Triangle LMN	Ratio of corresponding sides
$BC = 8$ cm	$MN =$ □ cm	$\frac{MN}{BC} = \frac{□}{8} =$ □
$AC =$ □ cm	$LN =$ □ cm	$\frac{LN}{AC} = \frac{□}{□} =$ □
$AB =$ □ cm	$LM =$ □ cm	$\frac{LM}{AB} = \frac{□}{□} =$ □

Each side of triangle LMN is □ times the corresponding side of triangle ABC.
The scale factor is □.
Triangles LMN and ABC are □.

If two triangles are **equiangular**, their corresponding sides are in proportion and the two triangles are said to be **similar**.

For two similar triangles the scale factor k can be found by calculating the ratio of **any pair** of corresponding sides. (Remember the corresponding sides are opposite the equal angles.)

Example

Triangles ABC and XYZ are equiangular as shown, so the triangles are similar and we can think of triangle XYZ as an enlargement of triangle ABC.
What is the scale factor k of this enlargement?

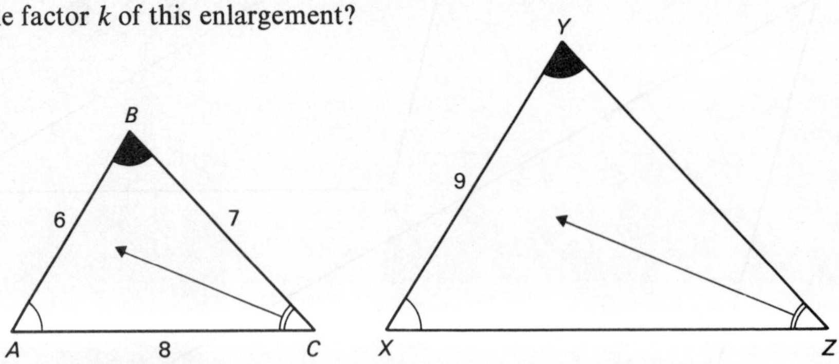

This is an enlargement, so $k > 1$.

$k =$ ratio of corresponding sides,

So $k = \dfrac{\text{length of side opposite } \widehat{Z}}{\text{length of side opposite } \widehat{C}} = \dfrac{9}{6} = 1.5$

Scale factor $k = 1.5$.

Example

Triangles *DEF* and *PQR* are equiangular as shown so the triangles are similar.
We can think of triangle *PQR* as a reduction of triangle *DEF*.
What is the scale factor *k* of this reduction?

This is a reduction, so $k < 1$.

$$k = \frac{\text{length of side opposite } \widehat{R}}{\text{length of side opposite } \widehat{F}} = \frac{4.2}{6.0} = 0.7$$

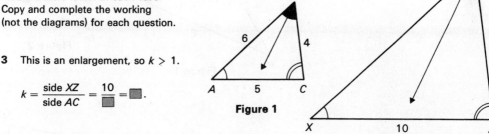

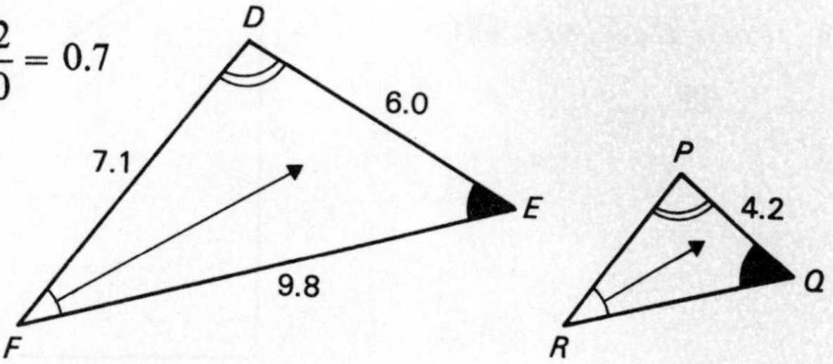

Scale factor $k = 0.7$.

Exercise

For each pair of equiangular triangles below,
decide whether the triangle in Fig. 2 is an enlargement
or a reduction of the triangle in Fig. 1.
Find the scale factor in each case.
Copy and complete the working
(not the diagrams) for each question.

3 This is an enlargement, so $k > 1$.

$$k = \frac{\text{side } XZ}{\text{side } AC} = \frac{10}{■} = ■.$$

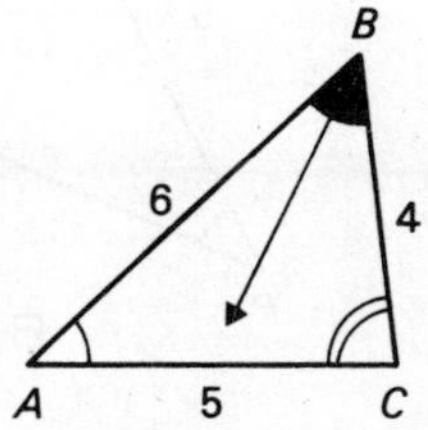

Figure 1

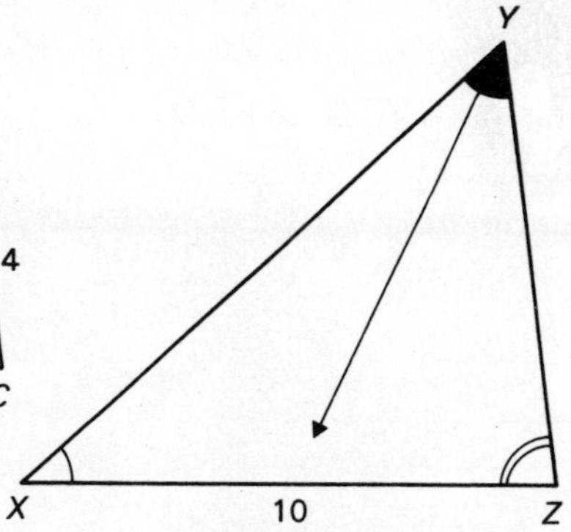

Figure 2

4 This is a reduction, so $k < 1$.

$$k = \frac{\text{side } TU}{■} = \frac{■}{■} = ■.$$

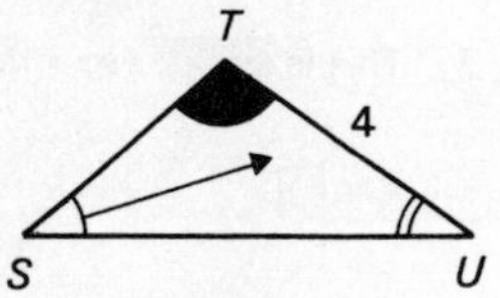

Figure 2

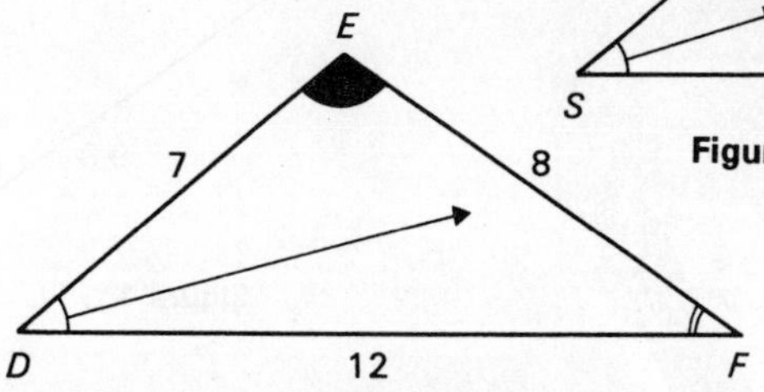

Figure 1

5 This is ___, so k ___ 1.

$k = \frac{\_\_\_}{\_\_\_} = \_\_\_$.

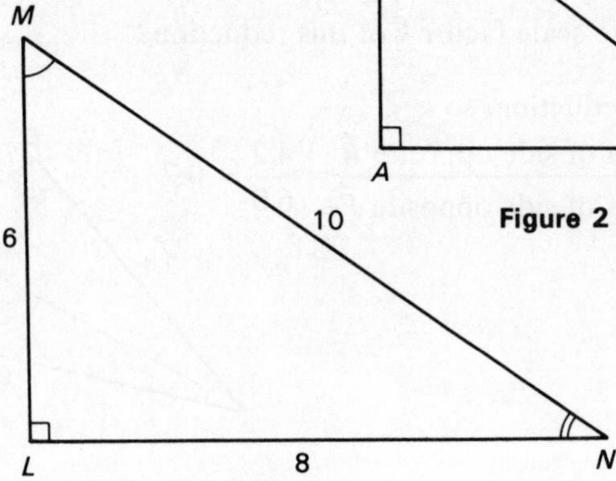

Figure 1

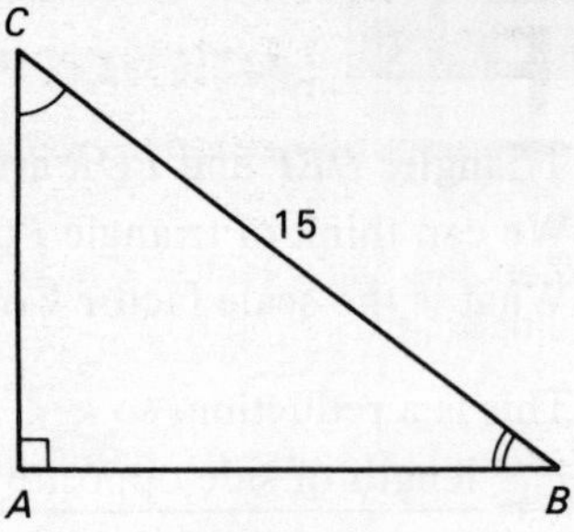

Figure 2

6 This is ___, so k ___ 1.

$k =$ ___.

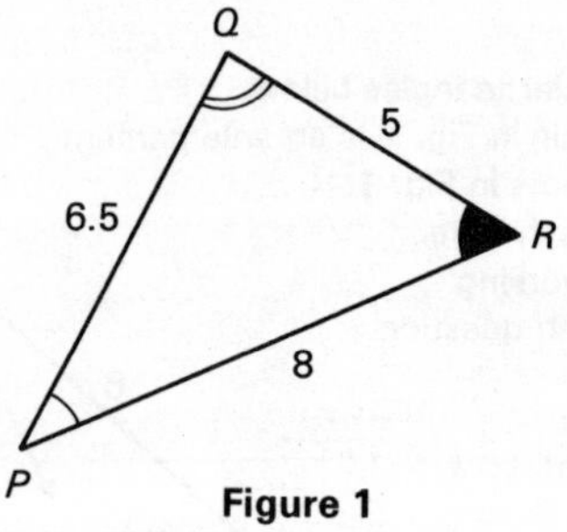

Figure 1

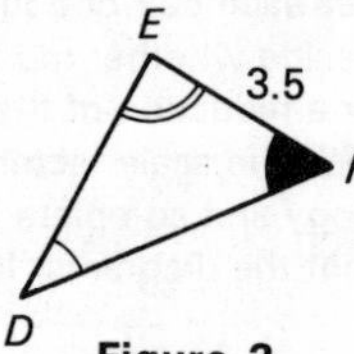

Figure 2

7 This is ___, so k ___ 1.

$k =$ ___.

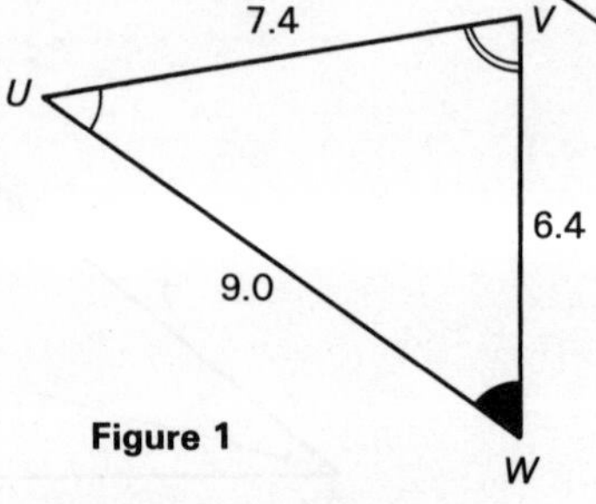

Figure 1

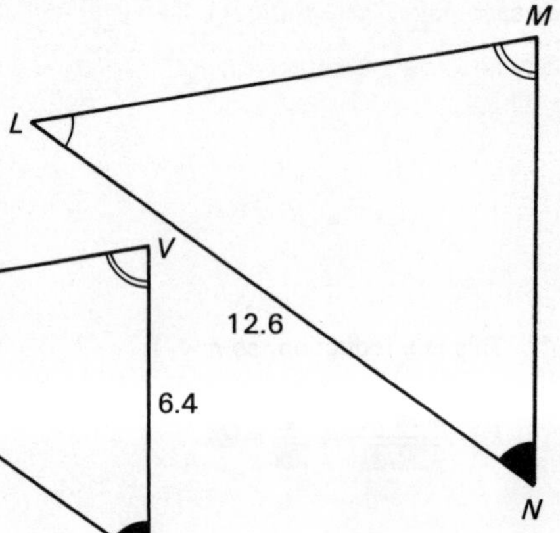

Figure 2

Continue with Section F

F Unknown sides

When the scale factor k is known, the lengths of the sides of one triangle can be found by multiplying the lengths of the corresponding sides of the other triangle by k.

Example

Calculate the lengths of the sides XY and YZ of triangle XYZ.

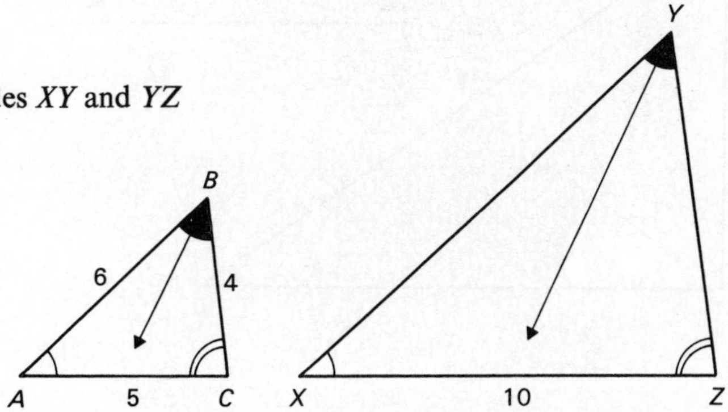

Step 1

Find k.

Triangle XYZ is an enlargement of triangle ABC. So $k = \frac{10}{5} = 2$.

Step 2

Each side of triangle XYZ is **twice** the corresponding side of triangle ABC.

$XY = 2 \times AB = 12$

and $YZ = 2 \times BC = 8$

Exercise

For each pair of equiangular triangles below, calculate the lengths of the unmarked sides.

Copy and complete the working (not the diagrams) for each question.

1

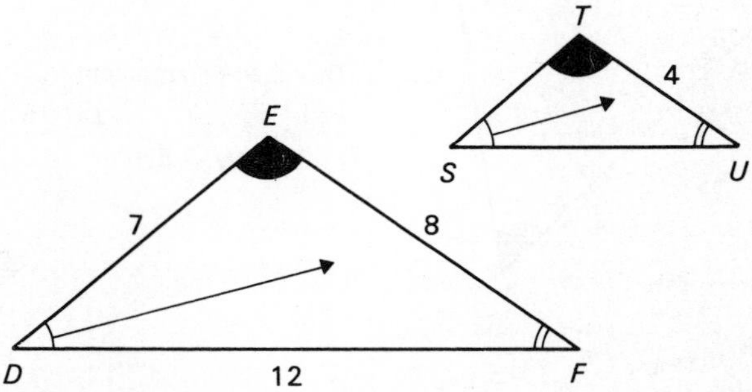

Triangle STU is a reduction of triangle DEF.

$k = \frac{4}{8} = 0.5$

$ST = 0.5 \times DE = 0.5 \times$ ▢

$= 3.5$

$US =$ ▢ $\times DF =$ ▢ $\times$ ▢

$=$ ▢

2

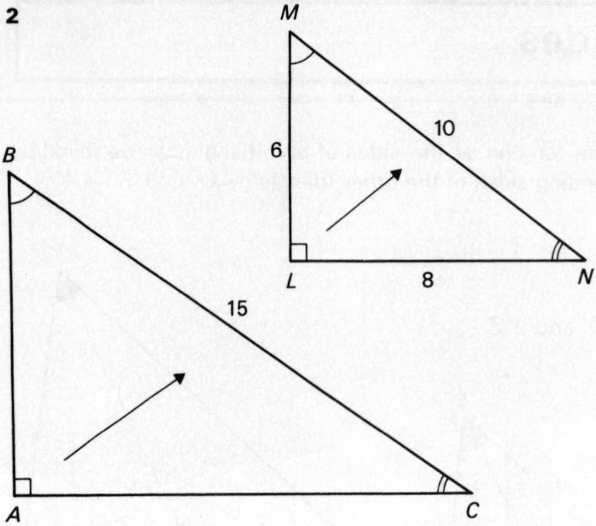

Triangle *ABC* is an enlargement of triangle *LMN*.

$k = \frac{15}{10} =$ ■, $AB =$ ■,

$CA =$ ■

3

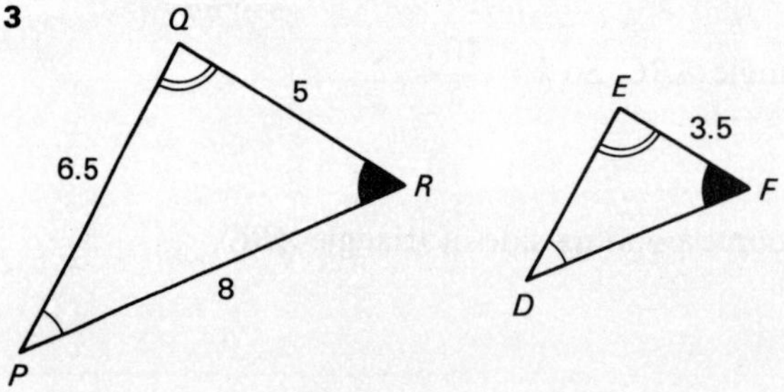

Triangle *DEF* is a reduction of triangle *PQR*.

$k =$ ■, $DE =$ ■,

$FD =$ ■

4

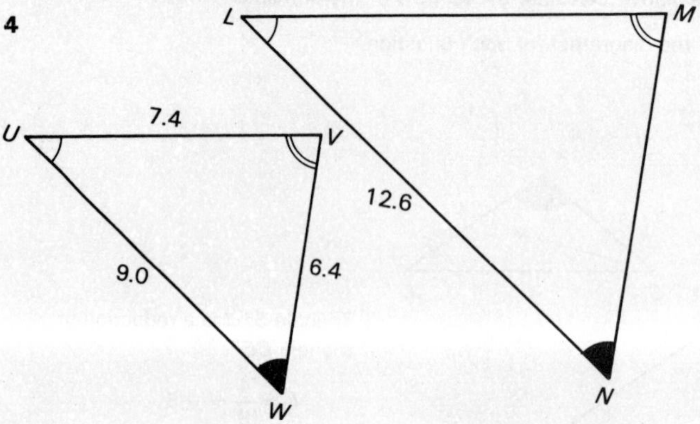

This is an enlargement.

$k =$ ■, $LM =$ ■,

$MN =$ ■

Continue with Section G

G Different positions

Similar triangles are not always found in the same position.

However the corresponding sides are **always** opposite the equal angles.

Example

Triangle XYZ is an enlargement of triangle ABC.
What is the scale factor k?

This is an enlargement, so $k > 1$.
k = ratio of corresponding sides.
XY is the side opposite $\hat{Z}$ and AB is the side opposite $\hat{C}$ and $\hat{Z} = \hat{C}$.

So $k = \frac{XY}{AB} = \frac{9}{6} = 1.5$

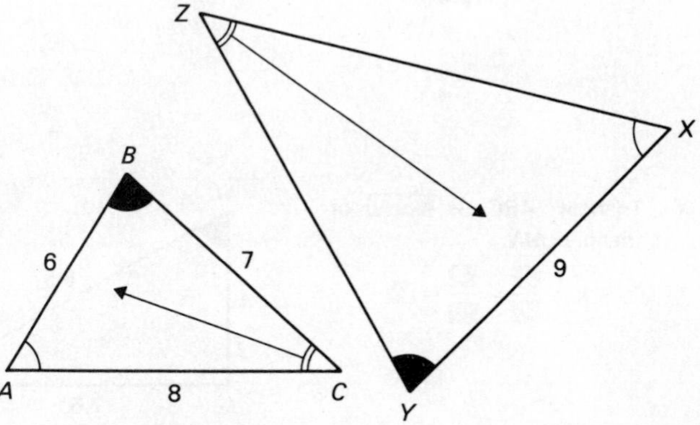

Scale factor $k = 1.5$

Exercise

For each pair of equiangular triangles below, decide whether the triangle in Fig. 2 is an enlargement or a reduction of the triangle in Fig. 1.

Calculate the scale factor k.
Copy and complete the working.

1 Triangle XYZ is ▭ of triangle ABC.

$k = \frac{YZ}{AC} = \frac{▭}{▭} = ▭$

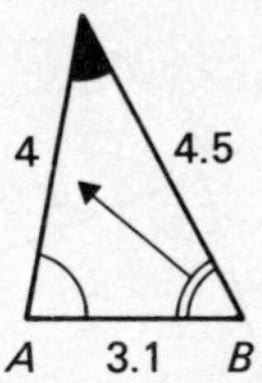

Figure 1

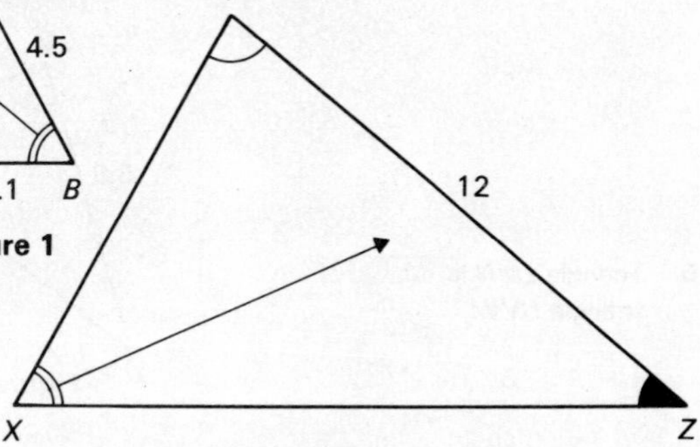

Figure 2

2

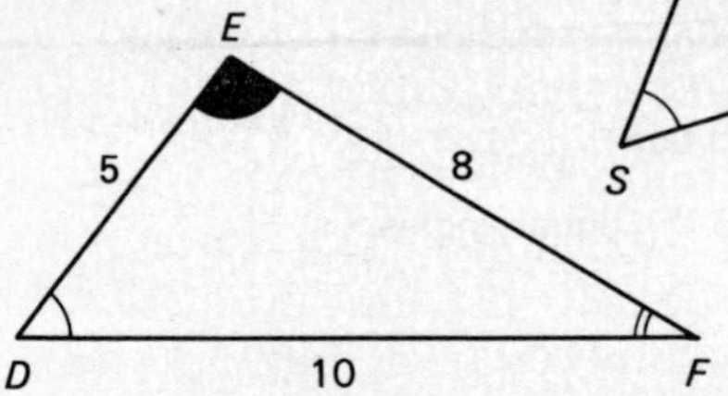

Figure 1

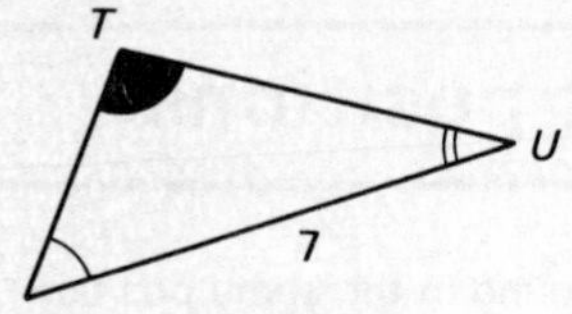

Figure 2

Triangle *STU* is ____ of triangle *DEF*.

$k = \frac{\square}{\square} = \frac{\square}{\square} = \square$

3 Triangle *ABC* is ____ of triangle *LMN*.

$k = \frac{\square}{\square} = \frac{\square}{\square} = \square$

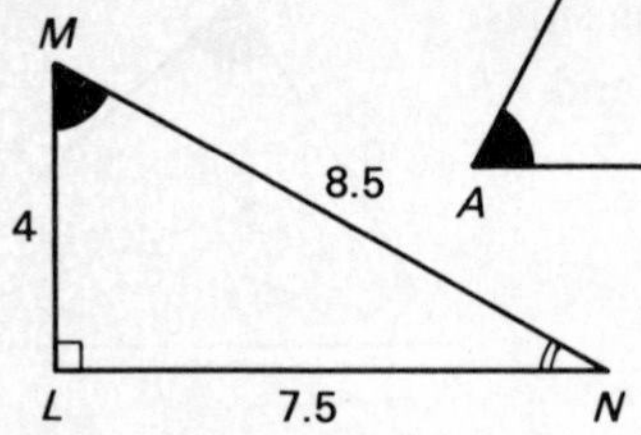

Figure 1

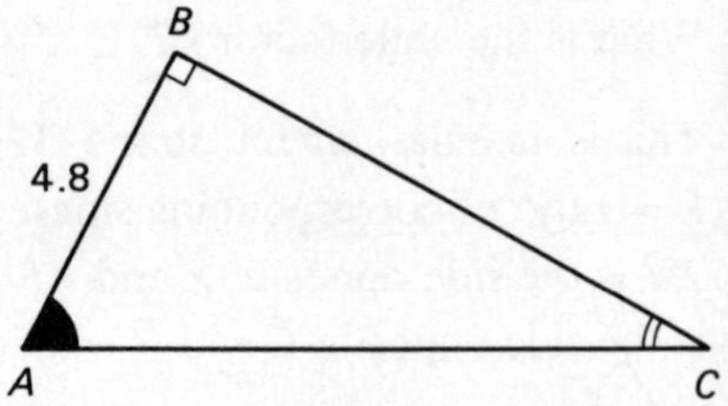

Figure 2

4

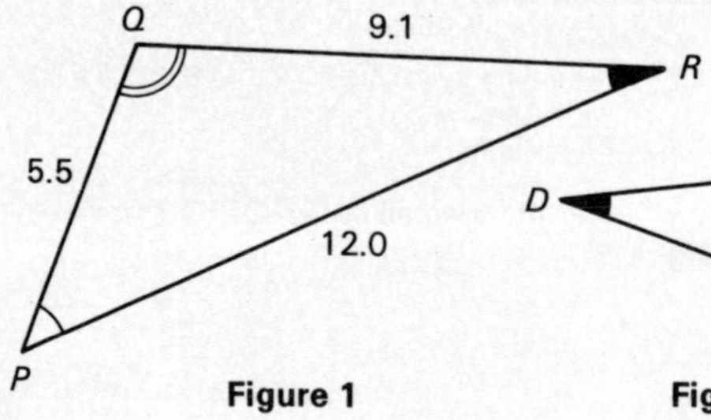

Figure 1

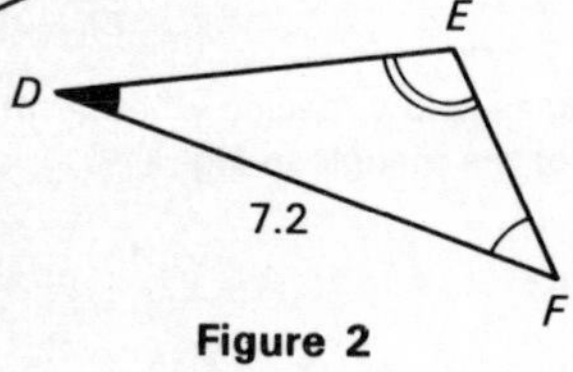

Figure 2

Triangle *DEF* is ____ of triangle *PQR*.

5 Triangle *LMN* is ____ of triangle *UVW*.

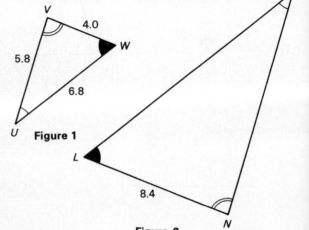

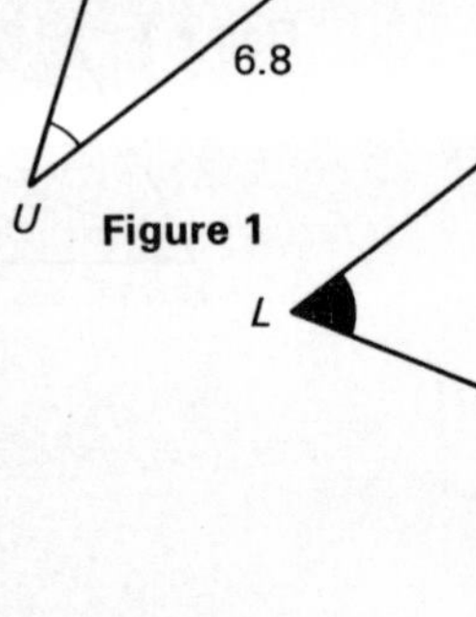

Figure 1

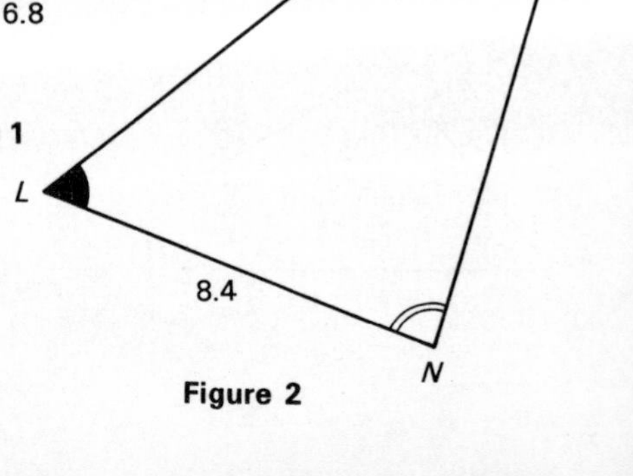

Figure 2

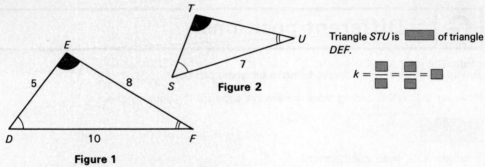

Example

Triangle *ABC* and triangle *XYZ* are similar triangles.
Find the lengths of the sides *XZ* and *YZ*.

Remember: The corresponding sides are opposite the equal angles.

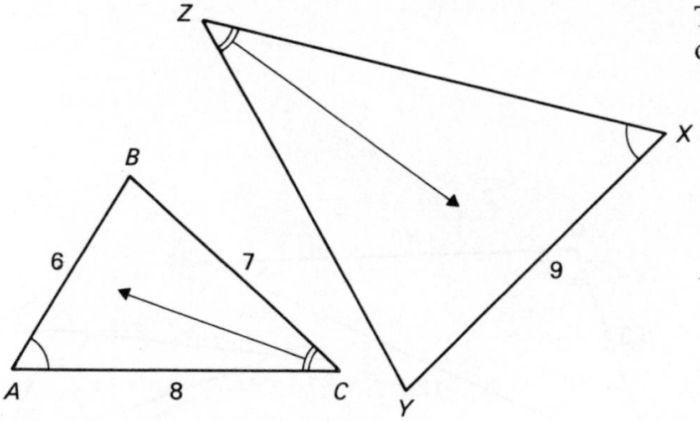

Triangle *XYZ* is an enlargement of triangle *ABC*.

$$k = \frac{XY}{AB} = \frac{9}{6} = 1.5$$

$$YZ = 1.5 \times 7 = 10.5$$

$$XZ = 1.5 \times 8 = 12.0$$

Exercise

For each pair of similar triangles, decide whether the triangle in Fig. 2 is an enlargement or a reduction of the triangle in Fig. 1.
Calculate the scale factor and find the lengths of the unmarked sides. Copy and complete the working.

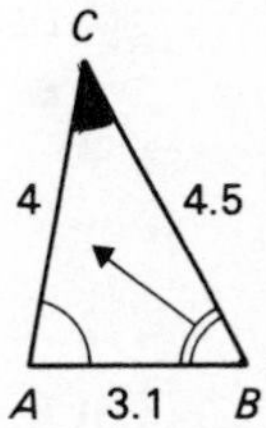

Figure 1

6 Triangle *XYZ* is an enlargement of triangle *ABC*.

$k = \frac{YZ}{AC} = \frac{12}{4} = 3$

$XY = 3 \times 3.1 =$ ■

$ZX =$ ■ $\times$ ■ $=$ ■

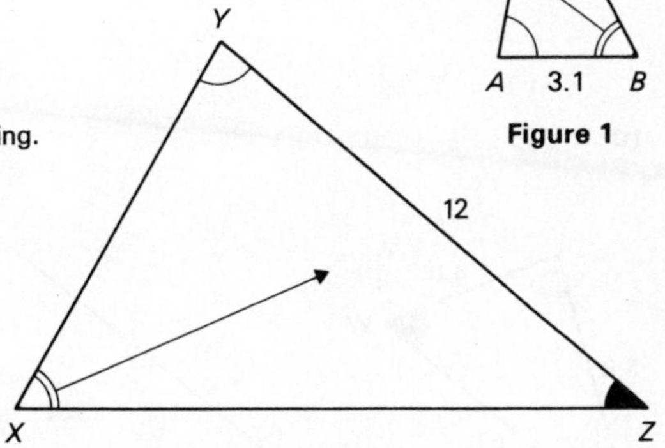

Figure 2

7

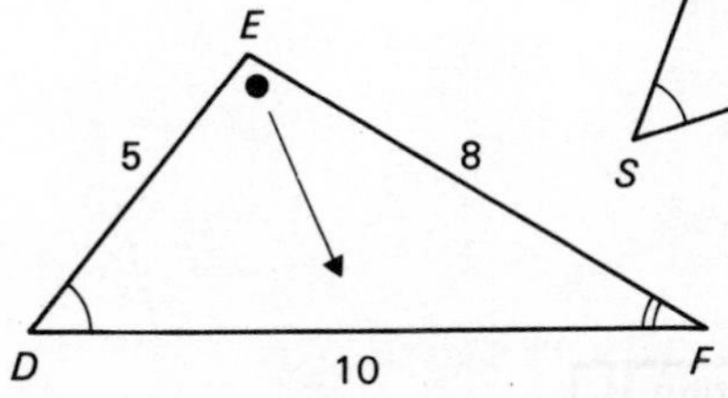

Figure 1

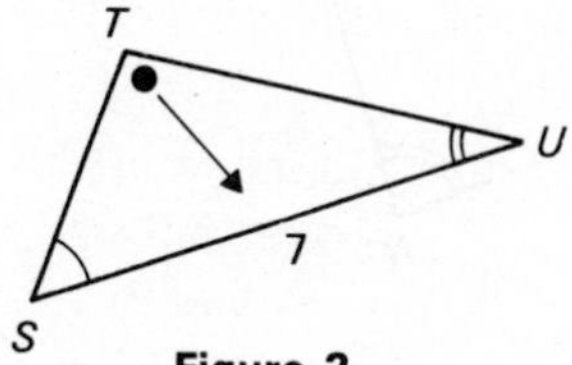

Figure 2

Triangle *STU* is ■ of triangle *DEF*.

$k = \frac{■}{■} = \frac{■}{■} =$ ■

$ST =$ ■ $\times$ ■ $=$ ■

$TU =$ ■ $\times$ ■ $=$ ■

8

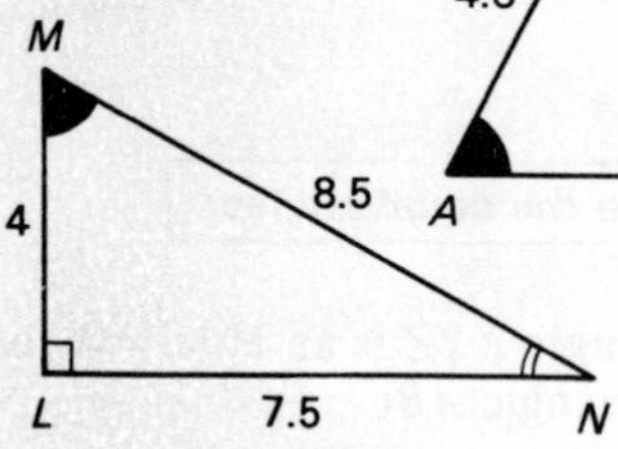

Figure 1

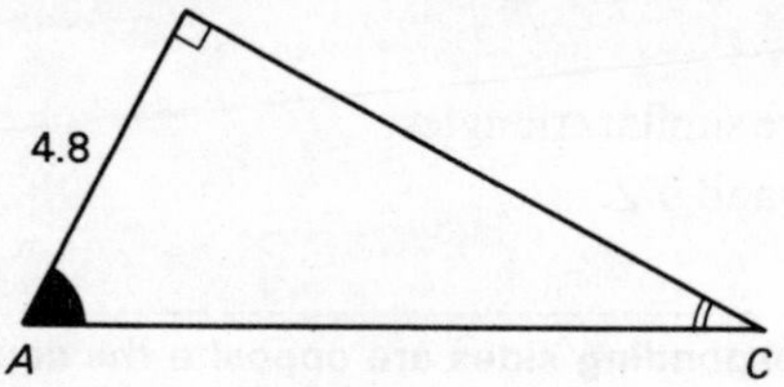

Figure 2

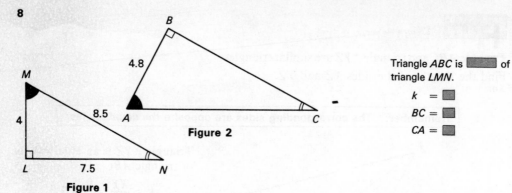

Triangle *ABC* is ___ of triangle *LMN*.

k = ___

BC = ___

CA = ___

9 Triangle *DEF* is ___ of triangle *PQR*.

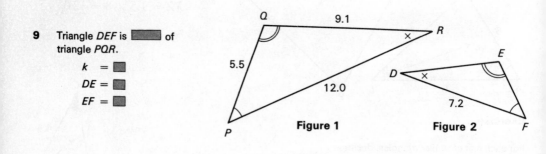

k = ___

DE = ___

EF = ___

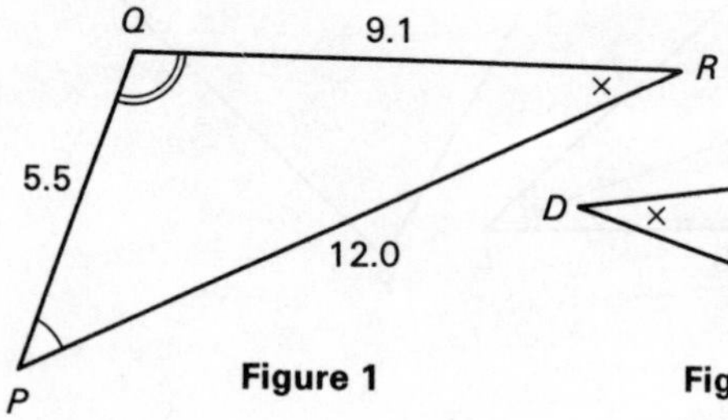

Figure 1

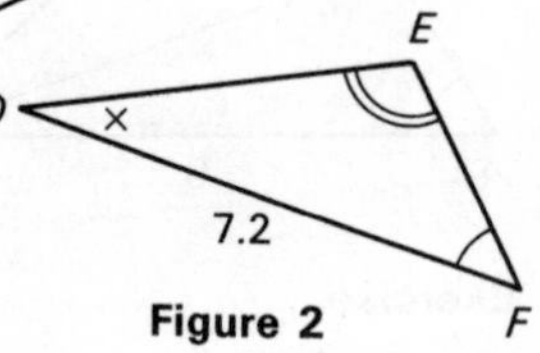

Figure 2

10

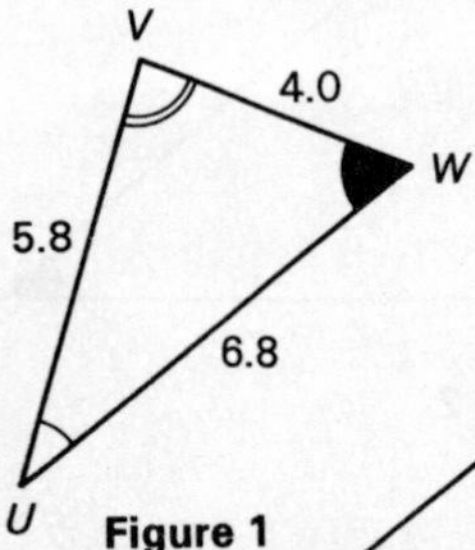

Figure 1

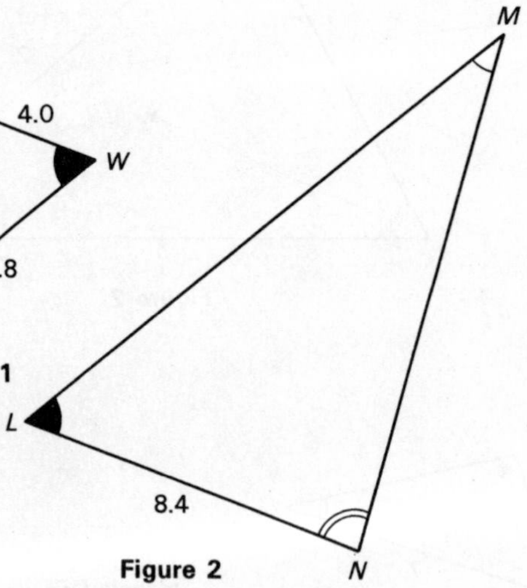

Figure 2

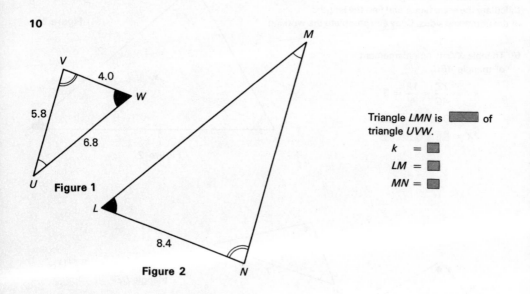

Triangle *LMN* is ___ of triangle *UVW*.

k = ___

LM = ___

MN = ___

Continue with Section H

H Progress check

Exercise

1 Which figure is *not* similar to the others?

Figure 1 **Figure 2** **Figure 3** **Figure 4**

2

An enlargement of 5 : 1 is to be made from this snapshot.

(a) What is the scale factor k?

(b) What will be the length of the enlargement?

(c) What will be the width of the enlargement?

3

A sports car is 4.8 m long, 1.4 m wide, and 1.2 m high.

A model of the sports car is made to the scale 1 : 50.

The scale factor $k = \frac{1}{50} = 0.02$.

(a) Calculate the **length** of the model in cm.

(b) Calculate the **width** of the model in cm.

(c) Calculate the **height** of the model in cm.

4 Using $\frac{1}{2}$ cm squared paper, copy this diagram and make an enlargement of the parallelogram in the ratio 3 : 2, that is using a scale factor of $\frac{3}{2}$ or 1.5.

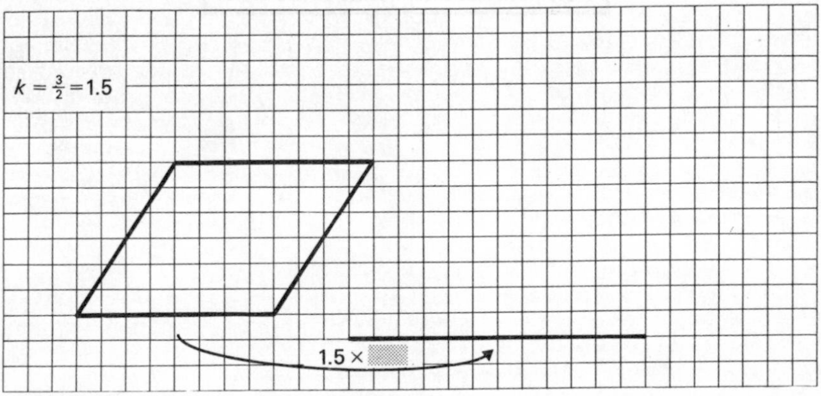

5 Calculate the value of the scale factor k and find the length of the unmarked sides.

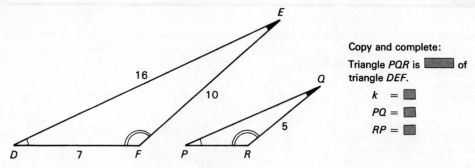

(a)

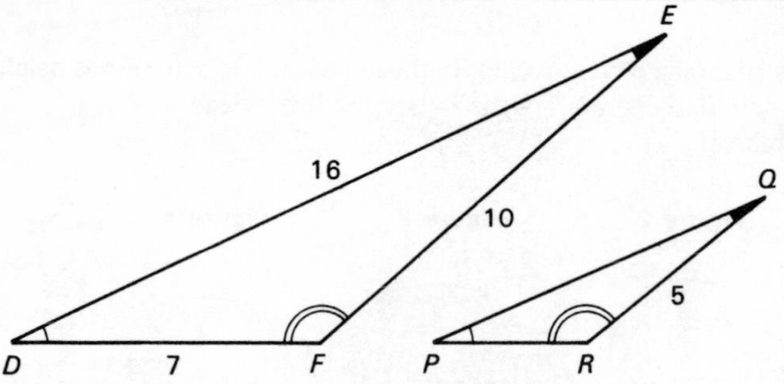

Copy and complete:

Triangle PQR is ____ of triangle DEF.

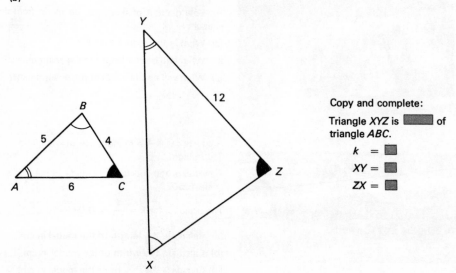

k = ____

PQ = ____

RP = ____

(b)

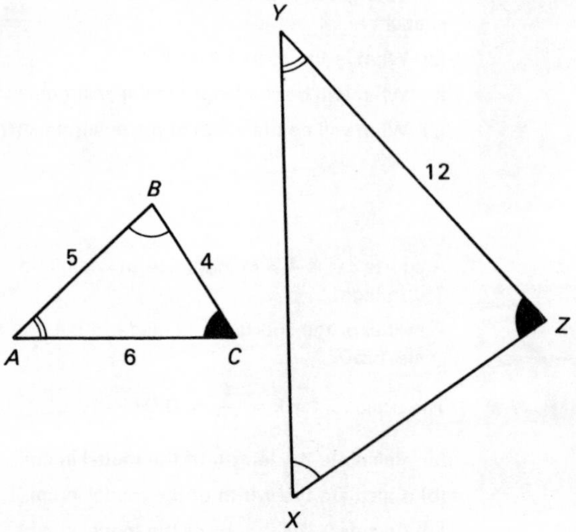

Copy and complete:

Triangle XYZ is ____ of triangle ABC.

k = ____

XY = ____

ZX = ____

Ask your teacher what to do next

I Practical problems

In practical problems, the similar triangles often overlap. In these cases, it is sometimes helpful to sketch the triangles apart to see clearly which are the corresponding sides.

Example

A man 2 metres tall standing 6 metres away from a lamp-post casts a shadow 3 metres long.

What is the height of the lamp-post?

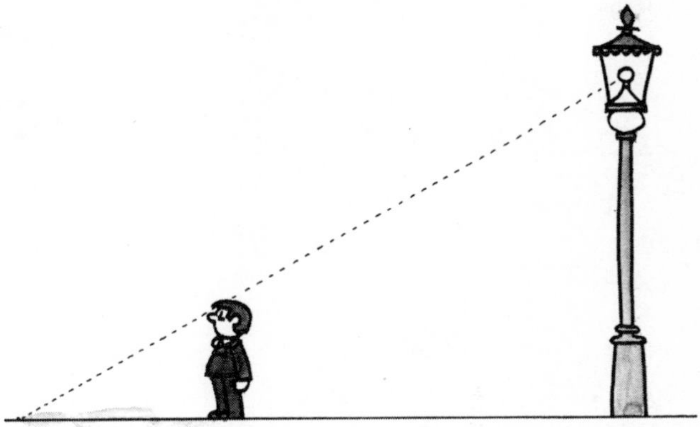

Step 1

Make a sketch **marking the known lengths and the equal angles.**

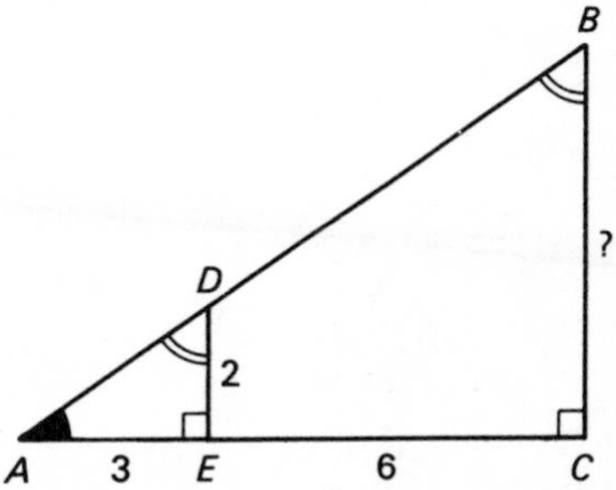

Step 2

Draw separate sketches of the triangles and calculate the scale factor.

$$k = \frac{9}{3} = 3$$

$$BC = 3 \times DE$$
$$= 3 \times 2$$
$$= 6$$

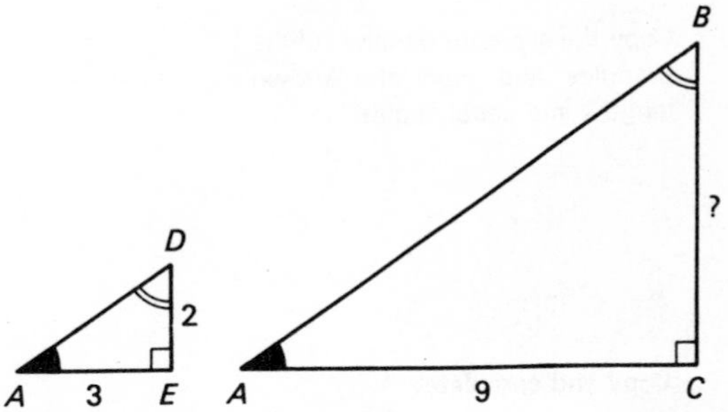

The height of the lamp-post is **6 metres**

Exercise

1 A ladder is placed against a house so that it reaches an upper window ledge while just passing over the garden wall which is 2.4 metres high. If the foot of the ladder is 2 metres from the wall and the wall is 5 metres from the house, calculate the height of the ledge.

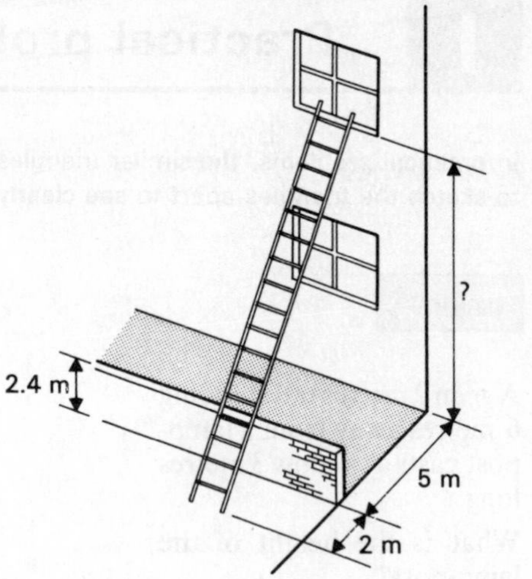

Step 1

Copy the sketch and **mark the known lengths and equal angles.**

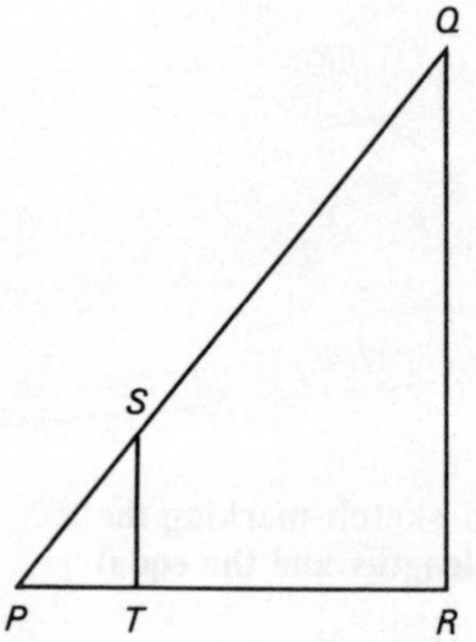

Step 2

Copy the separate sketches of the triangles and mark the known lengths and equal angles.

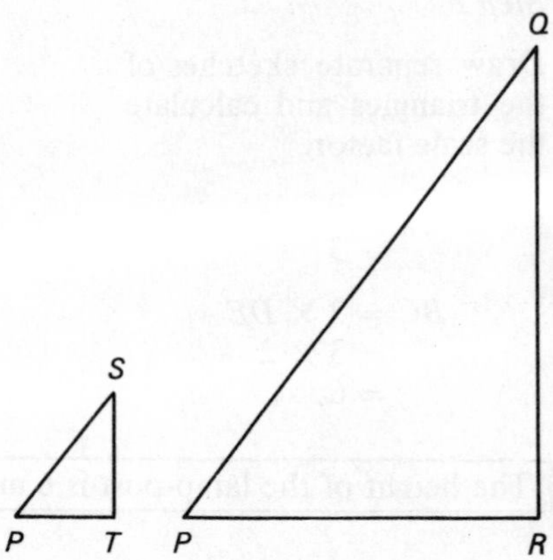

Copy and complete:

$k = \blacksquare$

$QR = \blacksquare$

The height of the ledge is $\blacksquare$ metres.

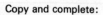

Do the following questions in the same way.

2 An advertising hoarding is held upright by tubular scaffolding supported by a vertical strut as shown in the diagram.

Calculate the height of the hoarding.

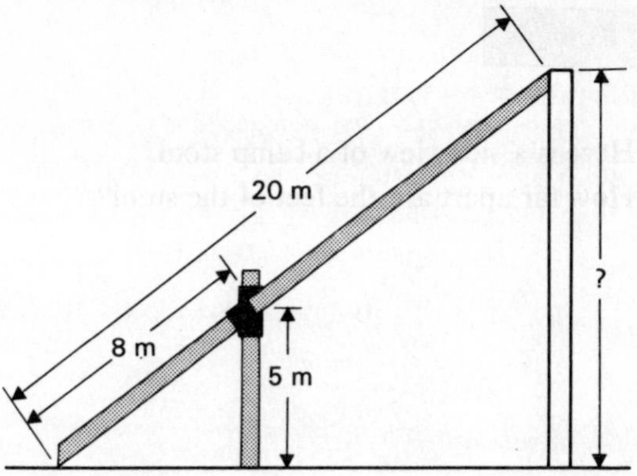

3 A step ladder is kept steady by a horizontal spar, 0.4 metres long.

How far apart are the feet of the ladder?

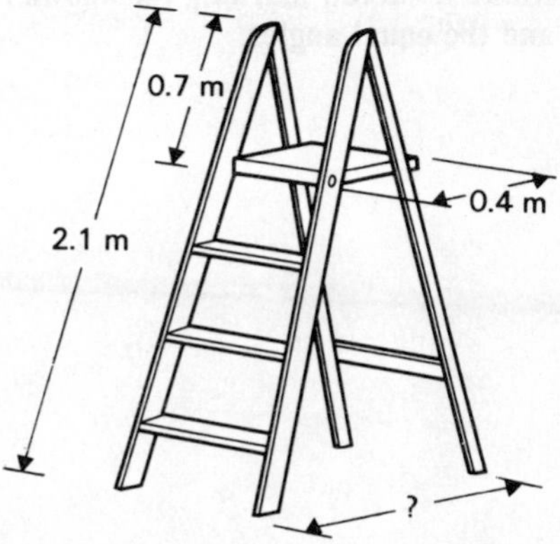

4 Find the value of *x*.

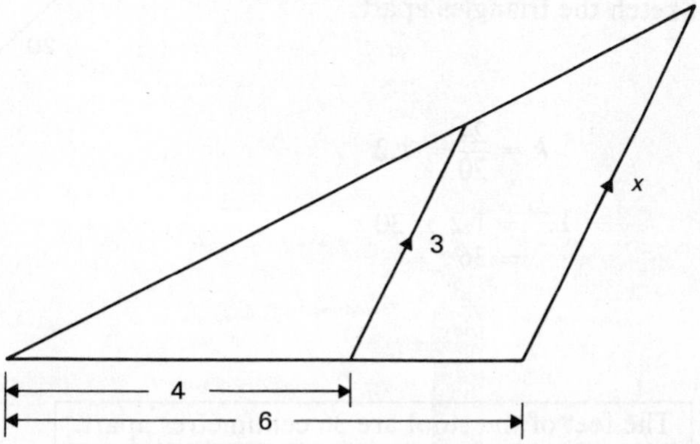

Example

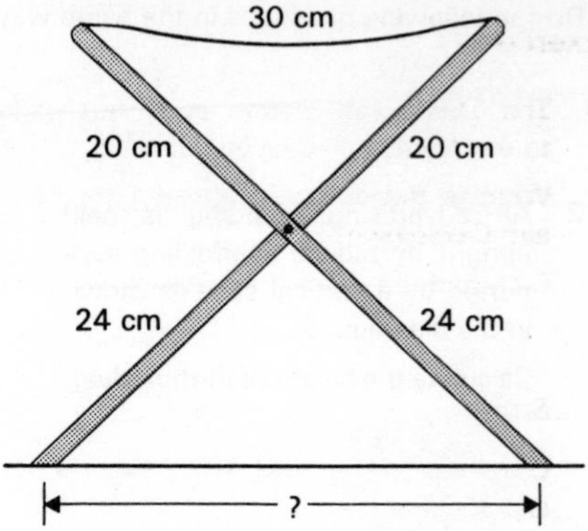

Here is a side view of a camp stool.
How far apart are the feet of the stool?

Step 1

Make a sketch **marking the known lengths and the equal angles.**

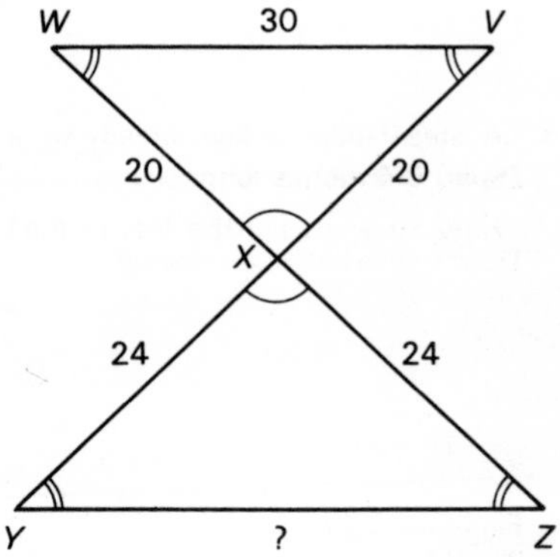

Step 2

Sketch the triangles apart.

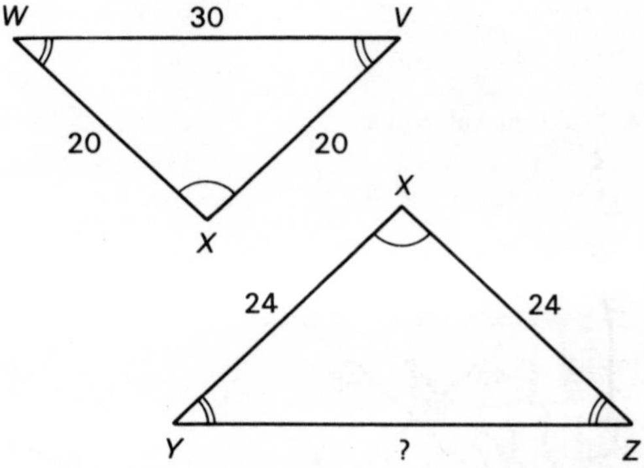

$$k = \frac{24}{20} = 1.2$$

$$YZ = 1.2 \times 30$$
$$= 36$$

The feet of the stool are 36 centimetres apart.

Exercise

5 The Dunsburgh–Barton road is parallel to the Alyntown–Castletown road.

What is the distance between Alyntown and Castletown?

Copy and complete the following working.

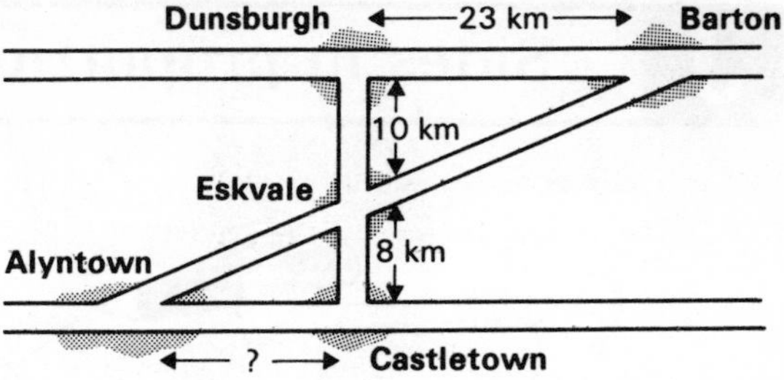

Step 1

Copy the sketch and mark the known lengths and equal angles.

Step 2

Draw separate sketches of the triangles.

k = ▢

AC = ▢

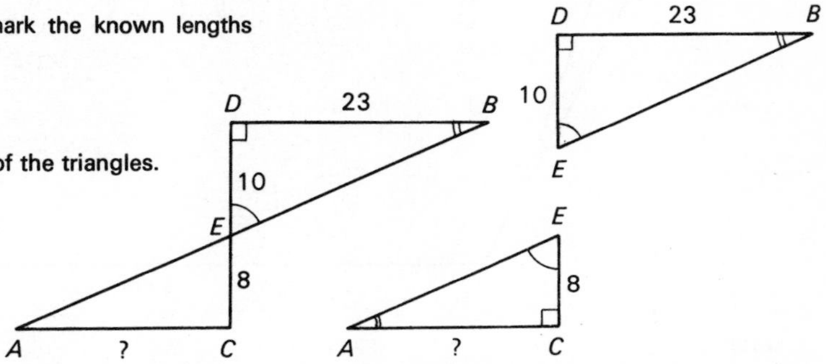

Distance between Alyntown and Castletown = ▢ km.

Do the following questions in the same way.

6 Find the value of x in this diagram.

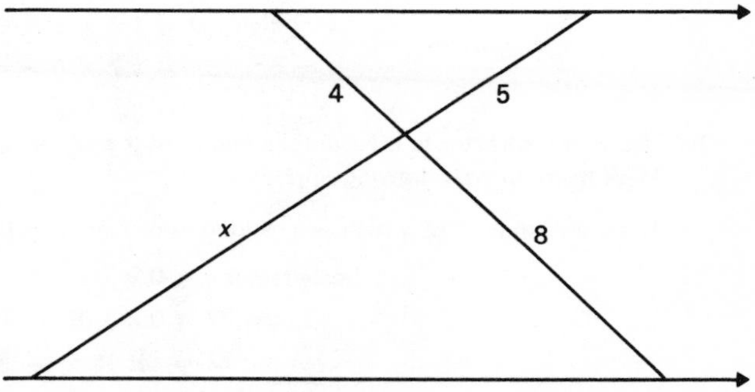

7

How far apart are the feet of this ironing board?

Continue with Section J

J Sides in proportion

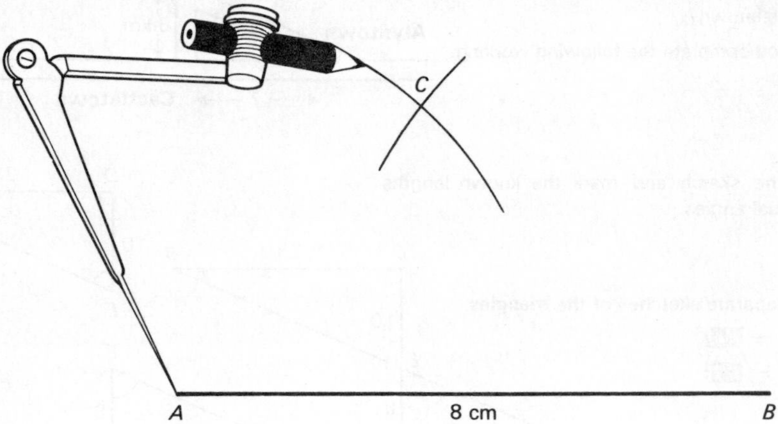

Exercise

1 (a) Use a ruler and compasses to draw triangle ABC with $AB = 8$ cm, $BC = 6$ cm and $CA = 5$ cm.

(b) Draw a triangle PQR which is an *enlargement* of triangle ABC using a scale factor of 1.2.

Scale factor $k = 1.2$

then $PQ = 1.2 \times 8 = 9.6$ cm

$QR = \square \times 6 = \square$ cm

$RP = \square \times \square = \square$ cm

(c) Use your protractor to measure the angles of triangle ABC and triangle PQR.
Mark them on your drawing.

(d) Draw a triangle XYZ which is a **reduction** of triangle ABC using a scale factor of 0.9.

Scale factor $k = 0.9$

then $XY = 0.9 \times 8 = 7.2$ cm

$YZ = \square \times 6 = \square$ cm

$ZX = \square \times \square = \square$ cm

Measure the angles of triangle XYZ and mark them on your drawing.

(e) Copy and complete the following table:

Triangle ABC	Triangle PQR	Triangle XYZ
$\hat{A} = 49°$	$\hat{P} = \square°$	$\hat{X} = \square°$
$\hat{B} = \square°$	$\hat{Q} = \square°$	$\hat{Y} = \square°$
$\hat{C} = \square°$	$\hat{R} = \square°$	$\hat{Z} = \square°$

(f) Copy and complete the following:

If one triangle is an enlargement or a reduction of the other, then the corresponding angles are $\square$ and the triangles are therefore $\square$.

You should have written:

> If one triangle is an enlargement or reduction of the other, then the corresponding angles are **equal** and the triangles are therefore **similar**.

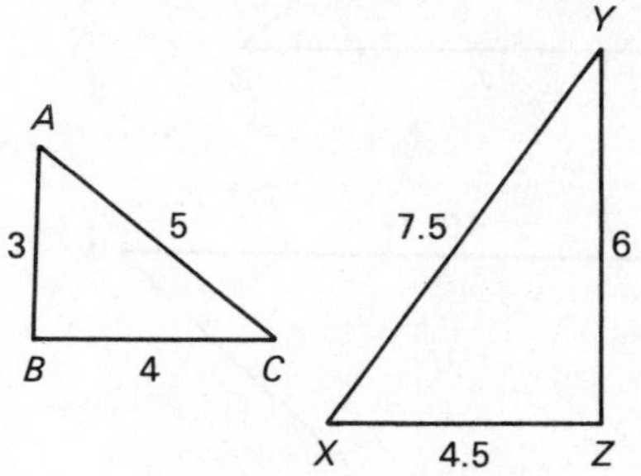

Example

Are triangle *ABC* and triangle *XYZ* similar?

Ratio of **largest** sides $= \frac{XY}{AC} = \frac{7.5}{5} = 1.5$

Ratio of **smallest** sides $= \frac{ZX}{AB} = \frac{4.5}{3} = 1.5$

Ratio of remaining sides $= \frac{YZ}{BC} = \frac{6}{4} = 1.5$

> **The corresponding sides are in proportion** and the triangles are therefore similar.

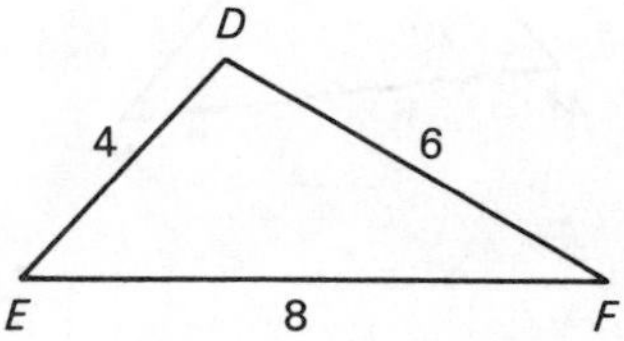

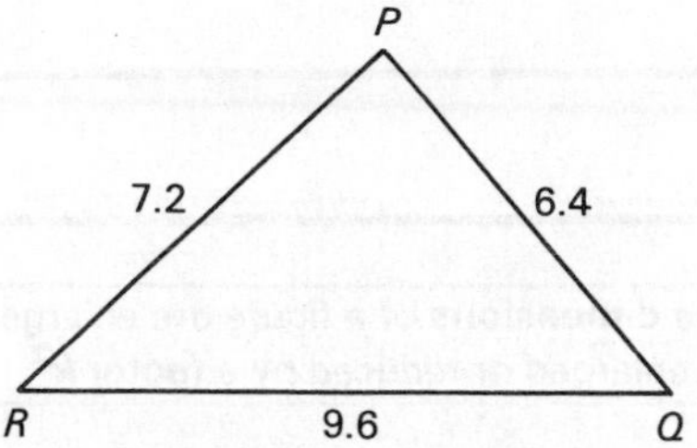

Example

Are triangle *DEF* and triangle *PQR* similar?

Ratio of largest sides $= \frac{RQ}{EF} = \frac{9.6}{8} = 1.2$

Ratio of smallest sides $= \frac{PQ}{DE} = \frac{6.4}{4} = 1.6$

Ratio of remaining sides $= \frac{PR}{DF} = \frac{7.2}{6} = 1.2$

> The corresponding sides are **not in proportion** and the triangles are therefore **not similar.**

Exercise

Find out which of the following pairs of triangles are similar.
Where they are similar write down the scale factor *k*.

2 Copy and complete:

Ratio of largest sides $= \frac{PR}{DF} = \frac{\square}{\square} = \square$

Ratio of smallest sides $= \frac{\square}{\square} = \frac{\square}{\square} = \square$

Ratio of remaining sides $= \frac{\square}{\square} = \frac{\square}{\square} = \square$

The triangles are $\square$

$k = \square$

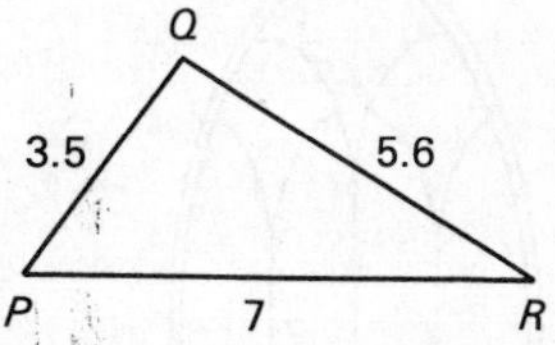

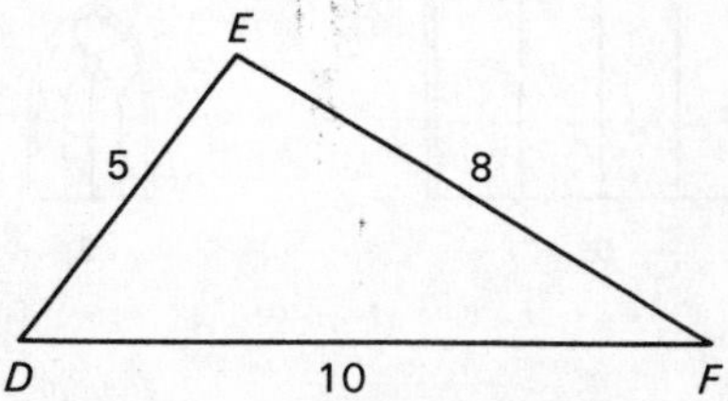

Do the following questions in the same way.

3

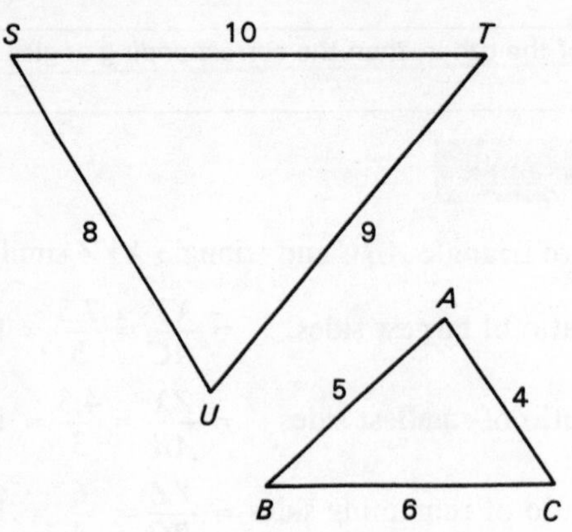

4

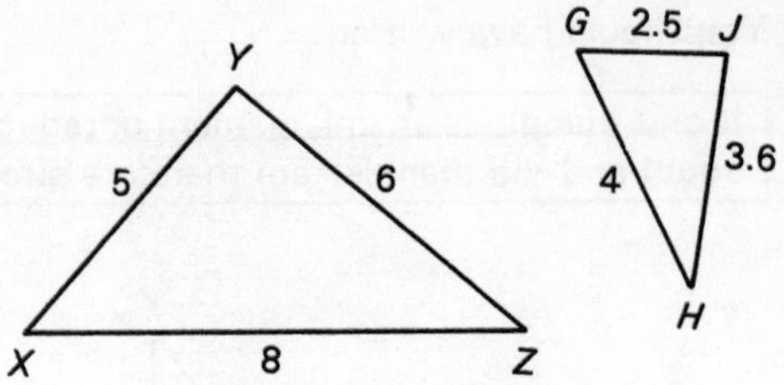

5

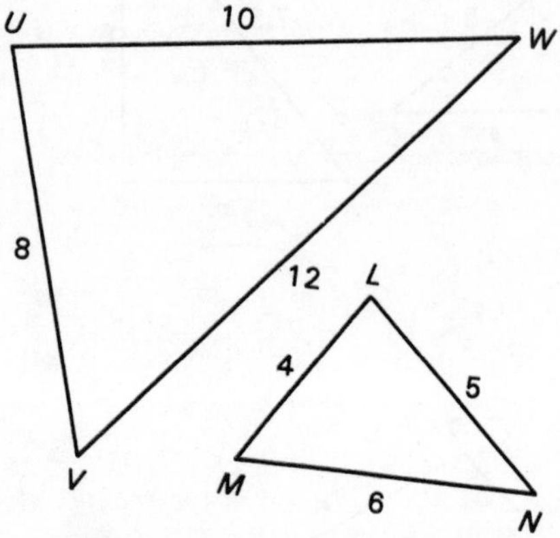

Continue with Sheet M1/2

K Areas

From Sheet M1/2 you will have found that when the **dimensions** of a figure are enlarged or reduced by a scale factor *k*, the **area** of the figure is enlarged or reduced by a **factor k^2**.

Example

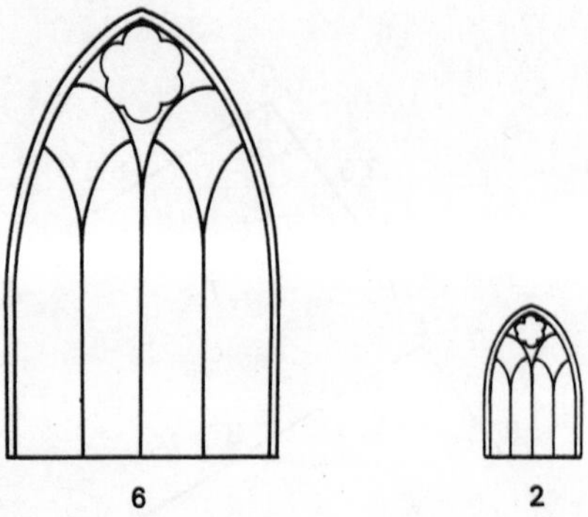

Here are two stained glass windows which are similar in shape. The area of the smaller window is 7 m². What is the area of the larger window?

Scale factor $k = \frac{6}{2} = 3$

Area of larger window $= k^2 \times$ area of smaller window

$= 3^2 \times 7$

$= 63 \text{ m}^2$

Exercise

1

A photograph is enlarged in the ratio 3:1. The area of the smaller photograph is 8.5 cm^2.

Find the area of the enlargement.

Copy and complete:

Scale factor $k = \frac{3}{1} = 3$

$$\text{Area of enlargement} = k^2 \times \text{area of photograph}$$
$$= \square \times 8.5$$
$$= \square \text{ cm}^2$$

Do the following questions in the same way.

2

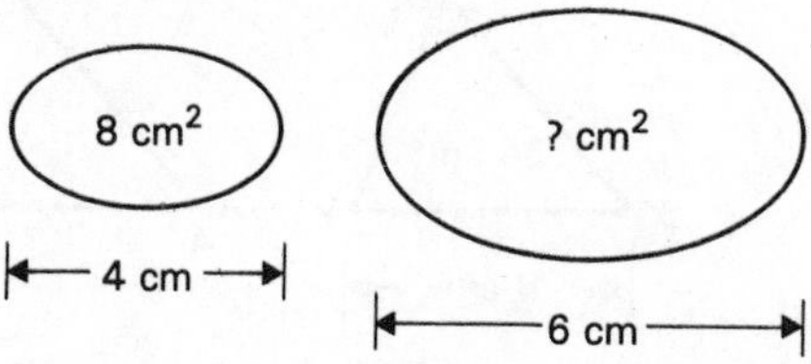

The area of the smaller ellipse is 8 cm^2.

What is the area of the larger ellipse?

3 A map was enlarged by a scale factor of 5.

If an island on the original map had an area of 3 cm^2 what is its area on the enlarged map?

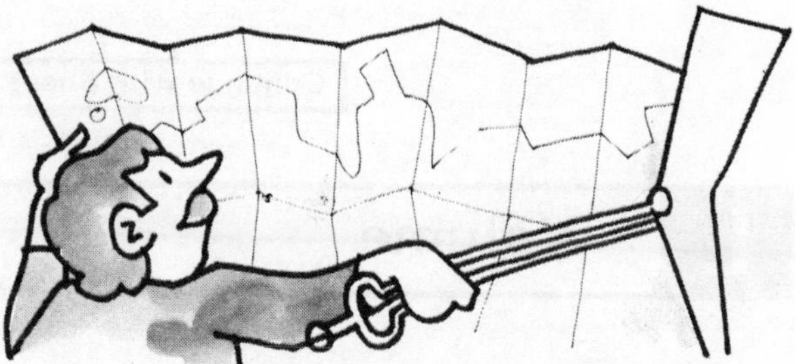

4

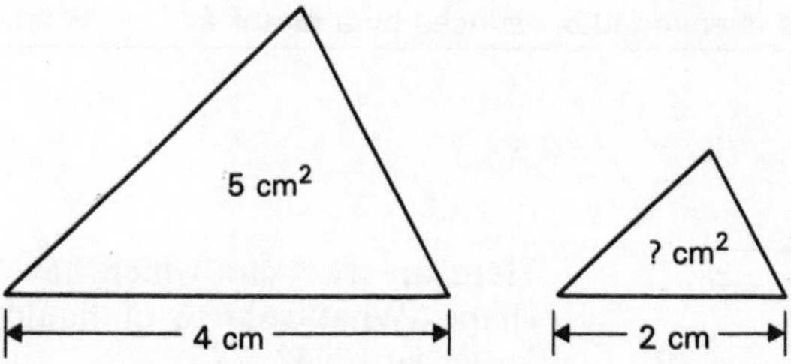

These triangles are similar. What is the area of the smaller triangle?

5 The diameter of a 1p coin is 2 cm and its area is 3.14 cm^2.

The diameter of a 2p coin is 2.6 cm. Find its area using

(a) the scale factor k^2, and (b) the area formula $A = \pi r^2$.

Compare your answers.

6 A photograph is reduced in the ratio 2 : 3, that is $k = \frac{2}{3}$.

The area of the larger photograph is 36 cm^2.

What is the area of the smaller photograph?

7 Triangles *XYZ* and *ABC* are similar.

The area of triangle *XYZ* is 24 cm^2 and the area of triangle *ABC* is 96 cm^2.

$XY = 8$ cm.

Calculate the length of *AB*.

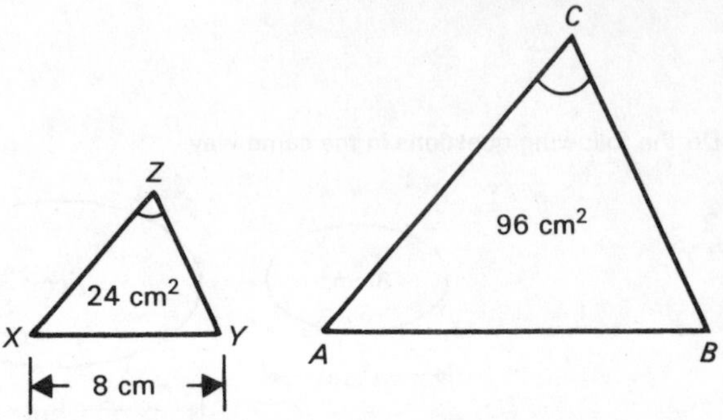

Continue with Sheet M1/3

L Volume

From Sheet M1/3 you will have found that when a figure is enlarged or reduced by a scale factor *k*, the **volume** of the figure is enlarged or reduced by a **factor** k^3.

Example

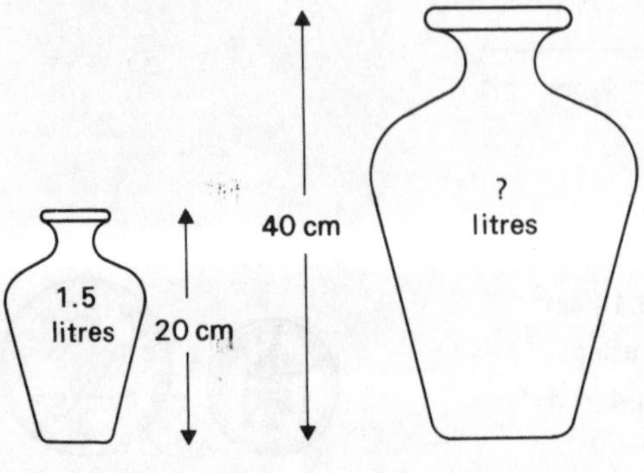

Here are two jars which have a similar shape. What volume of liquid does the larger jar hold?

Scale factor $k = \frac{40}{20} = 2$

Volume of liquid in larger jar

$= k^3 \times$ volume of liquid in smaller jar.

$= 2^3 \times 1.5$

$= 8 \times 1.5$

$= 12$ litres

The larger jar holds 12 litres

Exercise

1 The two tins are similarly shaped. The smaller one holds 2 litres.

What is the volume of the larger one?

Copy and complete:

Scale factor $k = \frac{\square}{\square} = \square$

Volume of larger tin

$= k^3 \times$ volume of smaller tin

$= \square \times 2$

$= \square$ litres

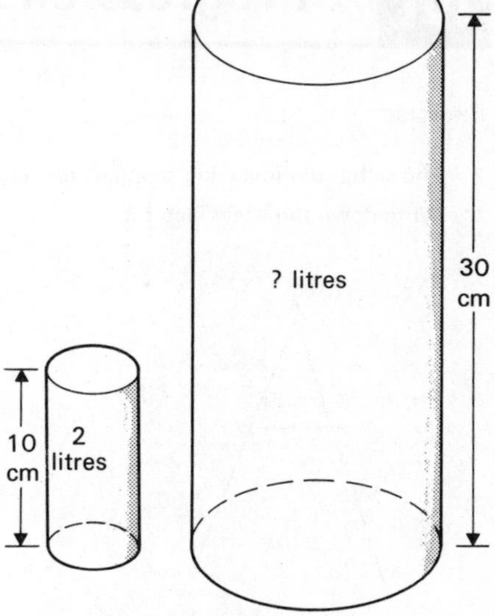

Do the following questions in the same way.

2 These boxes are similar.

The volume of the smaller one is 8 cubic centimetres.

What is the volume of the larger one?

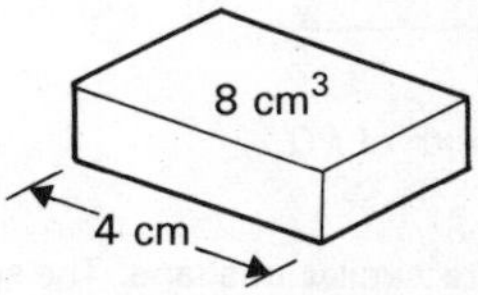

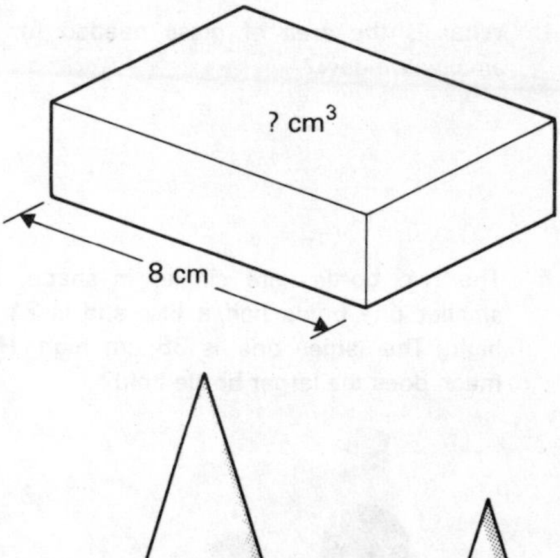

3

The smaller jug has the same shape as the larger, but is $\frac{1}{3}$ of its height.

The larger jug holds 13.5 litres.

How much does the smaller jug hold?

4 Here are two similar cones.

The larger one has a volume of 72 cubic centimetres.

What is the volume of the smaller one?

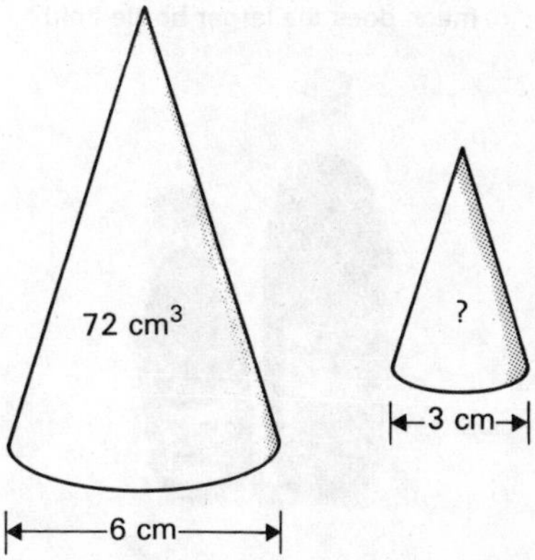

Continue with Section M

M Progress check

Exercise

1 Show that the following triangles are similar. Write down the scale factor *k*.

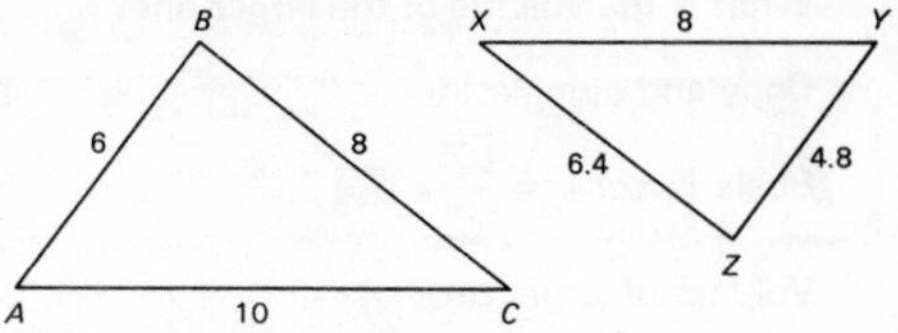

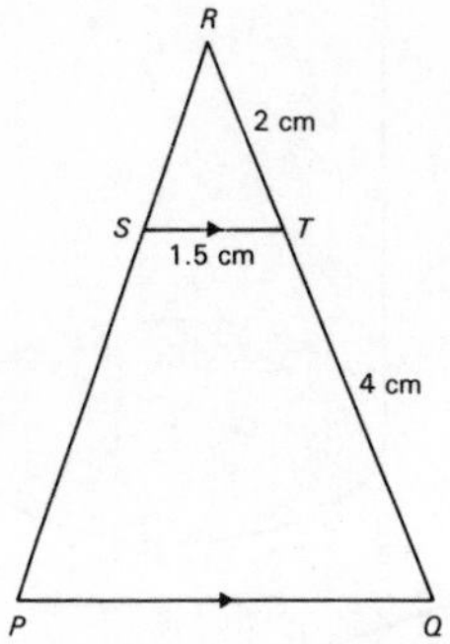

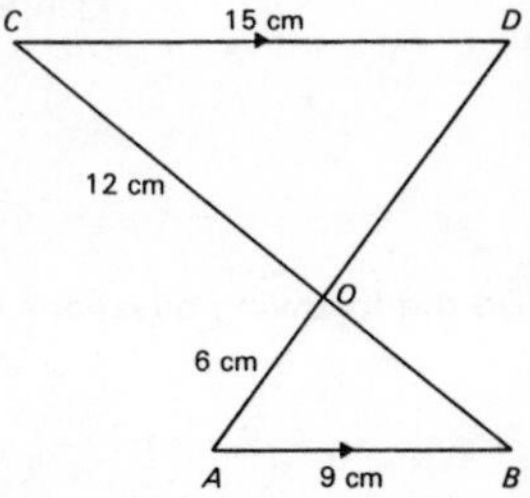

2 Calculate the length of *PQ*.

3 Calculate the length of *OB* and *OD*.

4 Two windows are similar in shape. The scale factor is 0.8.

What is the area of glass needed for the smaller window?

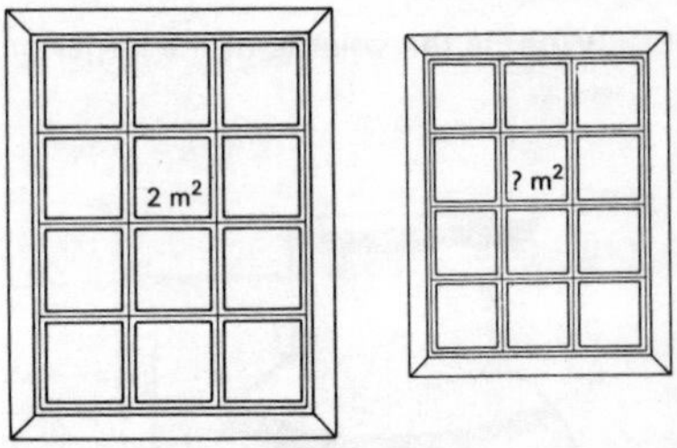

5 The two bottles are similar in shape. The smaller one holds half a litre and is 21 cm high. The larger one is 35 cm high. How much does the larger bottle hold?

6 A vertical strut supports the roof structure of a house.

Calculate the length of the strut.

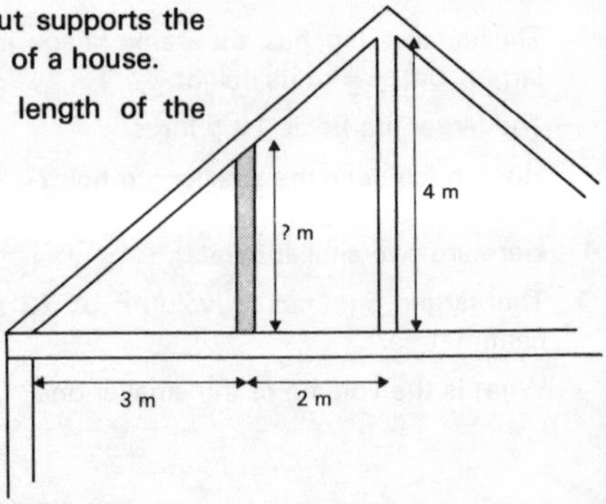

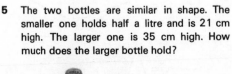

Tell your teacher that you have finished this unit

UNIT M2
Vectors

A | Moving a triangle

Here is a triangle on a square grid.

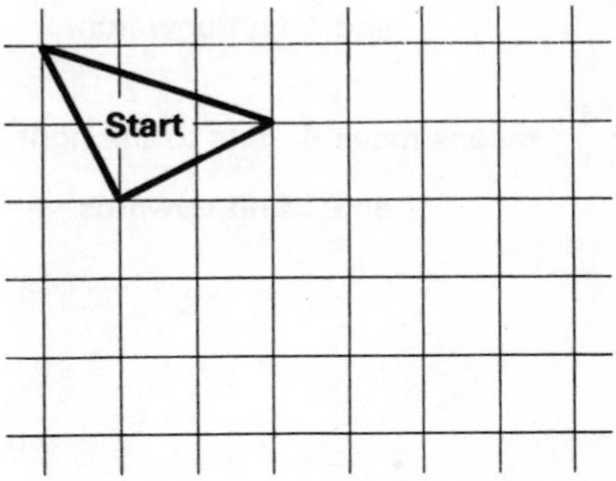

In this diagram the triangle has been moved four units to the right.

Notice that each vertex moves four units.

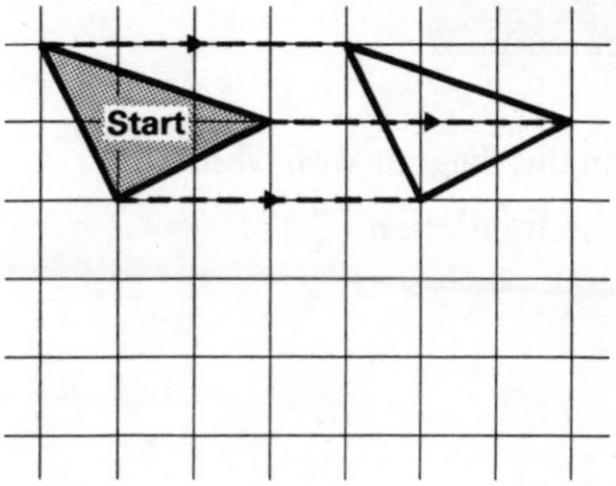

In this diagram the triangle has been moved again – this time three units downwards.

Notice that each vertex moves three units.

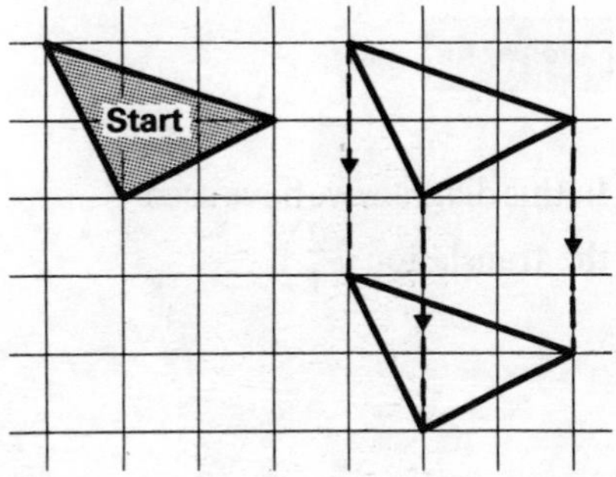

On Sheet M2/1 there is a diagram showing these moves.

Continue with Sheet M2/1

B Describing translations

Movements like those on Sheet M2/1 are called **translations**.

Instead of writing words like 'along' and 'upwards' each time we can use the following method to describe a translation.

$\begin{pmatrix}3\\1\end{pmatrix}$ means move 3 units to the right

and 1 unit upwards

$\begin{pmatrix}4\\1\end{pmatrix}$ means move 4 units to the right

and 1 unit upwards

Example

In this diagram we have used the translation $\begin{pmatrix}4\\1\end{pmatrix}$

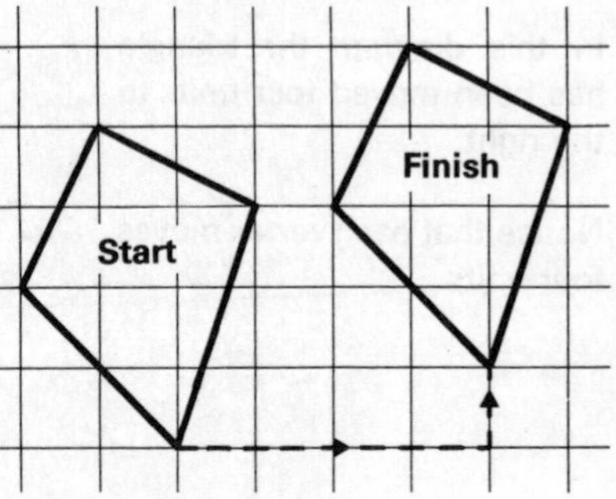

Example

In this diagram we have used the translation $\begin{pmatrix}2\\1\end{pmatrix}$

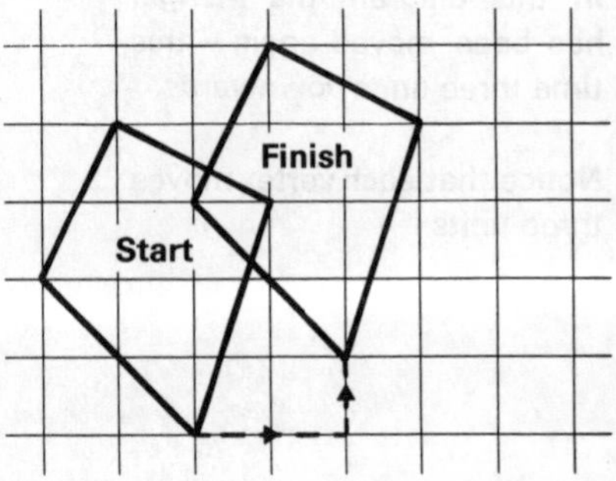

Continue with Sheet M2/1 (reverse)

C Components

The numbers which describe a translation are called the **components of the translation.**

In the translation $\begin{pmatrix} 2 \\ 3 \end{pmatrix}$

2 is the first component and shows the number of moves to the right.

3 is the second component and shows the number of moves upwards.

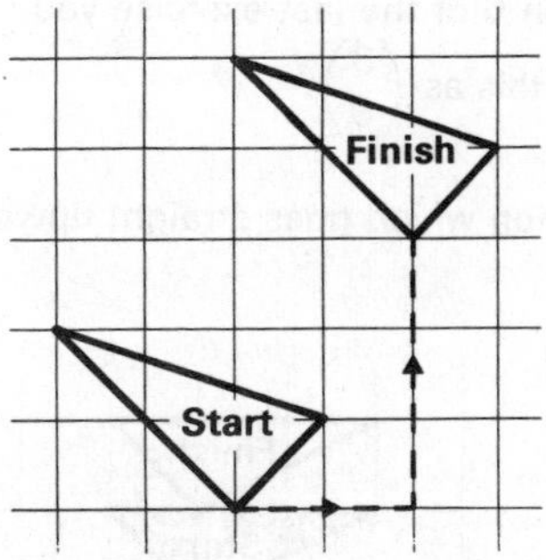

Exercise

Write down the components of the following translations, e.g. for question 1 write translation $\begin{pmatrix} 4 \\ 2 \end{pmatrix}$.

1

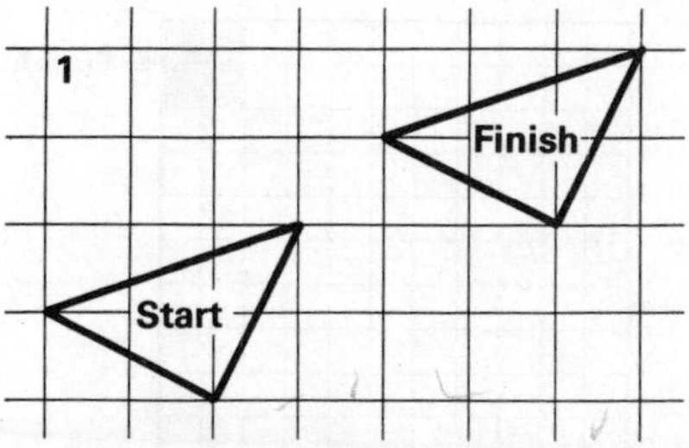

2

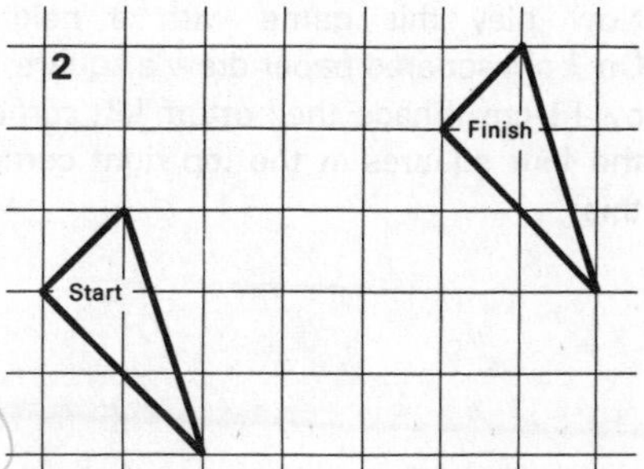

3

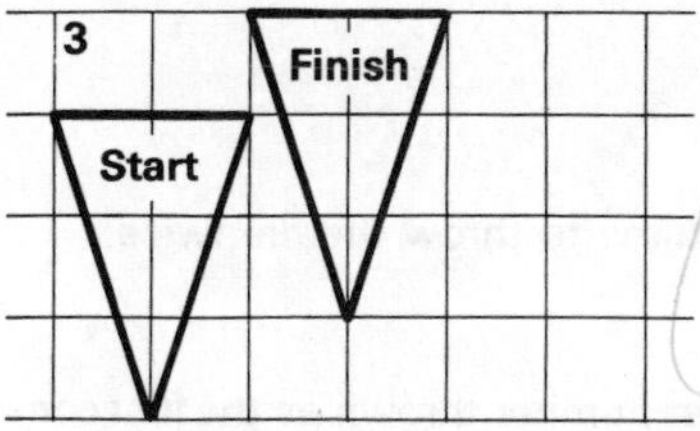

4

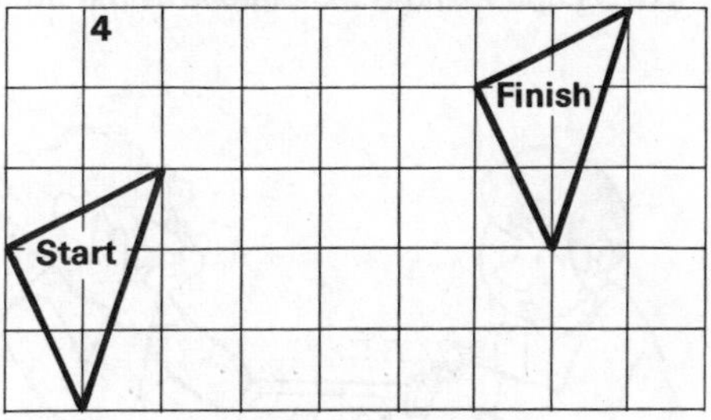

5

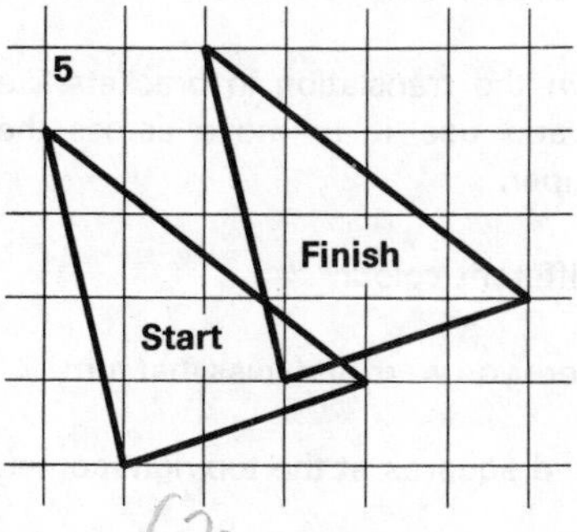

6

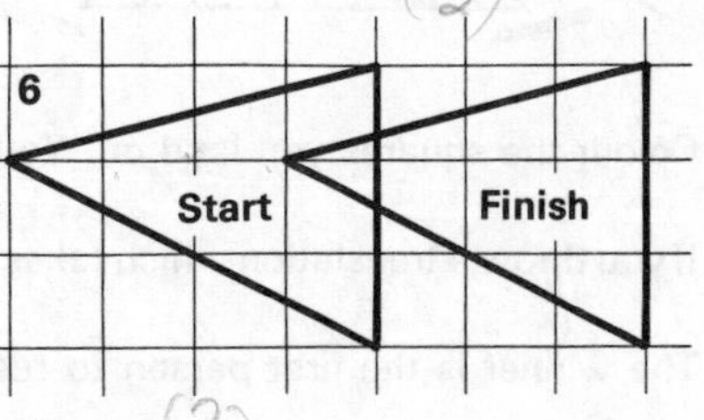

Continue with Section D

D A component game

In question 6 of the last exercise you should have found that the second component was zero. We write this as $\begin{pmatrix}3\\0\end{pmatrix}$.

A translation which goes straight upwards will have its first component equal to zero.

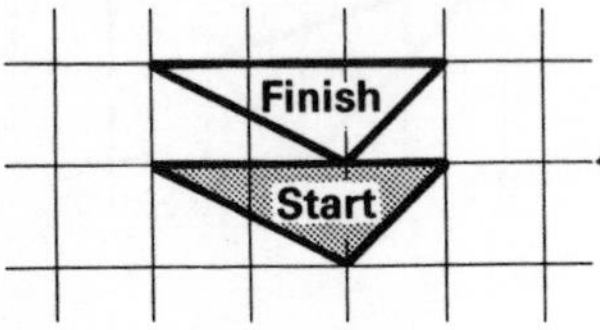

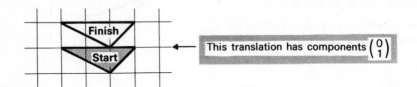

This translation has components $\begin{pmatrix}0\\1\end{pmatrix}$

Now play this game with a neighbour. On 1 cm squared paper draw a square 11 cm by 11 cm. Shade the bottom left corner and the four squares at the top right corner like this:

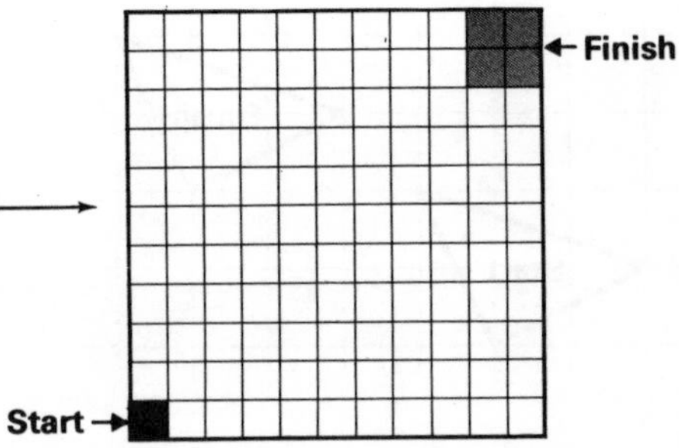

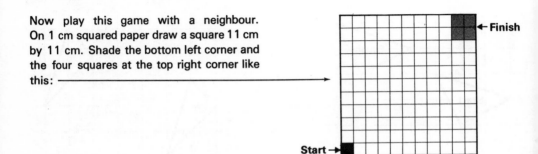

Take a cube marked as a die with the numbers 0, 1, 2, 3, 4, 5.

Take it in turns to throw the die twice.

Use the first number thrown as the first component of a translation and the second number as the second component.

Write down the translation in brackets like this ( ) and use it to move across the squared paper.

Colour the squares you land on. Your partner should use a different colour.

If you throw a translation which takes you off the page, stay where you were and miss that turn.

The winner is the first person to reach one of the four shaded squares at the top right corner.

After playing the game continue with Section E

E Negative components

We can use negative numbers to describe translations.

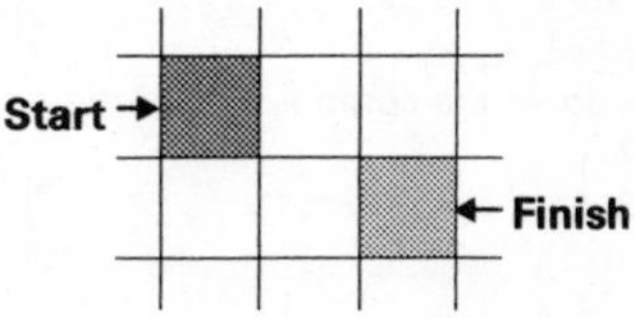

$\begin{pmatrix}2\\-1\end{pmatrix}$ means move 2 units right and 1 unit downwards.

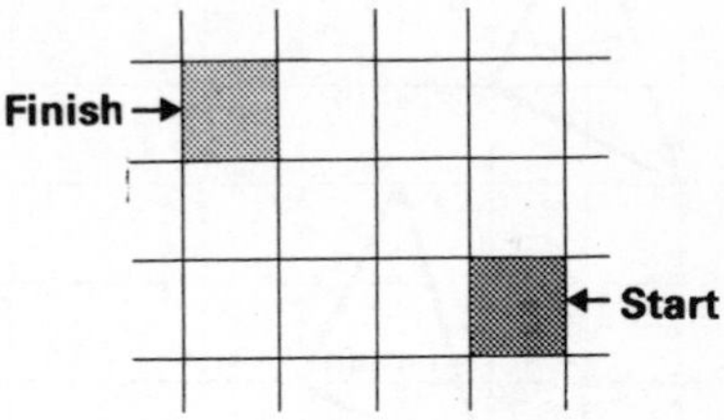

$\begin{pmatrix}-3\\2\end{pmatrix}$ means move 3 units left and 2 units upwards.

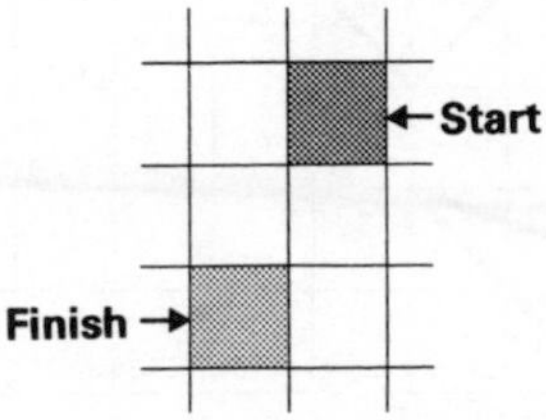

$\begin{pmatrix}-1\\-2\end{pmatrix}$ means move 1 unit to the left and 2 units downwards.

Example

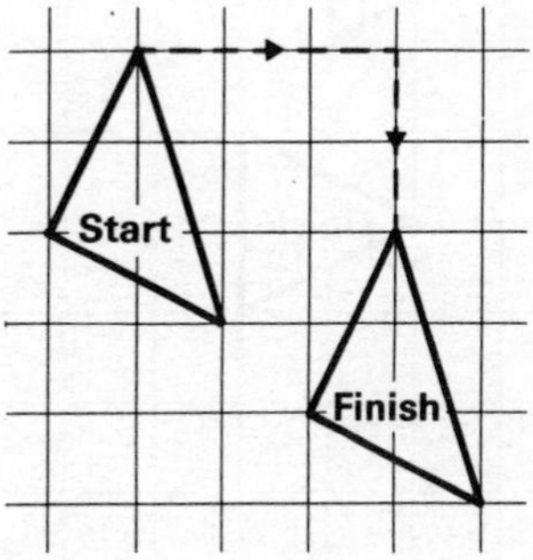

The translation $\begin{pmatrix}3\\-2\end{pmatrix}$ moves the triangle 3 units right and 2 units downwards.

Continue with Sheet M2/2

F Using negative components

Exercise

Write down the components of the translations which have been used, e.g. for question 1 write translation $\begin{pmatrix} 2 \\ -3 \end{pmatrix}$.

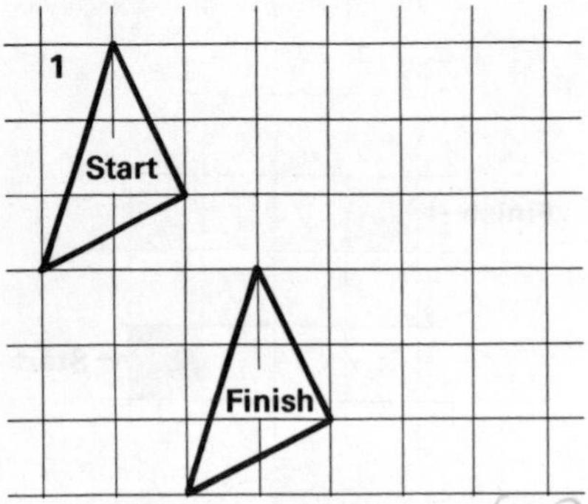

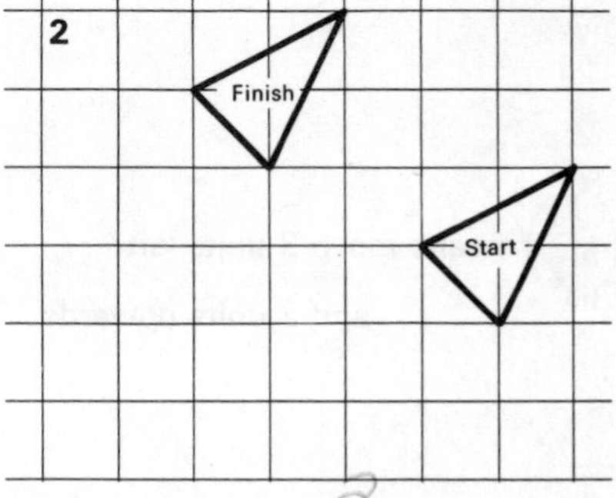

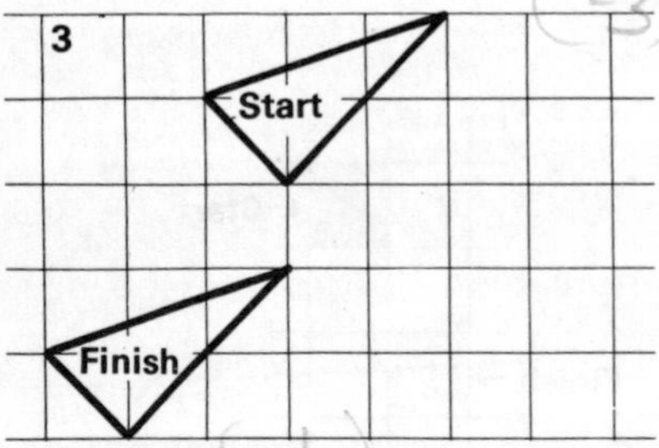

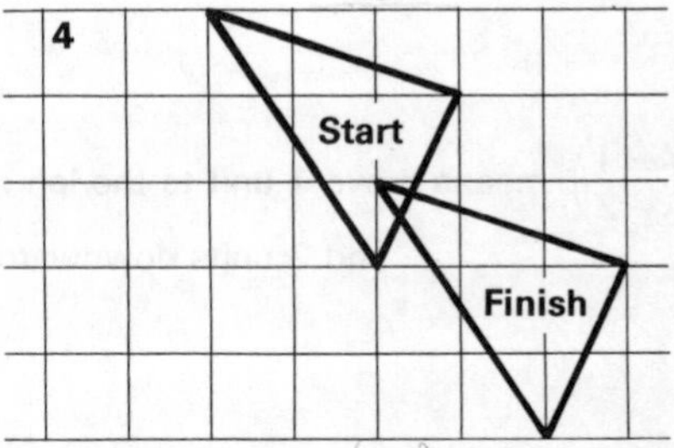

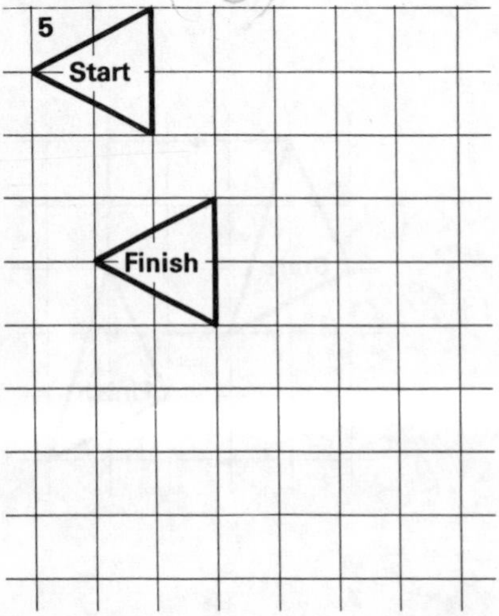

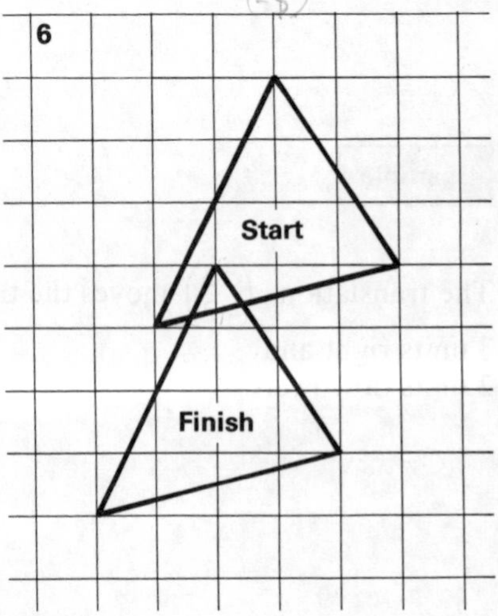

Continue with Section G

G Another component game

The game you played earlier can also be played using negative numbers.

This time take a cube marked as a die with the numbers −2, −1, 0, 1, 2, 3.

Play this game with a neighbour. On a piece of 1 cm squared paper draw a square 11 cm by 11 cm and shade the square at the middle like this:

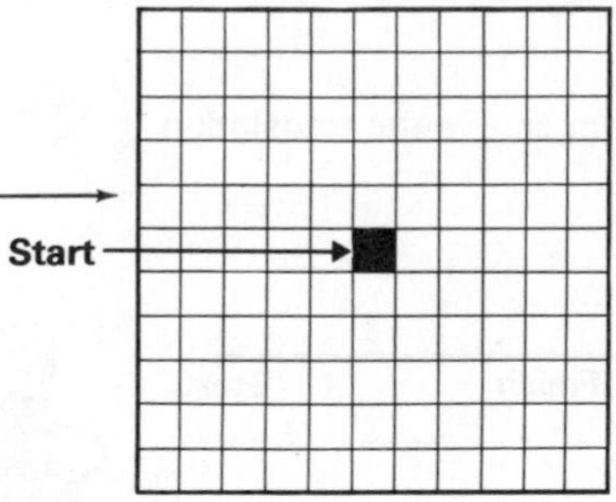

Take it in turns to throw the die twice using the first number as the first component and the second number as the second component of the translation.

Remember to write down the components of each translation.

Colour the squares you land on. Your partner should use a different colour.

The winner is the first person to reach the edge of the sheet.

After playing the game continue with Section H

H Arrow heads

The drawings show the movements of

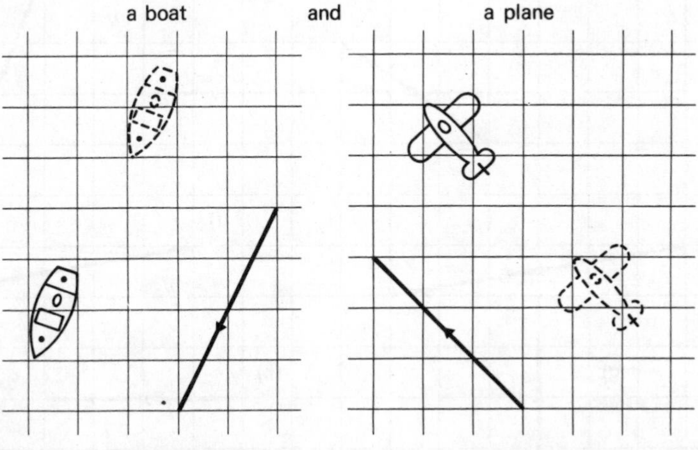

The movements are translations.

Translations can be shown by straight lines like those in the drawings.

The lines show the **distance** and the **direction** of the translation.

This diagram shows the translation $\begin{pmatrix} 3 \\ 1 \end{pmatrix}$.

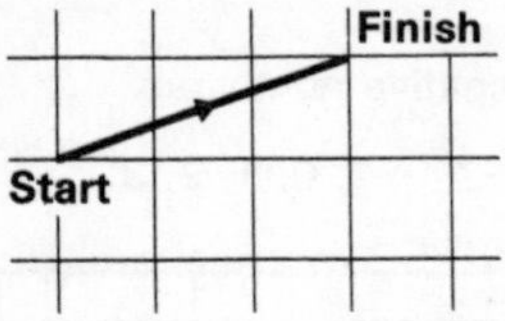

This diagram shows the translation $\begin{pmatrix} -2 \\ 1 \end{pmatrix}$.

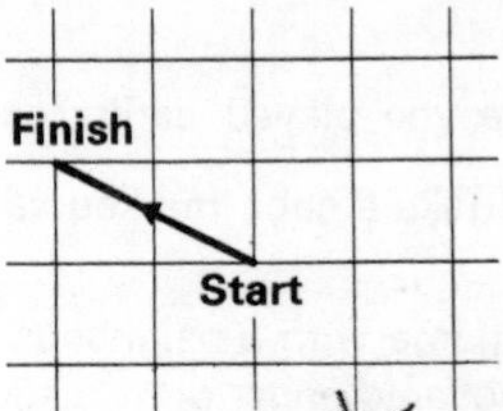

This diagram shows the translation $\begin{pmatrix} -4 \\ 0 \end{pmatrix}$.

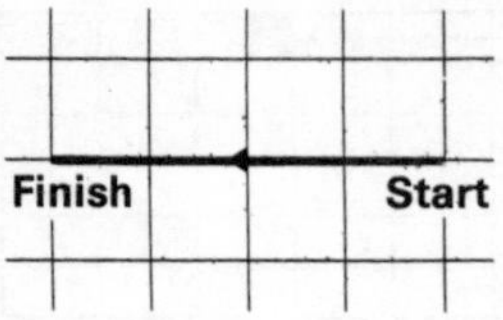

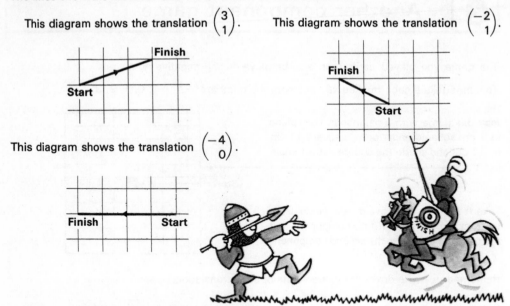

Note: Always make arrow point to **Finish**.

Exercise

1 Copy the following diagrams on 1 cm squared paper and write the components of each translation beside your drawing. **Remember to show the arrow heads.**

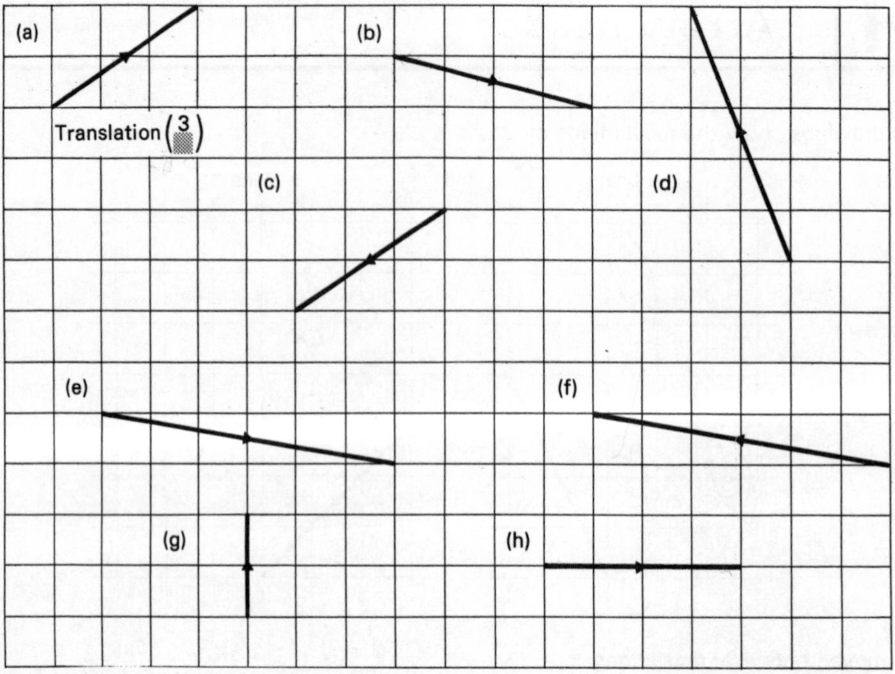

2 Draw diagrams on squared paper to show the following translations.
Remember the arrow heads.

(a) $\begin{pmatrix}4\\3\end{pmatrix}$ (b) $\begin{pmatrix}2\\5\end{pmatrix}$ (c) $\begin{pmatrix}-1\\5\end{pmatrix}$ (d) $\begin{pmatrix}-3\\-3\end{pmatrix}$

(e) $\begin{pmatrix}0\\6\end{pmatrix}$ (f) $\begin{pmatrix}7\\0\end{pmatrix}$ (g) $\begin{pmatrix}-3\\2\end{pmatrix}$ (h) $\begin{pmatrix}4\\-1\end{pmatrix}$

The number pairs, like (a) to (h) above, which we have used to describe translations are called vectors.

Continue with Section I

I Labelling vectors

Vectors can be used to describe other quantities in mathematics such as forces, velocities, accelerations.

Sometimes we use underlined letters to stand for vectors. For example: $\underline{v}$, $\underline{a}$, $\underline{d}$, $\underline{w}$, $\underline{s}$, $\underline{t}$.

Suppose that this shows the vector $\underline{u}$.

We say that $\underline{u} = \begin{pmatrix}2\\4\end{pmatrix}$.

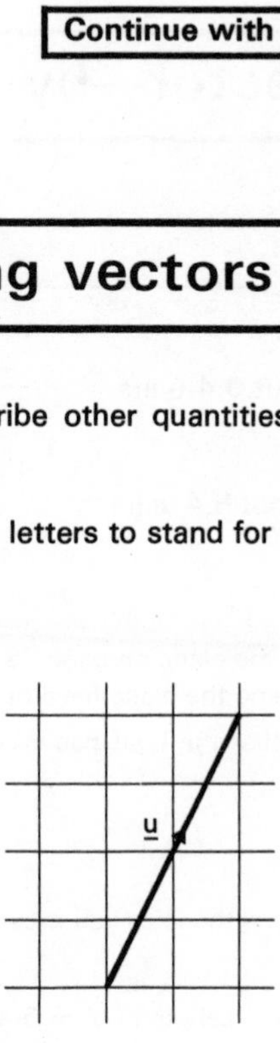

If this shows the vector $\underline{t}$, we say that $\underline{t} = \begin{pmatrix}-3\\-1\end{pmatrix}$.

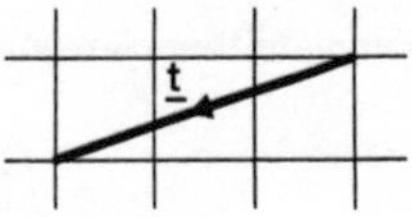

Exercise

1 Copy on 1 centimetre squared paper the drawings showing these vectors and write down their components.

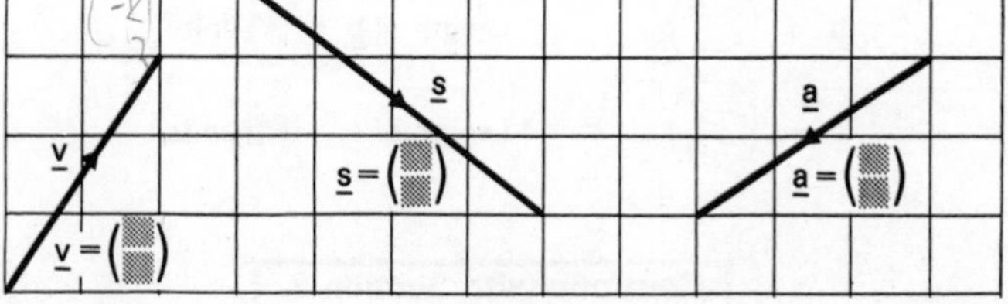

2 On 1 cm squared paper, draw lines to show the following vectors.
(Remember the arrow heads, and write the correct letter along each line.)

$\underline{u} = \begin{pmatrix}2\\5\end{pmatrix}$ $\underline{w} = \begin{pmatrix}-1\\4\end{pmatrix}$ $\underline{v} = \begin{pmatrix}-3\\2\end{pmatrix}$

$\underline{a} = \begin{pmatrix}3\\-4\end{pmatrix}$ $\underline{b} = \begin{pmatrix}-5\\-4\end{pmatrix}$ $\underline{c} = \begin{pmatrix}-2\\0\end{pmatrix}$

Continue with Section J

J Length of a vector—by measurement

The vector $\begin{pmatrix}2\\5\end{pmatrix}$ is shown by a line like this. →

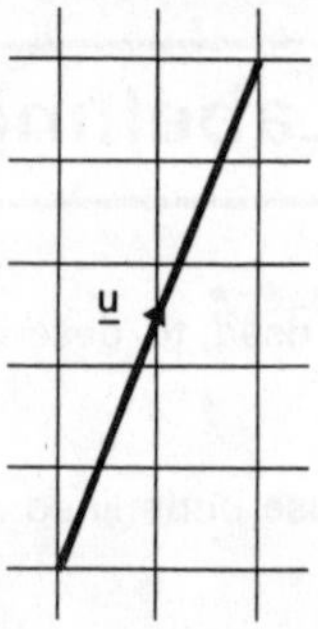

The length of the line in centimetres is about 5.4 units (measure it!).

We say that the length of the vector u is about 5.4 units.

Exercise

1 Look back at the drawings of the boat and the plane on page 39, Section H. Measure the lengths of the straight lines showing how far the boat and the plane have moved.

If 1 unit stands for 1 km you should find that the boat has moved about 4.5 km and the plane has moved about 4.2 km.

2 Copy and complete the following by measuring the lines you drew to show the vectors in question 2 of Section I.

$\underline{u} = \begin{pmatrix}2\\5\end{pmatrix}$ Length of $\underline{u}$ = 5.4 units.

$\underline{w} = \begin{pmatrix}-1\\4\end{pmatrix}$ Length of $\underline{w}$ = ■ units.

$\underline{v} = \begin{pmatrix}-3\\2\end{pmatrix}$ Length of $\underline{v}$ = ■ units.

$\underline{a} = \begin{pmatrix}3\\-4\end{pmatrix}$ Length of $\underline{a}$ = ■ units.

$\underline{b} = \begin{pmatrix}-5\\-4\end{pmatrix}$ Length of $\underline{b}$ = ■ units.

$\underline{c} = \begin{pmatrix}-2\\0\end{pmatrix}$ Length of $\underline{c}$ = ■ units.

Continue with Section K

K Length of a vector—by calculation

We can find the length of a vector without measuring it if we know its components.

Using Pythagoras' Theorem in any right-angled triangle, we can find the length of the longest side by:

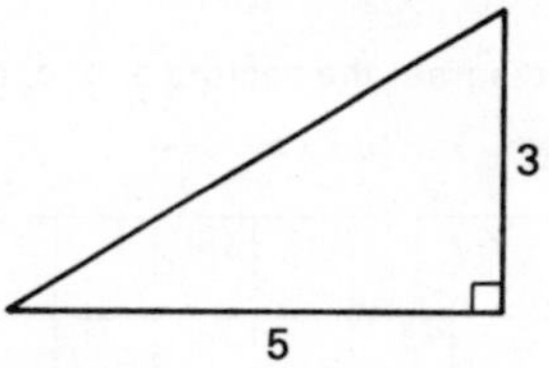

1 squaring the two shorter sides — $5^2, 3^2$

2 adding the squares together — $5^2 + 3^2$

3 taking the square root of the answer — $\sqrt{5^2 + 3^2} = \sqrt{25 + 9} = \sqrt{34}$
$= 5.83$ (from square root tables)

Example

This line shows the vector $\underline{v} = \begin{pmatrix} 6 \\ 2 \end{pmatrix}$

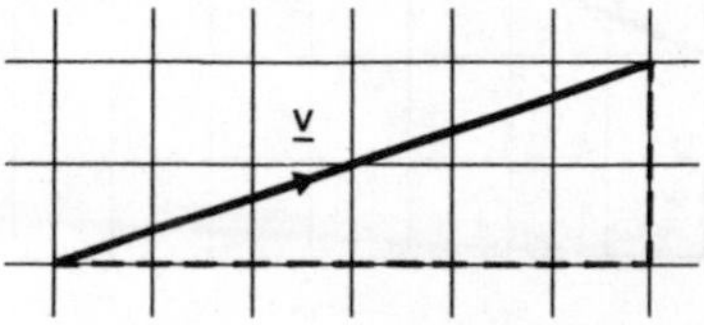

Its length is given by $\sqrt{6^2 + 2^2}$

$= \sqrt{36 + 4}$

$= \sqrt{40}$

$= 6.32$ (from square root tables)

We say that the length of $\underline{v}$ = 6.32 units

Exercise

Find the lengths of the vectors shown below by copying and completing the following:

1 Length of $\begin{pmatrix} 3 \\ 4 \end{pmatrix} = \sqrt{3^2 + 4^2} = \sqrt{\square + \square} = \sqrt{\square} = \square$ units

2 Length of $\begin{pmatrix} 2 \\ 6 \end{pmatrix} = \sqrt{\square + \square} = \sqrt{\square + \square} = \sqrt{\square} = \square$ units

3 Length of $\begin{pmatrix} 1 \\ 7 \end{pmatrix} = \sqrt{\square + \square} = \sqrt{\square + \square} = \sqrt{\square} = \square$ units

4 Length of $\begin{pmatrix} -2 \\ 3 \end{pmatrix} = \sqrt{(-2)^2 + 3^2} = \sqrt{4 + 9} = \sqrt{\square} = \square$ units

Remember that $(-2) \times (-2) = 4$.

5 Length of $\begin{pmatrix} 4 \\ -3 \end{pmatrix} = \sqrt{\blacksquare + \blacksquare} = \sqrt{\blacksquare + \blacksquare} = \sqrt{\blacksquare} = \blacksquare$ units

6 Length of $\begin{pmatrix} -3 \\ 1 \end{pmatrix} = \sqrt{\blacksquare + \blacksquare} = \sqrt{\blacksquare + \blacksquare} = \sqrt{\blacksquare} = \blacksquare$ units

In the following diagram the vectors $\underline{a}$, $\underline{b}$, $\underline{c}$, $\underline{d}$, $\underline{e}$, and $\underline{f}$ are shown.

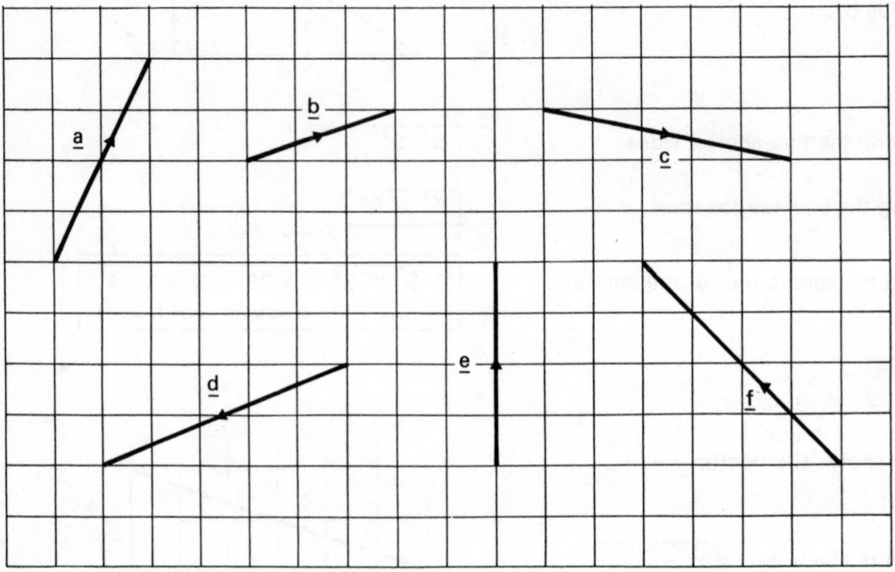

Copy and complete the following:

7 $\underline{a} = \begin{pmatrix} 2 \\ 4 \end{pmatrix}$ Length of $\underline{a} = \sqrt{\blacksquare + \blacksquare} = \sqrt{4 + \blacksquare} = \sqrt{\blacksquare} = \blacksquare$ units

8 $\underline{b} = \begin{pmatrix} \\ \end{pmatrix}$ Length of $\underline{b} = \sqrt{\blacksquare + \blacksquare} =$

9 $\underline{c} = \begin{pmatrix} \\ \end{pmatrix}$ Length of $\underline{c} =$

10 $\underline{d} = \begin{pmatrix} \\ \end{pmatrix}$ Length of $\underline{d} =$

11 $\underline{e} = \begin{pmatrix} \\ \end{pmatrix}$ Length of $\underline{e} =$

12 $\underline{f} = \begin{pmatrix} \\ \end{pmatrix}$ Length of $\underline{f} =$

Continue with Sheet M2/2 (reverse)

L 'Adding' vectors

Here are three possible successive moves in the translation game of Section D.

Stage 1

You throw

then

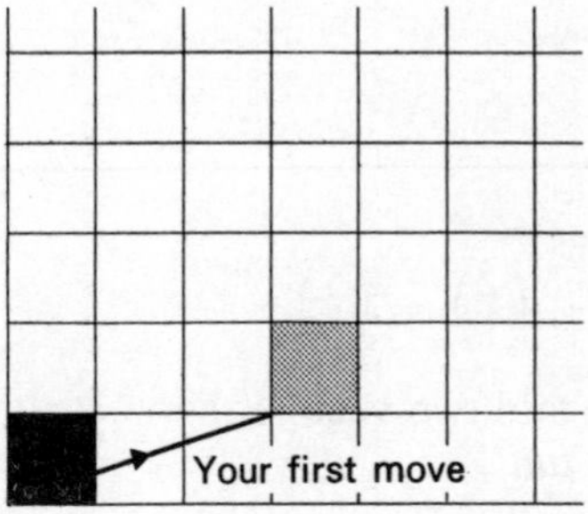

Your vector is $\begin{pmatrix}3\\1\end{pmatrix}$ so the result is

Stage 2

Your opponent throws

then

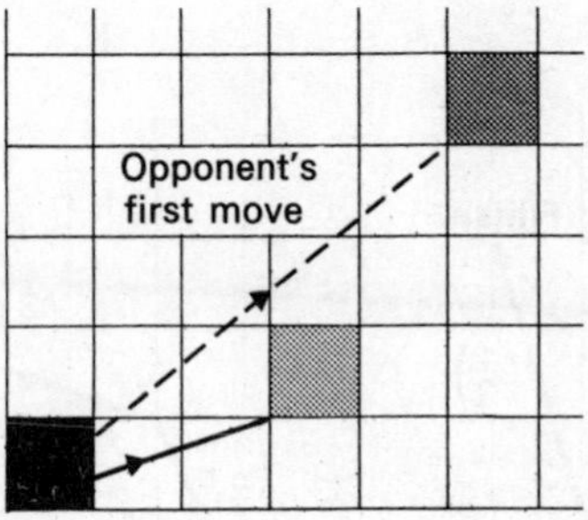

Opponent's vector is $\begin{pmatrix}5\\4\end{pmatrix}$

Stage 3

You throw

then

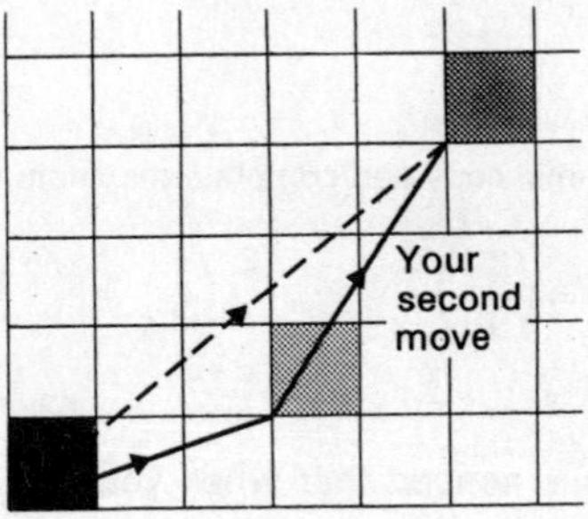

Your vector is $\begin{pmatrix}2\\3\end{pmatrix}$

So a move of $\begin{pmatrix}3\\1\end{pmatrix}$ followed by a move of $\begin{pmatrix}2\\3\end{pmatrix}$ gives the same effect as a move of $\begin{pmatrix}5\\4\end{pmatrix}$.

We call this method of combining moves '**addition**' and we write

$$\begin{pmatrix}4\\1\end{pmatrix} + \begin{pmatrix}2\\2\end{pmatrix} = \begin{pmatrix}6\\3\end{pmatrix}$$

When we add two vectors we get another vector.

Example

This diagram shows that

$$\begin{pmatrix}3\\5\end{pmatrix} + \begin{pmatrix}2\\1\end{pmatrix} = \begin{pmatrix}5\\6\end{pmatrix}$$

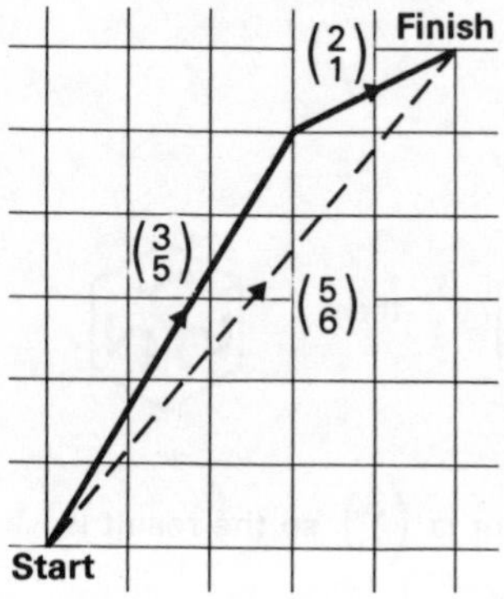

Notice when we add two vectors the lines go '*nose to tail*'.

We start the second line from the finish of the first one.

Exercise

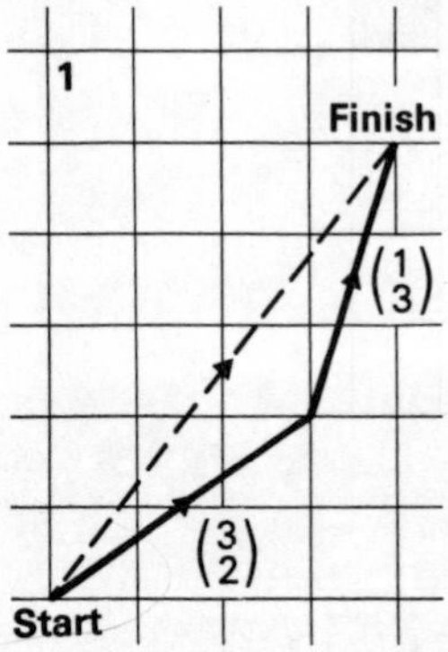

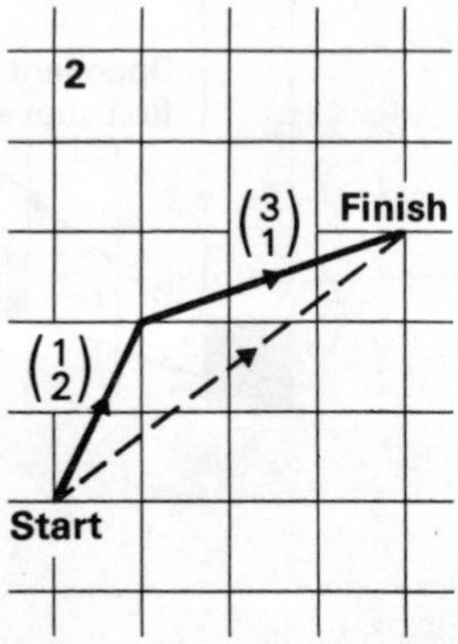

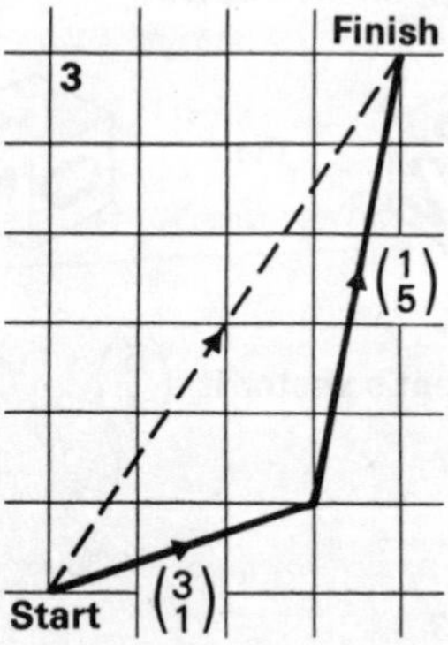

Using the diagrams, copy and complete the additions below.

1 $\begin{pmatrix}3\\2\end{pmatrix} + \begin{pmatrix}1\\3\end{pmatrix} = \begin{pmatrix}\blacksquare\\\blacksquare\end{pmatrix}$ **2** $\begin{pmatrix}1\\2\end{pmatrix} + \begin{pmatrix}3\\1\end{pmatrix} = \begin{pmatrix}\blacksquare\\\blacksquare\end{pmatrix}$ **3** $\begin{pmatrix}3\\1\end{pmatrix} + \begin{pmatrix}1\\5\end{pmatrix} = \begin{pmatrix}\blacksquare\\\blacksquare\end{pmatrix}$

You should have noticed that when you add two vectors you add the first components and the second components separately.

In question 1:

$$\begin{pmatrix}3\\2\end{pmatrix} + \begin{pmatrix}1\\3\end{pmatrix} = \begin{pmatrix}3+1\\2+3\end{pmatrix} = \begin{pmatrix}4\\5\end{pmatrix}$$

Example

$$\text{If } \underline{s} = \begin{pmatrix} 3 \\ 5 \end{pmatrix} \text{ and } \underline{t} = \begin{pmatrix} 2 \\ 1 \end{pmatrix} \text{ then } \underline{s} + \underline{t} = \begin{pmatrix} 3 + 2 \\ 5 + 1 \end{pmatrix} = \begin{pmatrix} 5 \\ 6 \end{pmatrix}$$

Exercise

Copy and complete the additions below.

4 $\underline{v} = \begin{pmatrix} 2 \\ 2 \end{pmatrix}$ $\quad\underline{w} = \begin{pmatrix} 0 \\ 4 \end{pmatrix}$ $\quad\underline{v} + \underline{w} = \begin{pmatrix} \square + \square \\ \square + \square \end{pmatrix} = \begin{pmatrix} \square \\ \square \end{pmatrix}$

5 $\underline{d} = \begin{pmatrix} 6 \\ 2 \end{pmatrix}$ $\quad\underline{y} = \begin{pmatrix} 2 \\ 3 \end{pmatrix}$ $\quad\underline{d} + \underline{y} = \begin{pmatrix} \square + \square \\ \square + \square \end{pmatrix} = \begin{pmatrix} \square \\ \square \end{pmatrix}$

6 $\underline{k} = \begin{pmatrix} 4 \\ 3 \end{pmatrix}$ $\quad\underline{s} = \begin{pmatrix} 1 \\ 4 \end{pmatrix}$ $\quad\underline{k} + \underline{s} = \begin{pmatrix} \square + \square \\ \square + \square \end{pmatrix} = \begin{pmatrix} \square \\ \square \end{pmatrix}$

7 $\underline{x} = \begin{pmatrix} 3 \\ 5 \end{pmatrix}$ $\quad\underline{y} = \begin{pmatrix} 4 \\ 2 \end{pmatrix}$ $\quad\underline{x} + \underline{y} = \begin{pmatrix} \square + \square \\ \square + \square \end{pmatrix} = \begin{pmatrix} \square \\ \square \end{pmatrix}$

8 $\underline{a} = \begin{pmatrix} 2 \\ 5 \end{pmatrix}$ $\quad\underline{b} = \begin{pmatrix} 3 \\ 2 \end{pmatrix}$ $\quad\underline{a} + \underline{b} = \begin{pmatrix} \square + \square \\ \square + \square \end{pmatrix} = \begin{pmatrix} \square \\ \square \end{pmatrix}$

Example

On 1 cm squared paper show the addition in question 4 above.

First draw $\underline{v}$.

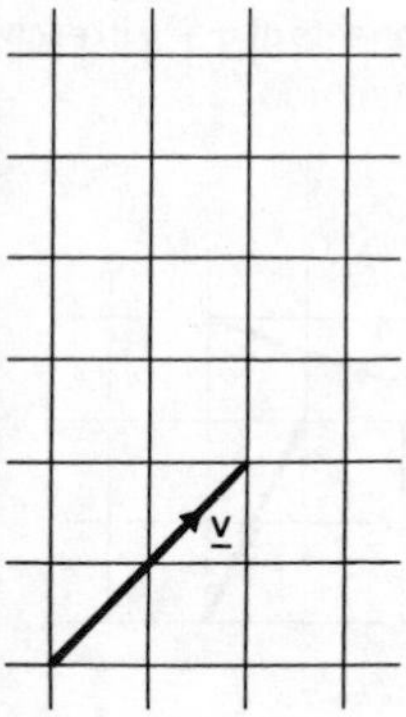

Using the **finish** of $\underline{v}$ as the **start** of $\underline{w}$, draw $\underline{w}$.

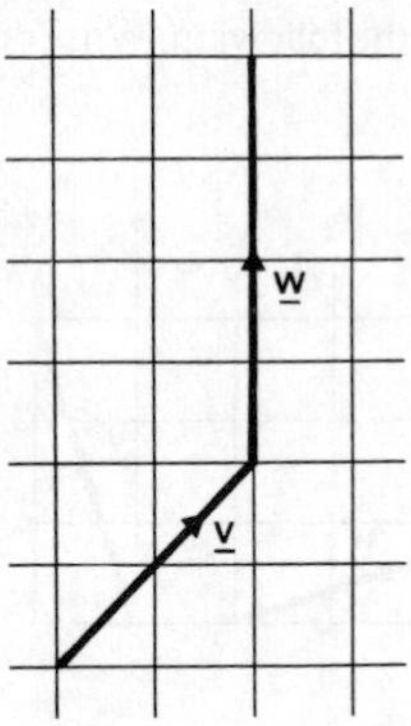

Draw the direct route from **start** to **finish** and label it $\underline{v} + \underline{w}$.

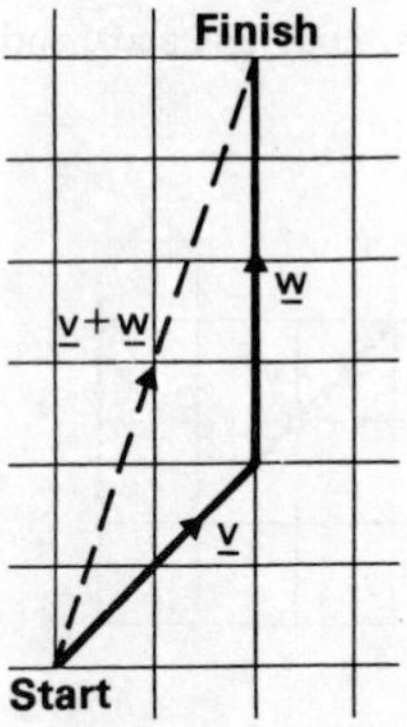

Exercise

9 On 1 cm squared paper show the additions in questions 5 to 8 above.

Continue with Section M

M The sum of two vectors

Example

Add the vectors u and v.

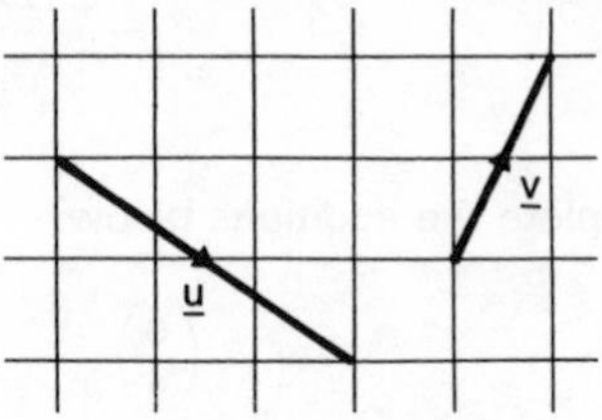

Copy the vector u.

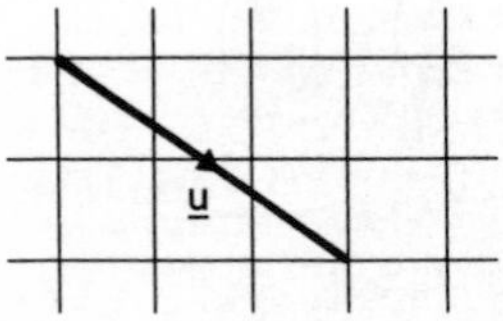

Using the **finish** of u as the **start** of v, copy v.

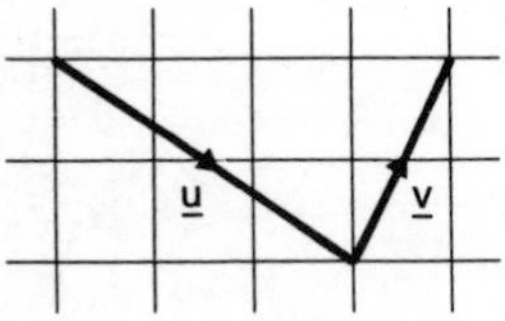

Draw the direct route from **start** to **finish** and label it u + v.

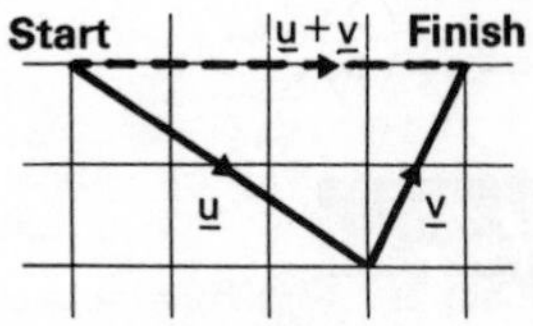

Exercise

In the same way copy and add u and v in each of the following. Write down the components of u + v in each case.

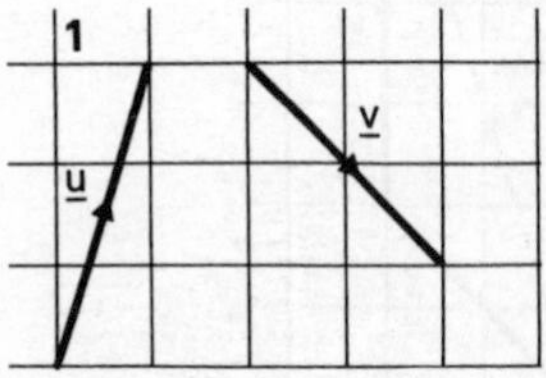

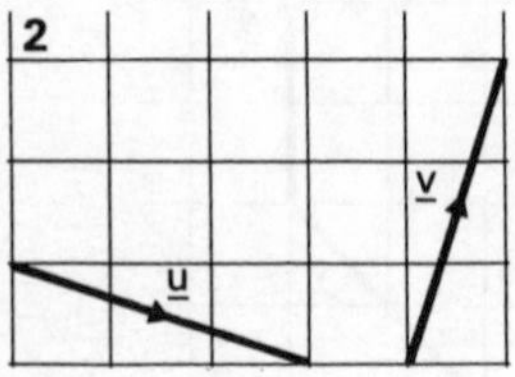

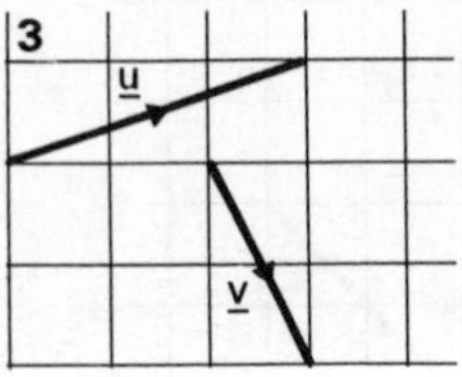

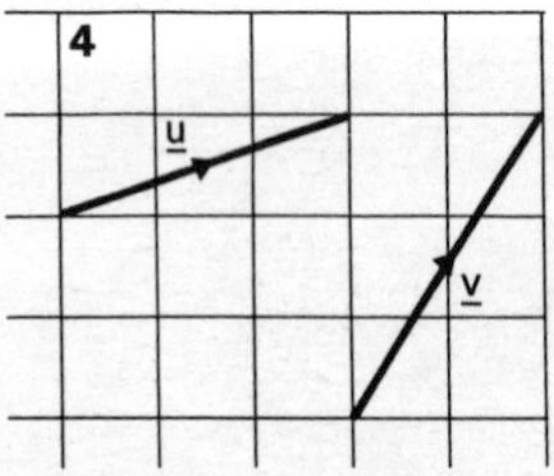

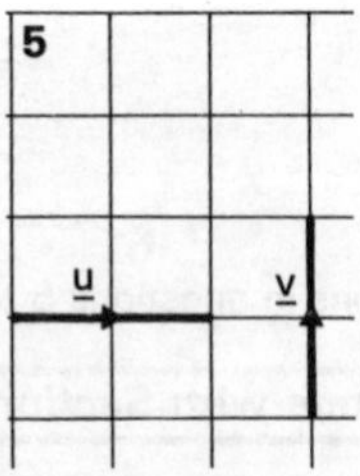

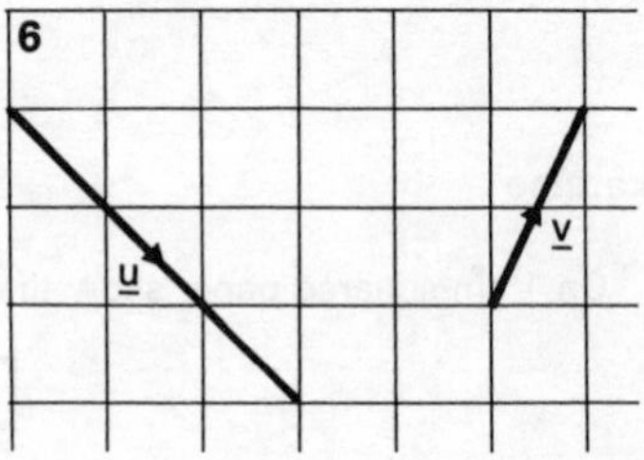

Example

For question 1 above find $\underline{u} + \underline{v}$ in component form.

$$\underline{u} = \begin{pmatrix} 1 \\ 3 \end{pmatrix} \qquad \underline{v} = \begin{pmatrix} 2 \\ -2 \end{pmatrix} \qquad \underline{u} + \underline{v} = \begin{pmatrix} 1 + 2 \\ 3 + (-2) \end{pmatrix} = \begin{pmatrix} 3 \\ 1 \end{pmatrix}$$

which should check with the answer obtained in your diagram.

Exercise

Calculate $\underline{u} + \underline{v}$ as above for questions 2 to 6 and check with the answers obtained from your diagrams.

Continue with Section N

N Negative of a vector

Exercise

Copy and complete the following:

1 $\begin{pmatrix} 2 \\ 3 \end{pmatrix} + \begin{pmatrix} -2 \\ -3 \end{pmatrix} = \begin{pmatrix} \blacksquare \\ \blacksquare \end{pmatrix}$

2 $\begin{pmatrix} 4 \\ 2 \end{pmatrix} + \begin{pmatrix} -4 \\ -2 \end{pmatrix} = \begin{pmatrix} \blacksquare \\ \blacksquare \end{pmatrix}$

3 $\begin{pmatrix} -5 \\ -2 \end{pmatrix} + \begin{pmatrix} 5 \\ 2 \end{pmatrix} = \begin{pmatrix} \blacksquare \\ \blacksquare \end{pmatrix}$

4 $\begin{pmatrix} -1 \\ -4 \end{pmatrix} + \begin{pmatrix} 1 \\ 4 \end{pmatrix} = \begin{pmatrix} \blacksquare \\ \blacksquare \end{pmatrix}$

5 $\begin{pmatrix} 1 \\ -2 \end{pmatrix} + \begin{pmatrix} -1 \\ 2 \end{pmatrix} = \begin{pmatrix} \blacksquare \\ \blacksquare \end{pmatrix}$

6 $\begin{pmatrix} -4 \\ 3 \end{pmatrix} + \begin{pmatrix} 4 \\ -3 \end{pmatrix} = \begin{pmatrix} \blacksquare \\ \blacksquare \end{pmatrix}$

Note: In each case you should have found the answer was $\begin{pmatrix} 0 \\ 0 \end{pmatrix}$, the zero vector.

Copy and complete:

7 $\begin{pmatrix} 7 \\ 6 \end{pmatrix} + \begin{pmatrix} 0 \\ 0 \end{pmatrix} = \begin{pmatrix} \blacksquare \\ \blacksquare \end{pmatrix}$

8 $\begin{pmatrix} 4 \\ 5 \end{pmatrix} + \begin{pmatrix} 0 \\ 0 \end{pmatrix} = \begin{pmatrix} \blacksquare \\ \blacksquare \end{pmatrix}$

9 $\begin{pmatrix} 5 \\ 2 \end{pmatrix} + \begin{pmatrix} 0 \\ 0 \end{pmatrix} = \begin{pmatrix} \blacksquare \\ \blacksquare \end{pmatrix}$

When two vectors add together to give the zero vector like this:

$$\begin{pmatrix}8\\2\end{pmatrix} + \begin{pmatrix}-8\\-2\end{pmatrix} = \begin{pmatrix}0\\0\end{pmatrix}$$

then each of them is said to be **the negative of the other.**

Example

$\begin{pmatrix}4\\3\end{pmatrix}$ is the negative of $\begin{pmatrix}-4\\-3\end{pmatrix}$ and

$\begin{pmatrix}-4\\-3\end{pmatrix}$ is the negative of $\begin{pmatrix}4\\3\end{pmatrix}$.

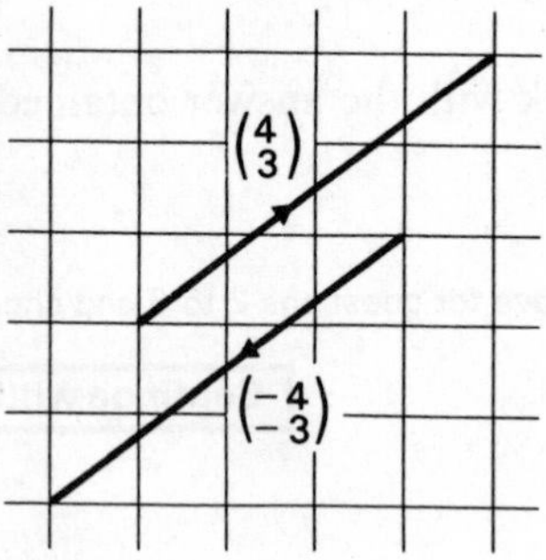

$\begin{pmatrix}-2\\5\end{pmatrix}$ is the negative of $\begin{pmatrix}2\\-5\end{pmatrix}$ $\qquad$ $\begin{pmatrix}-2\\-1\end{pmatrix}$ is the negative of $\begin{pmatrix}2\\1\end{pmatrix}$

Exercise

Write down the negative of each of the following vectors.

10 $\begin{pmatrix}2\\5\end{pmatrix}$ $\qquad$ **11** $\begin{pmatrix}1\\2\end{pmatrix}$ $\qquad$ **12** $\begin{pmatrix}4\\-1\end{pmatrix}$

13 $\begin{pmatrix}-3\\2\end{pmatrix}$ $\qquad$ **14** $\begin{pmatrix}-1\\-4\end{pmatrix}$ $\qquad$ **15** $\begin{pmatrix}-2\\0\end{pmatrix}$

> **Note:** The negative of a vector $\underline{a}$ is the vector $-\underline{a}$,
> so if $\underline{a} = \begin{pmatrix}8\\-2\end{pmatrix}$ then $-\underline{a} = \begin{pmatrix}-8\\2\end{pmatrix}$.

Copy and complete the following:

16 $\underline{x} = \begin{pmatrix}3\\4\end{pmatrix}$, $-\underline{x} = \begin{pmatrix}\blacksquare\\\blacksquare\end{pmatrix}$ $\qquad$ **17** $\underline{z} = \begin{pmatrix}7\\3\end{pmatrix}$, $-\underline{z} = \begin{pmatrix}\blacksquare\\\blacksquare\end{pmatrix}$

18 $\underline{w} = \begin{pmatrix}-2\\8\end{pmatrix}$, $-\underline{w} = \begin{pmatrix}\blacksquare\\\blacksquare\end{pmatrix}$ $\qquad$ **19** $\underline{t} = \begin{pmatrix}4\\-1\end{pmatrix}$, $-\underline{t} = \begin{pmatrix}\blacksquare\\\blacksquare\end{pmatrix}$

20 For the vectors in questions 16 to 19, draw the following vectors on 1 cm squared paper:

$\underline{x}$ and $-\underline{x}$ $\qquad$ $\underline{z}$ and $-\underline{z}$

$\underline{w}$ and $-\underline{w}$ $\qquad$ $\underline{t}$ and $-\underline{t}$

Continue with Section O

O Multiplication by a number

In this diagram the vector

$\underline{v} = \begin{pmatrix} 4 \\ 1 \end{pmatrix}$ has been added to itself.

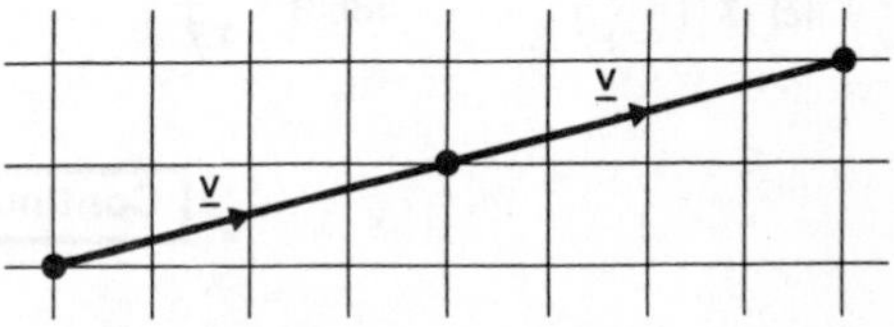

That is $\begin{pmatrix} 4 \\ 1 \end{pmatrix} + \begin{pmatrix} 4 \\ 1 \end{pmatrix} = \begin{pmatrix} 8 \\ 2 \end{pmatrix}$.

$\underline{v} + \underline{v} = 2\underline{v}$

We will write $\underline{v} + \underline{v}$ as $2\underline{v}$.

Notice that both the x component and the y component of $\underline{v}$ are doubled so that $2\underline{v} = 2\begin{pmatrix} 4 \\ 1 \end{pmatrix} = \begin{pmatrix} 2 \times 4 \\ 2 \times 1 \end{pmatrix} = \begin{pmatrix} 8 \\ 2 \end{pmatrix}$

In this diagram the vector $\underline{u} = \begin{pmatrix} -3 \\ -1 \end{pmatrix}$ is added to itself and then $\underline{u}$ is added to the sum.

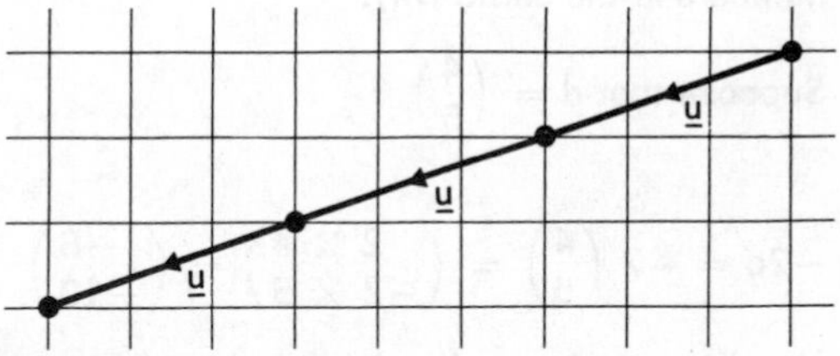

That is $\begin{pmatrix} -3 \\ -1 \end{pmatrix} + \begin{pmatrix} -3 \\ -1 \end{pmatrix} + \begin{pmatrix} -3 \\ -1 \end{pmatrix} = \begin{pmatrix} -9 \\ -3 \end{pmatrix}$

$\underline{u} + \underline{u} + \underline{u} = 3\underline{u}$

We will write $\underline{u} + \underline{u} + \underline{u}$ as $3\underline{u}$.

This time the x and y components are both multiplied by 3 so that

$$3\underline{u} = 3\begin{pmatrix} -3 \\ -1 \end{pmatrix} = \begin{pmatrix} 3 \times (-3) \\ 3 \times (-1) \end{pmatrix} = \begin{pmatrix} -9 \\ -3 \end{pmatrix}$$

Exercise

1 On 1 cm squared paper draw diagrams to show the following:

(a) $\begin{pmatrix} 3 \\ 5 \end{pmatrix} + \begin{pmatrix} 3 \\ 5 \end{pmatrix}$

(b) $\begin{pmatrix} 2 \\ -3 \end{pmatrix} + \begin{pmatrix} 2 \\ -3 \end{pmatrix} + \begin{pmatrix} 2 \\ -3 \end{pmatrix}$

2 Suppose that $\underline{s} = \begin{pmatrix} 2 \\ 3 \end{pmatrix}$, $\underline{t} = \begin{pmatrix} -3 \\ 4 \end{pmatrix}$, and $\underline{a} = \begin{pmatrix} -1 \\ -5 \end{pmatrix}$.

Draw diagrams on squared paper to show

$\underline{s}$, $2\underline{s}$, $4\underline{s}$, $\underline{t}$, $3\underline{t}$, $\underline{a}$, $3\underline{a}$

3 Copy and complete (a) and then do (b) to (f) in the same way:

(a) $3\begin{pmatrix}4\\3\end{pmatrix} = \begin{pmatrix}3\times 4\\3\times 3\end{pmatrix} = \begin{pmatrix}\blacksquare\\\blacksquare\end{pmatrix}$ (b) $5\begin{pmatrix}-2\\1\end{pmatrix}$

(c) $7\begin{pmatrix}-3\\-1\end{pmatrix}$ (d) $3\begin{pmatrix}5\\1\end{pmatrix}$ (e) $2\begin{pmatrix}0\\4\end{pmatrix}$ (f) $4\begin{pmatrix}3\\-2\end{pmatrix}$

Continue with Section P

P Multiplication by a negative number

We can multiply vectors by negative numbers in the same way.

Suppose that $\underline{d} = \begin{pmatrix}4\\5\end{pmatrix}$.

$$-2\underline{d} = -2\begin{pmatrix}4\\5\end{pmatrix} = \begin{pmatrix}-2\times 4\\-2\times 5\end{pmatrix} = \begin{pmatrix}-8\\-10\end{pmatrix}$$

The diagram shows $\underline{d}$ and $-2\underline{d}$.

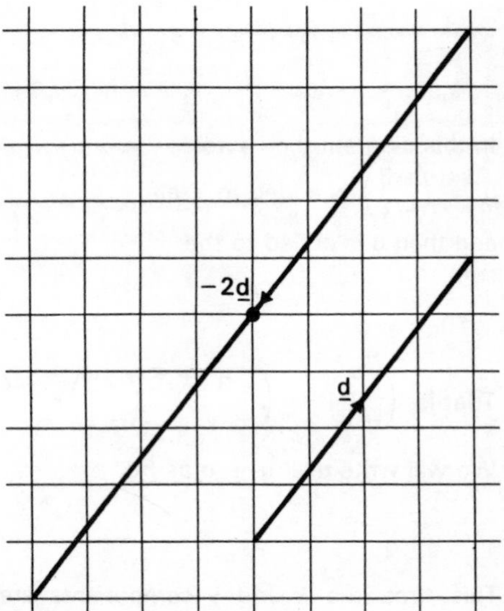

Notice the direction of the arrows.

Example

This diagram shows the vectors

$$\underline{k} = \begin{pmatrix}1\\2\end{pmatrix} \text{ and } -3\underline{k} = -3\begin{pmatrix}1\\2\end{pmatrix} = \begin{pmatrix}-3\times 1\\-3\times 2\end{pmatrix} = \begin{pmatrix}-3\\-6\end{pmatrix}$$

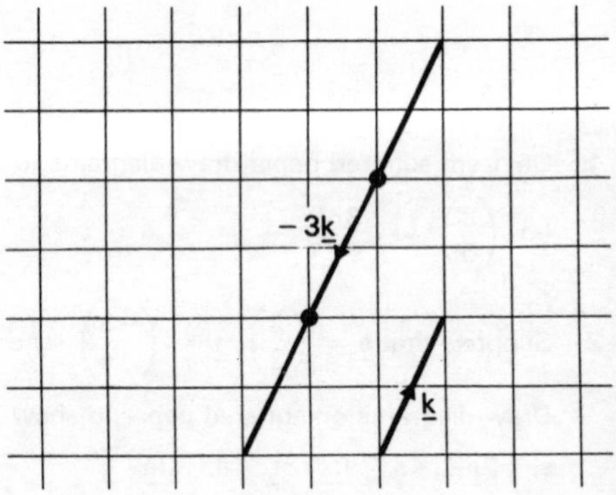

Notice the direction of the arrows.

Exercise

1 Copy and complete (a) and then do (b) to (f) in the same way:

(a) $-5\begin{pmatrix}2\\1\end{pmatrix} = \begin{pmatrix}-5\times 2\\-5\times 1\end{pmatrix} = \begin{pmatrix}\blacksquare\\\blacksquare\end{pmatrix}$ (b) $-4\begin{pmatrix}3\\1\end{pmatrix}$

(c) $-3\begin{pmatrix}-2\\1\end{pmatrix}$ (d) $-2\begin{pmatrix}4\\0\end{pmatrix}$ (e) $-5\begin{pmatrix}2\\-1\end{pmatrix}$ (f) $-3\begin{pmatrix}-3\\-1\end{pmatrix}$

2 If $\underline{m} = \begin{pmatrix}2\\-1\end{pmatrix}$ and $\underline{n} = \begin{pmatrix}-3\\2\end{pmatrix}$ draw on squared paper diagrams to show:

$\underline{m}$, $-3\underline{m}$, $-5\underline{m}$, $\underline{n}$, $-2\underline{n}$, $-3\underline{n}$

Continue with Section Q

Q Progress check

Exercise

1 What are the components of the following vectors?

Copy and complete:

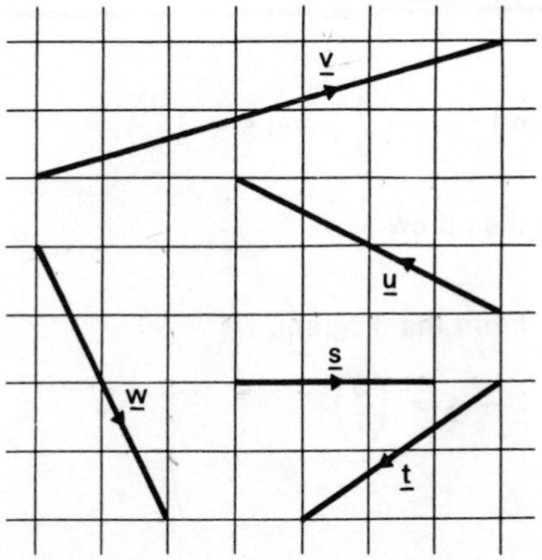

$\underline{v} = \begin{pmatrix}\blacksquare\\\blacksquare\end{pmatrix}$

$\underline{u} = \begin{pmatrix}\blacksquare\\\blacksquare\end{pmatrix}$

$\underline{w} = \begin{pmatrix}\blacksquare\\\blacksquare\end{pmatrix}$

$\underline{s} = \begin{pmatrix}\blacksquare\\\blacksquare\end{pmatrix}$

$\underline{t} = \begin{pmatrix}\blacksquare\\\blacksquare\end{pmatrix}$

2 On 1 cm squared paper draw diagrams to show the following vectors:

$\underline{a} = \begin{pmatrix}3\\5\end{pmatrix}$ $\underline{b} = \begin{pmatrix}2\\-3\end{pmatrix}$ $\underline{c} = \begin{pmatrix}-4\\0\end{pmatrix}$ $\underline{d} = \begin{pmatrix}0\\3\end{pmatrix}$ $\underline{e} = \begin{pmatrix}-3\\2\end{pmatrix}$

Calculate the length of each of these vectors. Write your answer beside each drawing.

3 If $\underline{u} = \begin{pmatrix}4\\1\end{pmatrix}$, $\underline{v} = \begin{pmatrix}5\\3\end{pmatrix}$, and $\underline{w} = \begin{pmatrix}-2\\2\end{pmatrix}$, draw diagrams on squared paper to show the additions

$\underline{u} + \underline{v}$ and $\underline{u} + \underline{w}$.

4 Copy and complete the following additions:

(a) $\begin{pmatrix} 4 \\ 2 \end{pmatrix} + \begin{pmatrix} 2 \\ 4 \end{pmatrix} = \begin{pmatrix} \blacksquare \\ \blacksquare \end{pmatrix}$ (b) $\begin{pmatrix} 3 \\ 1 \end{pmatrix} + \begin{pmatrix} 0 \\ 4 \end{pmatrix} = \begin{pmatrix} \blacksquare \\ \blacksquare \end{pmatrix}$

(c) $\begin{pmatrix} 2 \\ -1 \end{pmatrix} + \begin{pmatrix} 4 \\ 3 \end{pmatrix} = \begin{pmatrix} \blacksquare \\ \blacksquare \end{pmatrix}$ (d) $\begin{pmatrix} 6 \\ 2 \end{pmatrix} + \begin{pmatrix} -1 \\ -2 \end{pmatrix} = \begin{pmatrix} \blacksquare \\ \blacksquare \end{pmatrix}$

5 What is the negative of each of the following vectors?

$\underline{x} = \begin{pmatrix} 2 \\ 7 \end{pmatrix}$ $\underline{y} = \begin{pmatrix} 3 \\ -1 \end{pmatrix}$ $\underline{v} = \begin{pmatrix} -4 \\ -3 \end{pmatrix}$

Copy and complete: $-\underline{x} = \begin{pmatrix} \blacksquare \\ \blacksquare \end{pmatrix}$, $-\underline{y} = \begin{pmatrix} \blacksquare \\ \blacksquare \end{pmatrix}$, $-\underline{v} = \begin{pmatrix} \blacksquare \\ \blacksquare \end{pmatrix}$

6 $\underline{u} = \begin{pmatrix} 3 \\ 4 \end{pmatrix}$ and $\underline{a} = \begin{pmatrix} 2 \\ 4 \end{pmatrix}$

Copy and complete: $2\underline{u} = \begin{pmatrix} \blacksquare \\ \blacksquare \end{pmatrix}$, $-3\underline{a} = \begin{pmatrix} \blacksquare \\ \blacksquare \end{pmatrix}$

Draw $\underline{u}$, $2\underline{u}$, $\underline{a}$, and $-3\underline{a}$.

Ask your teacher what to do next

R Order of addition

In question 6 of the exercise in Section L, $\underline{k} = \begin{pmatrix} 4 \\ 3 \end{pmatrix}$ and $\underline{s} = \begin{pmatrix} 1 \\ 4 \end{pmatrix}$.

To find $\underline{k} + \underline{s}$, you started with $\underline{k}$ and then drew $\underline{s}$.

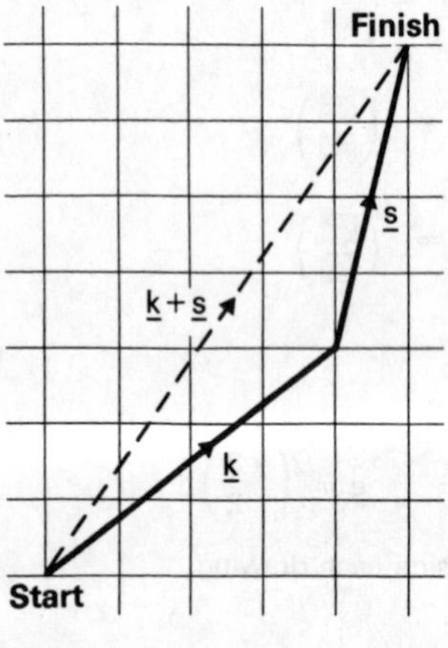

From the diagram,

$\underline{k} + \underline{s} = \begin{pmatrix} 5 \\ 7 \end{pmatrix}$

What is the vector $\underline{s} + \underline{k}$?

This time we start by drawing $\underline{s}$ and then draw $\underline{k}$.

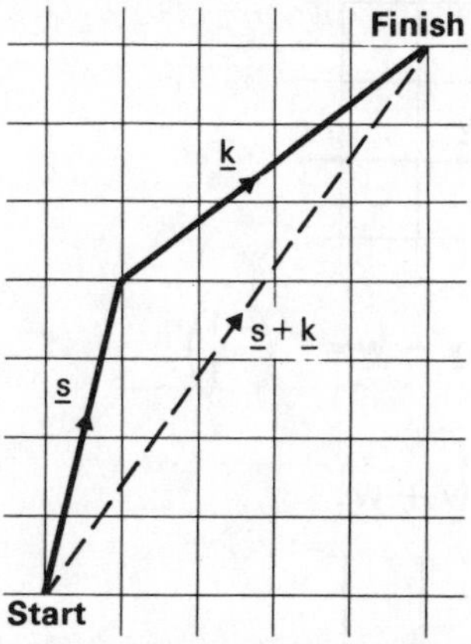

From the diagram,

$$\underline{s} + \underline{k} = \begin{pmatrix} 5 \\ 7 \end{pmatrix}$$

So starting with $\underline{k}$ and adding $\underline{s}$ gives the same result as starting with $\underline{s}$ and adding $\underline{k}$.

We have shown that the order in which we add two vectors is not important.

Continue with Sheet M2/3

S Adding three vectors

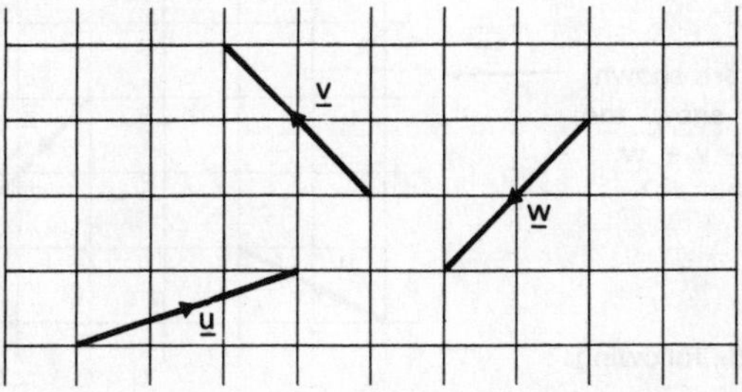

$$\underline{u} = \begin{pmatrix} 3 \\ 1 \end{pmatrix} \qquad \underline{v} = \begin{pmatrix} -2 \\ 2 \end{pmatrix} \qquad \text{and} \qquad \underline{w} = \begin{pmatrix} -2 \\ -2 \end{pmatrix}$$

Let us find the sum of these three vectors.

Method 1

Start by adding $\underline{u}$ and $\underline{v}$.

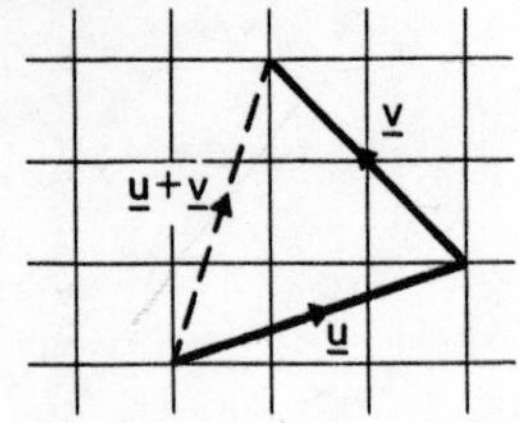

Next, to ($\underline{u} + \underline{v}$) add $\underline{w}$.

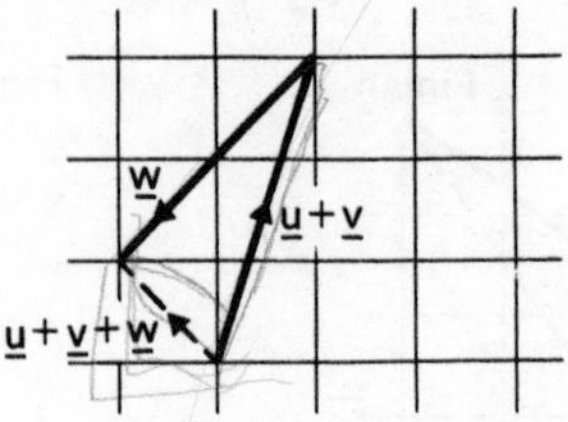

From the diagram $\underline{u} + \underline{v} + \underline{w} = \begin{pmatrix} -1 \\ 1 \end{pmatrix}$

Method 2

Suppose we start by finding $\underline{v} + \underline{w}$ first.

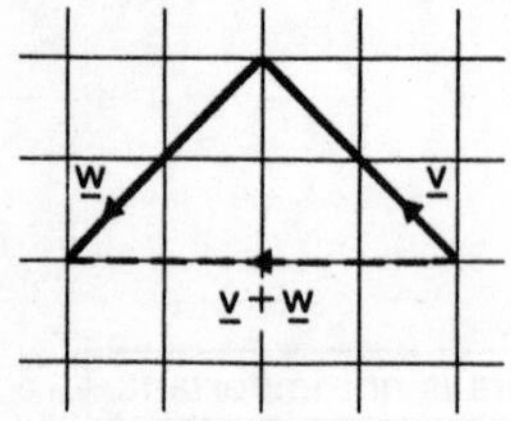

Next, to $\underline{u}$ add ($\underline{v} + \underline{w}$).

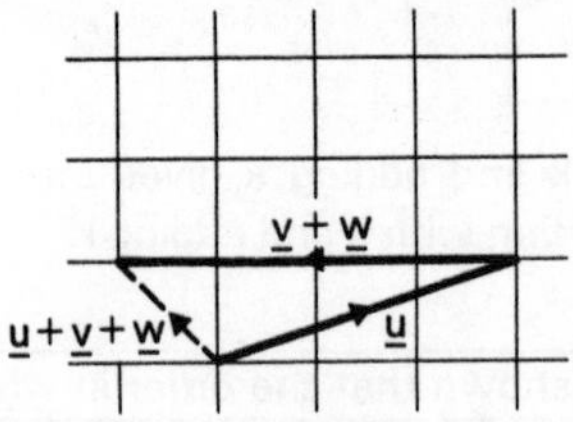

From the diagram $\underline{u} + \underline{v} + \underline{w} = \begin{pmatrix} -1 \\ 1 \end{pmatrix}$.

So adding ($\underline{u} + \underline{v}$) and $\underline{w}$ gives the same result as adding $\underline{u}$ and ($\underline{v} + \underline{w}$).

The order in which we add three vectors is not important.

Exercise

1 Vectors $\underline{u}$, $\underline{v}$, and $\underline{w}$ are shown. Draw diagrams to show the vectors $\underline{u} + \underline{v}$ and $\underline{u} + \underline{v} + \underline{w}$. →

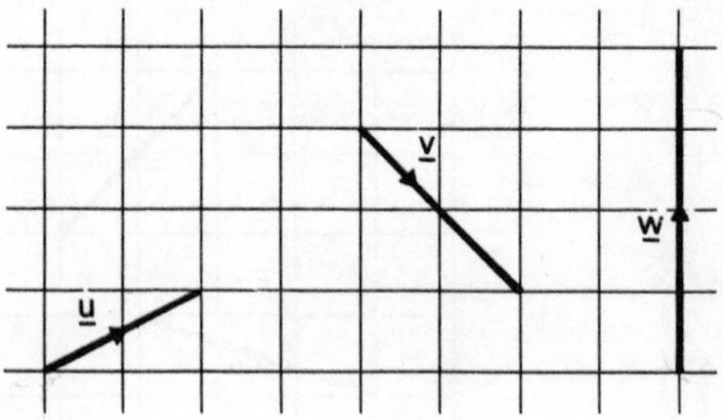

Copy and complete the following:

$\underline{u} = \begin{pmatrix} 2 \\ 1 \end{pmatrix}$ $\underline{v} = \begin{pmatrix} \blacksquare \\ \blacksquare \end{pmatrix}$ $\underline{w} = \begin{pmatrix} \blacksquare \\ \blacksquare \end{pmatrix}$

$\underline{u} + \underline{v} = \begin{pmatrix} \blacksquare + \blacksquare \\ \blacksquare + \blacksquare \end{pmatrix} = \begin{pmatrix} \blacksquare \\ \blacksquare \end{pmatrix}$

$\underline{u} + \underline{v} + \underline{w} = \begin{pmatrix} 4 + \blacksquare \\ -1 + \blacksquare \end{pmatrix} = \begin{pmatrix} \blacksquare \\ \blacksquare \end{pmatrix}$

Check that the vector $\underline{u} + \underline{v} + \underline{w}$ you have drawn has these components.

2 Vectors $\underline{a}$, $\underline{b}$ and $\underline{c}$ are shown. Draw diagrams to show the vectors $\underline{a} + \underline{b}$ and $\underline{a} + \underline{b} + \underline{c}$.

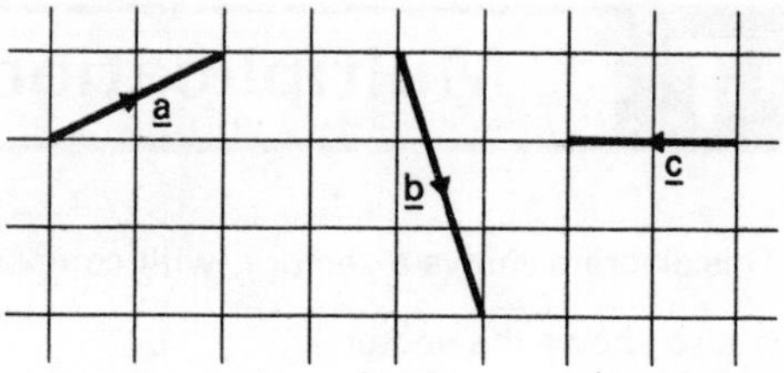

Copy and complete the following:

$\underline{a} = \begin{pmatrix} 2 \\ 1 \end{pmatrix}$ $\quad \underline{b} = \begin{pmatrix} \square \\ \square \end{pmatrix}$ $\quad \underline{c} = \begin{pmatrix} \square \\ \square \end{pmatrix}$

$\underline{a} + \underline{b} = \begin{pmatrix} \square + \square \\ \square + \square \end{pmatrix} = \begin{pmatrix} \square \\ \square \end{pmatrix}$

$\underline{a} + \underline{b} + \underline{c} = \begin{pmatrix} \square + \square \\ \square + \square \end{pmatrix} = \begin{pmatrix} \square \\ \square \end{pmatrix}$

Check that the vector $\underline{a} + \underline{b} + \underline{c}$ you have drawn has these components.

3 Vectors $\underline{u}$, $\underline{v}$, and $\underline{w}$ are shown. Draw diagrams to show the vectors $\underline{u} + \underline{v}$ and $\underline{u} + \underline{v} + \underline{w}$.

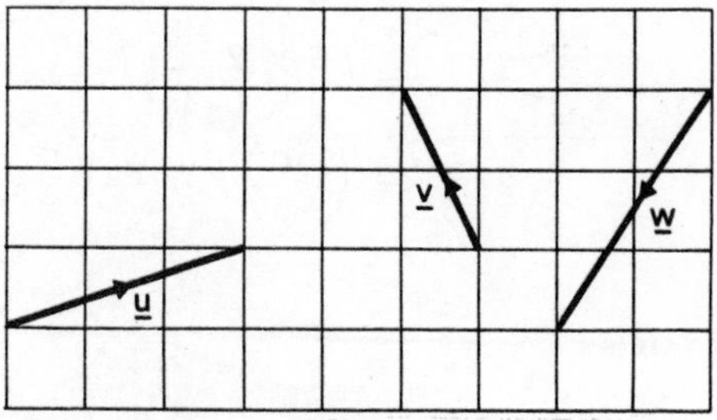

Copy and complete the following:

$\underline{u} = \begin{pmatrix} 3 \\ 1 \end{pmatrix}$ $\quad \underline{v} = \begin{pmatrix} \square \\ \square \end{pmatrix}$ $\quad \underline{w} = \begin{pmatrix} \square \\ \square \end{pmatrix}$

$\underline{u} + \underline{v} = \begin{pmatrix} \square + \square \\ \square + \square \end{pmatrix} = \begin{pmatrix} \square \\ \square \end{pmatrix}$

$\underline{u} + \underline{v} + \underline{w} = \begin{pmatrix} \square + \square \\ \square + \square \end{pmatrix} = \begin{pmatrix} \square \\ \square \end{pmatrix}$

> **Note:** You should have found that the translation $\underline{u}$ followed by $\underline{v}$ followed by $\underline{w}$ brought you back to your starting point. That is, $\underline{u} + \underline{v} + \underline{w}$ has no effect. We say that $\underline{u} + \underline{v} + \underline{w}$ is the **zero vector**.
>
> In terms of components the zero vector is $\begin{pmatrix} 0 \\ 0 \end{pmatrix}$. It is also written as $\underline{0}$.

4 Copy diagram (a). On your diagram draw another vector so that the vectors in the diagram add up to $\begin{pmatrix} 0 \\ 0 \end{pmatrix}$.

Beside this last vector write its components.

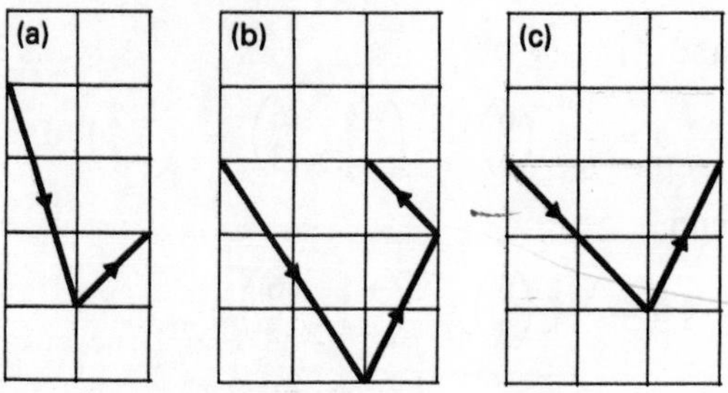

Repeat this for diagrams (b) and (c).

Continue with Section T

T Multiplication by a fraction

This diagram shows a vector $\underline{r}$, with components $\begin{pmatrix} 4 \\ -2 \end{pmatrix}$.

It also shows the vector $\frac{1}{2}\underline{r}$.

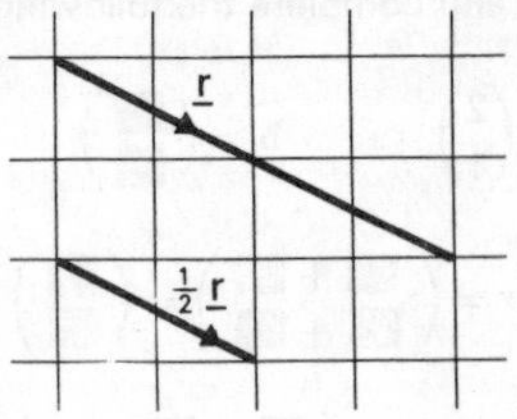

That is, $\frac{1}{2}\begin{pmatrix} 4 \\ -2 \end{pmatrix} = \begin{pmatrix} \frac{1}{2} \times 4 \\ \frac{1}{2} \times -2 \end{pmatrix} = \begin{pmatrix} 2 \\ -1 \end{pmatrix}$

This diagram shows $\frac{5}{2}\underline{r}$, which means $5 \times \frac{1}{2}\underline{r}$.

$$\frac{5}{2}\begin{pmatrix} 4 \\ -2 \end{pmatrix} = \begin{pmatrix} \frac{5}{2} \times 4 \\ \frac{5}{2} \times -2 \end{pmatrix} = \begin{pmatrix} 5 \times \frac{1}{2} \text{ of } 4 \\ 5 \times \frac{1}{2} \text{ of } (-2) \end{pmatrix} = \begin{pmatrix} 5 \times 2 \\ 5 \times (-1) \end{pmatrix} = \begin{pmatrix} 10 \\ -5 \end{pmatrix}$$

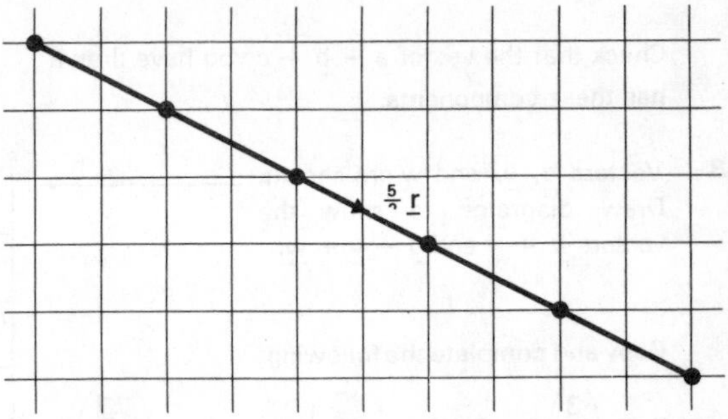

Exercise

1 If $\underline{v} = \begin{pmatrix} 6 \\ -4 \end{pmatrix}$ and $\underline{w} = \begin{pmatrix} -3 \\ 6 \end{pmatrix}$ draw diagrams on 1 cm squared paper to show $\underline{v}$, $\frac{1}{2}\underline{v}$, $\frac{3}{2}\underline{v}$, $\underline{w}$, $\frac{1}{3}\underline{w}$, and $\frac{4}{3}\underline{w}$.

2 Find the value of each of the following:

(a) $\frac{1}{2}\begin{pmatrix} 10 \\ -4 \end{pmatrix}$ (b) $\frac{2}{3}\begin{pmatrix} -6 \\ 9 \end{pmatrix}$ (c) $\frac{3}{2}\begin{pmatrix} 4 \\ 2 \end{pmatrix}$ (d) $\frac{5}{3}\begin{pmatrix} 12 \\ -3 \end{pmatrix}$

Example

This diagram shows the vector $\underline{a} = \begin{pmatrix} 6 \\ 3 \end{pmatrix}$

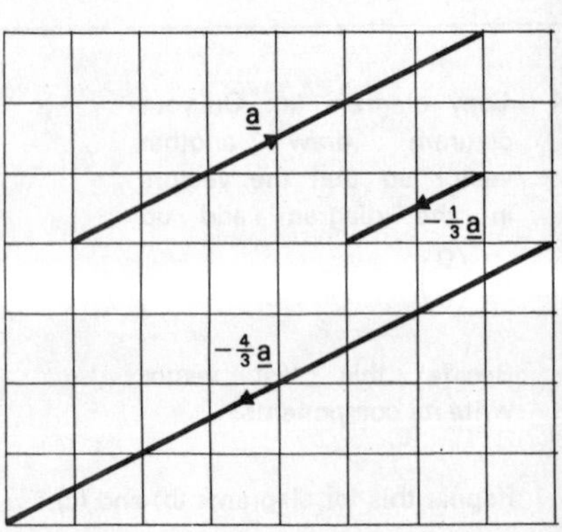

and

$$-\tfrac{1}{3}\underline{a} = -\tfrac{1}{3}\begin{pmatrix} 6 \\ 3 \end{pmatrix} = \begin{pmatrix} -\frac{1}{3} \times 6 \\ -\frac{1}{3} \times 3 \end{pmatrix} = \begin{pmatrix} -2 \\ -1 \end{pmatrix}$$

and

$$-\tfrac{4}{3}\underline{a} = -\tfrac{4}{3}\begin{pmatrix} 6 \\ 3 \end{pmatrix} = \begin{pmatrix} -\frac{4}{3} \times 6 \\ -\frac{4}{3} \times 3 \end{pmatrix} = \begin{pmatrix} -4 \times \frac{1}{3} \text{ of } 6 \\ -4 \times \frac{1}{3} \text{ of } 3 \end{pmatrix} = \begin{pmatrix} -4 \times 2 \\ -4 \times 1 \end{pmatrix} = \begin{pmatrix} -8 \\ -4 \end{pmatrix}$$

Exercise

3 If $\underline{b} = \begin{pmatrix} 4 \\ 2 \end{pmatrix}$ and $\underline{c} = \begin{pmatrix} 10 \\ 4 \end{pmatrix}$ draw diagrams on 1 cm squared paper to show: $\underline{b}$, $-\frac{1}{2}$, $-\frac{5}{2}\underline{b}$, $\underline{c}$, $-\frac{1}{2}\underline{c}$, $-\frac{3}{2}\underline{c}$.

4 Find the value of each of the following:

(a) $-\frac{1}{3}\begin{pmatrix} 3 \\ 6 \end{pmatrix}$ (b) $-\frac{1}{2}\begin{pmatrix} 10 \\ -6 \end{pmatrix}$ (c) $-\frac{3}{2}\begin{pmatrix} 4 \\ 8 \end{pmatrix}$ (d) $-\frac{5}{4}\begin{pmatrix} -8 \\ -12 \end{pmatrix}$

Continue with Section U

U Use of brackets

Example

On squared paper draw diagrams to show
(a) $\underline{a} + \underline{b}$ and $2(\underline{a} + \underline{b})$,
(b) $2\underline{a}$, $2\underline{b}$, and $2\underline{a} + 2\underline{b}$.

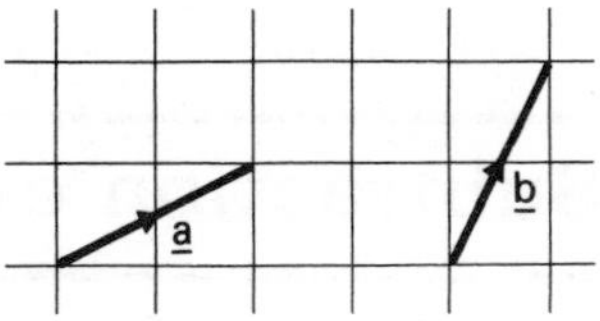

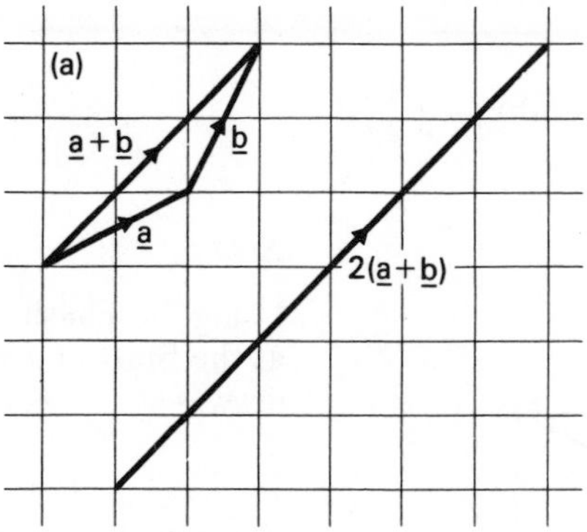

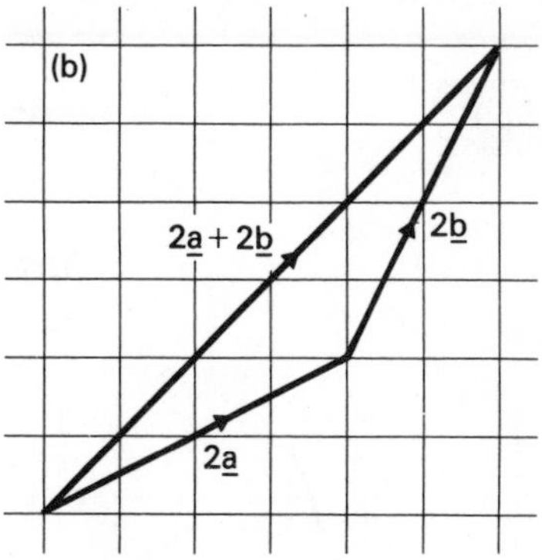

Notice that $2(\underline{a} + \underline{b}) = 2\underline{a} + 2\underline{b}$.

Exercise

1 Copy and complete the following:

If $\underline{u} = \begin{pmatrix} 3 \\ 4 \end{pmatrix}$ and $\underline{v} = \begin{pmatrix} 1 \\ 2 \end{pmatrix}$ $\underline{u} + \underline{v} = \begin{pmatrix} \square \\ \square \end{pmatrix}$ $2(\underline{u} + \underline{v}) = \begin{pmatrix} \square \\ \square \end{pmatrix}$

$2\underline{u} = \begin{pmatrix} \square \\ \square \end{pmatrix}$ $2\underline{v} = \begin{pmatrix} \square \\ \square \end{pmatrix}$ $2\underline{u} + 2\underline{v} = \begin{pmatrix} \square \\ \square \end{pmatrix}$

What do you notice?

2 On squared paper copy $\underline{a}$ and $\underline{b}$ and draw diagrams to show

(a) $\underline{a} + \underline{b}$ and $\frac{1}{2}(\underline{a} + \underline{b})$,

(b) $\frac{1}{2}\underline{a}$, $\frac{1}{2}\underline{b}$ and $\frac{1}{2}\underline{a} + \frac{1}{2}\underline{b}$.

You should find that $\frac{1}{2}(\underline{a} + \underline{b})$ is the same as $\frac{1}{2}\underline{a} + \frac{1}{2}\underline{b}$.

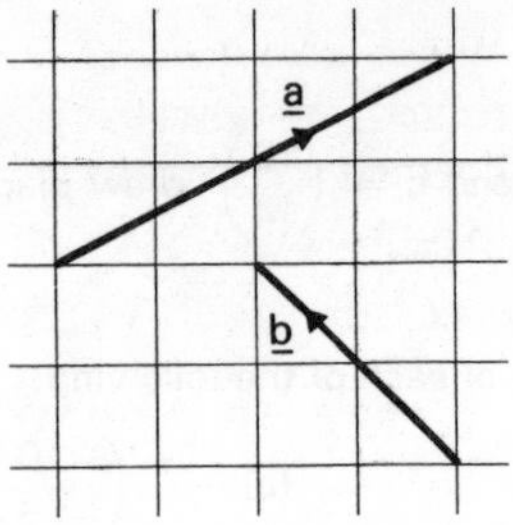

3 Copy and complete the following:

If $\underline{u} = \begin{pmatrix} 6 \\ 4 \end{pmatrix}$ and $\underline{v} = \begin{pmatrix} 4 \\ 8 \end{pmatrix}$

$\underline{u} + \underline{v} = \begin{pmatrix} \blacksquare \\ \blacksquare \end{pmatrix}$ $\qquad \frac{1}{2}(\underline{u} + \underline{v}) = \begin{pmatrix} \blacksquare \\ \blacksquare \end{pmatrix}$

$\frac{1}{2}\underline{u} = \begin{pmatrix} \blacksquare \\ \blacksquare \end{pmatrix}$ $\qquad \frac{1}{2}\underline{v} = \begin{pmatrix} \blacksquare \\ \blacksquare \end{pmatrix}$ $\qquad \frac{1}{2}\underline{u} + \frac{1}{2}\underline{v} = \begin{pmatrix} \blacksquare \\ \blacksquare \end{pmatrix}$

What do you notice?

Continue with Section V

V Subtraction of vectors

If $\underline{w}$ and $\underline{v}$ are two vectors we can find $\underline{w} - \underline{v}$ in the following way.

Example

Suppose $\underline{w} = \begin{pmatrix} 2 \\ 5 \end{pmatrix}$ and $\underline{v} = \begin{pmatrix} 4 \\ 2 \end{pmatrix}$.

Step 1

Draw $\underline{w}$.

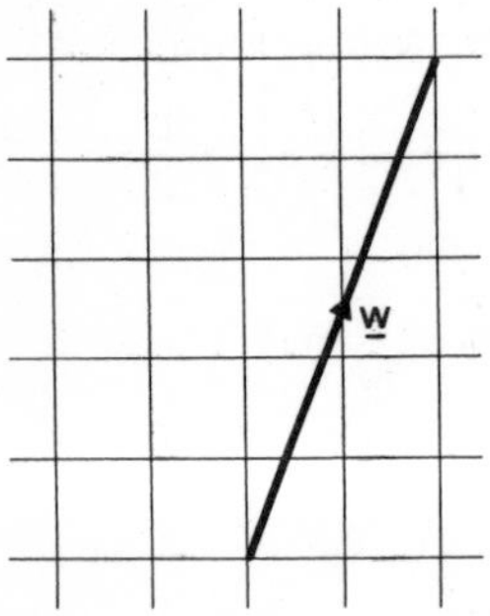

Step 2

Draw $\underline{v}$.

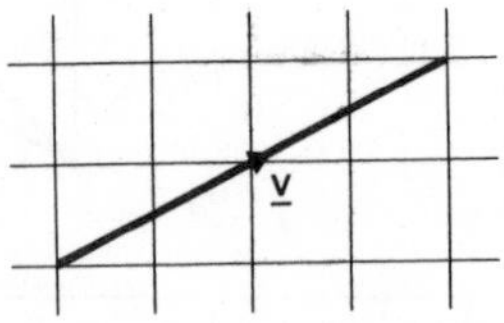

Step 3

Using the **Finish** of $\underline{w}$ as the **Start** of $-\underline{v}$, draw $-\underline{v}$.

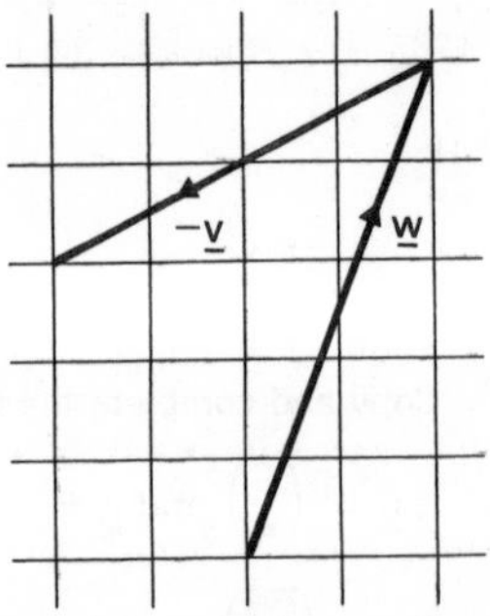

Remember: $-\underline{v}$ is the same length as $\underline{v}$ but in the **opposite** direction.

Step 4

Draw the direct route from **Start** to **Finish**. This is $\underline{w} + (-\underline{v})$, which we write as $\underline{w} - \underline{v}$ and label in the diagram.

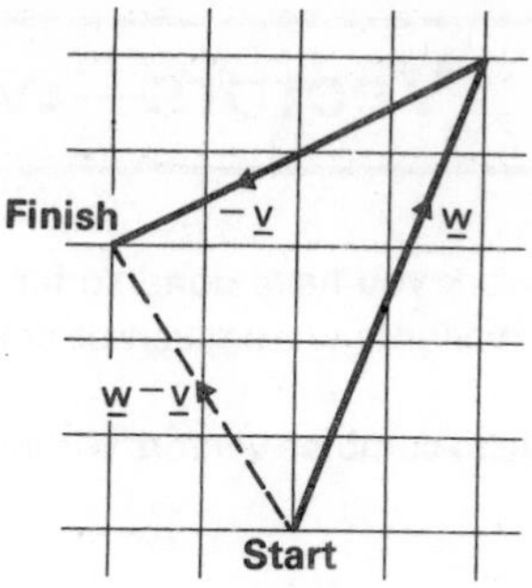

Exercise

1 $\underline{w} = \begin{pmatrix} 3 \\ 4 \end{pmatrix}$, $\underline{v} = \begin{pmatrix} 1 \\ 3 \end{pmatrix}$. Draw a diagram on 1 cm squared paper to show the vector $\underline{w} - \underline{v}$ and write down the components of $\underline{w} - \underline{v}$.

2 $\underline{w} = \begin{pmatrix} 5 \\ 7 \end{pmatrix}$, $\underline{v} = \begin{pmatrix} 3 \\ 2 \end{pmatrix}$. Draw a diagram on 1 cm squared paper to show the vector $\underline{w} - \underline{v}$ and write down the components of $\underline{w} - \underline{v}$. Check that this answer can be obtained by subtracting the components, i.e. $\begin{pmatrix} 5 - 3 \\ 7 - 2 \end{pmatrix}$.

3 Repeat question 2 for $\underline{w} = \begin{pmatrix} 5 \\ 1 \end{pmatrix}$, $\underline{v} = \begin{pmatrix} 3 \\ -4 \end{pmatrix}$.

Example

$\underline{w} = \begin{pmatrix} 4 \\ -1 \end{pmatrix}$, $\underline{v} = \begin{pmatrix} 2 \\ -4 \end{pmatrix}$. Calculate $\underline{w} - \underline{v}$ without drawing a diagram.

$$\underline{w} - \underline{v} = \begin{pmatrix} 4 - 2 \\ -1 - (-4) \end{pmatrix} = \begin{pmatrix} 2 \\ -1 + 4 \end{pmatrix} = \begin{pmatrix} 2 \\ 3 \end{pmatrix}.$$

Exercise

In each of the following calculate $\underline{w} - \underline{v}$ without drawing a diagram.

4 $\underline{w} = \begin{pmatrix} 4 \\ 1 \end{pmatrix}$ $\underline{v} = \begin{pmatrix} 2 \\ -1 \end{pmatrix}$

5 $\underline{w} = \begin{pmatrix} -5 \\ 2 \end{pmatrix}$ $\underline{v} = \begin{pmatrix} 1 \\ 3 \end{pmatrix}$

6 $\underline{w} = \begin{pmatrix} -6 \\ -2 \end{pmatrix}$ $\underline{v} = \begin{pmatrix} -3 \\ 1 \end{pmatrix}$

7 $\underline{w} = \begin{pmatrix} 4 \\ -3 \end{pmatrix}$ $\underline{v} = \begin{pmatrix} 7 \\ 1 \end{pmatrix}$

Continue with Section W

W Vectors—without a grid

In all the work you have done so far on adding vectors you have been concerned with vectors whose components were given or could be read off from a grid.

It is possible to combine vectors without a grid, provided you remember how to draw parallel lines.

How do you draw a line through the point *Z* parallel to the line *XY*?

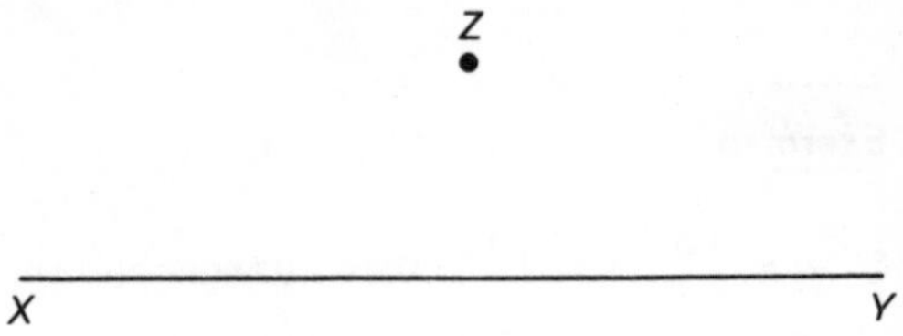

Step 1

Place one edge of your set square along the line *XY*.

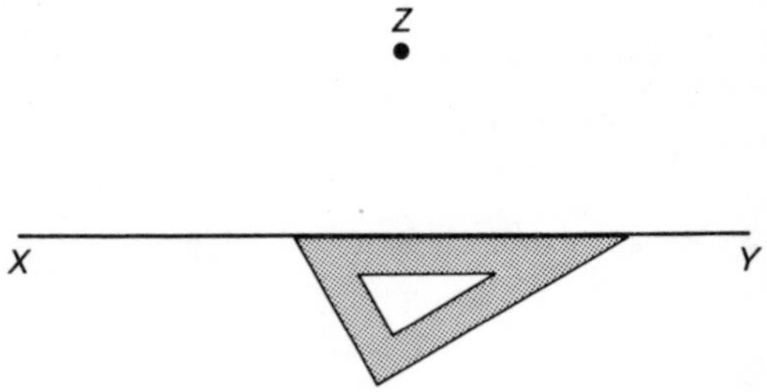

Step 2

Lay a ruler along another edge of the set square.

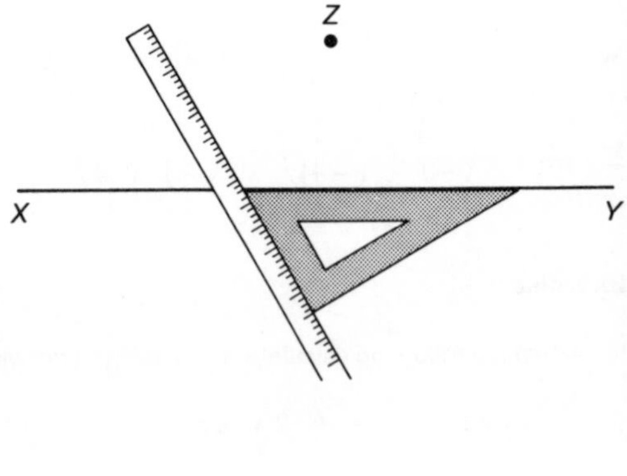

Step 3

Pressing firmly on the ruler so that it cannot move, slide the set square up until the top edge is just below the point *Z*.

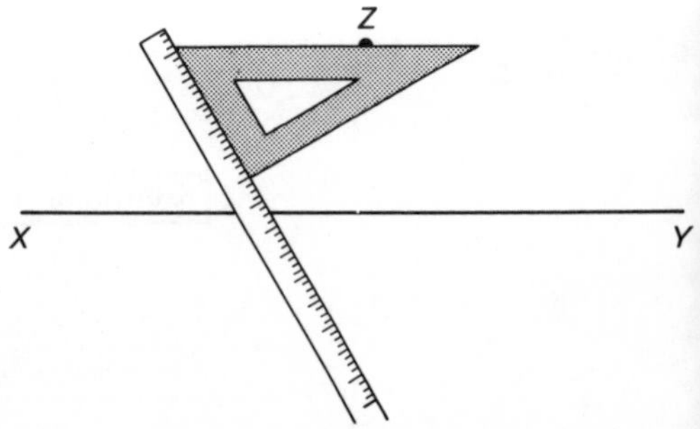

Step 4

Draw a line along the edge of the set square passing through the point *Z*.

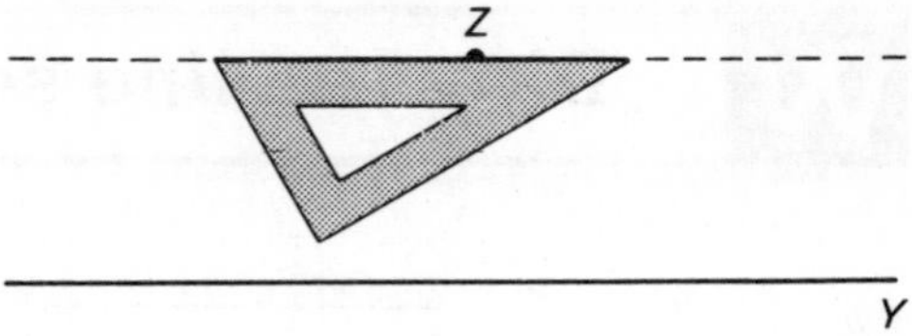

This second line is **parallel** to the first one.

Example

$\underline{u}$, $\underline{v}$, and $\underline{w}$ are the vectors shown.

To find $\underline{u} + \underline{v} + \underline{w}$ we do the following:

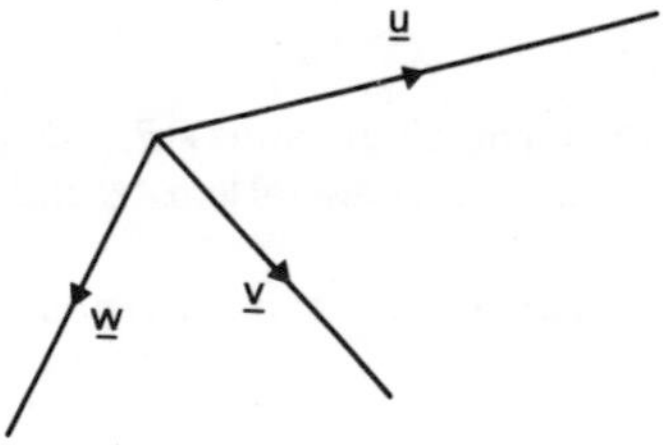

Step 1

Draw a line parallel to $\underline{u}$ of length equal to $\underline{u}$.

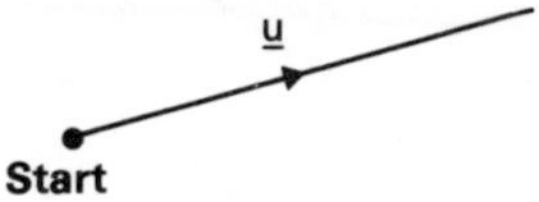

Step 2

From the finish of $\underline{u}$ draw a line parallel and equal in length to $\underline{v}$.

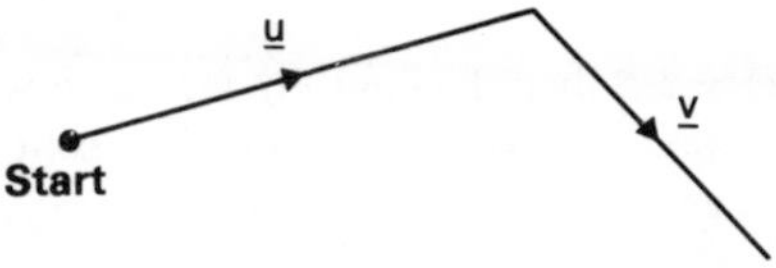

Step 3

From the finish of $\underline{v}$ draw a line parallel and equal in length to $\underline{w}$.

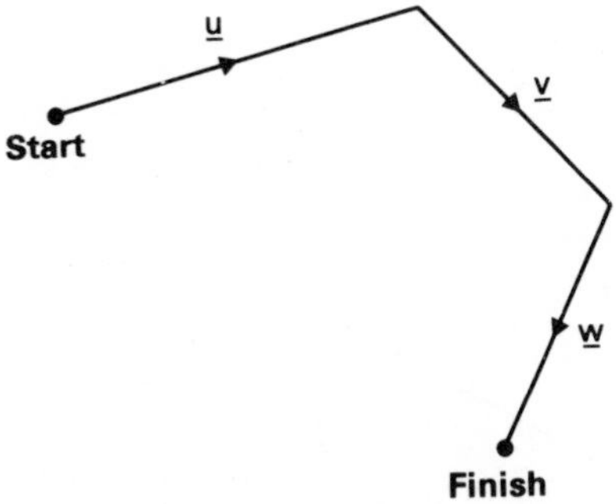

Step 4

Join **Start** to **Finish**.
This gives $\underline{u} + \underline{v} + \underline{w}$.

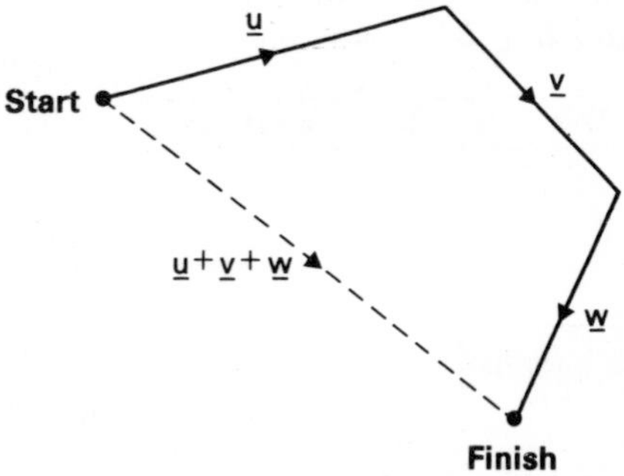

Continue with Sheet M2/3 (reverse)

X Directed line segments

Point 1

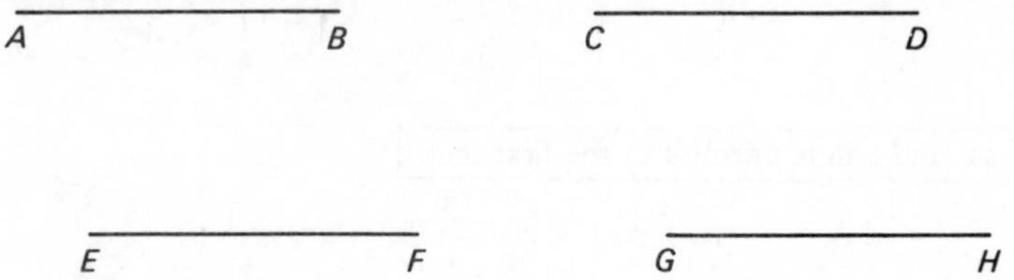

In the diagram above, all the lines *AB*, *CD*, *EF*, and *GH* are of the same length and have the same direction (either they are parallel like *AB* and *EF*, or they are in line like *AB* and *CD*).

Each of these lines could be used as a representative of the vector $\underline{u}$.

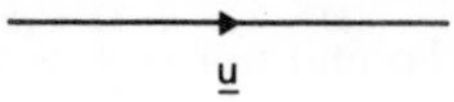

When we want to show that the line *AB* is a representative of a vector we write it as $\overrightarrow{AB}$ and call it a **directed line segment**. (Read $\overrightarrow{AB}$ as '*A* to *B*'.)

The fact that each of the lines above represents $\underline{u}$ would be shown by writing $\overrightarrow{AB} = \overrightarrow{CD} = \overrightarrow{EF} = \overrightarrow{GH} = \underline{u}$.

Point 2

If $\overrightarrow{PQ} = \overrightarrow{RS}$ then the lines *PQ* and *RS* must be equal and parallel since they represent the same vector.

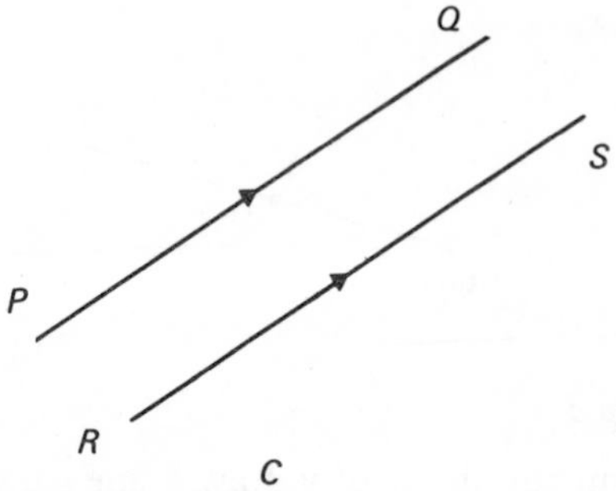

Point 3

If *ABC* is any triangle,
then $\overrightarrow{AB} + \overrightarrow{BC} = \overrightarrow{AC}$
but $AB + BC \neq AC$

This means **'is not equal to'**

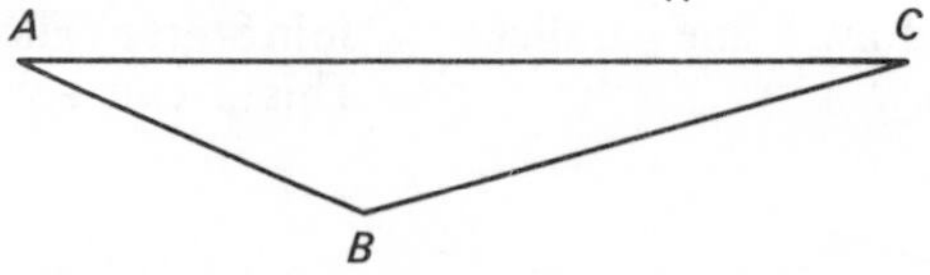

Example

PQRS is a quadrilateral.

$\overrightarrow{PQ} + \overrightarrow{QR} = \overrightarrow{PR}$
$\overrightarrow{PQ} + \overrightarrow{QR} + \overrightarrow{RS} + \overrightarrow{SP} = \underline{0}$

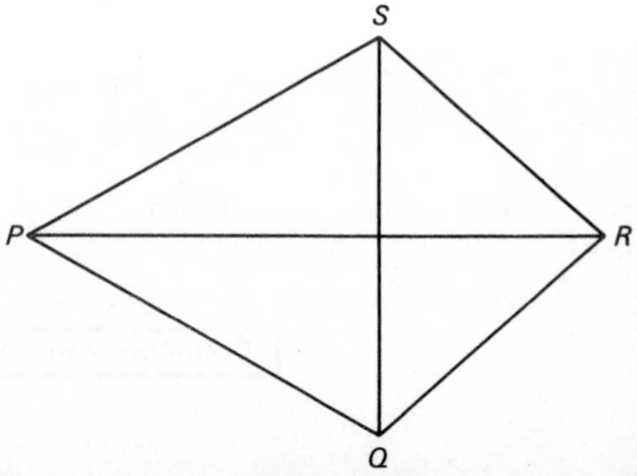

Exercise

1 Copy and complete the following for the diagram above:

(a) $\overrightarrow{RS} + \overrightarrow{SP} = \square$ (b) $\overrightarrow{PQ} + \overrightarrow{QS} = \square$ (c) $\overrightarrow{PR} + \overrightarrow{RQ} = \square$

(d) $\overrightarrow{RQ} + \overrightarrow{QP} = \square$ (e) $\overrightarrow{RQ} + \overrightarrow{QS} + \overrightarrow{SP} = \square$ (f) $\overrightarrow{QP} + \overrightarrow{PS} = \square$

(g) $\overrightarrow{PQ} + \overrightarrow{QR} + \overrightarrow{RP} = \square$ (h) $\overrightarrow{QR} + \overrightarrow{RS} + \overrightarrow{SQ} = \square$

2 In the diagram opposite

(a) What can you say about the direction of lines WX and ZY?

(b) What can you say about the lengths of lines WX and ZY?

(c) What is $\overrightarrow{XY}$ in terms of $\underline{a}$ and $\underline{b}$?

Copy and complete:

$$\begin{aligned}\overrightarrow{XY} &= \overrightarrow{XW} + \overrightarrow{WZ} + \square \\ &= -\underline{a} + \square + \square \\ &= \square\end{aligned}$$

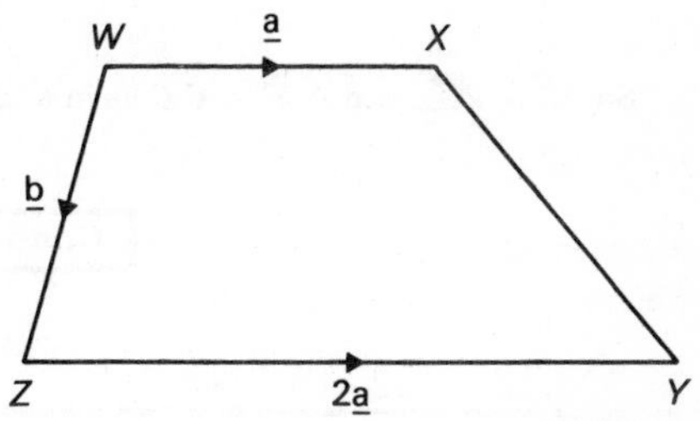

3 In the diagram, $ABCD$ is a parallelogram and CD has been **produced** its own length to E. $\overrightarrow{AB}$ and $\overrightarrow{CB}$ are representatives of $\underline{u}$ and $\underline{v}$.

In terms of $\underline{u}$ and $\underline{v}$, find:

(a) $\overrightarrow{DC}$ (b) $\overrightarrow{DB}$

(c) $\overrightarrow{DA}$ (d) $\overrightarrow{ED}$ (e) $\overrightarrow{EA}$

By looking at the answers for (b) and (e), what can you say about DB and EA?

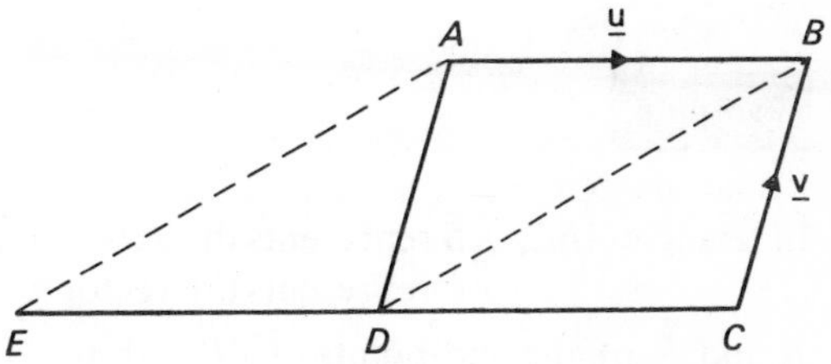

4 In the diagram, $\overrightarrow{KM}$ and $\overrightarrow{KL}$ represent vectors $2\underline{a}$ and $2\underline{b}$. LN represents the vector $\underline{a} - \underline{b}$.

In terms of $\underline{a}$ and $\underline{b}$, find:

(a) $\overrightarrow{KN}$

(b) $\overrightarrow{NM}$

What can you say about the position of N on the line LM?

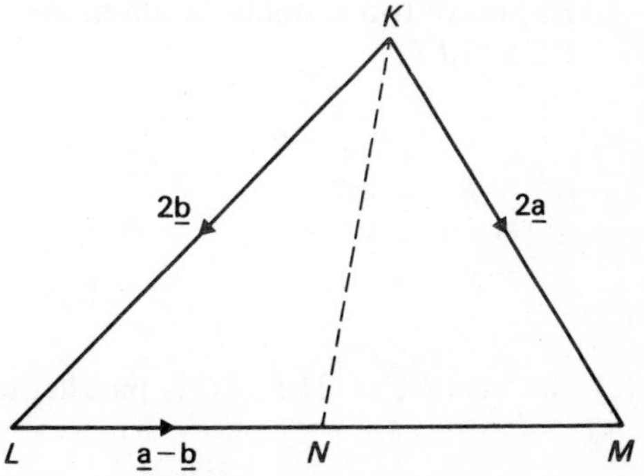

5 In the diagram *ABCD* and *AEFG* are rhombuses with *E* and *G* the mid-points of *AB* and *AD* respectively.

$\overrightarrow{AE}$ represents the vector $\underline{x}$ and $\overrightarrow{AG}$ represents the vector $\underline{y}$.

In terms of $\underline{x}$ and $\underline{y}$, find:

(a) $\overrightarrow{EF} = ▢$ (b) $\overrightarrow{AF} = ▢$

(c) $2\overrightarrow{AF} = ▢$ (d) $\overrightarrow{AB} = ▢$

(e) $\overrightarrow{BC} = ▢$ (f) $\overrightarrow{AC} = ▢$

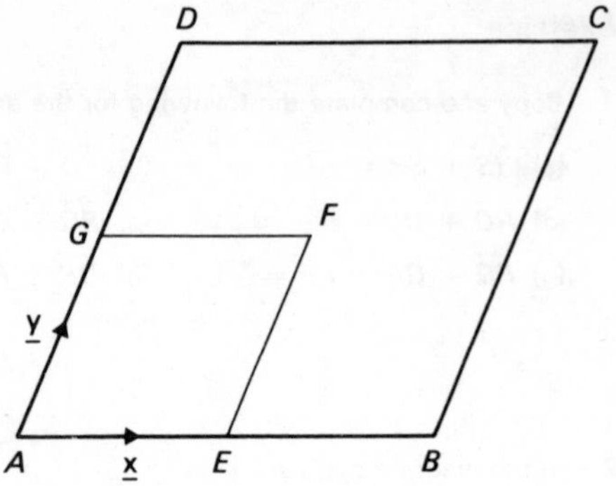

Copy and complete:

So $\overrightarrow{AC} = 2$▢, and *A*, *F*, and *C* lie in a ▢.

Continue with Section Y

Y Vectors applied to geometry

We can use vectors in geometry to establish some properties of figures.

Example

In triangle *ABC*, $\overrightarrow{AB}$ represents the vector $\underline{u}$ and $\overrightarrow{AC}$ represents the vector $\underline{v}$.

E and *F* are the mid-points of *AB* and *AC* respectively.

(a) Express $\overrightarrow{BC}$ in terms of $\underline{u}$ and $\underline{v}$.

(b) Express $\overrightarrow{EF}$ in terms of $\underline{u}$ and $\underline{v}$.

(c) By comparing the results for $\overrightarrow{BC}$ and $\overrightarrow{EF}$, make two statements about lines *BC* and *EF*.

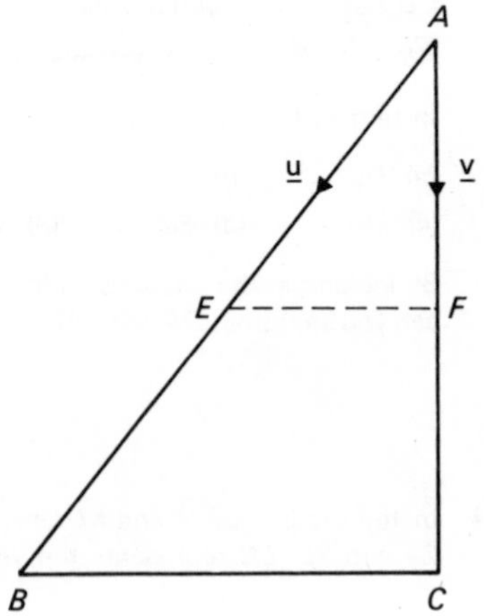

(a) $\overrightarrow{BC} = \overrightarrow{BA} + \overrightarrow{AC}$
$= -\underline{u} + \underline{v}$
$= \underline{v} - \underline{u}$

(b) $\overrightarrow{EF} = \overrightarrow{EA} + \overrightarrow{AF}$
$= -\tfrac{1}{2}\underline{u} + \tfrac{1}{2}\underline{v}$
$= \tfrac{1}{2}\underline{v} - \tfrac{1}{2}\underline{u}$
So $2\overrightarrow{EF} = \underline{v} - \underline{u}$

(c) Because $\overrightarrow{BC} = 2\overrightarrow{EF}$, *BC* is parallel to *EF* and *BC* is twice the length of *EF*.

Exercise

1 In triangle ABC, P and Q are points on AB and AC respectively such that $AP = \frac{1}{4}AB$ and $AQ = \frac{1}{4}AC$.

Show that PQ is parallel to BC and $PQ = \frac{1}{4}BC$. (In the figure $\overrightarrow{BA} = \underline{u}$ and $\overrightarrow{AC} = \underline{v}$.)

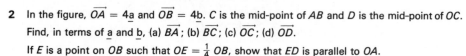

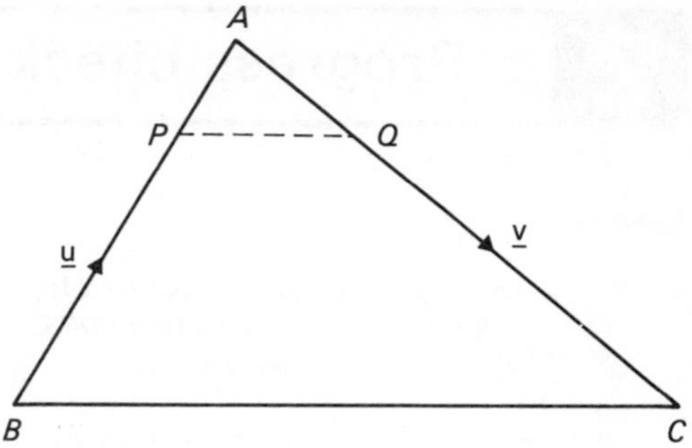

Copy and complete:

$\overrightarrow{BC} = \overrightarrow{BA} + \square$
$= \underline{u} + \square$

$\overrightarrow{PQ} = \overrightarrow{PA} + \square$
$= \square + \square$

So $4\overrightarrow{PQ} = \square$

Because $\overrightarrow{BC} = 4\overrightarrow{\square}$, PQ is parallel to $\square$ and PQ is a $\square$ of the length of BC.

2 In the figure, $\overrightarrow{OA} = 4\underline{a}$ and $\overrightarrow{OB} = 4\underline{b}$. C is the mid-point of AB and D is the mid-point of OC.
Find, in terms of $\underline{a}$ and $\underline{b}$, (a) $\overrightarrow{BA}$; (b) $\overrightarrow{BC}$; (c) $\overrightarrow{OC}$; (d) $\overrightarrow{OD}$.
If E is a point on OB such that $OE = \frac{1}{4}OB$, show that ED is parallel to OA.

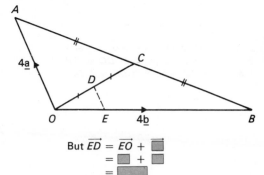

Copy and complete:

(a) $\overrightarrow{BA} = \overrightarrow{BO} + \square$
$= \square + 4\underline{a}$
$= 4\underline{a} - \square$

(b) $\overrightarrow{OC} = \overrightarrow{OB} + \overrightarrow{\square}$
$= \square + \square$
$= \square$

(c) $\overrightarrow{BC} = \frac{1}{2}\overrightarrow{BA}$
$= \square$

(d) $\overrightarrow{OD} = \frac{1}{2}\overrightarrow{\square}$
$= \square$

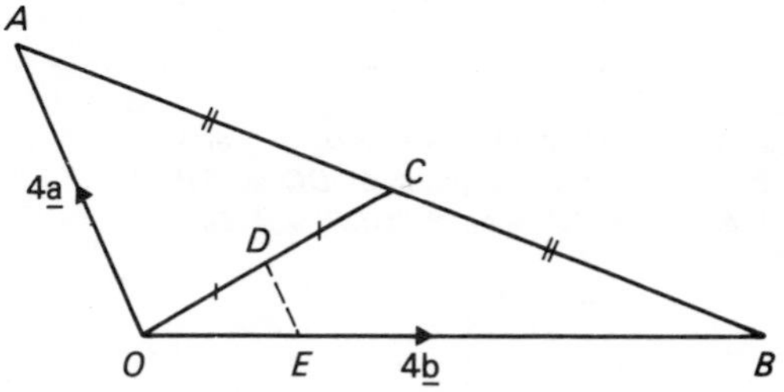

But $\overrightarrow{ED} = \overrightarrow{EO} + \overrightarrow{\square}$
$= \square + \square$
$= \square$

So $\overrightarrow{ED} = \frac{1}{4}\overrightarrow{OA}$, So ED is parallel to $\square$.

3 $OWXYZ$ represents a path from O to Z with OW equal and parallel to YZ.

(a) If $\overrightarrow{OW}$, $\overrightarrow{WX}$, and $\overrightarrow{XY}$ represent vectors $\underline{a}$, $\underline{b}$, and $\underline{c}$ respectively, find the vector represented by $\overrightarrow{OZ}$ in terms of $\underline{a}$, $\underline{b}$, and $\underline{c}$.

(b) If OZ is parallel to WX and $OZ = 2WX$, show that $2\underline{a} = \underline{b} - \underline{c}$

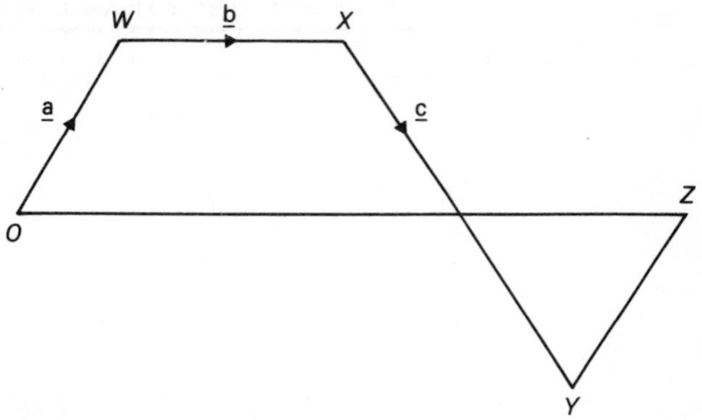

Copy and complete:

(c) $\overrightarrow{OZ} = \overrightarrow{OW} + \overrightarrow{\square} + \overrightarrow{\square} + \overrightarrow{\square}$
$= \underline{a} + \square + \square + \square$
$= \square$

(d) But $\overrightarrow{OZ} = 2\overrightarrow{WX}$
So $\square + \square + \square = 2\underline{b}$
So . . . .

Continue with Section Z

Z Progress check

Exercise

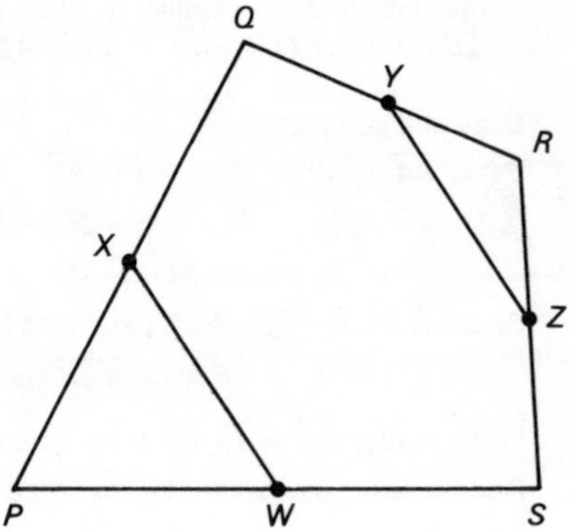

1 X, Y, Z, and W are the mid-points of the sides PQ, QR, RS, and SP of a quadrilateral $PQRS$. $\overrightarrow{QP} = \underline{a}$, $\overrightarrow{QR} = \underline{b}$, $\overrightarrow{RS} = \underline{c}$, and $\overrightarrow{PS} = \underline{d}$.

(a) Express $\overrightarrow{QS}$ and $\overrightarrow{XW}$ in terms of $\underline{a}$ and $\underline{d}$.
(b) Express $\overrightarrow{QS}$ and $\overrightarrow{YZ}$ in terms of $\underline{b}$ and $\underline{c}$.
(c) What can you say about XW and YZ?

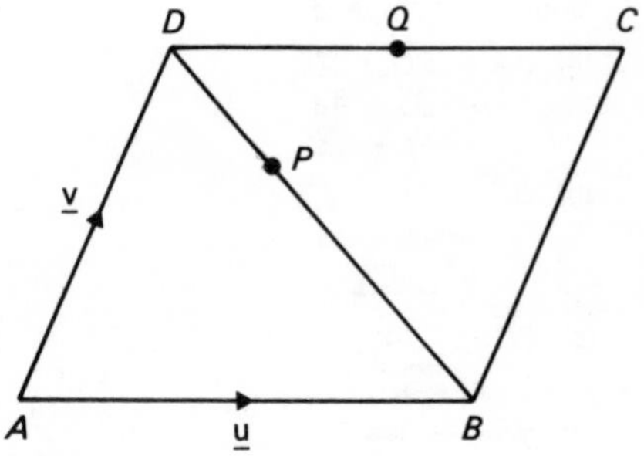

2 $ABCD$ is a parallelogram with $\overrightarrow{AB} = \underline{u}$ and $\overrightarrow{AD} = \underline{v}$. Q is the mid-point of DC and P is the point on DB such that $DP = \frac{1}{3}DB$.

(a) Express $\overrightarrow{DQ}$ in terms of $\underline{u}$.
(b) Express $\overrightarrow{AQ}$ in terms of $\underline{u}$ and $\underline{v}$. What is $\frac{2}{3}\overrightarrow{AQ}$ in terms of $\underline{u}$ and $\underline{v}$?
(c) Express $\overrightarrow{DB}$, $\overrightarrow{DP}$, and $\overrightarrow{AP}$ in terms of $\underline{u}$ and $\underline{v}$.
(d) Using the results for $\overrightarrow{AQ}$ and $\overrightarrow{AP}$, what can you say about A, P, and Q?

Tell your teacher you have finished this Unit

UNIT M3
Simple Equations and Inequations

A True replacements

Here are some examples of mathematical statements:

$$y + 3 = 5$$
$$x(x + 1) = 20$$
$$n + \frac{1}{n} = 2$$
$$2\,(\text{perimeter}) + 6 = 18$$

Each statement contains a **variable.**

In these statements the variables are y, x, n, 'perimeter'.

To solve equations we find numbers which can replace the variables to give **true** statements.

In the equation $y + 3 = 5$, the only possible replacement for y which makes the statement **true** is 2. So $y = 2$ is the **solution** of the equation.

Exercise

1 The statement $2x + 3 = 9$ may be made **true** by choosing the correct replacement for x from the set $\{0, 1, 2, 3, 4\}$.

Copy and complete the following table.

Statement	Replacement	Statement	True/False
$2x + 3 = 9$	0	$0 + 3 = 9$	False
	1	$2 + 3 = 9$	False
	2		
	3	$6 + 3 = 9$	True
	4		

You should have found that the only replacement which makes $2x + 3 = 9$ **true** is

$$\boxed{x = 3.}$$

So the solution of the equation $2x + 3 = 9$ is $x =$ ■.

2 The statement $x(x + 1) = 20$ may be made **true** by choosing the correct replacement for x from the set $\{0, 1, 2, 3, 4\}$. Copy and complete the following table:

Statement	Replacement	Statement	True/False
$x(x + 1) = 20$	0		
	1		
	2		
	3	$3(3 + 1) = 20$	False
	4		

Copy and complete: A *solution* of the equation $x(x + 1) = 20$ is $x = \blacksquare$.

Complete a table like the one above for each of the following statements and write below it a solution of the equation.

3 $5x - 8 = 7$

4 $x(x - 1) = 12$

5 $x^2 + x = 2$

6 $x^2 - 4 = 0$

7 $\dfrac{x^2}{x + 4} = 2$

8 $10x + 1 = 1$

Continue with Section B

B Equation dominoes

A pack of 25 dominoes can be used for playing an equation game. The game can be played by 2, 3, or 4 players.

Each domino has printed on it an equation and one of the numbers 1, 2, 3, 4 or 5 (see Worksheet M3/1).

In playing the game you match an equation with a solution of the equation from the set 1, 2, 3, 4, or 5.

The dealer deals five dominoes to each player and an extra domino face up on the table. The rest of the dominoes are placed face down on the table.

Each player examines the dominoes he has been given. The first player (the one on the left of the dealer) has to play a domino which matches one end of the exposed domino.

If the exposed domino was

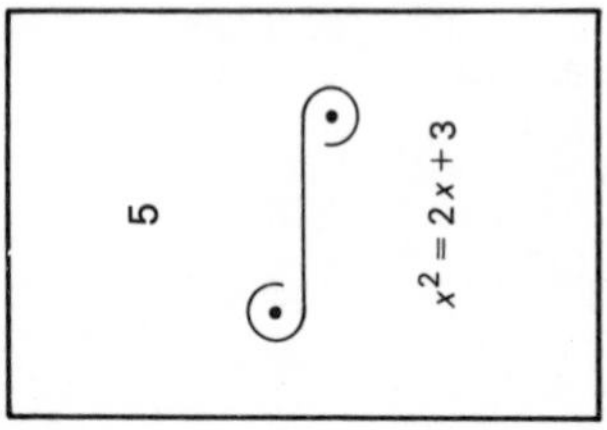

then the first player could play

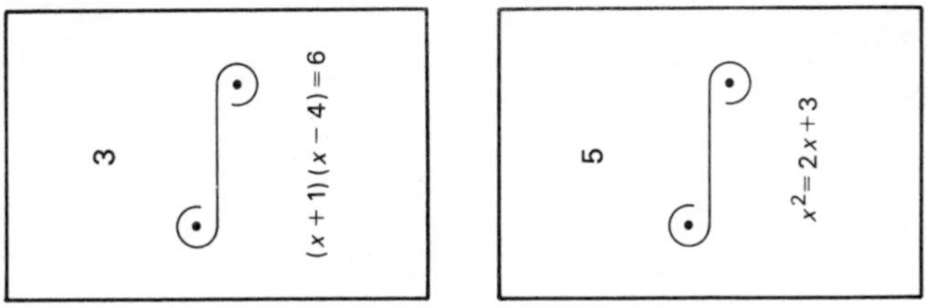

because 5 is a true replacement for x in $(x + 1)(x - 4) = 6$.

OR

He could play

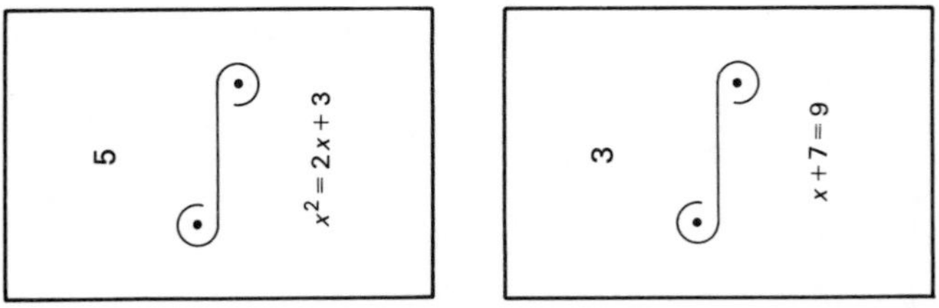

because 3 is a true replacement for x in $x^2 = 2x + 3$.

If a player cannot play he takes an extra domino from the stack but does not play it until his next turn.

If a player plays a wrong domino he takes it back and takes an extra one from the stack.

The next player plays in the same way, trying to match one of the ends. Play continues until one player has played all his dominoes or until no one can play any of the remaining dominoes. In this case the winner is the player with least dominoes left.

Continue with Section C

C Solving equations

You could solve the equations in Sections A and B because you knew that you had only **five** possible replacements to try. Usually, however, there is an infinite number of possible replacements. We are going to develop ways of solving equations when we cannot try all possible replacements.

> To solve an equation you may
> **add** the same number to both sides, or
> **subtract** the same number from both sides.

Example

Solve the equation $x + 3 = 7$.
Subtract 3 from both sides:

$$x = 7 - 3$$

$$x = 4$$

Exercise

In the same way solve the following equations:

1 $x + 3 = 15$
2 $y + 10 = 15$
3 $t + 5 = 12$
4 $y + 1 = 7$
5 $2 + x = 8$
6 $10 + z = 50$

Example

Solve the equation $y - 5 = 11$.
Add 5 to both sides:

$$y = 11 + 5$$

$$y = 16$$

Exercise

In the same way solve the following equations:

7 $x - 7 = 1$
8 $y - 3 = 9$
9 $x - 5 = 7$
10 $t - 9 = 10$
11 $y - 12 = 8$
12 $z - 4 = 0$

Solutions of equations may be **negative** numbers as well as **positive** numbers.

Example

Solve the equation $x + 11 = 5$.
Subtract 11 from both sides:

$$x = 5 - 11$$

$$x = -6$$

Exercise
Solve the following equations:

13 $y + 4 = 1$
14 $x - 5 = -8$
15 $t + 7 = 7$
16 $x + 5 = -2$
17 $y + 3 = -5$
18 $z - 3 = -5$
19 $a - 6 = 5$
20 $t + 9 = 3$
21 $b - 4 = -8$

Sometimes an equation contains more than one variable and we are asked to express one variable in terms of the others.

Example

Solve the equation $x + b = 8$ for x.

Here we want to express x in terms of b and 8. We use the same method as before.

$$x + b = 8$$

Subtract b from both sides:

$$x + b - b = 8 - b$$
$$x = 8 - b$$

Example

Solve the equation $x - p = 10$ for x.

Add p to both sides:

$$x - p + p = 10 + p$$
$$x = 10 + p$$

Exercise

Solve the following equations for x:

22 $x + a = 10$ **23** $x + b = 9$ **24** $x + p = 20$

25 $x + q = -15$ **26** $t + x = 1$ **27** $b + x = -2$

28 $x - b = 10$ **29** $x - r = 4$ **30** $x - c = 9$

31 $-a + x = 7$ **32** $-c + x = 11$

Copy and complete:

33 $x - p = q$

Add p to both sides:

$x - p + \square = q + \square$

$x = q + p$

34 $x + r = t$

Subtract r from both sides:

$x + r - \square = t - \square$

$x = \square$

In the same way solve each of the following equations for x:

35 $x - a = b$ **36** $x + q = s$ **37** $x - y = z$

38 $x + a = d$ **39** $d + x = r$ **40** $-t + x = v$

Continue with Section D

D Dividing both sides of an equation

Here is another method you may use to solve an equation.

> To solve an equation you may
> **divide** both sides by the same number.

Example

Solve the equation $3x = 12$.
Divide both sides by 3:

$$x = 4$$

Exercise

Copy and complete the following:

1 $5y = 35$
Divide both sides by $\square$:
$y = \square$

2 $6t = 42$
Divide both sides by $\square$:
$t = \square$

Solve the following equations:

3 $6n = 24$ **4** $2x = 42$ **5** $5t = 60$
6 $7w = 21$ **7** $3y = 39$ **8** $8p = 72$

Remember the following rules:

(a)	A **positive** number divided by a **positive** number gives a **positive** number.
(b)	A **negative** number divided by a **positive** number gives a **negative** number.
(c)	A **positive** number divided by a **negative** number gives a **negative** number.
(d)	A **negative** number divided by a **negative** number gives a **positive** number.

Exercise

Copy and complete the following:

9 $4r = -16$
Divide both sides by $\square$:
$r = \dfrac{-16}{4}$
$r = -4$

10 $-3k = -27$
Divide both sides by $\square$:
$k = \dfrac{-27}{-3}$
$k = \square$

Solve the following equations:

11 $5y = -35$ **12** $8t = -32$ **13** $-7x = 49$

14 $-12z = -60$ **15** $-10x = 80$ **16** $-9y = -54$

In all the above equations the solutions, or replacements, were **integers**. This need not always be so. In the rest of this unit we will try to find replacements from the set of rational numbers, that is, **integers and fractions**.

Example

Solve the equation $5x = 12$.

Divide both sides by 5:

$$x = \frac{12}{5}$$

$$x = 2.4$$

Exercise

In the same way find solutions for the following equations:

17 $2y = 9$ **18** $4x = 10$ **19** $-5t = 16$ **20** $6t = -15$

21 $-3x = 1.5$ **22** $-8y = -20$ **23** $5t = -14$ **24** $-7y = -8.4$

Example

Solve the equation $ax = 10$ for x.

Use the same method as before.

Divide both sides by a:

$$\frac{ax}{a} = \frac{10}{a}$$

so $$x = \frac{10}{a}$$

Example

Solve for x, $px = q$.

Divide both sides by p:

$$x = \frac{q}{p}$$

Exercise

Solve the following equations for x:

25 $px = 5$ **26** $rx = -8$ **27** $5x = p$ **28** $7x = -d$

29 $ax = b$ **30** $bx = -k$ **31** $-ax = -p$ **32** $-cx = -10$

Continue with Section E

E Multiplying both sides of an equation

In the last section you solved each equation by dividing both sides by the same number.

> To solve an equation you may **multiply** both sides by the same number.

Example

Solve the equation $\frac{x}{3} = 5$.

Multiply both sides by 3:

$$x = 5 \times 3$$
$$x = 15$$

To check that $x = 15$ is a solution of the equation $\frac{x}{3} = 5$, we must check that $\frac{15}{3} = 5$ is a **true** statement. It is!

Exercise

In the same way solve the following equations and check your solutions:

1 $\frac{x}{4} = 7$ **2** $\frac{z}{5} = 7$ **3** $\frac{t}{3} = 8$ **4** $\frac{y}{7} = 3$

5 $\frac{p}{8} = 2$ **6** $\frac{x}{6} = 1$ **7** $\frac{y}{10} = 9$ **8** $\frac{t}{11} = 2$

Remember the following rules:

(a) A **positive** number multiplied by a **positive** number gives a **positive** number.
(b) A **negative** number multiplied by a **positive** number gives a **negative** number.
(c) A **positive** number multiplied by a **negative** number gives a **negative** number.
(d) A **negative** number multiplied by a **negative** number gives a **positive** number.

Example

Solve $\frac{a}{-2} = 6$.

Multiply both sides by -2:

$$a = (-2) \times 6$$

$$a = -12$$

Check: $\frac{-12}{-2} = 6$ is a true statement.

Example

Solve $\frac{b}{-6} = -7$.

Multiply both sides by -6:

$$b = (-6) \times (-7)$$

$$b = 42$$

Check: $\frac{42}{-6} = -7$ is a true statement.

Exercise

In the same way solve the following equations and check each solution:

9 $\frac{x}{-8} = 6$ **10** $\frac{y}{9} = 7$ **11** $\frac{z}{-2} = -5$ **12** $\frac{t}{11} = -4$

13 $\frac{y}{-3} = 5$ **14** $\frac{x}{7} = -8$ **15** $\frac{z}{-4} = -10$ **16** $\frac{w}{10} = -1.5$

In solving the following equations, sometimes you will need to **multiply** and sometimes you will need to **divide**.

17 $7x = 28$ **18** $\frac{x}{5} = 6$ **19** $\frac{z}{3} = -7$ **20** $11z = 88$

21 $-10z = 70$ **22** $\frac{k}{-4} = -11$ **23** $4w = -16$ **24** $\frac{t}{-7} = 14$

Example

Solve for x, $\frac{x}{a} = 7$.

Multiply both sides by a:

$$x = a \times 7$$

$$x = 7a$$

Example

Solve $\frac{x}{p} = q$ for x.

Multiply both sides by p:

$$x = p \times q$$

$$x = pq$$

Exercise

In the same way solve the following equations for x.

25 $\frac{x}{b} = 9$ **26** $\frac{x}{k} = -10$ **27** $\frac{x}{8} = c$

28 $\frac{x}{a} = p$ **29** $\frac{x}{a} = -b$ **30** $\frac{x}{-c} = d$

Continue with Section F

F Two step equations

Example

Solve $5x + 1 = 16$.
Subtract 1 from both sides:

$$5x = 16 - 1$$
$$5x = 15$$

Divide both sides by 5:

$$x = 3$$

Example

Solve $5x - 3 = 9$.
Add 3 to both sides:

$$5x = 9 + 3$$
$$5x = 12$$

Divide both sides by 5:

$$x = 2.4$$

Exercise

In the same way solve the following equations:

1 $4x + 3 = 19$	**2** $3x + 5 = 17$	**3** $5x + 2 = 12$
4 $6x + 5 = 23$	**5** $2x + 1 = 30$	**6** $7x + 10 = 17$
7 $2x - 5 = 6$	**8** $5x - 3 = 18$	**9** $4x - 1 = 3$
10 $3x - 4 = 6.5$	**11** $6x - 5 = 4$	**12** $4x - 6 = 6.4$

Example

Solve $7x = 3x - 20$.
Subtract $3x$ from both sides to get the terms in x on the **same** side of the equation:

$$7x - 3x = -20$$
$$4x = -20$$

Divide both sides by 4:

$$x = -5$$

Check: $7(-5) = 3(-5) - 20$
that is, $-35 = -15 - 20$
is a true statement.

Example

Solve $5x = -x + 12$.
Add x to both sides to get the terms in x on the **same** side:

$$5x + x = 12$$
$$6x = 12$$

Divide both sides by 6:

$$x = 2$$

Check: $5(2) = -2 + 12$
that is, $10 = -2 + 12$
is a true statement.

Exercise

Solve the following equations for x:

13 $9x = 4x + 15$	**14** $5x = x - 20$	**15** $6x = 2x - 8$
16 $10x = 3x - 14$	**17** $8x = 3x + 10$	**18** $2x = x - 8$
19 $5x = -3x + 16$	**20** $3x = -3x - 24$	**21** $6x = -2x + 4$
22 $2x = -7x + 27$	**23** $x = -3x - 24$	**24** $10x = -x - 11$

Example

Solve $2x + 7 = 3x$.
Subtract $2x$ from both sides:

$$7 = 3x - 2x$$
$$7 = x$$

and this means

$$x = 7$$

Example

Solve $2x = 3x - 6$.
Subtract $3x$ from both sides:

$$2x - 3x = -6$$
$$-x = -6$$

Divide both sides by -1:

$$x = 6$$

Exercise

Solve the following equations:

25 $3x - 9 = 4x$ **26** $x + 5 = 3x$ **27** $2x - 5 = 6x$
28 $4x + 12 = 7x$ **29** $5x - 12 = 6x$ **30** $x + 8 = 6x$
31 $x = 2x + 5$ **32** $2x = 5x - 9$ **33** $3x = 5x + 8$
34 $7x = 10x - 27$ **35** $5x = 7x + 9$ **36** $x = 6x - 27$

Continue with Section G

G More equations

Exercise

Copy and complete the following to solve the equations for x:

1 $5 + 3x = 8 + 2x$

Subtract $2x$ from both sides:

$$5 + 3x - 2x = 8$$
$$5 + \square = 8$$

Subtract 5 from both sides:

$$x = 8 - \square$$
$$x = \square$$

2 $5x + 7 = 2x + 16$

Subtract $2x$ from both sides:

$$5x - 2x + 7 = 16$$
$$3x + 7 = 16$$

Subtract 7 from both sides:

$$\square = 16 - \square$$
$$\square = \square$$

Divide both sides by $\square$

$$x = \square$$

3 $28 - 3x = 8 + 2x$

Add $3x$ to both sides:

$$28 = 8 + 2x + \square$$
$$\square = 8 + \square$$

Subtract 8 from both sides:

$$28 - \square = \square$$
$$\square = 5x$$
$$5x = \square$$

Divide both sides by 5:

$$x = \square$$

4 $27 - 4x = 8x + 3$

Add $\square$ to both sides:

$$\square = 8x + \square + 3$$
$$\square = \square + 3$$

Subtract $\square$ from both sides:

$$\square - \square = \square$$
$$\square = 12x$$
$$12x = \square$$

Divide both sides by $\square$:

$$x = \square$$

5 $4x - 8 = 2x - 2$

Subtract $2x$ from both sides:

$\square - \square = \square$

Add 8 to both sides:

$\square = \square + 8$

$\square = \square$

Divide both sides by 2:

$\square = \square$

6 $px - 3 = q$

Add 3 to both sides:

$\square = q + 3$

Divide both sides by p:

$x = \dfrac{\square}{\square}$

7 $ax + 1 = b$

Subtract 1 from both sides:

$ax = \square$

Divide both sides by a:

$x = \dfrac{b - 1}{\square}$

8 $bx - d = c$

Add d to both sides:

$bx = c + \square$

Divide both sides by $\square$:

$x = \dfrac{\square}{\square}$

9 $cx + d = p$

Subtract $\square$ from both sides:

$\square = p - \square$

Divide both sides by $\square$:

$x = \dfrac{\square}{\square}$

Solve the following equations for x:

10 $11x - 6 = 6x + 14$

11 $7x + 2 = 2x + 12$

12 $7x - 5 = 3x + 7$

13 $x - 3 = 3 - 5x$

14 $5x - 9 = 3x - 11$

15 $x + 3 = 2x - 7$

16 $5x + 4 = 2x - 11$

17 $3 - 2x = 5x - 11$

18 $2x + 7 = 9x - 21$

19 $5 - 4x = 7 - 6x$

20 $px - 5 = q$

21 $rx + 7 = s$

22 $ax + b = c$

23 $tx - v = w$

Continue with Section H

H Equations with brackets

Remember that

$3 + 3$ means '2 times 3' which is 6

$y + y$ means '2 times y' which is written as $2y$

and

$(y + 3) + (y + 3)$ is the same as '2 times $(y + 3)$' or $2(y + 3)$

$(y + 3) + (y + 3)$ is the same as $y + y + 3 + 3$ or $2y + 6$

So

times

$$2(y + 3) = 2 \; (y + 3)$$
$$= (2 \times y) + (2 \times 3)$$
$$= 2y + 6$$

Example

Expand $-5(y-2)$.

$$-5(y-2) = -5\ (y-2)$$
$$= -5y + 10$$

Remember that $(-5) \times (-2) = +10$

Example

Expand $a(x-b)$.

$$a(x-b) = a\ (x-b)$$
$$= ax - ab$$

Exercise

Expand, that is 'multiply out', each of the following:

1	$3(x+2)$	**2**	$4(y-3)$	**3**	$3(p+7)$	**4**	$-2(p+5)$
5	$-3(a-3)$	**6**	$-(x-3)$	**7**	$-4(-x+7)$	**8**	$2(p+q)$
9	$a(y-3)$	**10**	$a(x+q)$	**11**	$b(c-d)$	**12**	$-a(p-q)$

To solve an equation containing brackets the first step is to multiply out the brackets and arrange the terms so that you get back to the kind of equation that you have solved before.

Example

Solve $12 + 3(x-2) = 2x$

Multiply out the brackets:

$$12 + 3x - 6 = 2x$$
$$3x + 6 = 2x$$

Subtract $3x$ from both sides:

$$6 = 2x - 3x$$
$$6 = -x$$

so $$-x = 6$$

Divide both sides by -1:

$$x = -6$$

Exercise

In the same way solve the following equations:

13	$4(x-2) = 12$	**14**	$3(y+1) - 4 = 2y$	**15**	$4(p+2) = 3p$
16	$2(q-3) + 3 = 7$	**17**	$2(s+2) + 8 = 15$	**18**	$5(t-1) - t = 3$
19	$2(x-6) + 3 = 5x$	**20**	$4(3-x) = 3x - 16$	**21**	$9y + 4 = 7(3-y) - 1$

Example

Solve the equation $3 - 2(p-3) = 7$.

Multiply out the brackets:

$$3 - 2p + 6 = 7 \qquad (-2) \times (-3) = +6$$
$$9 - 2p = 7$$

Subtract 9 from both sides: $-2p = 7 - 9$

$$-2p = -2$$

Divide both sides by -2: $p = 1$

Exercise

Solve the following equations:

22 $5 - 3(p - 2) = 5$ **23** $3 - 2(x + 1) = 5$ **24** $7p - 3(p - 5) = 31$

25 $6 - 3(s - 1) = s - 19$ **26** $7 - (5x - 2) = 25 - x$ **27** $5 - (t - 1) = 7 - 2(t - 3)$

Example

Solve $b(x - 2) = c$ for x.

We need to express x in terms of b and c, and so we want to get x by itself on the left hand side of the equation. This is sometimes called 'making x the subject of the formula or equation'.

$$b(x - 2) = c$$

Multiply out the brackets:

$$bx - 2b = c$$

Add $2b$ to both sides:

$$bx = c + 2b$$

Divide both sides by b:

$$x = \frac{c + 2b}{b}$$

Example

Make x the subject of the formula $c(x + b) = d$, that is, solve the equation for x.

$$c(x + b) = d$$

Multiply out the brackets:

$$cx + cb = d$$

Subtract cb from both sides:

$$cx = d - cb$$

Divide both sides by c:

$$x = \frac{d - cb}{c}$$

Exercise

Make x the subject of each of the following formulae:

28 $p(x + 3) = q$ **29** $3(x - 10) = d$ **30** $a(x - b) = c$

31 $3 + a(x - b) = d$ **32** $a + c(x - d) = b$

Continue with Section I

I Progress check

Exercise

1 Find replacements from the set {0, 1, 2, 3, 4} which make the following statements true:

(a) $\frac{x+1}{x} = 2$ (b) $\frac{x}{x+1} = x$ (c) $2^x = x + 2$ (d) $x(x + 1) = 20$

2 Find the value of x in each of the following equations:

(a) $x - 7 = 11$ (b) $x + 10 = 2$ (c) $5x = 20$ (d) $\frac{x}{-4} = 7$

3 Find x in terms of the other variables in each of the following equations:

(a) $a + x = 20$ (b) $x - p = q$ (c) $tx = 8$ (d) $\frac{x}{r} = s$

4 Solve the following equations:

(a) $5 + 3x = 25 - 2x$ (b) $8 - 6x = 3 - 4x$

5 Expand the following:

(a) $3(x - 4)$ (b) $-2(y - 3)$ (c) $-3(5 - 2p)$

6 Solve the following equations:

(a) $3(x + 2) - 4 = 17$ (b) $5 - 3(x - 2) = 2$

7 Make x the subject of each formula, that is, solve each equation for x:

(a) $c(x + 1) = d$ (b) $c(x - p) = q$

Ask your teacher what to do next

J Inequations

This sign on a motorway means that you may travel at a speed of 70 m.p.h. or at any speed **less than** 70 m.p.h.

So,

$$\text{speed} \leq 70.$$

This is an example of an **inequation**.

You will remember the meaning of the inequality signs:

$<$ means **is less than**
$\leq$ means **is less than or equal to**
$>$ means **is greater than**
$\geq$ means **is greater than or equal to**

An **inequation** is a mathematical statement involving the inequality signs $<$, $\leq$, $>$, or $\geq$, and one or more variables.

Example

The statement $x + 3 < 9$ is an inequation.

If x is replaced by **any number less than 6**, say 3, or 5, or 5.9, or 5.99, and so on, then the statement is **true.**

So, $x < 6$ is the solution of the inequation $x + 3 < 9$.

Many of the rules used to solve equations may be used to solve inequations, **but not all.**

Example

Solve $a + 4 < 10$

Subtract 4 from both sides:

$$a < 10 - 4$$
$$a < 6$$

Example

Solve $y - 5 \geq -2$

Add 5 to both sides:

$$y \geq -2 + 5$$
$$y \geq 3$$

Exercise

Solve the following inequations:

1 $x + 4 < 9$	**2** $x - 2 > 3$	**3** $y + 7 < 5$	**4** $a - 2 \leq 4$
5 $t + 3 \geq -2$	**6** $p - 7 < -3$	**7** $y - 5 > -8$	**8** $7 + x < 1$
9 $-2 + x \geq 10$	**10** $p + 7 < 7$	**11** $p + 7 \geq 7$	**12** $x + 100 > 101$

Continue with Section K

K Showing solutions on the number line

We can show the solution of the inequation $x < 2$ on the real number line :

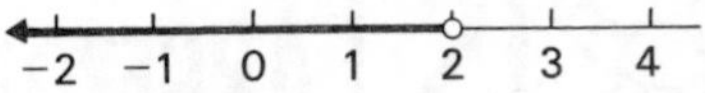

Note the **open** circle at 2 showing that 2 itself is *not a* possible solution.

To show the solution $x \geq -1$ we draw the graph thus:

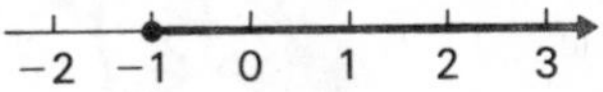

The **shaded** circle shows that $x = -1$ is included in the possible values which x may take.

Exercise

Copy each of the number lines below and show the solutions of the inequations.

1 $x \geq 4$

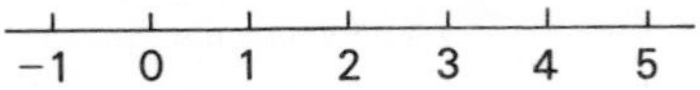

2 $x < -3$

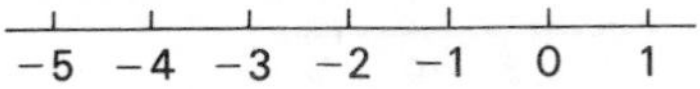

3 $x \geq -2$

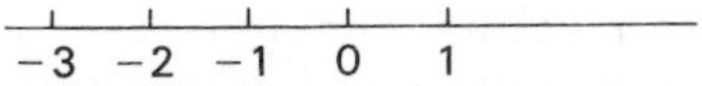

4 $x \leq -2$

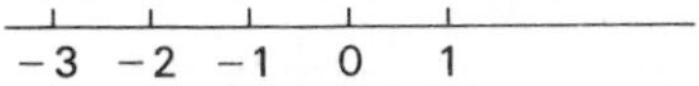

5 $x > -1$

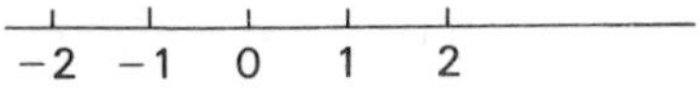

Example

Write an inequation whose solution is given by the following graph.

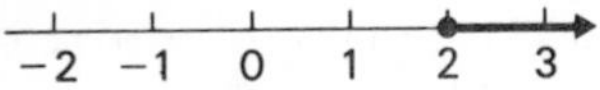

Answer: $x \geq 2$

Exercise

Write down inequations whose solutions are given by the following graphs.

6

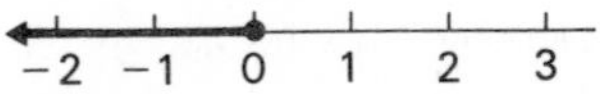

7

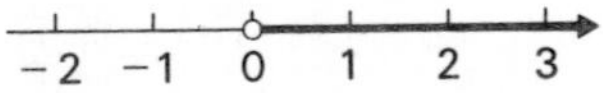

8

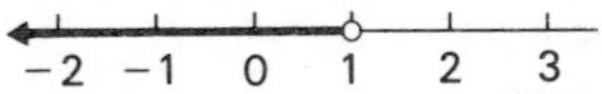

9

10

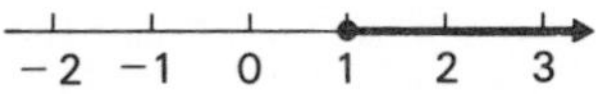

11

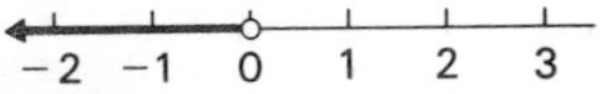

12

Continue with Section L

L Comparisons

Example

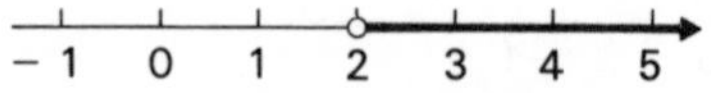

The graph shows the solution of the inequation $x > 2$. It shows that

x can take any value **greater than** 2

and also that

2 is **less than** each value of x

So

$2 < x$ is the same as $x > 2$

When solving **equations** we sometimes arrived at a result such as

$$20 = 5x$$

This was re-arranged, by turning it round, to give

$$5x = 20$$

and so $x = 4$

> When **inequations** are 'turned round' in this way,
> '**less than**' becomes '**greater than**'
> and '**greater than**' becomes '**less than**'

Example

$3 < 7$ means 3 **is less than** 7.
So 7 **is greater than** 3,
that is, $7 > 3$.

Example

$14 \geq 2x$ means 14 is **greater than or equal to** $2x$.
So $2x$ **is less than or equal to** 14,
that is, $2x \leq 14$.

Exercise

Copy and complete the following statements:

1 $9 > 6$ means 9 is **greater** than 6
so, 6 is ____ than 9
that is, $6 < 9$

2 $-2 > -5$ means -2 ____ -5
so, -5 ____ -2
that is, -5 ____ -2

3 $12 < 3x$ means 12 ____ $3x$
so, $3x$ ____ 12
that is, $3x$ ____ 12

4 $17 > 5x$ means ____
so, $5x$ ____
that is, $5x$ ____

5 $19 < 2x$ means ____
so, $2x$ ____
that is, $2x$ ____

6 $15 \geq 3x$
so, $3x$ ____ 15

7 $25 \leq 7x$
so, $7x$ ____

8 $14 \geq 8x$
so, $8x$ ____

Example

Show the solution of $3x \leq 12$ on a number line.

$$3x \leq 12$$

Divide both sides by 3:

$$x \leq 4$$

The graph is

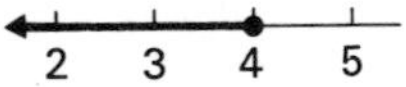

Example

Show the solution of $15 > 3x$ on a number line.

$$15 > 3x$$

Turn the inequation round so that the term in x is on the left hand side:

$$3x < 15$$

Notice that the sign has changed.

Divide both sides by 3:

$$x < 5$$

The graph is

Exercise

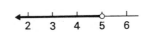

Solve the following inequations and show each solution on a number line:

9 $2x > 12$ **10** $7x > 14$ **11** $5x \leq 15$

12 $3x \geq 21$ **13** $4x < -20$ **14** $16 < 8x$

15 $-6 \leq 3x$ **16** $30 < 6x$ **17** $14 \geq 2x$

18 $-4 \geq 2x$ **19** $4x \geq 10$ **20** $9 < 6x$

Continue with Section M

M Solving inequations

Example

Draw the graph of the solution of

$$5y + 7 < 2y + 19$$

Subtract $2y$ from both sides:

$$3y + 7 < 19$$

Subtract 7 from both sides:

$$3y < 19 - 7$$
$$3y < 12$$

Divide both sides by 3: $y < 4$ *Graph*

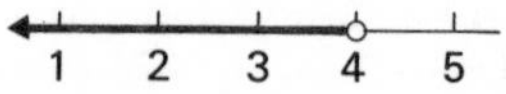

Exercise

Solve the following inequations in the same way and show each solution on a number line:

1 $6x + 4 < 3x + 7$
2 $7x + 5 \geq 2x + 30$
3 $7x + 11 > 5x - 9$
4 $10x - 3 \leq x + 6$
5 $3y - 11 > 2y + 5$
6 $5p - 9 < 2p$
7 $8p + 14 \geq p$
8 $3a + 2 \leq a + 2$
9 $9q - 1 > 2q - 1$
10 $13q + 10 \leq 3q - 40$

Example

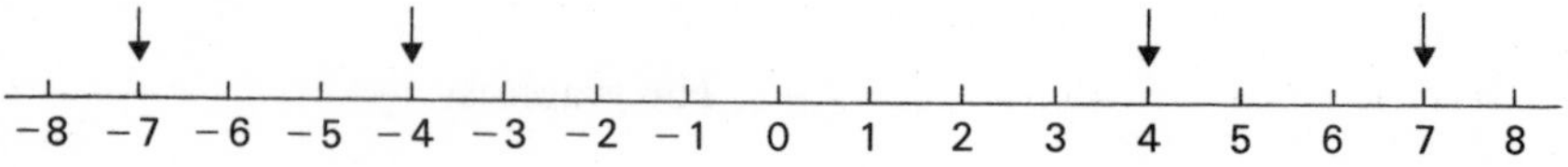

Which of the signs, > or <, should be put between the following pairs of numbers to make true statements?

(a) −7 □ −4. −7 **is less than** −4 so, the answer is $-7 < -4$.

(b) 7 □ 4. 7 **is greater than 4** so, the answer is $7 > 4$.

Exercise

In the same way, copy and complete the following statements putting the correct inequality sign (either > or <) between each pair of numbers:

11 (a) −8 □ −3 (b) 8 □ 3
12 (a) −1 □ −6 (b) 1 □ 6
13 (a) −5 □ 7 (b) 5 □ −7
14 (a) −4 □ −8 (b) 1 □ 2
15 (a) −3 □ 6 (b) 1 □ −2
16 (a) −5 □ 10 (b) 1 □ −2

Example

From the number line we see that $-6 < -4$

Divide both sides by -2:

$$\frac{-6}{-2} \;\square\; \frac{-4}{-2}$$

$$3 \;\square\; 2$$

What sign goes here?
Clearly 3 is greater than 2 so $3 > 2$

> When you divide both sides of an inequation by a **negative** number you must **change** the inequality sign from
> **'less than'** to **'greater than'**
> or from **'greater than'** to **'less than'**.

Example

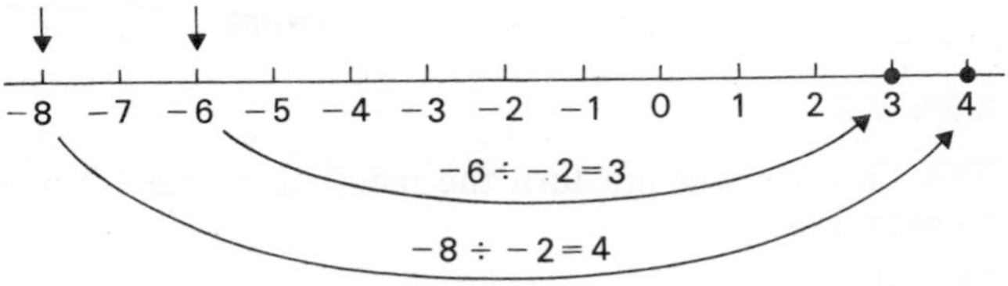

$-6 > -8$

Divide both sides by -2:

$3 < 4$

Example

Solve for x

$-5x > 10$

Divide both sides by -5 and change the sign:

$$x < \frac{10}{-5}$$

$$x < -2$$

Example

Solve for y

$-3y \leq -12$

Divide both sides by -3 and change the sign:

$$y \geq \frac{-12}{-3}$$

$$y \geq 4$$

Exercise

Solve the following inequations:

17 $-4p > 16$ **18** $-3q \leq 3$ **19** $-7p < -14$
20 $-10x \geq -20$ **21** $-5y > 30$ **22** $-x > -1$
23 $-y \leq 8$ **24** $-x < 0$ **25** $-p \geq 0$

Continue with Section N

N Beware of the minus

Example

Solve $5x - 4 < 7x - 2$

Method 1

Turn the inequation round:

$$7x - 2 > 5x - 4$$

The inequality sign is changed.

Subtract $5x$ from both sides:

$$2x - 2 > -4$$

Add 2 to both sides

$$2x > -4 + 2$$
$$2x > -2$$
$$x > -1$$

Graph 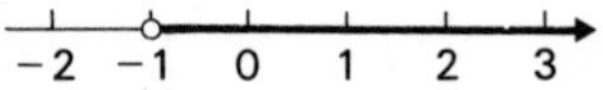

Method 2

This time we will not turn the inequation round but will subtract $7x$ from both sides straight away.

$$5x - 4 - 7x < -2$$
$$-2x - 4 < -2$$

Add 4 to both sides:

$$-2x < -2 + 4$$
$$-2x < 2$$

Divide both sides by -2:

Remember: Change the sign when dividing by a negative number.

$$x > \frac{2}{-2}$$
$$x > -1$$

and this is the same result as before.

Exercise

Solve the following inequations using either of the above methods.

1 $4x - 6 > 5x + 4$ **2** $2x - 4 < 5x + 8$ **3** $9x + 4 \geq 10x - 5$

4 $x + 9 \leq 3x + 5$ **5** $3x - 5 > 7x - 5$ **6** $2x \leq 7x - 5$

Example

Solve $4 - 3y \geq 7 - 6y$
Add $6y$ to both sides:
$$4 + 3y \geq 7$$
Subtract 4 from both sides:
$$3y \geq 3$$
Divide both sides by 3:
$$y \geq 1$$

Example

Solve $4 + 3y < 7 + 5y$
Subtract $3y$ from both sides:
$$4 < 7 + 2y$$
Subtract 7 from both sides:
$$-3 < 2y$$
Turn the inequation round and change sign:
$$2y > -3$$
Divide both sides by 2:
$$y > -1.5$$

Exercise

Solve the following inequations and show each solution on a number line:

7 $4 - x > 5 - 2x$
8 $5x - 43 < 5 - 7x$
9 $4 - a > 7 - 2a$
10 $3 - 2t > 5 + 3t$
11 $x + 5 \geq 7$
12 $x - 2 \leq -3$
13 $3x + 5 \leq 11$
14 $4 - 3x \geq x$
15 $2x - 4 \geq x - 3$
16 $5x - 7 < 3x - 3$
17 $8x + 5 > 3x - 15$
18 $5 - 3x < 6 - 4x$
19 $8x - 3 \geq 6x + 2$
20 $7x - 1 < 10x + 20$

Continue with Section O

O (In)equations with fractions

Example

Solve $8x - 2(3x - 8) \leq 24$
Multiply out the brackets:
$$8x - 6x + 16 \leq 24$$
$$2x + 16 \leq 24$$
Subtract 16 from both sides:
$$2x \leq 8$$
Divide both sides by 2:
$$x \leq 4$$

Exercise

Solve the following inequations:

1 $5(x - 3) - 2x \leq 9$
2 $4(x - 1) \geq 6 - x$
3 $3 + 2(x + 5) \geq 27$
4 $4x \leq 7(x - 2) + 5$
5 $x + 1 < 6(7 + x) + 1$

Example

Solve $\frac{3x}{4} + 5 = 17$

To solve an equation involving fractions we first of all multiply both sides of the equation by some number so that there are no fractions in the result.

$$\frac{3x}{4} + 5 = 17$$

Multiply both sides by 4:

$$4\left(\frac{3x}{4} + 5\right) = 4 \times 17$$

$$3x + 20 = 68$$

Subtract 20 from both sides:

$$3x = 48$$

Divide both sides by 3:

$$x = 16$$

Exercise

Solve the following:

6 $\frac{2x}{5} + 3 = 5$ **7** $\frac{3x}{7} - 2 = 1$ **8** $4 + \frac{2x}{3} = x + 1$

9 $\frac{5x}{4} - 7 \geq 8$ **10** $4 - \frac{x}{5} < x + 16$ **11** $2 + \frac{3x}{7} \leq x - \frac{2}{7}$

12 $\frac{5x}{2} - 6 > \frac{x}{2} + 1$ **13** $2(x + 1) > \frac{7x}{4} + 1$

Example

Solve $\frac{5}{4} - \frac{2x}{5} = 2$

Multiply both sides by 20:

$$20\left(\frac{5}{4} - \frac{2x}{5}\right) = 20 \times 2$$

$$\frac{100}{4} - \frac{40x}{5} = 40$$

$$25 - 8x = 40$$

Subtract 25 from both sides:

$$-8x = 15$$

Divide both sides by -8:

$$x = \frac{15}{-8} = -1.875$$

Exercise

Solve the following:

14 $\frac{3}{5} - \frac{x}{2} = 4$ **15** $\frac{x}{2} + \frac{x}{3} \leq 5$ **16** $\frac{x}{3} - \frac{x}{5} < 2$

17 $\frac{5x}{6} + x \geq \frac{22}{4}$ **18** $\frac{3x}{4} \leq \frac{x}{3} + 10$ **19** $\frac{x}{2} > \frac{2}{7} - \frac{x}{14}$

Example

Solve $\frac{3x}{2} - \frac{2(1-2x)}{3} < 5$

Multiply both sides by 6:

$$6\left(\frac{3x}{2} - \frac{2(1-2x)}{3}\right) < 6 \times 5$$
$$\frac{18x}{2} - \frac{12(1-2x)}{3} < 30$$
$$9x - 4(1-2x) < 30$$
$$9x - 4 + 8x < 30$$
$$17x - 4 < 30$$

Add 4 to both sides:

$$17x < 34$$

Divide both sides by 17:

$$x < 2$$

Exercise

Solve the following:

20 $\frac{3x}{2} - \frac{(x-2)}{5} = 3$ **21** $\frac{2x}{5} - \frac{(x+1)}{3} \geq 2$ **22** $\frac{(x+1)}{2} - \frac{3}{4} < 6$

23 $2x - \frac{(x+27)}{3} = 16$ **24** $x - \frac{(x-2)}{7} \geq \frac{x}{2} + 1$ **25** $\frac{x}{4} - \frac{(x+1)}{3} > \frac{1}{4}$

Continue with Section P

P Setting up (in)equations

So far we have solved equations and inequations without worrying about where they came from. It is just as important in mathematics to be able to make up equations as it is to solve them. You must be able to translate a problem from words into algebra. You may in fact be able to solve the problem without doing the algebra but once you can do the simple ones by algebra you will be ready to go on to more realistic problems.

Example

I think of a number, double it and add ten. The result is thirty-eight. What was the number?
Let the original number be x, so

$$2x + 10 = 38$$

Subtract 10 from both sides:

$$2x = 28$$

Divide both sides by 2:

$$x = 14$$

Exercise

For each of the following write an equation and solve it.

1 To three times a certain number I add eleven, and then find I have thirty-five. What is the number?

2 From twice a certain number I took seven and obtained fifty-three as a result. What was the original number?

3 A man is 25 years older than his son, and the sum of the ages of father and son is 65. Find their ages. (Let the son be x years old.)

4 A box contains enough sweets to give each boy in a group 8. If each boy took only 5 sweets, there would be 36 left. How many boys are in the group?

5 The length of a rectangular garden is 3 metres more than twice its width. If the perimeter of the garden is 72 metres, find the length and breadth of the garden. (Let the width be x metres and form an equation.)

6 The sum of three numbers is 66. The second number is twice the first and the third number is six more than the second. What are the numbers? (Let x be the first number.)

Example

To a certain whole number is added 6, and the answer is then doubled. If the result exceeds 100, form an inequation and find the possible numbers.

Let x be the number.

$$2(x + 6) > 100$$

Multiply out the brackets:

$$2x + 12 > 100$$

Subtract 12 from both sides:

$$2x > 88$$

Divide both sides by 2:

$$x > 44$$

The possible numbers are 45, 46, 47, . . .

Exercise

7 I think of a whole number, double it, and add 5. The result is less than 20. What can you say about the number I started with? (Let x be the number and form an inequation.)

8 I subtract 5 from a whole number and then treble the answer. The result is less than 45. Form an inequation and solve it to find the possible whole numbers.

9 A mother is four times as old as her son. She is also more than 30 years older than her son. Let the son's age be x years and form an inequation. What can you discover about the son's age?

10 Carol is 3 years older than Jane. The sum of their ages is less than 35 years. Let Jane's age be x years and form an inequation. What can you say about Jane's age?

11 The width of a rectangle is 2 cm less than its length. The perimeter of the rectangle is less than 44 cm. Find possible values for its length.

Continue with Section Q

Q Changing the subject of a formula

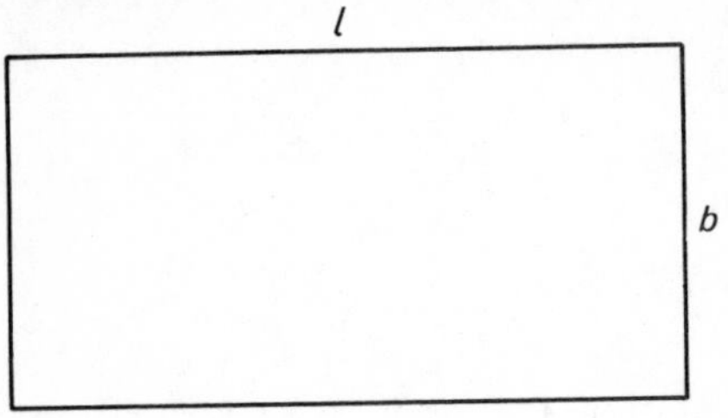

The **formula** $P = 2(l + b)$ enables us to calculate the perimeter P of a rectangle when we know the length l and the breadth b of the rectangle. P is called the **subject of the formula.**

We can rearrange the formula so that b becomes the subject instead of P. To do this we express b in terms of P and l and this is the same as **solving the equation** (or formula) for b.

Example

Make b the subject of the formula $P = 2(l + b)$.

$$P = 2(l + b)$$

Multiply out the brackets:

$$P = 2l + 2b$$

Subtract $2l$ from both sides:

$$P - 2l = 2b$$

Divide both sides by 2:

$$\frac{P - 2l}{2} = b$$

And so

$$b = \frac{P - 21}{2}$$

Example

The area A of a circle of radius r is given by $A = \pi r^2$. Make r the subject of this formula.

$$A = \pi r^2$$

Divide both sides by π:

$$\frac{A}{\pi} = r^2$$

To obtain r we must take the **square root** of both sides:

$$\sqrt{\frac{A}{\pi}} = r$$

$$r = \sqrt{\frac{A}{\pi}}$$

Exercise

Change each formula to the subject indicated:

1 $P = 2r + 2w$ to r

2 $2S = n(a + b)$ to b

3 $S = \frac{1}{2}b(a + b)$ to a

4 $S = \frac{1}{2}at^2$ to t

5 $E = \frac{1}{2}mv^2$ to v

6 $V = \pi r^2 h$ to r

Example

Make l the subject of the formula

$$T = 2\pi\sqrt{\frac{l}{g}}$$

Divide both sides by 2π

$$\frac{T}{2\pi} = \sqrt{\frac{l}{g}}$$

To obtain an expression without a square root we must **square both sides** of the equation:

$$\frac{T^2}{4\pi^2} = \frac{l}{g}$$

Multiply both sides by g:

$$\frac{T^2 g}{4\pi^2} = l$$

So,

$$l = \frac{T^2 g}{4\pi^2}$$

Exercise

7 Make d the subject of the formula $r = p\sqrt{d}$

8 Make a the subject of the formula $D = \sqrt{b^2 - 4ac}$

9 Make R the subject of the formula $c = \sqrt{2hR - h^2}$

10 Make d the subject of the formula $V = d^2\sqrt{H}$

Example

Make n the subject of the formula $an = b + cn$.

$$an = b + cn$$

Subtract cn from both sides:

$$an - cn = b$$

n is a common factor of each term on the left, so

$$n(a - c) = b$$

Divide both sides by $(a - c)$:

$$n = \frac{b}{a - c}$$

Exercise

Change each formula to the subject indicated:

11 $ax + bx = c$ to x

12 $kr = c - br$ to r

13 $d = \frac{t(n - 1)}{n}$ to n

14 $nE = I(r + Rn)$ to n

15 $V = \frac{1}{3}\pi r^2 h$ to h

16 $A = \pi r(r + l)$ to l

17 $v^2 = u^2 + 2fs$ to (a) s, (b) u

18 $T = a + (n - 1)d$ to n

19 $F = \frac{mv^2}{r}$ to (a) r, (b) v

20 $M = P\sqrt{1 + t}$ to t

21 $R = \frac{p}{p + q}$ to (a) q, (b) p

22 $C = \frac{5}{9}(F - 32)$ to F

Continue with Section R

R Progress check

Exercise

1 Solve the following inequations:

(a) $x - 9 \geq -7$ (b) $-6 \leq 3x$ (c) $\frac{x}{5} > -1$

2 Solve the following inequations and show your solution on a number line:

(a) $-10y \geq 80$ (b) $3x + 4 < 8x - 11$
(c) $x + 1 < 6(7 + x) + 1$ (d) $2(3 - x) > 6x - 10$

3 (a) Solve the equation $\frac{x + 3}{2} - \frac{x - 1}{3} = 4$

(b) Solve the inequation $\frac{2x - 1}{3} + \frac{2x + 1}{4} < \frac{5}{6}$

4 Two numbers differ by 5. Three times the smaller number exceeds twice the larger by 8. Let x be the smaller number and form an equation. Solve the equation and find both numbers.

5 I buy a rubber for 7p, and 2 pencils. The total cost is less than 25p. What can you say about the cost of one pencil?

6 Change the subject of the formula

(a) $I = \frac{PTR}{100}$ to R (b) $A = 4\pi r^2$ to r

(c) $D = \sqrt{b^2 - 4ac}$ to (i) c (ii) b

Tell your teacher you have finished this Unit

UNIT M4
Solution of Right-angled Triangles

A Similar triangles

How high are the towers?

How high is this cliff?

It is usually impossible to answer questions like these by direct measurement.

On a sunny day, however, we can use shadows.

We will try to answer the question 'How high is this cliff?'

We need a measuring tape, a pole, and someone to hold the pole upright. We can measure the height of the pole and the lengths of the two shadows.

We then calculate the height of the cliff.

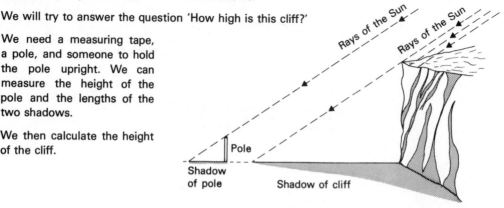

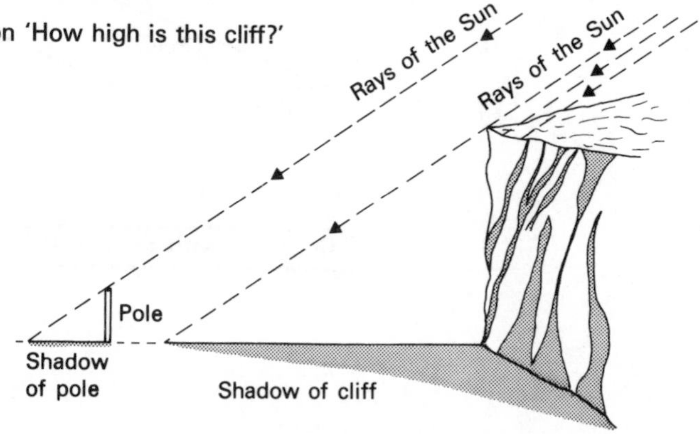

Example

Suppose the height of the pole is 2 metres, the length of the shadow of the pole is 3 metres, and the length of the shadow of the cliff is 12 metres.

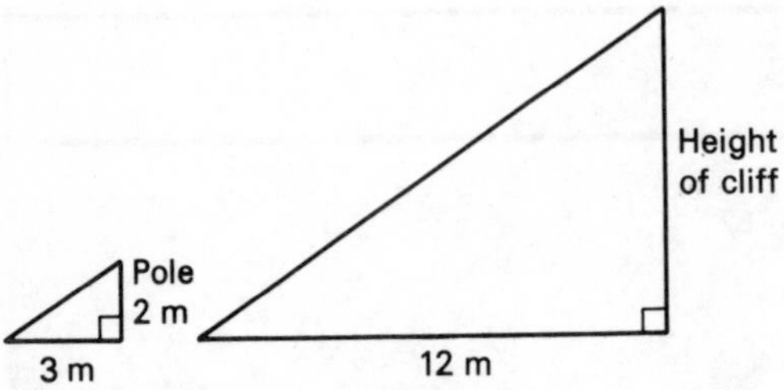

These drawings show the two triangles formed.

Notice that they are **right angled.**

Since the rays of the Sun are parallel, the triangles are also **similar**.

We first calculate the scale factor:

$$k = \frac{12}{3} = 4$$

$$\begin{aligned} \text{Height of cliff} &= k \times \text{height of pole} \\ &= 4 \times 2 \\ &= 8 \text{ metres} \end{aligned}$$

Exercise

1 The diagrams show the shadows cast by a 2 metre pole and a flagpole. Two **right angled** triangles are formed and they are **similar.** What is the height of the flagpole?

Copy and complete: $k = \frac{\square}{5}$

Height of flagpole $= k \times$ height of pole

$= \frac{\square}{\square} \times \square$

$=$ 6 metres

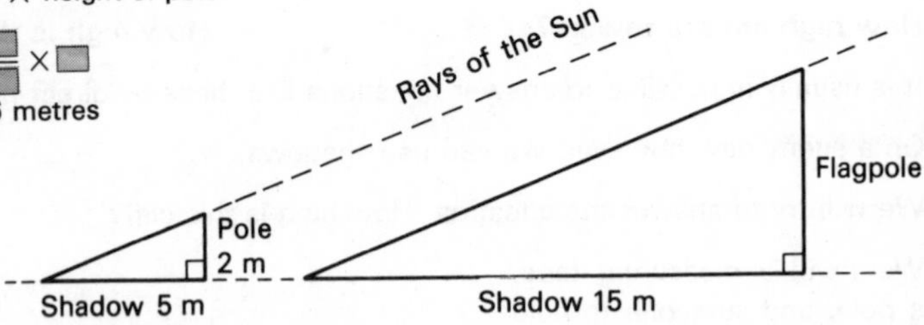

Continue with Section B

B Height and shadow

It is only possible to use the method of Section A when the Sun shines. In this Unit we are going to study other ways of solving such problems using the methods of **trigonometry**.

Consider the exercise above:

$$\frac{\text{Height of pole}}{\text{Length of its shadow}} = \frac{2}{5} \qquad \frac{\text{Height of flagpole}}{\text{Length of its shadow}} = \frac{6}{15} = \frac{2}{5}$$

Notice that the **right-angled** triangles above are **similar** and that in each triangle

$$\frac{\text{Height}}{\text{Shadow}} = \frac{2}{5}$$

Example

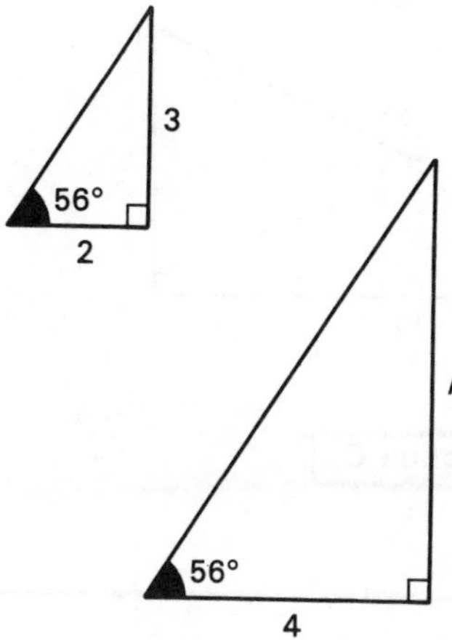

The scale factor $k = \frac{4}{2}$
$= 2$
$h = k \times 3$
$= 2 \times 3$
$= 6$

In the smaller triangle $\frac{\text{height}}{\text{shadow}} = \frac{3}{2}$

In the larger triangle $\frac{\text{height}}{\text{shadow}} = \frac{6}{4}$
$= \frac{3}{2}$

Exercise

Pairs of **similar right-angled** triangles are drawn below. Find *h* in each case.

1

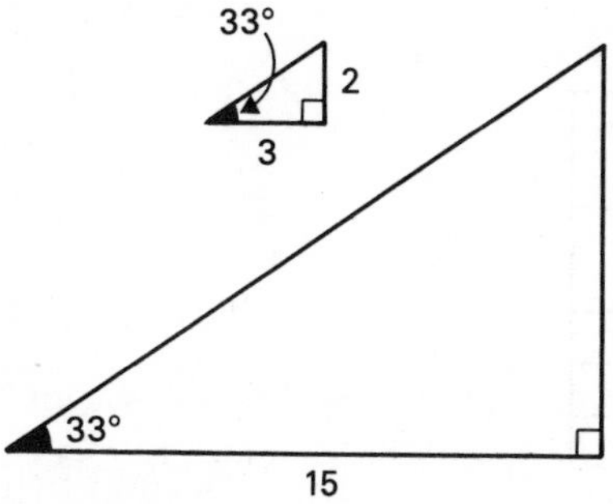

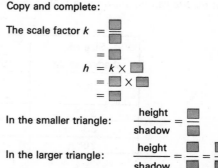

Copy and complete:

The scale factor $k = \frac{■}{■}$
$= ■$
$h = k \times ■$
$= ■ \times ■$
$= ■$

In the smaller triangle: $\frac{\text{height}}{\text{shadow}} = \frac{■}{■}$

In the larger triangle: $\frac{\text{height}}{\text{shadow}} = \frac{■}{■} = \frac{■}{■}$

2

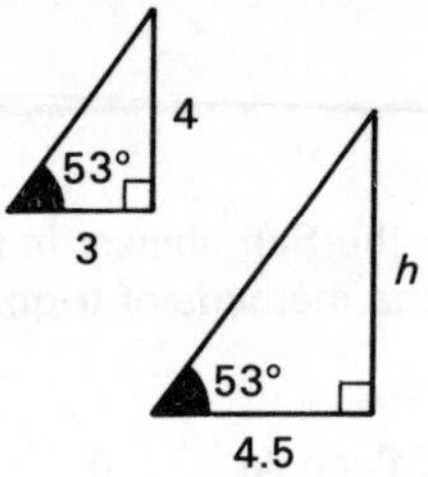

Copy and complete:

The scale factor $k = \frac{■}{■}$

$= ■$

$h = k \times ■$

$= ■ \times ■$

$= ■$

In the smaller triangle: $\frac{\text{height}}{\text{shadow}} = \frac{■}{■}$

In the larger triangle: $\frac{\text{height}}{\text{shadow}} = \frac{■}{■} = \frac{■}{■}$

3 Complete the working as before.

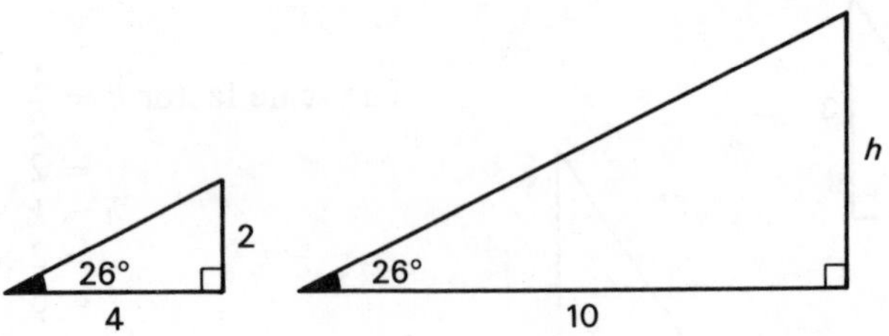

Continue with Section C

C Tangent

In the exercise in Section B, you should have found that in similar right-angled triangles the value of $\frac{\text{height}}{\text{shadow}}$ remains the same no matter how big the triangles are.

Your results can be shown in a table like this:

Size of shaded angle	$\frac{\text{Height}}{\text{Shadow}}$
56°	$\frac{3}{2} = 1.5$
33°	
53°	
26°	

Copy the table and complete it.

So the value of $\frac{\text{height}}{\text{shadow}}$ is the same for similar right-angled triangles, but changes with the size of the shaded angle.

We give the value of $\frac{\text{height}}{\text{shadow}}$ the name **tangent** and write

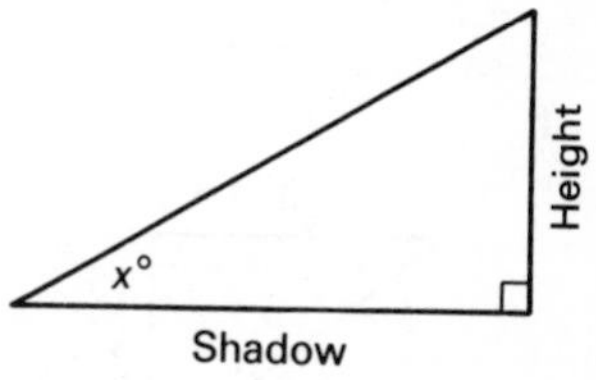

$$\tan x^\circ = \frac{\text{height}}{\text{shadow}}$$

This is a shorthand for tangent

Instead of **height** and **shadow** we will use **opposite** and **adjacent**.

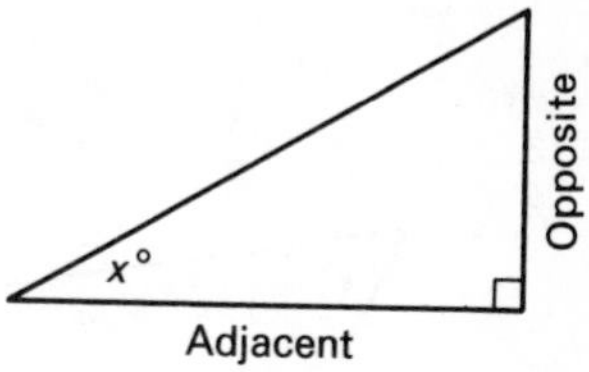

So $$\boxed{\tan x^\circ = \frac{\text{opposite}}{\text{adjacent}}}$$

Example

For this right angled triangle find the value of tan $x°$.

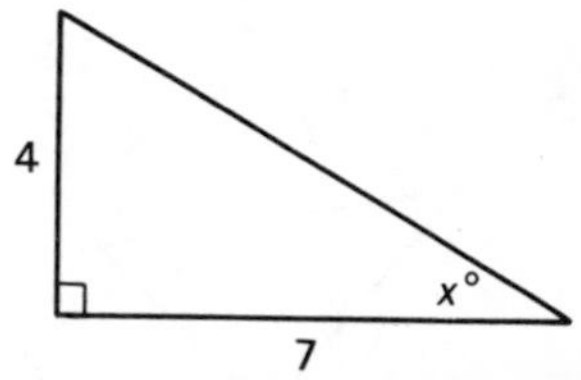

Step 1

Draw an arrow to the side opposite the $x°$ angle and write 'opposite'.

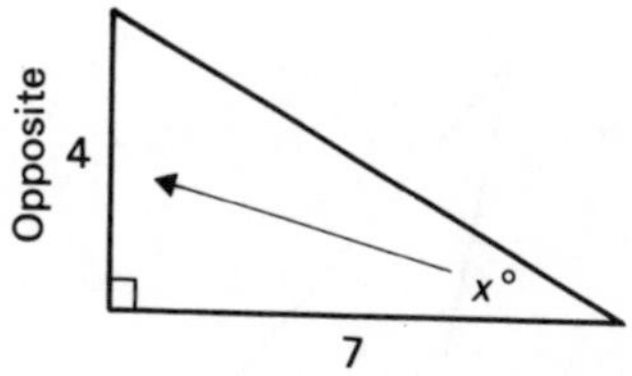

Step 2

The side opposite the right angle is the hypotenuse. Label it 'hypotenuse'.

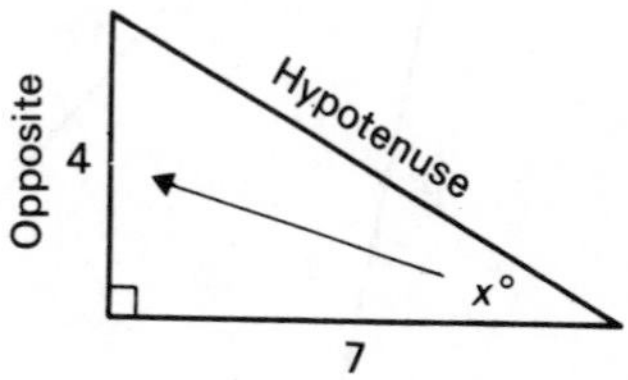

Step 3

The remaining side is adjacent to the $x°$ angle. Label it 'adjacent'.

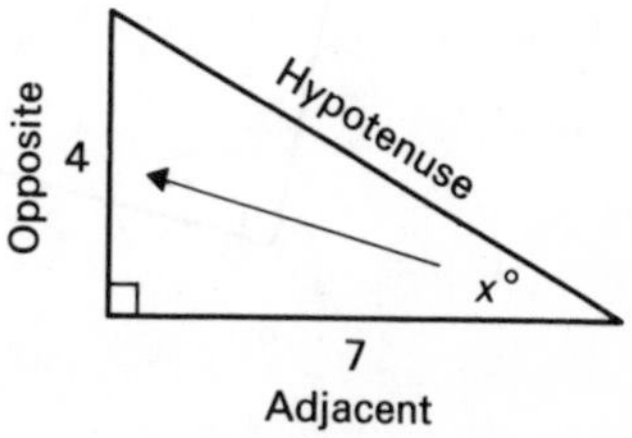

Step 4

Write $\tan x^\circ = \frac{4}{7}$.

Exercise

Make a sketch of each of the triangles below and, using Steps 1 to 4, find tan $x°$ in each case.

1

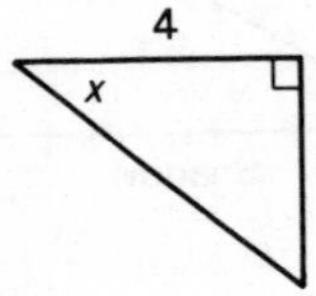

2

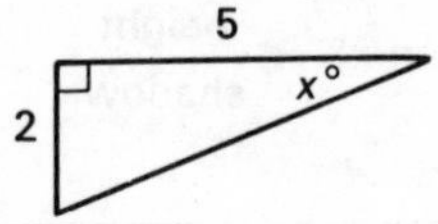

3

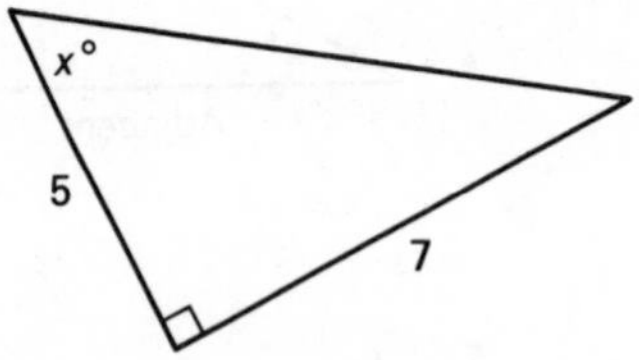

4

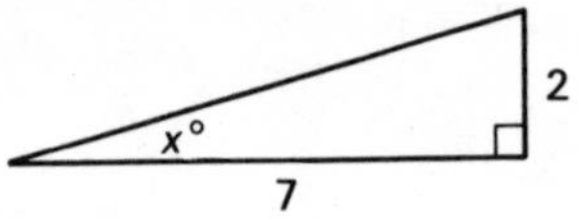

5

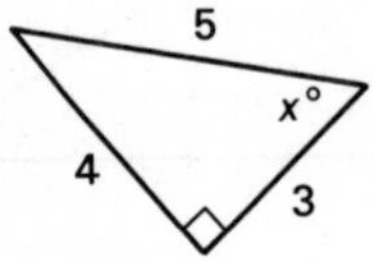

6

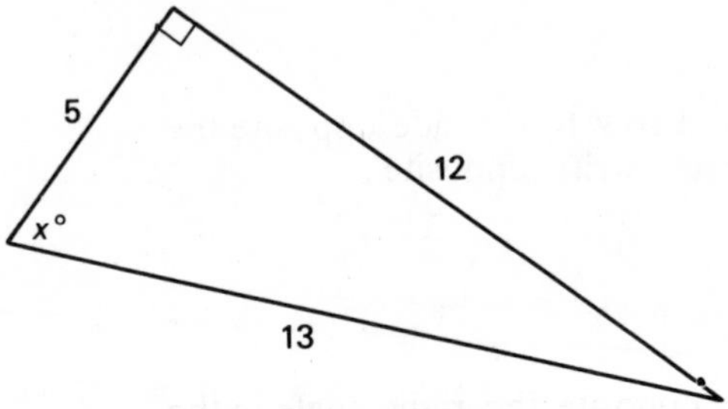

7

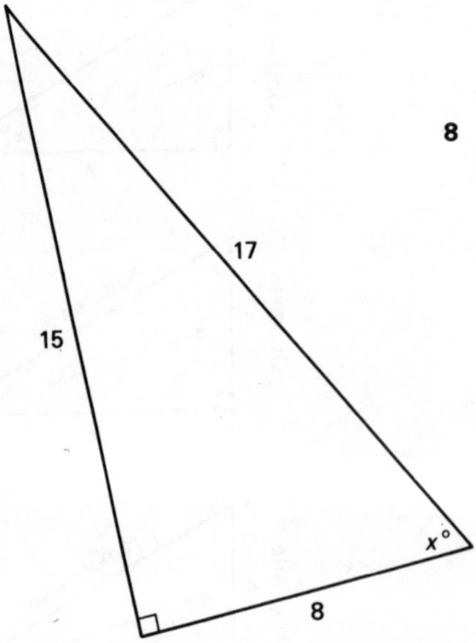

8

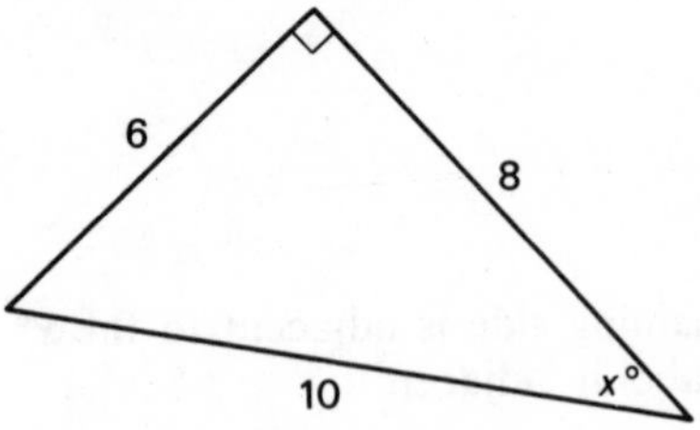

Continue with Section D

D Tangent by drawing

This diagram can be used to find the tangent of angles of 10°, 20°, 30°, 40°, 50°, and 60°.

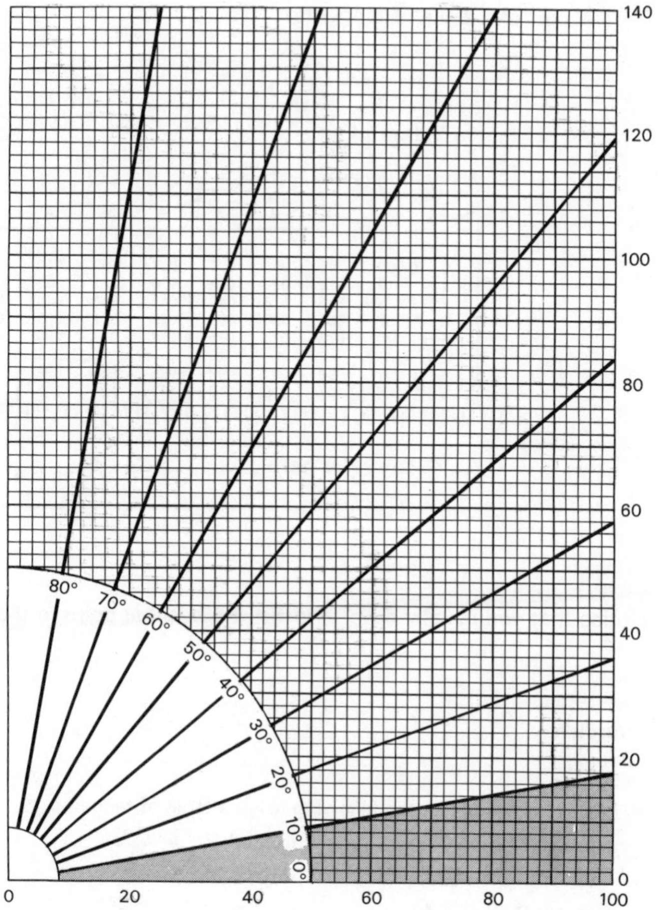

Example

To find tan 10° we use the shaded right-angled triangle.

The adjacent side is 100 units and the opposite side is 18 units.

(Each little square has a side measuring 2 units.)

So $\tan 10° = \dfrac{\text{opposite}}{\text{adjacent}}$

$= \dfrac{18}{100}$

$\tan 10° = 0.18$

Exercise

1 Copy this table and complete it using the diagram above.

Angle	0°	10°	20°	30°	40°	50°
Opposite side	0	18				119
Adjacent side	100	100	100	100	100	100
Tangent	0	0.18				1.19

Continue with Section E

E Tangent from tables

Using a set of Mathematical Tables we can find the values of the tangent of angles from 0° to 89.9° (sometimes called 'natural tangents').

Here is part of a table of tangents.

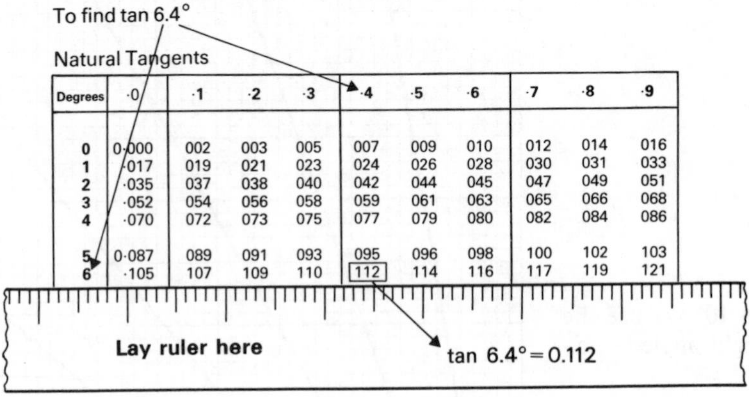

Degrees	·0	·1	·2	·3	·4	·5	·6	·7	·8	·9
0	0·000	002	003	005	007	009	010	012	014	016
1	·017	019	021	023	024	026	028	030	031	033
2	·035	037	038	040	042	044	045	047	049	051
3	·052	054	056	058	059	061	063	065	066	068
4	·070	072	073	075	077	079	080	082	084	086
5	0·087	089	091	093	095	096	098	100	102	103
6	·105	107	109	110	112	114	116	117	119	121

Notice that you usually have to insert the decimal point in the table reading.

Exercise

1 Copy and complete the following using a table of tangents.

(a) tan 5° = 0.087 (b) tan 10° = ▭ (c) tan 15° = ▭

(d) tan 20° = ▭ (e) tan 35° = ▭ (f) tan 5.2° = ▭

(g) tan 9.8° = ▭ (h) tan 10.7° = ▭ (i) tan 35.3° = ▭

(j) tan 44.9° = ▭ (k) tan 4.3° = ▭ (l) tan 27.5° = ▭

2 Copy and complete the following using a table of tangents.

Angle	0°	10°	20°	30°	40°	50°	60°
Tangent	0	0.176	0.364				

Compare your answers with those obtained in Section D.

Here is part of a table of tangents starting at 45°.

Notice that for angles between 45° and 90° the tangent is greater than 1 but the whole number part is only printed every 5°.

Natural Tangents

Degrees	·0	·1	·2	·3	·4	·5	·6	·7	·8	·9
45	1·000	003	007	011	014	018	021	025	028	032
46	·036	039	043	046	050	054	057	061	065	069
47	·072	076	080	084	087	091	095	099	103	107
48	·111	115	118	122	126	130	134	138	142	146
49	·150	154	159	163	167	171	175	179	183	188
50	1·192	196	200	205	209	213	217	222	226	230
51	·235	239	244	248	253	257	262	266	271	275
52	·280	285	289	294	299	303	308	313	317	322
53	·327	332	337	342	347	351	356	361	366	371
54	·376	381	387	392	397	402	407	412	418	423
55	1·428	433	439	444	450	455	460	466	471	477
56	·483	488	494	499	505	511	517	522	528	534
57	·540	546	552	558	564	570	576	582	588	594
58	·600	607	613	619	625	632	638	645	651	658
59	·664	671	678	684	691	698	704	711	718	725
60	1·732	739	746	753	760	767	775	782	789	797
61	·804	811	819	827	834	842	849	857	865	873
62	·881	889	897	905	913	921	929	937	946	954
63	1·963	971	980	988	997	2·006	2·014	2·023	2·032	2·041
64	2·050	059	069	078	087	097	106	116	125	135

Note: (a) The tangent of 53° is 1.327 (not 0.327).
(b) The tangent of 63.4° is 1.997 but the tangent of 63.5° is 2.006. The whole number changes in the middle of the table.

Example

Use tables of tangents to write down the value of tan 47.6°.

Degrees	·0	·1	·2	·3	·4	·5	·6	·7
45	1·000	003	007	011	014	018	021	025
46	·036	039	043	046	050	054	057	061
47	·072	076	080	084	087	091	095	099

tan 47.6° = 1.095

Exercise

3 Copy and complete the following using a table of tangents.

(a) tan 48.9° = ▢ (b) tan 70.0° = ▢ (c) tan 50.6° = ▢

(d) tan 59.9° = ▢ (e) tan 45° = ▢ (f) tan 80° = ▢

(g) tan 62.2° = ▢ (h) tan 73.3° = ▢ (i) tan 86.4° = ▢

Continue with Section F

F Calculating angle sizes

We can calculate the size of the $x°$ angle in this right-angled triangle.

$$\tan x° = \frac{\text{opposite}}{\text{adjacent}}$$

$$= \frac{12}{10}$$

$$= 1.2$$

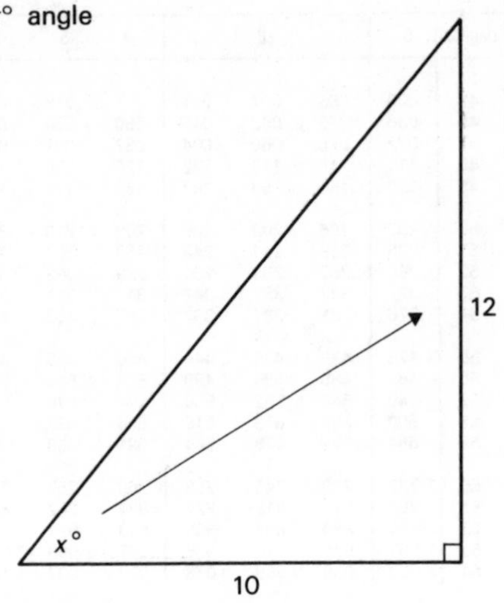

We look in a table of tangents to find the angle which has a tangent of 1.2.

Natural Tangents

Degrees	·0	·1	·2	·3	·4	·5	·6	·7	·8	·9
45	1·000	003	007	011	014	018	021	025	028	032
46	·036	039	043	046	050	054	057	061	065	069
47	·072	076	080	084	087	091	095	099	103	107
48	·111	115	118	122	126	130	134	138	142	146
49	·150	154	159	163	167	171	175	179	183	188
50	1·192	196	200	205	209	213	217	222	226	230
51	·235	239	244	248	253	257	262	266	271	275
52	·280	285	289	294	299	300	308	313	317	322

1.2 appears in the table as 1.200 (the 1. is at the beginning of the line only).

So the angle whose tangent is 1.2 is 50.2°.

$x° = 50.2°$

Example

Use a table of tangents to find the angle whose tangent is 1.163.

$$\tan x° = 1.163$$

From the table $x° = 49.3°$

Exercise

In the following exercise, use a table of tangents.

1 (a) Copy and complete

$\tan x° = 0.374$

So $x° = $ ▭

Find $x°$ in the following, setting down your working as above.

(b) $\tan x° = 0.827$ (c) $\tan x° = 1.564$ (d) $\tan x° = 2.808$

(e) $\tan x° = 1.505$ (f) $\tan x° = 1.732$ (g) $\tan x° = 3.133$

Example

$\tan x° = 0.276$, find $x°$

In the tangent tables you will not find the entry 0.276.
You will find 0.275 and 0.277. Either 15.4° or 15.5° would do.
If you cannot find the exact value you are looking for, take the **nearest value** to it.

Exercise

2 (a) Copy and complete:

$\tan x° = 1.500$

So $x° = $ ▭

Find $x°$ in the following, setting your work down as above.

(b) $\tan x° = 3.000$ (c) $\tan x° = 0.258$ (d) $\tan x° = 0.856$

(e) $\tan x° = 5.720$ (f) $\tan x° = 3.012$ (g) $\tan x° = 1.544$

Example

In the following triangle, find $x°$.

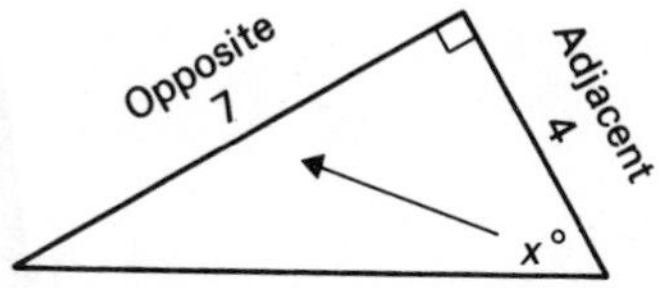

$$\text{tangent} = \frac{\text{opposite}}{\text{adjacent}}$$

$$\tan x° = \frac{7}{4} = 1.75$$

So $x° = 60.3°$ (since 1.75 is nearer 1.753 than 1.746)

Exercise

3 Sketch the following triangle:

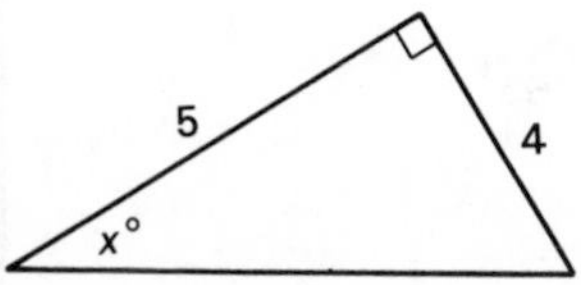

Mark the opposite and adjacent sides.

Copy and complete:

$\tan x° = \frac{▭}{▭} = $ ▭

So $x° = $ ▭

In the following, sketch the triangles, mark the opposite and adjacent sides, and set out your work in the same way as in question 3.

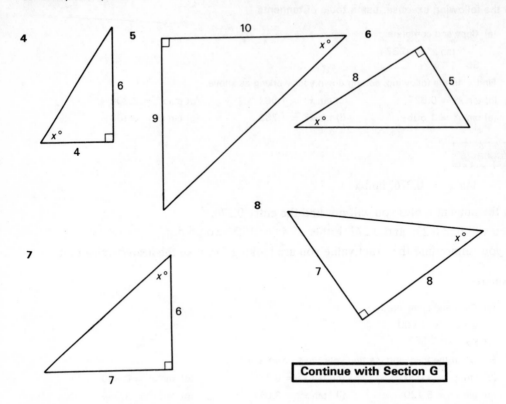

4

5

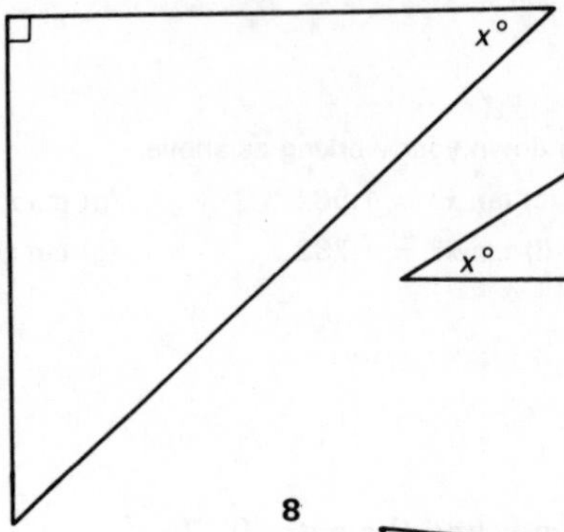

6

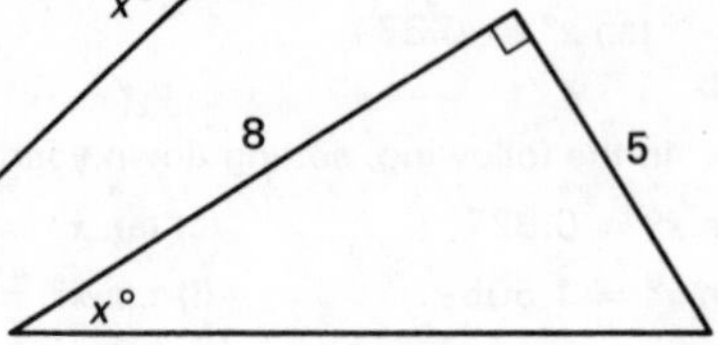

7

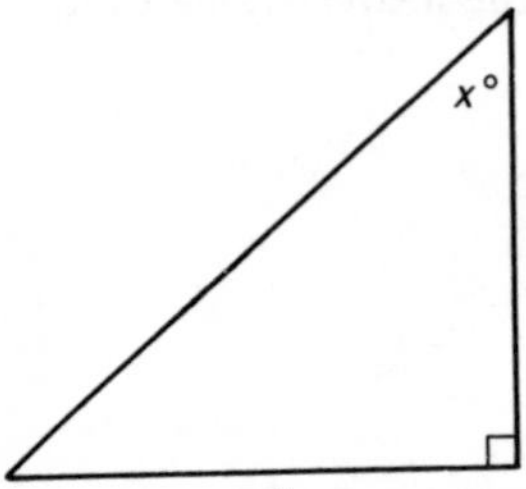

8

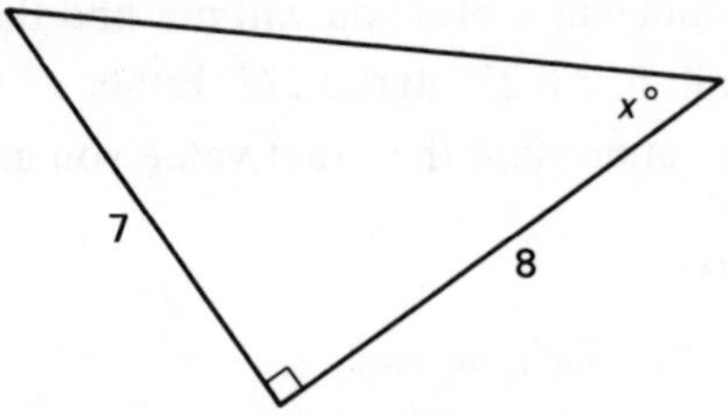

Continue with Section G

G Calculating lengths of sides

The drawing shows a clinometer being used to find the height of a tower.

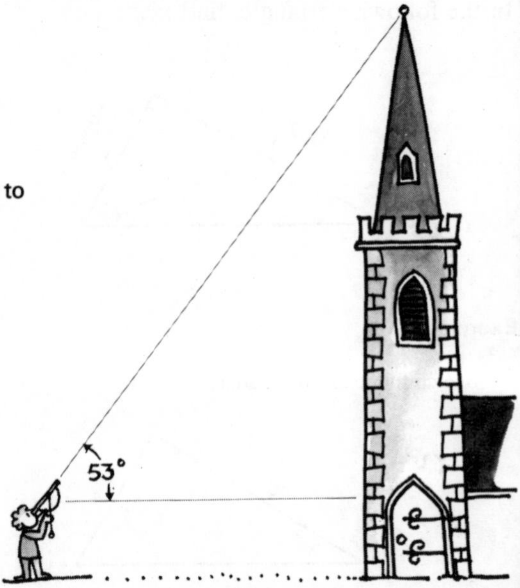

In order to find this height, we have to solve a triangle like this.

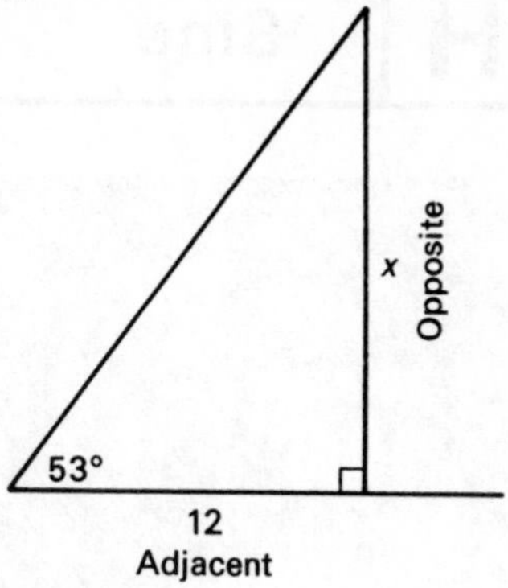

$$\frac{x}{12} = \tan 53°$$

So $\frac{x}{12} = 1.327$ (from a table of tangents)

$$x = 12 \times 1.327$$

$$x = 15.9$$

Exercise

1 Find x in the following triangles, setting down your work as above.

(a)

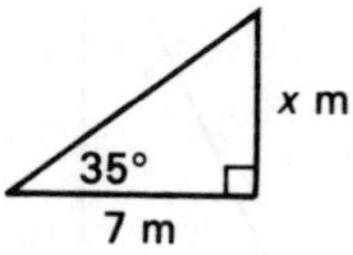

(b)

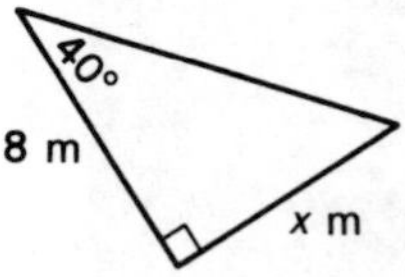

(c)

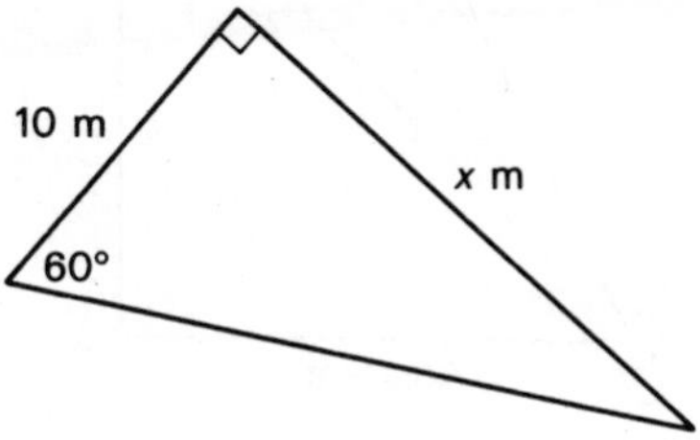

(d)

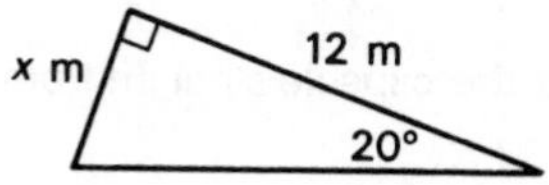

(e)

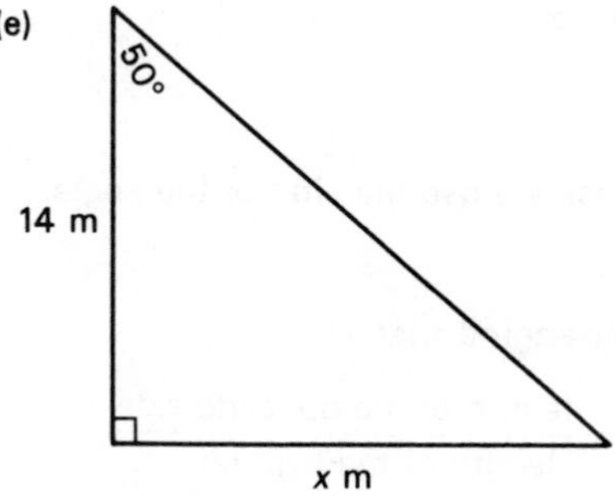

Continue with Section H

H Sine

A radar tracking station tracks a space capsule as it descends towards the earth.

It measures the angle of elevation of the capsule and its distance from the station.

This is shown in the diagram below.

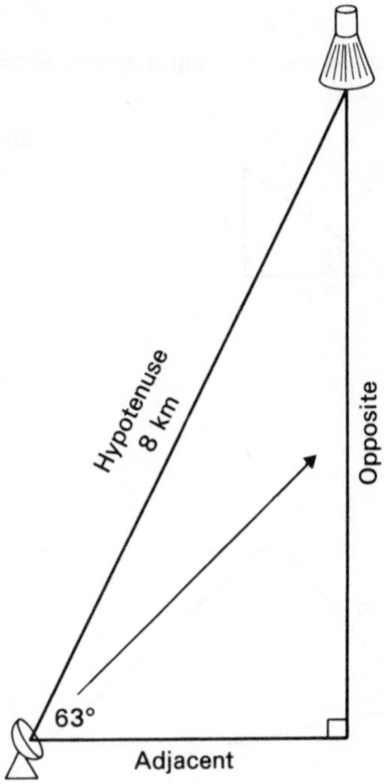

What is wanted is the capsule's height from the ground.

The tangent of 63° is no use here since we know neither the opposite side nor the adjacent side.

In this case we use the **sine** of the angle.

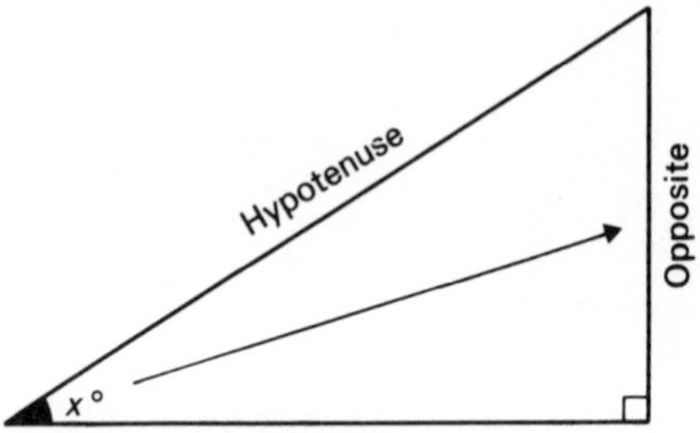

In a **right-angled** triangle.

$$\text{sine } x° = \frac{\text{length of the opposite side}}{\text{length of the hypotenuse}}$$

This is shortened to

$$\sin x° = \frac{\text{opposite}}{\text{hypotenuse}}$$

Example

For the triangle drawn here find sin $x°$.

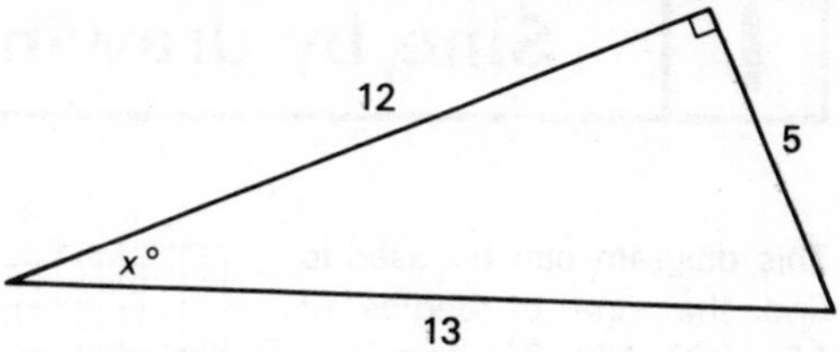

Decide first which side is opposite the $x°$ angle and which is the hypotenuse.

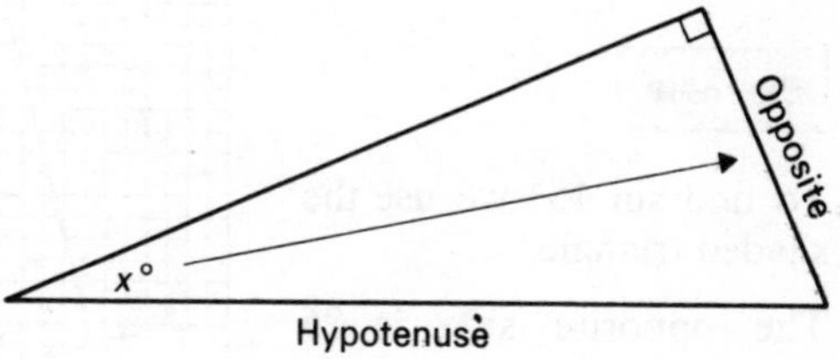

$$\sin x° = \frac{\text{opposite}}{\text{hypotenuse}} = \frac{5}{13}$$

Exercise

Find the value of sin $x°$ in each of the following triangles.

1

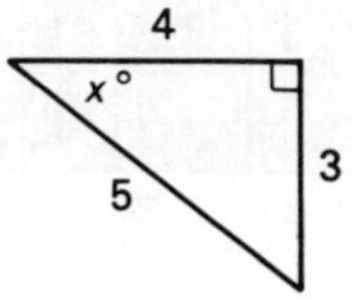

Copy and complete:

$\sin x° = \frac{\square}{\square}$

2

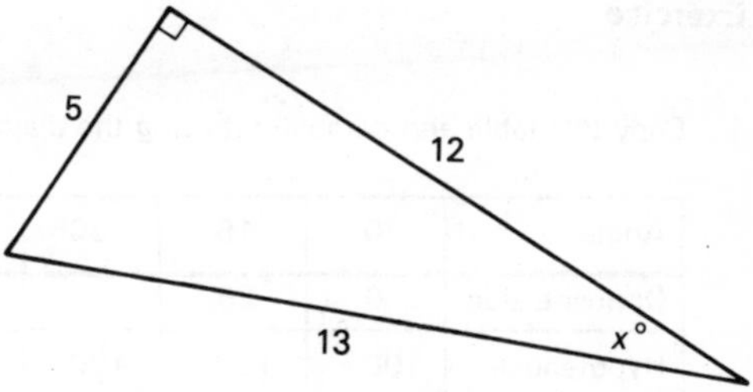

3

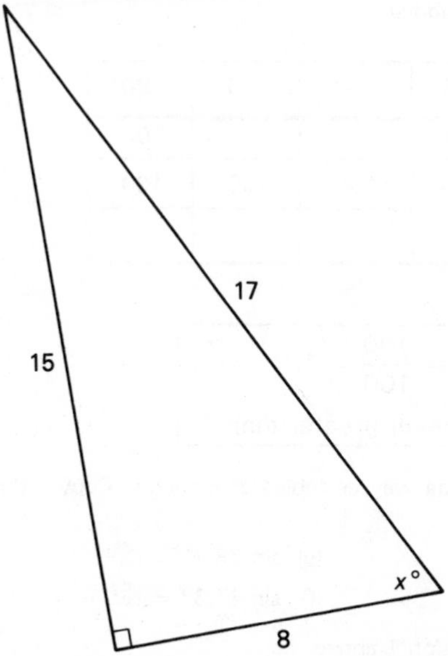

4

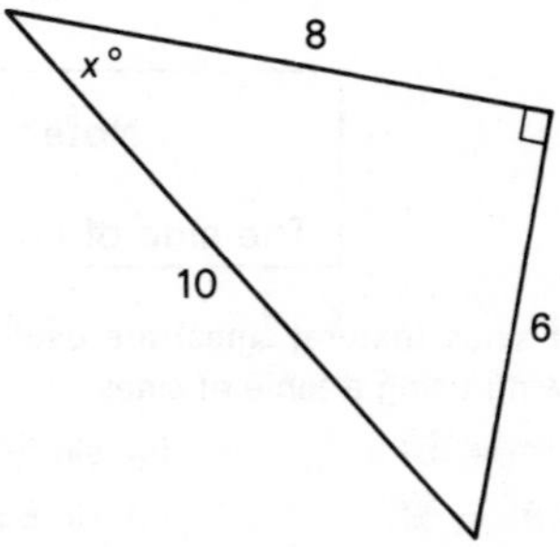

Continue with Section I

I Sine by drawing and from tables

This diagram can be used to find the sine of angles of 15°, 30°, 45°, 60° and 75°.

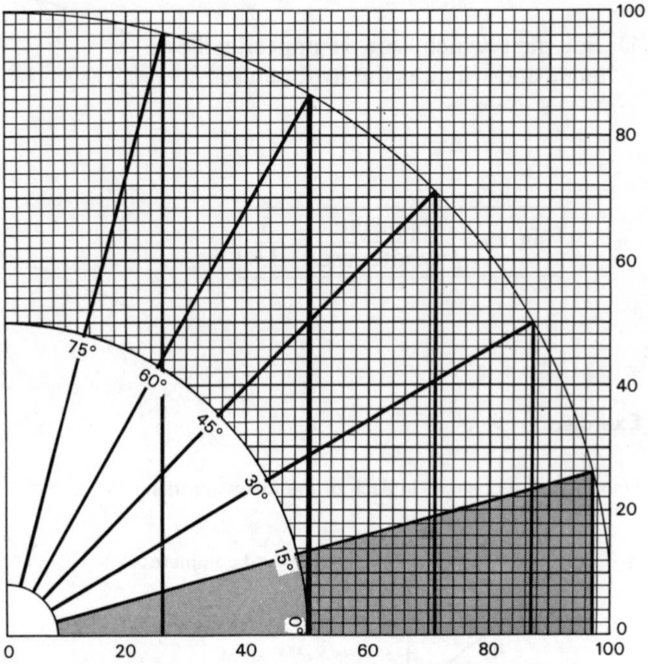

Example

To find sin 15° we use the shaded triangle.

The opposite side is 26 units and the hypotenuse is 100 units.

So $\sin 15° = \dfrac{\text{opposite}}{\text{hypotenuse}}$

$= \dfrac{26}{100}$

$\sin 15° = 0.26$

Exercise

1 Copy this table and complete it using the diagram above.

Angle	0°	15°	30°	45°	60°	75°	90°
Opposite side	0	26		71			100
Hypotenuse	100	100	100	100	100	100	100
Sine	0	0.26					

> Note: $\sin 90° = \dfrac{100}{100} = 1.$
>
> The sine of an angle is never greater than 1.

2 Tables of sines (natural sines) are used in the same way as tables of tangents. Copy and complete the following using a table of sines.

(a) sin 35° = ▢ (b) sin 54° = ▢ (c) sin 28.7° = ▢

(d) sin 5.9° = ▢ (e) sin 85.2° = ▢ (f) sin 47.3° = ▢

3 Use a table of sines to check your answers to question 1 above.

Continue with Section J

J Sine from tables

Example

To find the angle whose sine is 0.984.

78	·978	979	979	979	980	980	980	981	981	981
79	·982	982	982	983	983	983	984	984	984	985
							987	987	987	

From the tables, we see that angles of 79.6°, 79.7°, 79.8° all have a sine equal to 0.984.

You could give any of these as your answer.

In the following Exercise, use a table of sines.

Exercise

1 (a) Copy and complete:

$\sin x° = 0.866$

so $x° =$ ▭

Find $x°$ in the following, setting your work down as above.

(b) $\sin x° = 0.755$ (c) $\sin x° = 0.326$ (d) $\sin x° = 0.727$

(e) $\sin x° = 0.988$ (f) $\sin x° = 0.903$ (g) $\sin x° = 0.248$

Continue with Section K

K Calculating sides

We are now able to solve the space capsule problem in Section H.

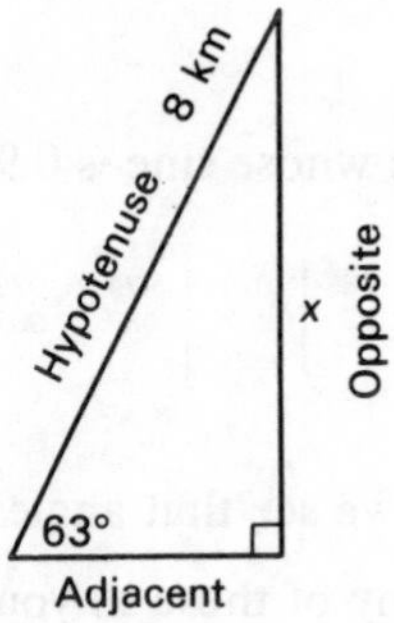

Let the height of the capsule above the ground be x km.

$$\frac{x}{8} = \sin 63°$$

$$\frac{x}{8} = 0.891 \text{ (from a table of sines)}$$

Multiply both sides by 8 :

$$x = 8 \times 0.891$$
$$= 7.128$$

The capsule is 7.128 km above the ground.

Exercise

1 Find x in each of the following triangles, setting down your work as above.

(a)

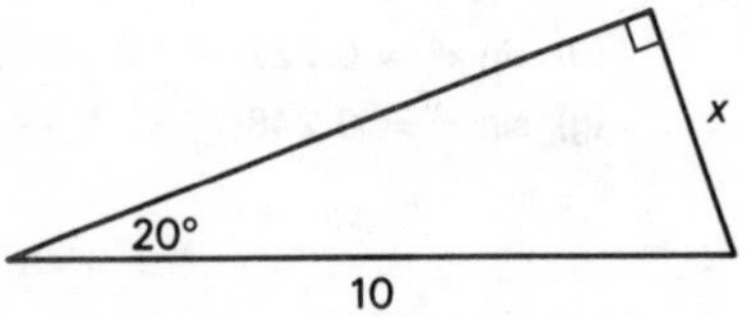

(b)

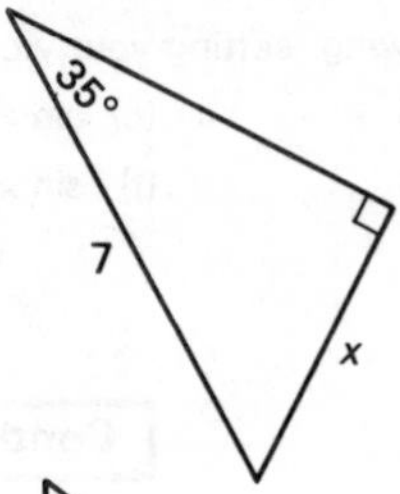

(c)

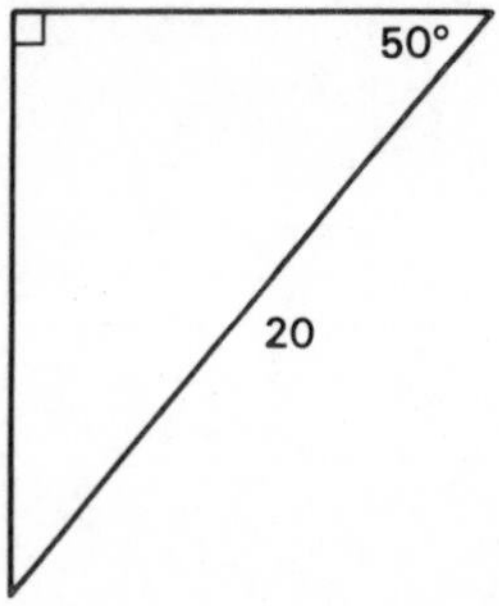

(d)

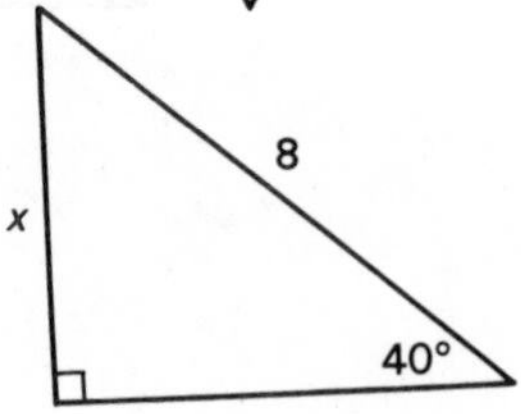

(e)

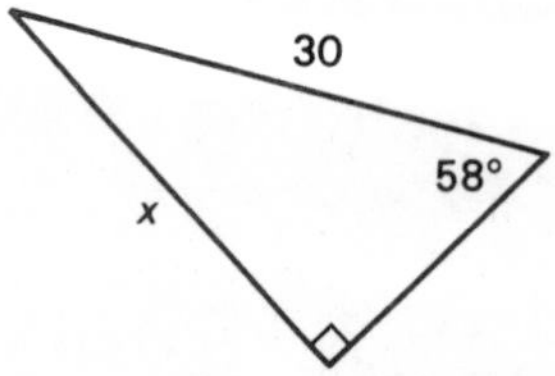

(f)

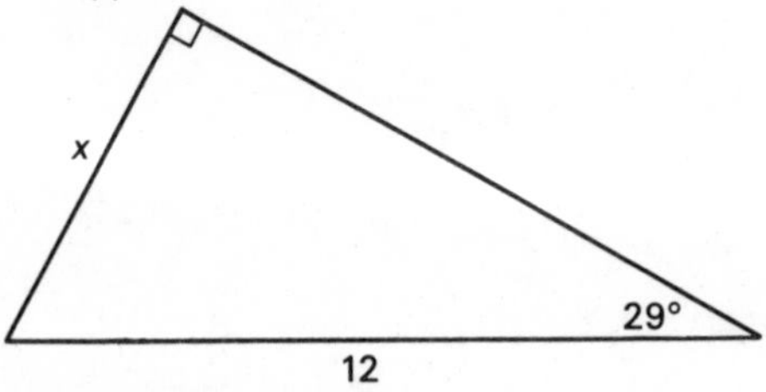

Continue with Section L

L Calculating angles

Example

Use a table of sines to calculate the size of the $x°$ angle in this triangle.

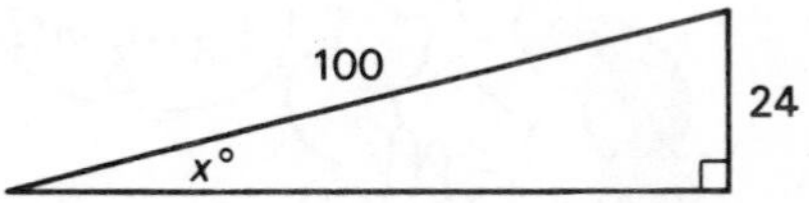

$$\sin x° = \frac{24}{100}$$
$$= 0.24$$

12	·208	210	211	213	215	216	218	220	222	223
13	·225	227	228	230	232	233	235	237	239	240
14	·242	244	245	247	249	250	252	254	255	257

Hence $x° = 13.9°$

Exercise

Use a table of sines to calculate the size of the $x°$ angle in each of the following triangles.

1

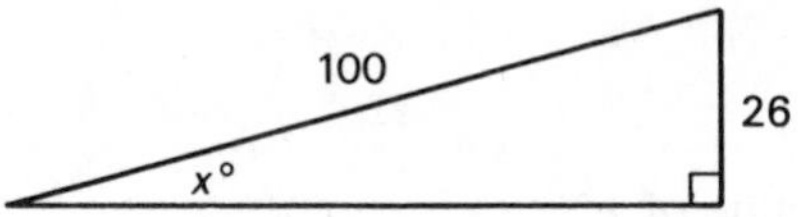

2

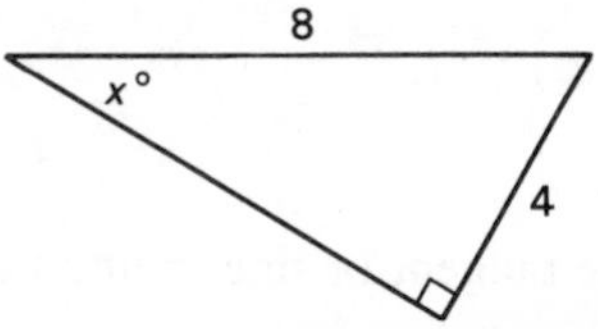

3

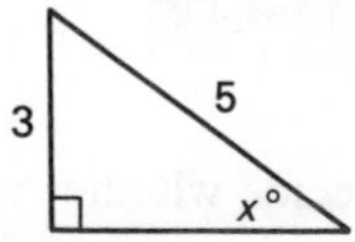

4

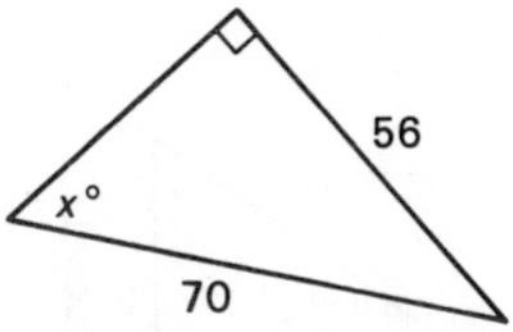

5

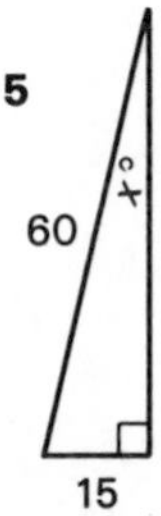

6

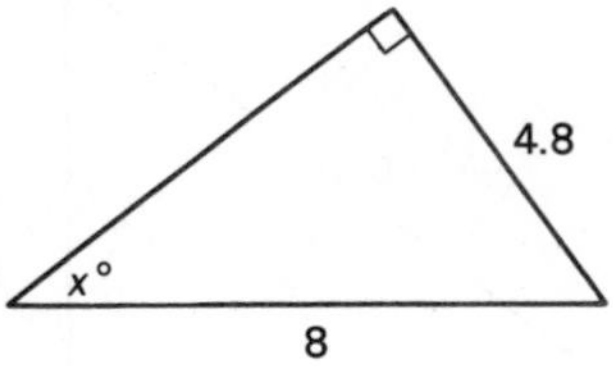

Continue with Section M

M Sine or tangent?

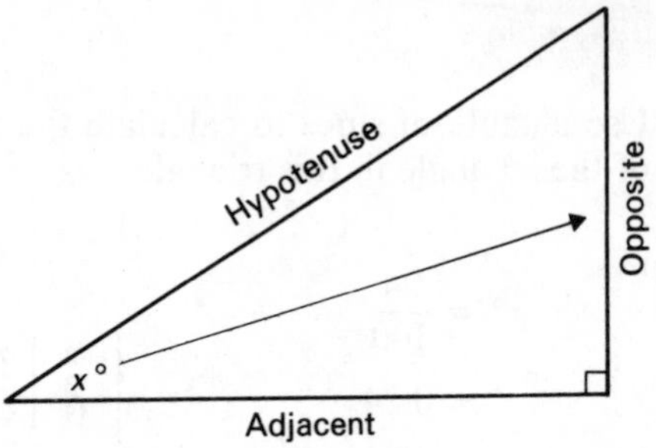

$$\tan x° = \frac{\text{opposite}}{\text{adjacent}}$$

$$\sin x° = \frac{\text{opposite}}{\text{hypotenuse}}$$

Example

Decide whether to use tangent or sine to find the value of $x°$.

Then find the value of $x°$ using tables.

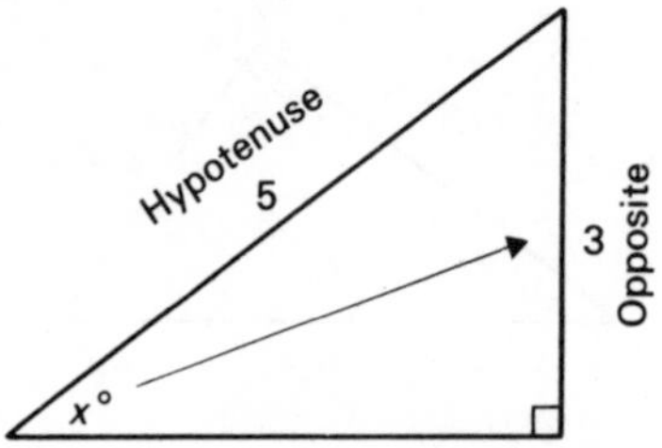

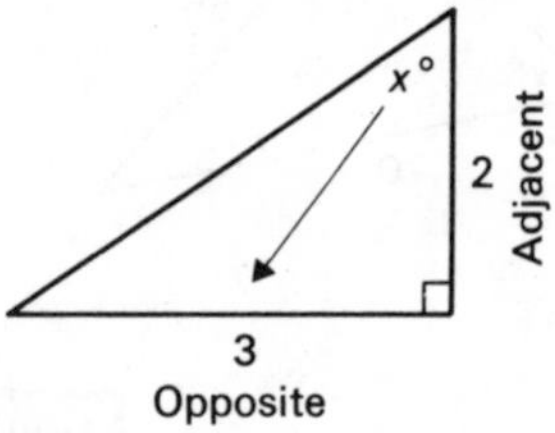

(a) Opposite and hypotenuse known, so sine is used.

$$\sin x° = \frac{3}{5} = 0.6$$

$$x° = 36.9°$$

(b) Opposite and adjacent known, so tangent is used.

$$\tan y° = \frac{3}{2} = 1.5$$

$$y° = 56.3°$$

Exercise

(a) Decide whether to use tangent or sine to find the value of $x°$ in the following triangles.

(b) Find the value of $x°$.

1

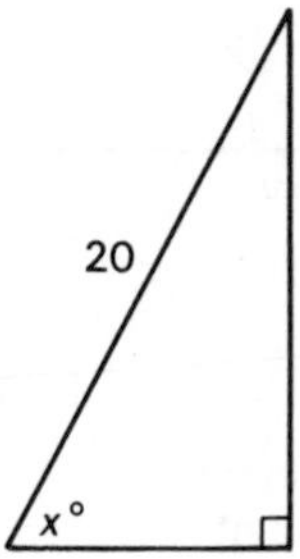

2

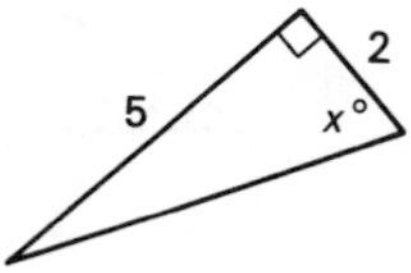

3

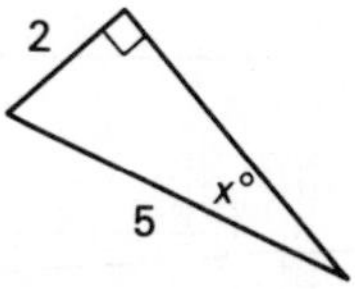

4

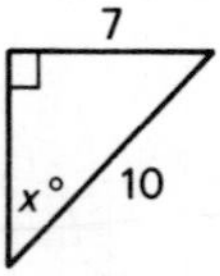

5

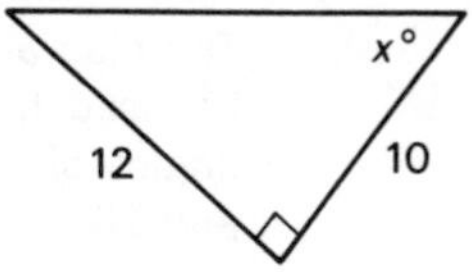

6

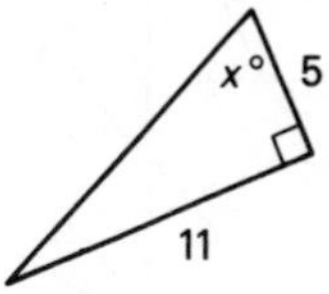

Continue with Section N

N Cosine

A miner had to drive a horizontal tunnel into a hill to meet up with a vertical ventilation shaft. The distance up the hill to the opening of the ventilation shaft is 1500 metres. The hillside makes an angle of 30° with the horizontal.

How long is the tunnel?

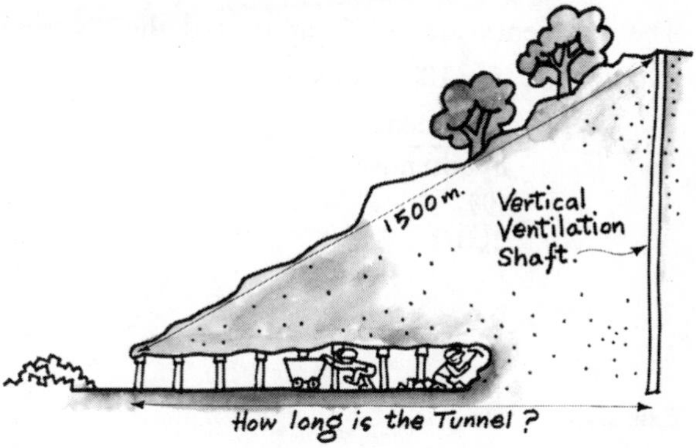

First make a drawing to show the details.

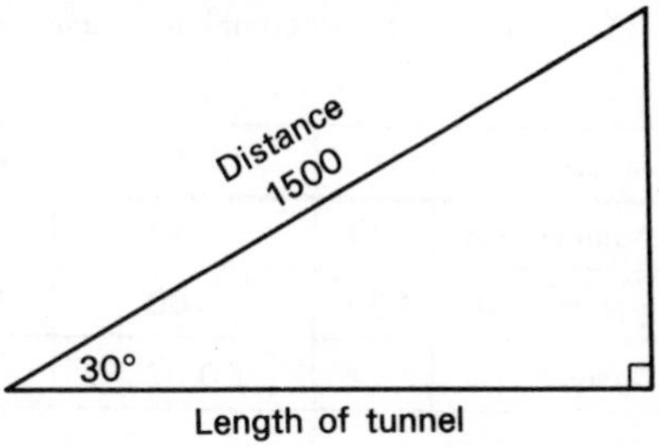

Here we know the hypotenuse and we want to find the adjacent side, so neither the tangent nor the sine will do.

In this case we use the **cosine** of the angle.

In a right-angled triangle,

$$\text{cosine } x^\circ = \frac{\text{length of adjacent side}}{\text{length of the hypotenuse}}$$

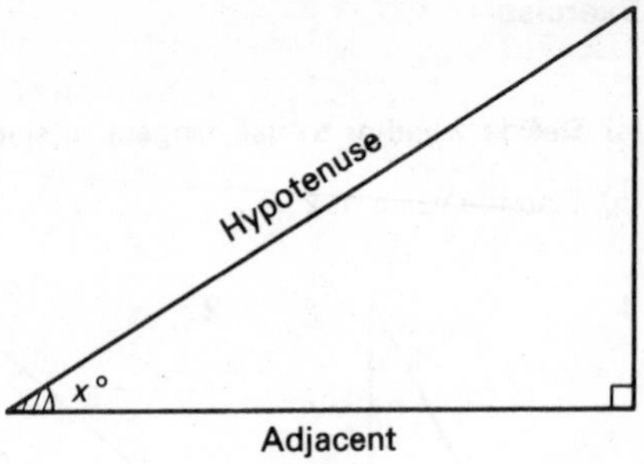

This is shortened to $\boxed{\cos x^\circ = \dfrac{\text{adjacent}}{\text{hypotenuse}}}$

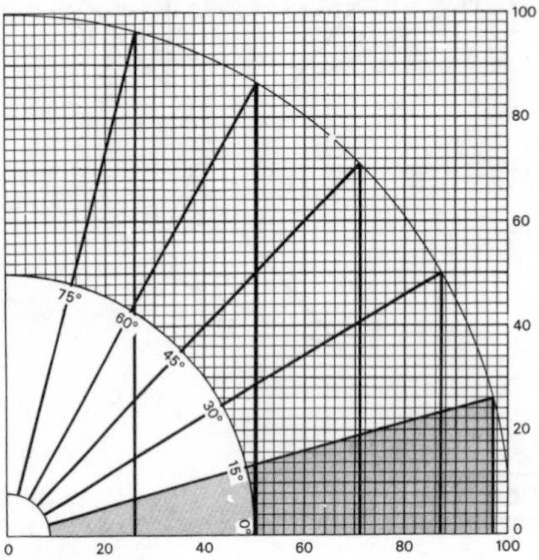

The diagram in Section I may be used to find the cosine of angles of 15°, 30°, 45°, 60°, and 75°.

Example

To find cos 15° we use the shaded triangle. The adjacent side is 97 units and the hypotenuse is 100 units.

$$\text{So } \cos 15^\circ = \frac{\text{adjacent}}{\text{hypotenuse}}$$

$$= \frac{97}{100}$$

$$\cos 15^\circ = 0.97$$

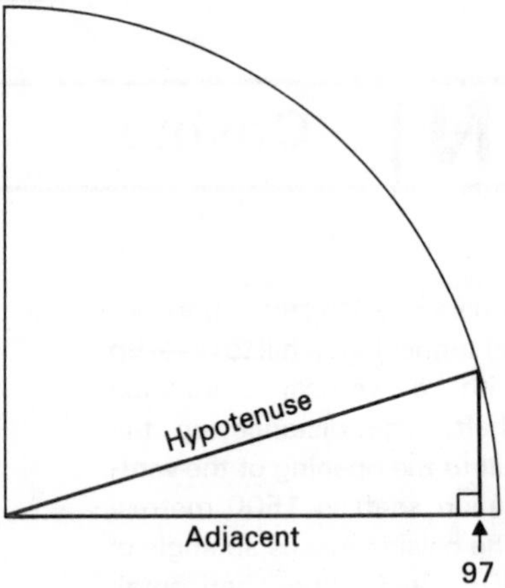

Exercise

1 Copy this table and complete it, using the diagram in Section I.

Angle	0°	15°	30°	45°	60°	75°	90°
Adjacent side	100	97					0
Hypotenuse	100	100	100	100	100	100	100
Cosine	1	0.97					0

We use tables of cosines in the same way as we use tables of tangents and sines.

Example

To find cos 16.4°.

16.4°

Natural Cosines

Degrees	·0	·1	·2	·3	·4	·5	·6	·7	·8	·9
0	1·000	000	000	000	000	000	000	000	000	000
1	1·000	000	000	000	000	000	000	000	000	0·999
2	0·999	999	999	999	999	999	999	999	999	999
3	·999	999	998	998	998	998	998	998	998	998
4	·998	997	997	997	997	997	997	997	996	996
5	0·996	996	996	996	996	995	995	995	995	995
6	·995	994	994	994	994	994	993	993	993	993
7	·993	992	992	992	992	991	991	991	991	991
8	·990	990	990	990	989	989	989	988	988	988
9	·998	987	987	987	987	986	986	986	985	985
10	0·985	985	984	984	984	983	983	983	982	982
11	·982	981	981	981	980	980	980	979	979	979
12	·978	978	977	977	977	976	976	976	975	975
13	·974	974	974	973	973	972	972	972	971	971
14	·970	970	969	969	969	968	968	967	967	966
15	0·966	965	965	965	964	964	963	963	962	962
16	·961	961	960	960	959	959	958	958	957	957
24	·914	913	912	911	911	910	909	909	908	907
25	0·906	906	905	904	903	903	902	901	900	900

Lay ruler here

cos 16.4° = 0.959

Exercise

2 Copy and complete the following using a table of cosines.

(a) cos 5° = ▢ (b) cos 10° = ▢ (c) cos 20° = ▢

(d) cos 40° = ▢ (e) cos 7.9° = ▢ (f) cos 24.9° = ▢

(g) cos 82.6° = ▢ (h) cos 3° = ▢ (i) cos 57.3° = ▢

3 Use a table of sines to check your answers to the Exercise.

Continue with Section O

O Use of cosine

Example

Find the value of x in this triangle.

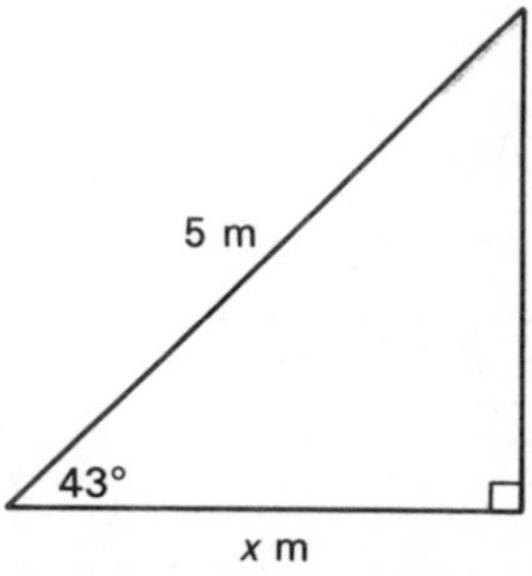

$$\frac{x}{5} = \cos 43°$$

$$\frac{x}{5} = 0.731 \text{ (from table of cosines)}$$

Multiply both sides by 5:

$$x = 5 \times 0.731$$

$$x = 3.655$$

Exercise

Find x in each of the following triangles, setting out your work as above.

1

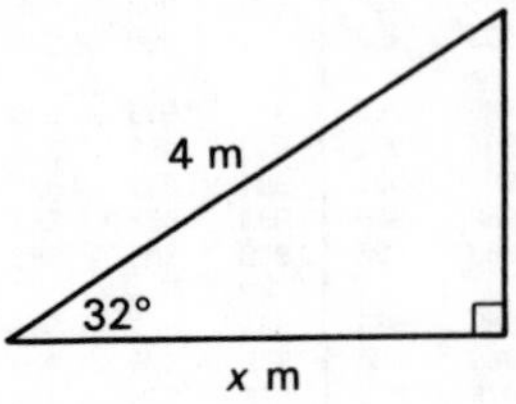

2

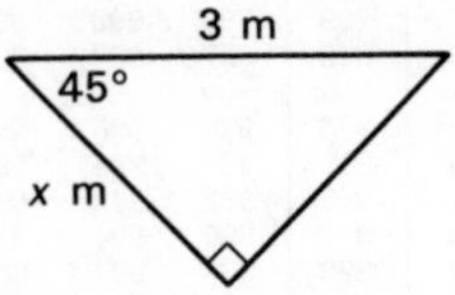

3

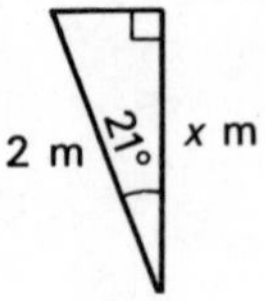

4

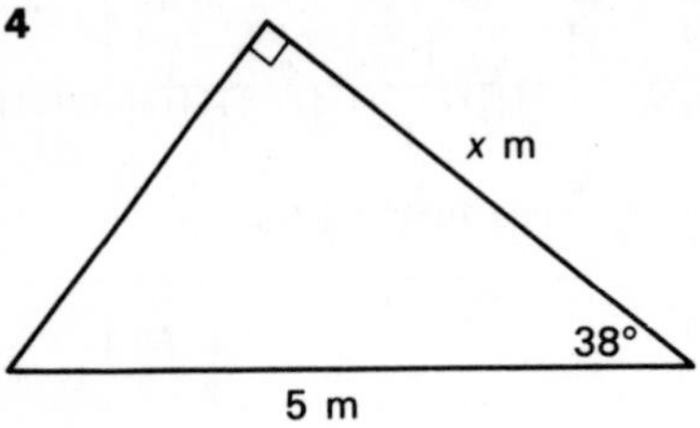

5

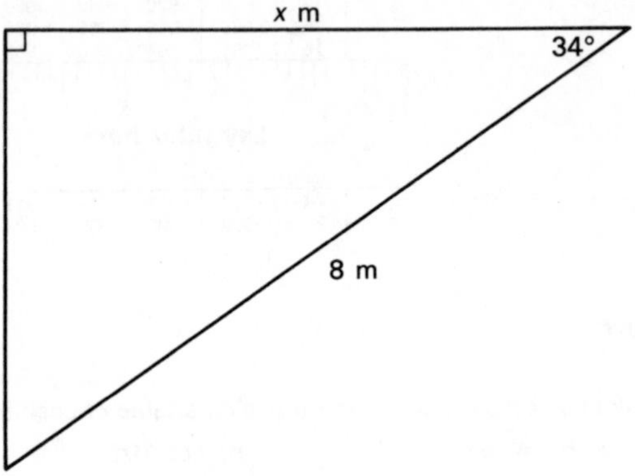

6

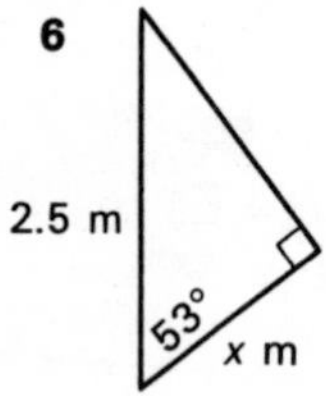

7 We can now find the length of the tunnel in Section L.

Let the length of the tunnel be x metres, and continue as for questions 1 to 6.

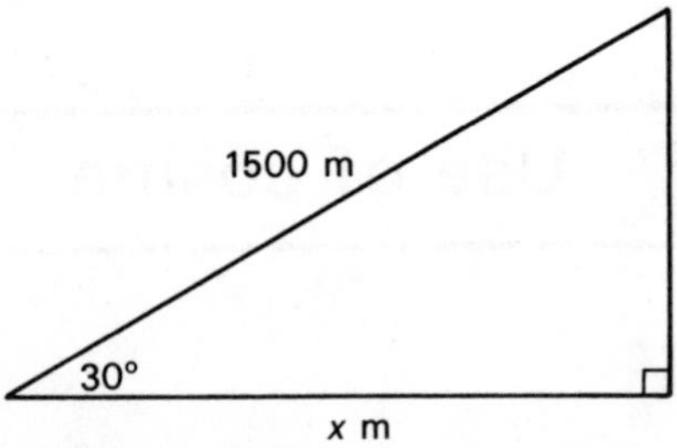

Continue with Section P

P Cosine used to find angles

When we know the lengths of the adjacent side and the hypotenuse we can use cosine tables to find the size of the angle enclosed.

Example

Find the value of the $x°$ angle in the triangle.

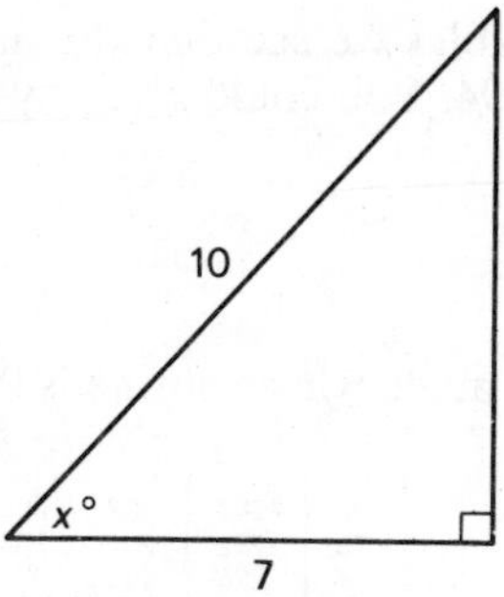

$$\cos x° = \frac{\text{adjacent}}{\text{hypotenuse}} = \frac{7}{10} = 0.7$$

We look in tables of cosines to find the angle which has a cosine of 0.700.

Natural Cosines

Degrees	·0	·1	·2	·3	·4	·5	·6	·7	·8	·9
45	0·707	706	705	703	702	701	700	698	697	696
46	·695	693	692	691	696	688	687	686	685	683
47	·682	681	679	678	677	676	674	673	672	670
48	·669	668	667	666	664	663	661	660	659	657
49	·656	655	653	652	651	649	648	647	645	644

So $x° = 45.6°$

In the following exercise, use a table of cosines.

Exercise

1 (a) Copy and complete:

$\cos x° = 0.950$

So $x° =$ ▭

Find $x°$ in the following, setting down your work as above.

(b) $\cos x° = 0.894$ (c) $\cos x° = 0.779$ (d) $\cos x° = 0.711$

(e) $\cos x° = 0.588$ (f) $\cos x° = 0.438$ (g) $\cos x° = 0.239$

Example

To find the angle whose cosine is 0.994.

5	0·996	996	996	996	996	995	995	995	995	995
6	·995	994	994	994	994	994	993	993	993	993
7	·993	992	992	992	992	991	991	991	991	991

From the tables we see that the angles 6.1°, 6.2°, 6.3°, 6.4° and 6.5° all have a cosine equal to 0.994. You could give any of these as your answer.

Example

To find the angle whose cosine is 0.270.

72	·309	307	306	304	302	301	299	297	200	294
73	·292	291	289	287	286	284	282	281	279	277
74	·276	274	272	271	269	267	266	264	262	261

In the tables you will not find the entry 0.270. You will find cos 74.3° = 0.271 and cos 74.4° = 0.269. Either 74.3° or 74.4° would be a correct answer.

> If you cannot find the exact value you are looking for, take **the nearest value** to it.

In the following Exercise, use a table of cosines.

Exercise

2 (a) Copy and complete:

$\cos x° = 0.997$

So $x° =$ ▭

Find $x°$ in the following, setting down your work as above.

(b) $\cos x° = 0.980$ (c) $\cos x° = 0.178$ (d) $\cos x° = 0.100$

(e) $\cos x° = 0.300$ (f) $\cos x° = 0.050$ (g) $\cos x° = 0.053$

Example

Use a table of cosines to calculate the size of the $x°$ angle in this triangle.

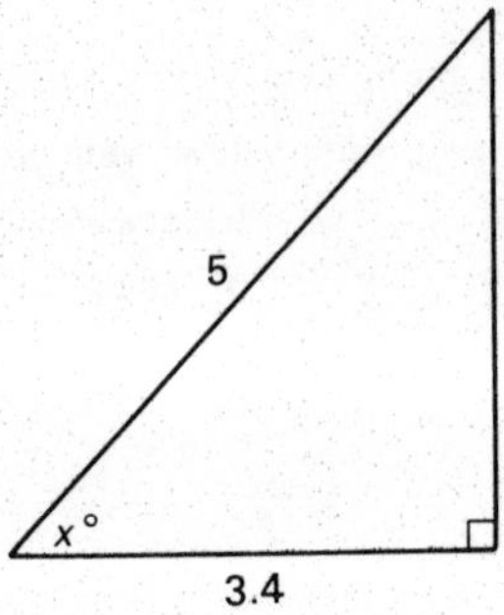

$$\cos x° = \frac{3.4}{5}$$

$$= 0.68$$

So $x° = 47.1°$ or $47.2°$

Exercise

Calculate the size of the $x°$ angle in each of the following triangles.

3

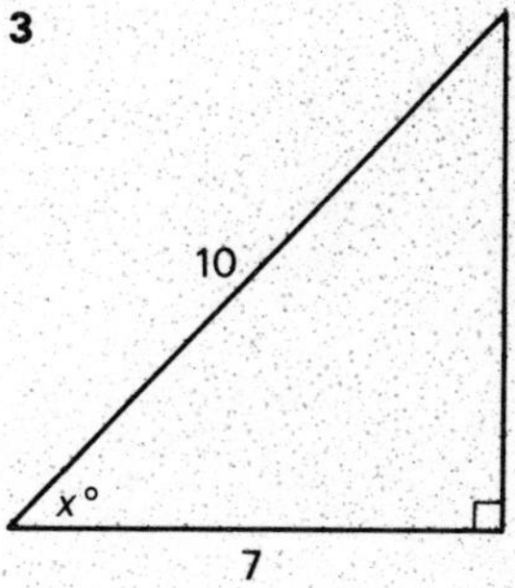

4

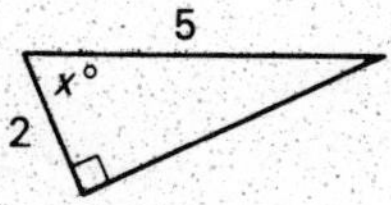

5

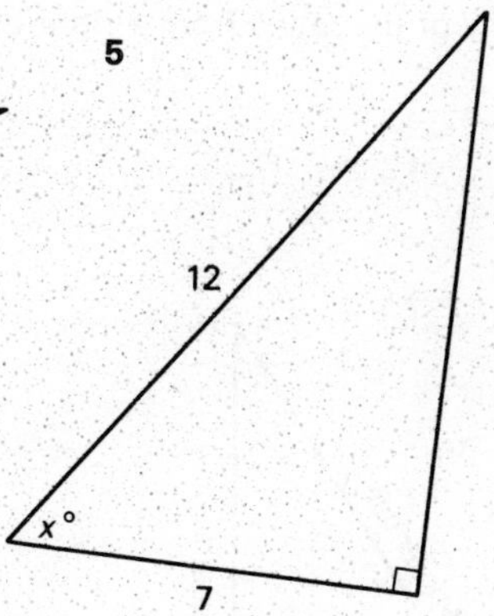

6

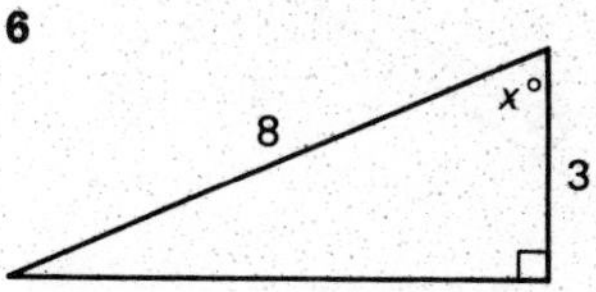

7

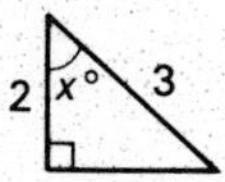

8

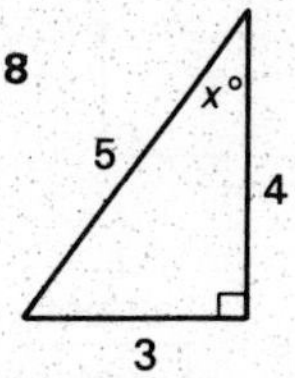

Continue with Section Q

Q Sine, cosine, or tangent?

Tangent, sine, and cosine can only be used in **right-angled triangles**. You must be able to pick out any of the ratios from a right-angled triangle.

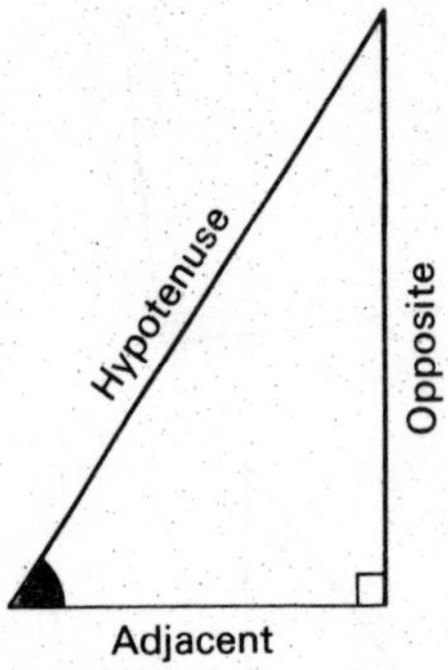

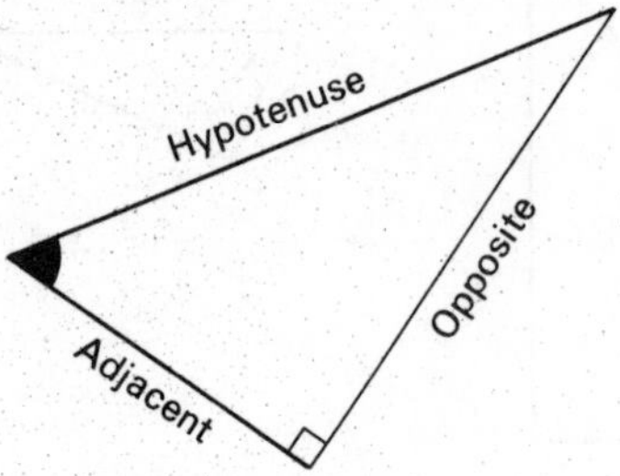

$$\text{cosine of angle} = \frac{\text{adjacent}}{\text{hypotenuse}}$$

$$\text{sine of angle} = \frac{\text{opposite}}{\text{hypotenuse}}$$

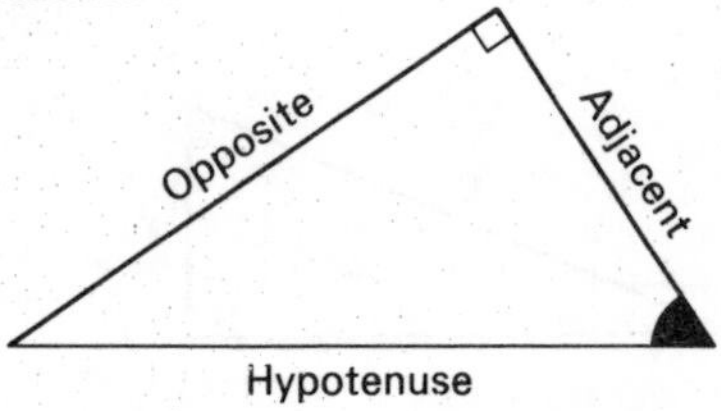

$$\text{tangent of angle} = \frac{\text{opposite}}{\text{adjacent}}$$

(a) Decide whether to use sine, cosine, or tangent to find the value of x in each of the following triangles.

(b) Find the value of x.

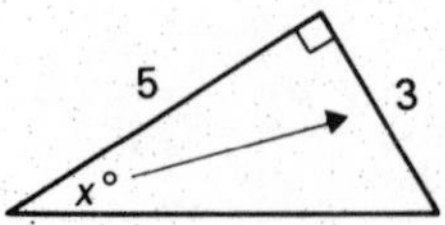

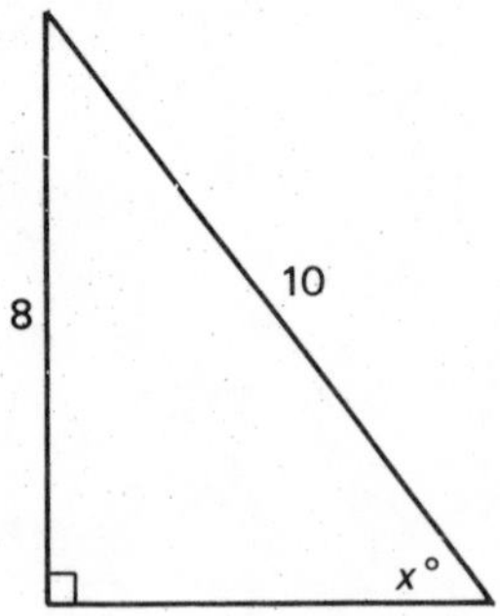

(a) **Opposite** and **adjacent** known
So tangent is used.

(b) $\tan x° = \frac{3}{5} = 0.6$

So $x° = 31.0°$

(a) **Opposite** and **hypotenuse** known
So sine is used.

(b) $\sin x° = \frac{8}{10} = 0.8$

So $x° = 53.1°$

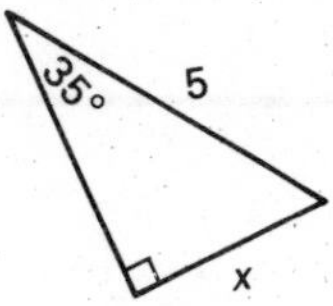

(a) **Hypotenuse** known and **opposite** wanted; so sine is used.

(b) $\dfrac{x}{5} = \sin 35°$

$\dfrac{x}{5} = 0.574$

$x = 5 \times 0.574$
$= 2.87$

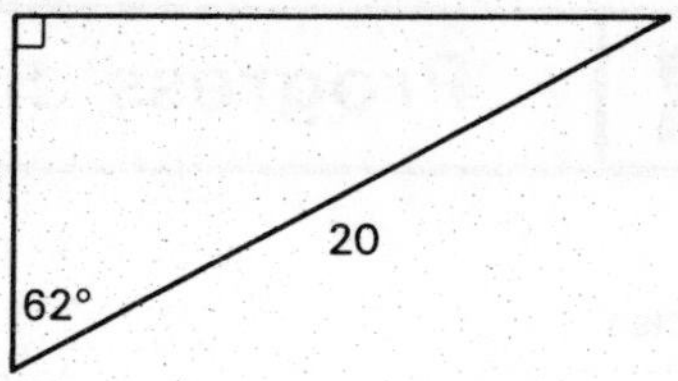

(a) **Hypotenuse** known and **adjacent** wanted; so cosine is used.

(b) $\dfrac{x}{20} = \cos 62°$

$\dfrac{x}{20} = 0.469$

$x = 20 \times 0.469$
$= 9.38$

Exercise

(a) Decide whether to use sine, cosine, or tangent to find the value of *x* in each of the following triangles.
(b) Find the value of *x*.

1

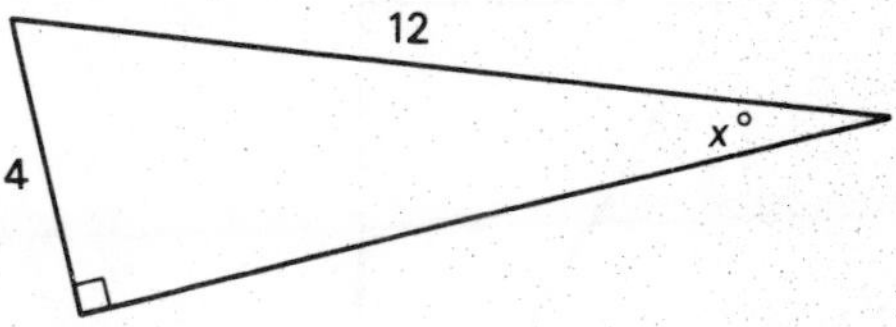

2

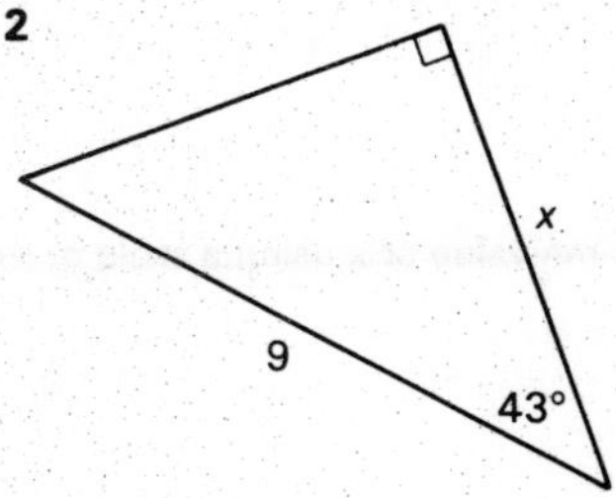

3

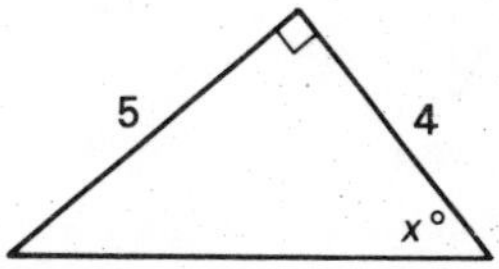

4

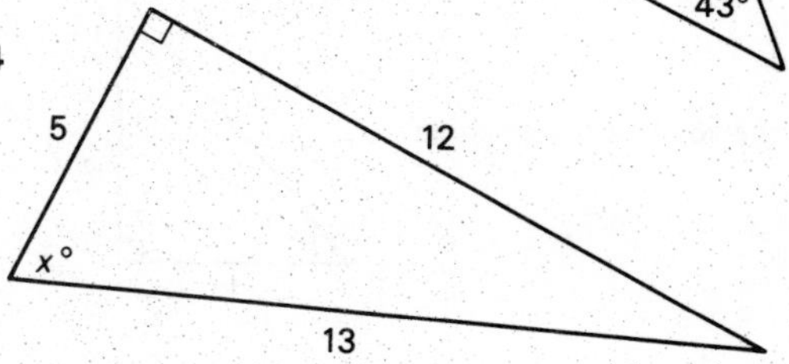

5

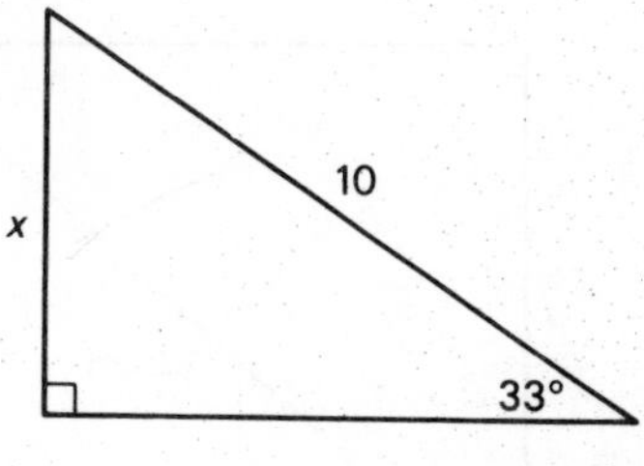

6

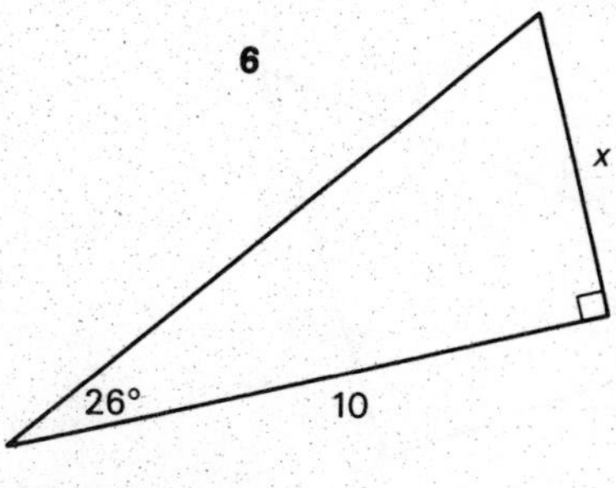

Continue with Section R

R Progress check

Exercise

1 Use tables to find the following:

(a) cos 53° (b) cos 35.7° (c) sin 25° (d) sin 43.8°

(e) tan 32° (f) tan 35.7° (g) tan 54° (h) tan 63.8°

2 Use tables to find the value of $x°$ in each of the following:

(a) $\cos x° = 0.629$ (b) $\cos x° = 0.461$ (c) $\tan x° = 0.445$

(d) $\tan x° = 2.194$ (e) $\tan x° = 1.700$ (f) $\tan x° = 2.014$

(g) $\sin x° = 0.857$ (h) $\sin x° = 0.926$

3 Find the value of $x°$ using a table of tangents.

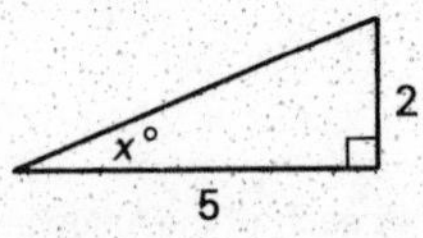

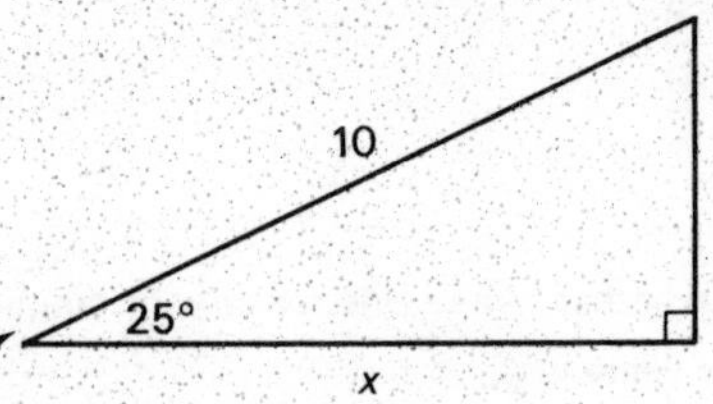

4 Find the value of $x°$ using a table of cosines.

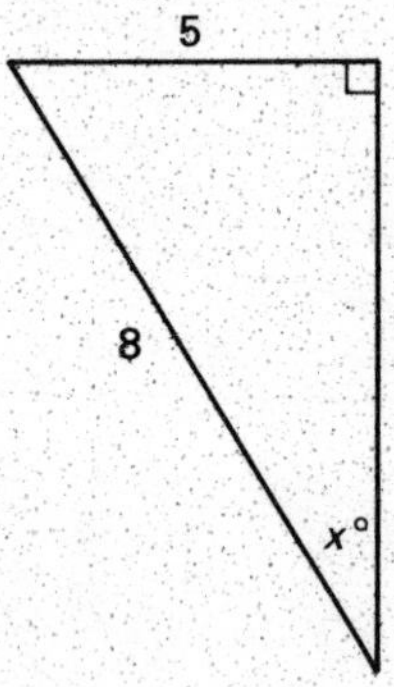

5 Find the value of x using a table of sines.

6 Find the value of the $x°$ angle.

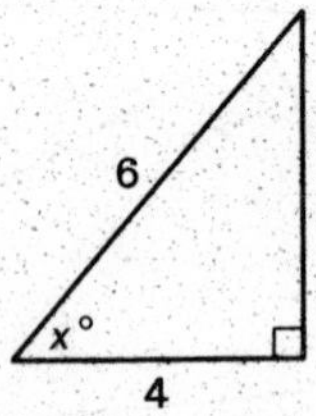

7 Find the value of x.

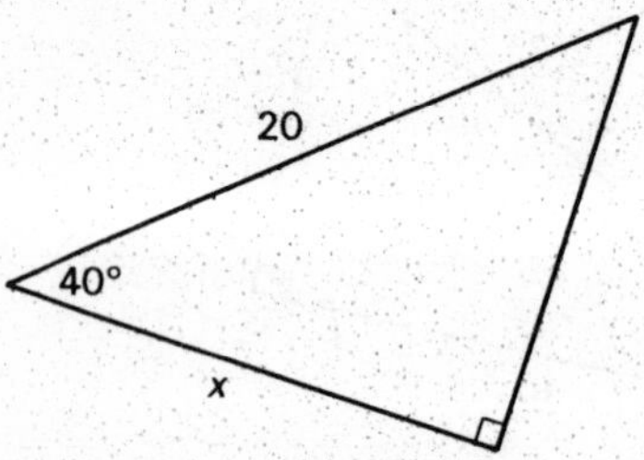

8 Find the value of x.

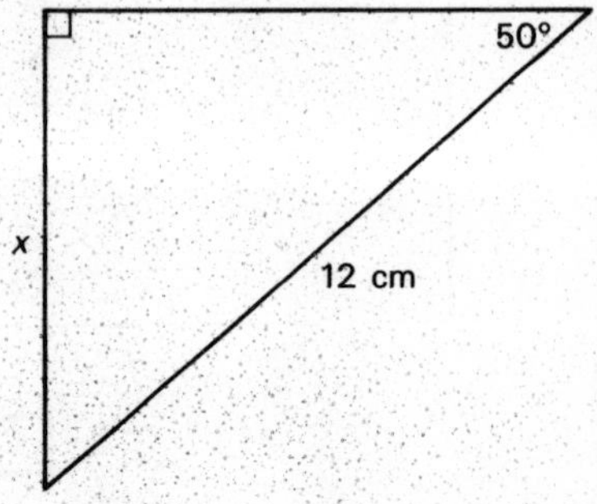

Ask your teacher what to do next

S The hypotenuse

Example

Find the value of x in this right-angled triangle.

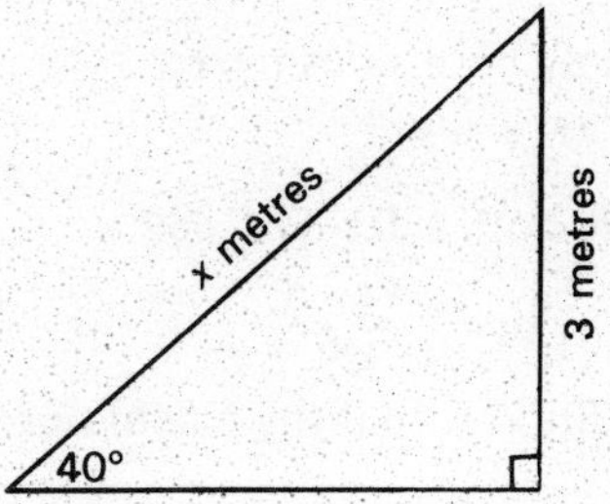

$$\sin 40° = \frac{3}{x}$$

$$0.643 = \frac{3}{x} \quad \text{(from sine tables)}$$

Multiply both sides by x:

$$0.643x = 3$$

Divide both sides by 0.643:

$$x = \frac{3}{0.643}$$

So $x = 4.67$ (by calculator or long division)

Exercise

In the same way find the hypotenuse in each of the following right-angled triangles.

1

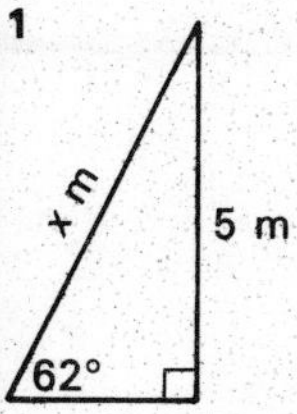

2

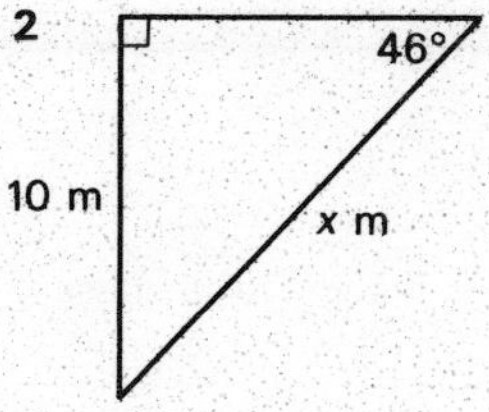

3

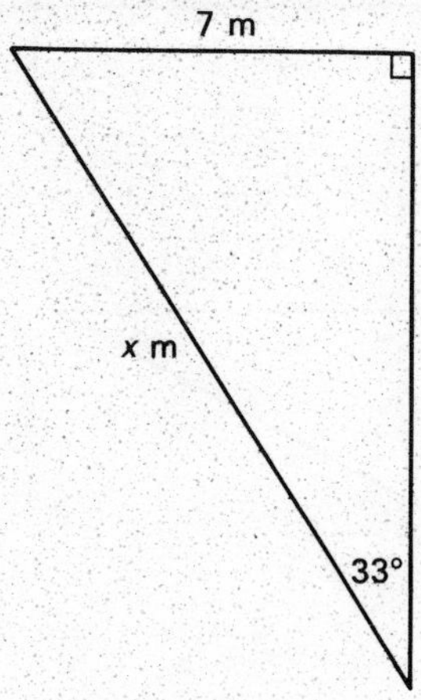

4

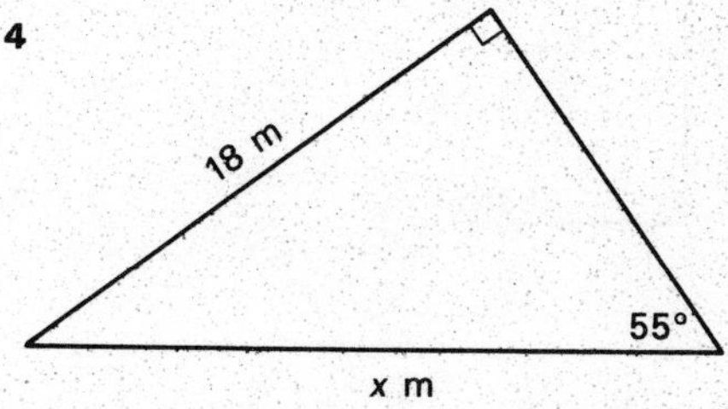

Example

Find the value of x in this right angled triangle.

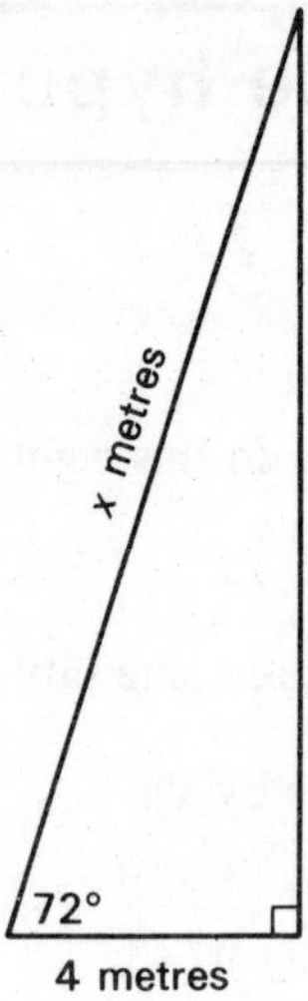

$$\cos 72° = \frac{4}{x}$$

$$0.309 = \frac{4}{x}$$

Multiply both sides by x:

$$0.309x = 4$$

Divide both sides by 0.309:

$$x = \frac{4}{0.309}$$

So $x = 13.0$ (by calculator or long division)

Exercise

5 In the same way find the hypotenuse in each of the following right-angled triangles.

(a)

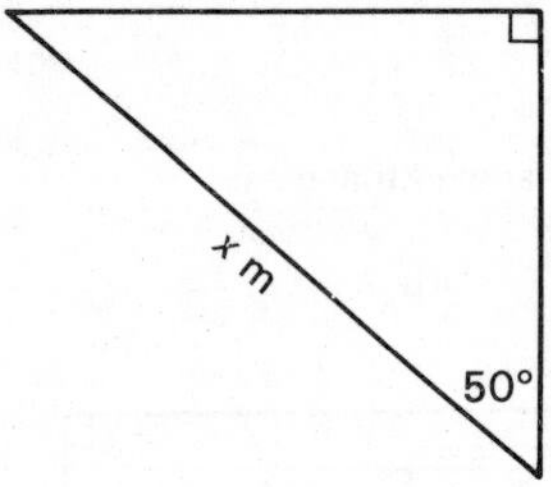

(b)

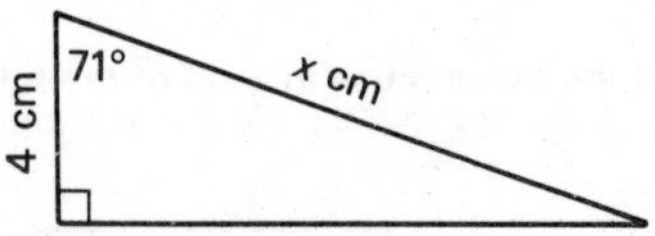

6 In this question decide which ratio to use and then find the hypotenuse.

(a)

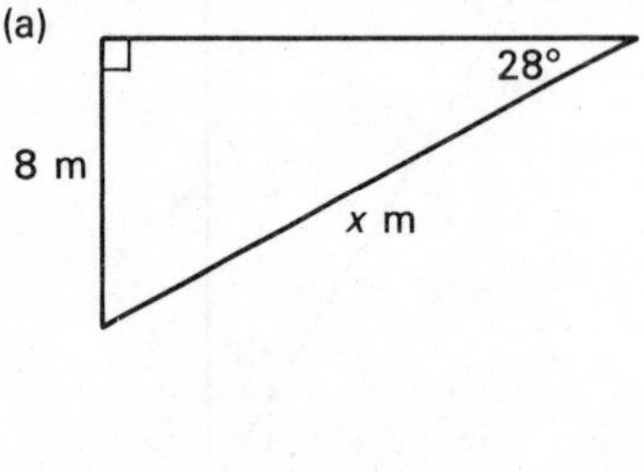

(b)

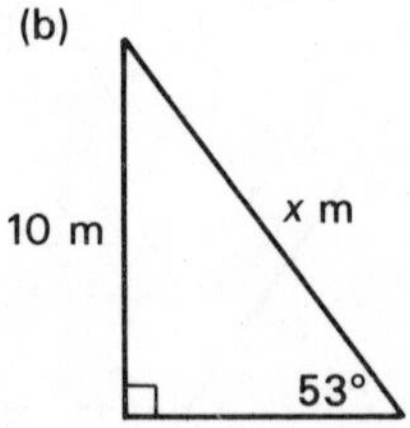

(c)

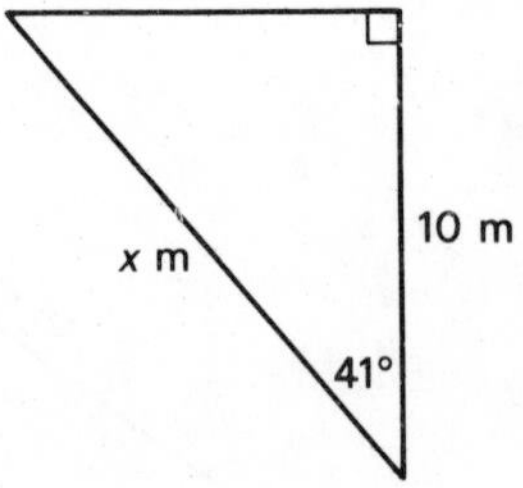

7 For each of the following triangles draw a **rough** diagram and then calculate the required length.

(a) $P\widehat{Q}R = 90°$, $P\widehat{R}Q = 42°$, and $PQ = 6$ cm. Find the length of PR.

(b) $L\widehat{M}N = 90°$, $M\widehat{L}N = 54°$, and $LM = 10$ cm. Find the length of LN.

(c) $R\widehat{S}T = 90°$, $S\widehat{R}T = 28°$, and $RS = 8$ cm. Find the length of RT.

Continue with Section T

T Some problems

Example

A ladder 6 m long rests against a vertical wall with its foot 2 m from the wall on horizontal ground. What is the angle between the ladder and the wall?

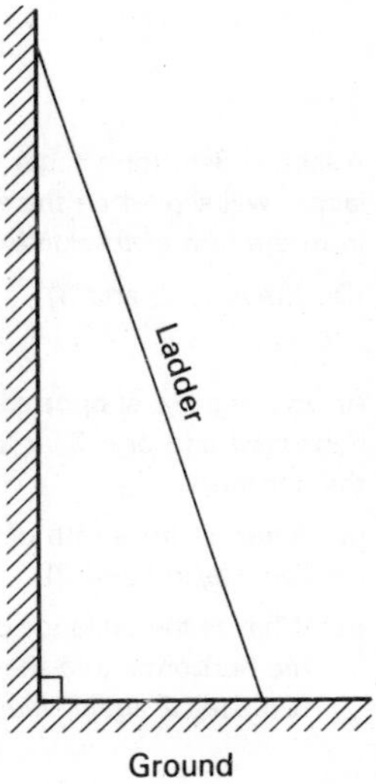

Step 1

Make a sketch of the situation.

Step 2

Look for a right-angled triangle and make a rough drawing of it.

Mark it with known lengths and angles, and mark x on the angle or side which has to be found.

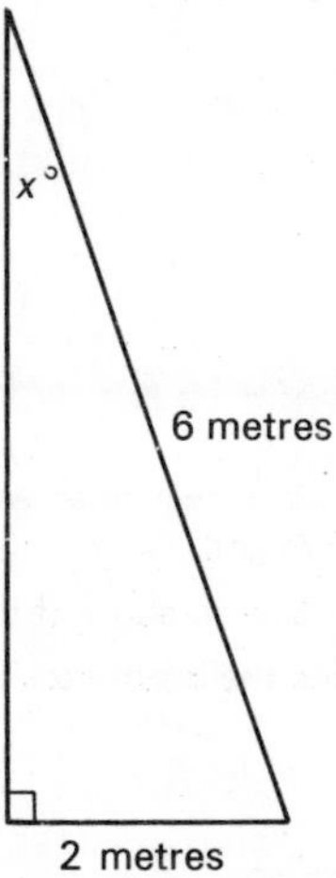

Step 3

Solve the problem using sine, cosine, or tangent.

Opposite side and hypotenuse are known, so the **sine** is used.

$$\sin x° = \frac{2}{6}$$
$$= 0.333$$
$$x° = 19.5°$$

Exercise

1 An aircraft coming in to land on an airfield descends at a constant angle of 15° to the horizontal. At what height is the aircraft when it is 2000 m horizontally from the airfield?

Here is *Step 1*, a sketch of the situation. Do *Steps 2 and 3* as instructed above.

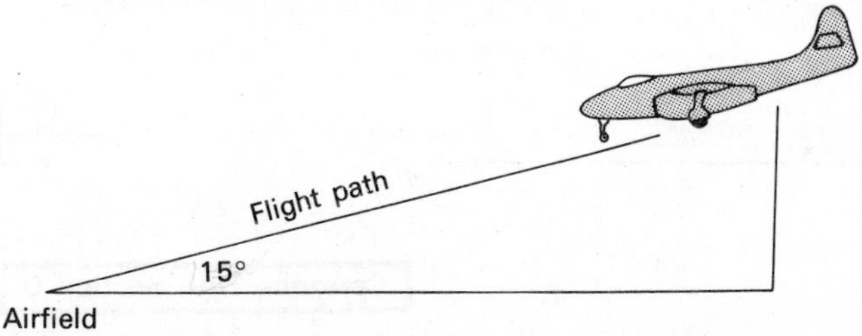

2 An arrow is fired and travels initially in a straight line at 75° to the horizontal. What is the height of the arrow when it is 100 m horizontally from the bow?

(Do *Steps 1, 2,* and *3*)

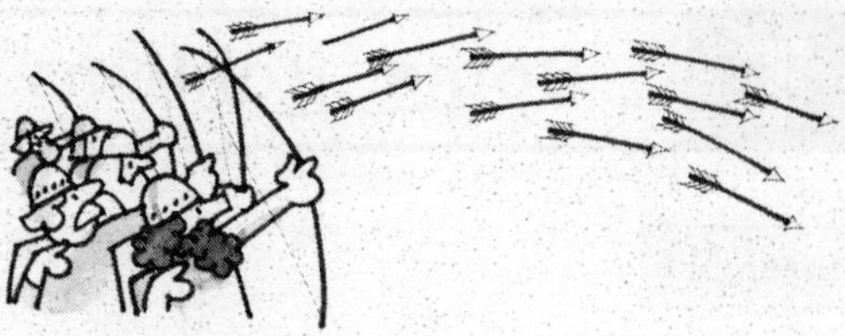

3 A ladder 3 m long rests with one end on a vertical wall and the other on horizontal ground. If the ladder will slip when the angle to the horizontal is less than 65°, what is the greatest possible distance from the foot of the ladder to the wall?

(Do *Steps 1, 2,* and *3*)

4 An inn sign is supported by two stays, one horizontal and one 3 m long fixed at 40° to the horizontal.

(a) What is the length of the horizontal stay? (Do *Steps 2* and *3*)

(b) What is the distance on the wall between the horizontal and the slant stay? (Do *Step 2* again, then *Step 3*)

5 A searchlight beam lights up a helicopter which is descending vertically at a horizontal distance of 1500 metres from the searchlight.

(a) If the searchlight beam is at an angle of 50° to the horizontal, what is the height of the helicopter?

(b) Through what angle does the beam turn as the helicopter descends 200 m?

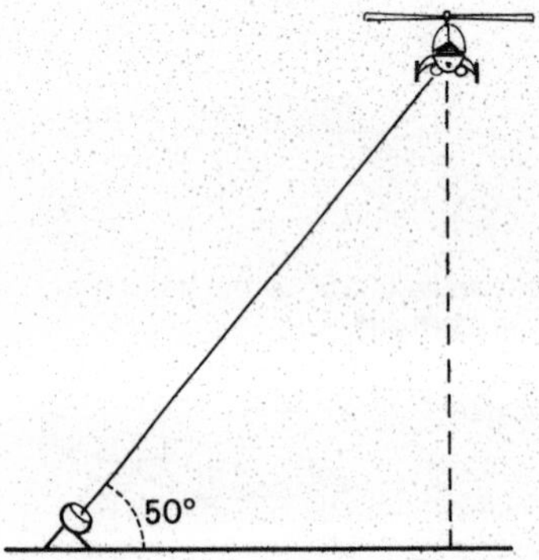

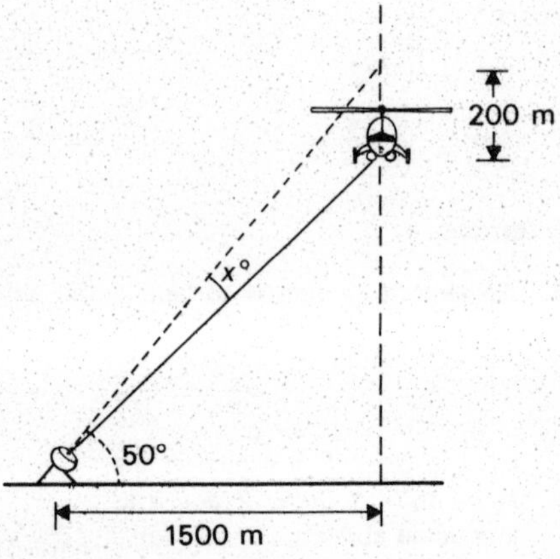

Continue with Section U

U Isosceles triangles

Example

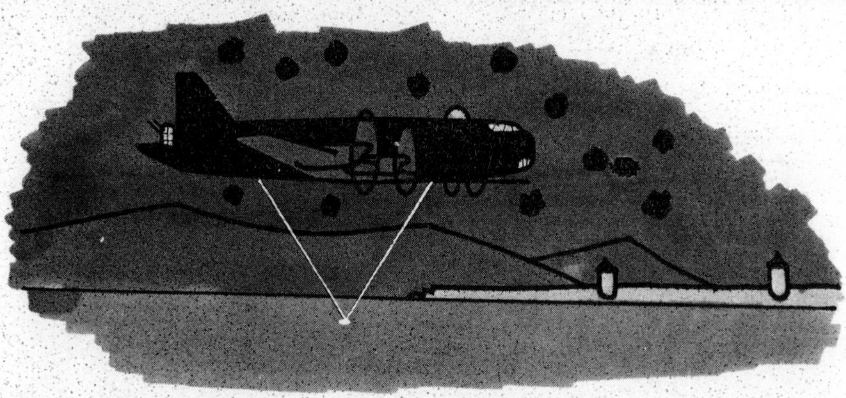

During the last war it was necessary for an aircraft to fly at exactly 20 metres above the surface of a dam during a bombing raid. To make this possible, two spot lights were fitted to the aircraft, angled as shown in the sketch, so that when the aircraft was at the correct height, the two lights would light up at the same point.

If the lights were fitted 24 metres apart, at what angle should they be set?

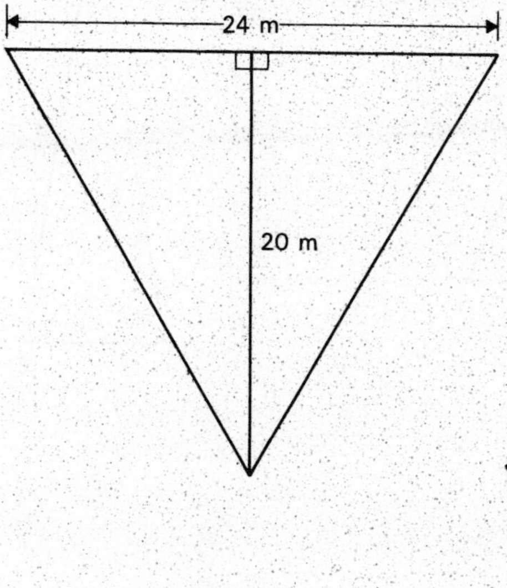

Step 1

Make a sketch marking known lengths and angles.

Notice that the figure is an **isosceles** triangle divided into two right-angled triangles.

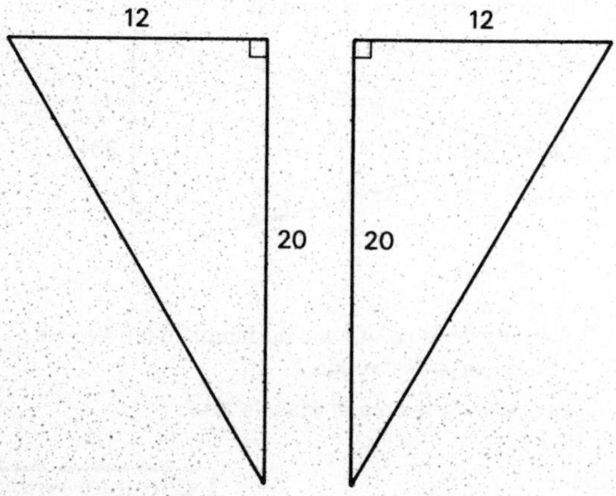

Step 2

Sketch the triangles apart.

Notice that they are congruent. (That is, they are the same size and shape, even though one is a 'turned over' view.)

Step 3

Since the triangles are congruent we can use one of them to find the angle ($x°$).

$$\tan x° = \frac{20}{12} = \frac{5}{3}$$
$$= 1.667$$
$$x° = 59°$$

Angle should be set at 59°

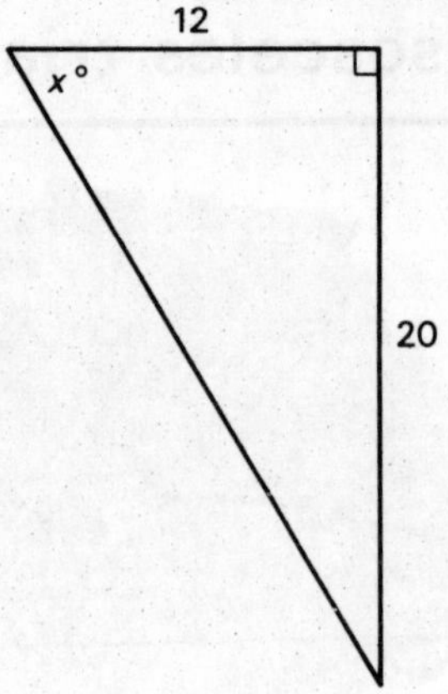

Exercise

For the following questions draw sketches each time and mark them with known lengths and angles.

1 (a) If the aircraft mentioned on the previous page was required to fly at 30 m, at what angle should the lights be set?

(b) What angle is required for a height of 40 m?

2 Find the length of *QR*.

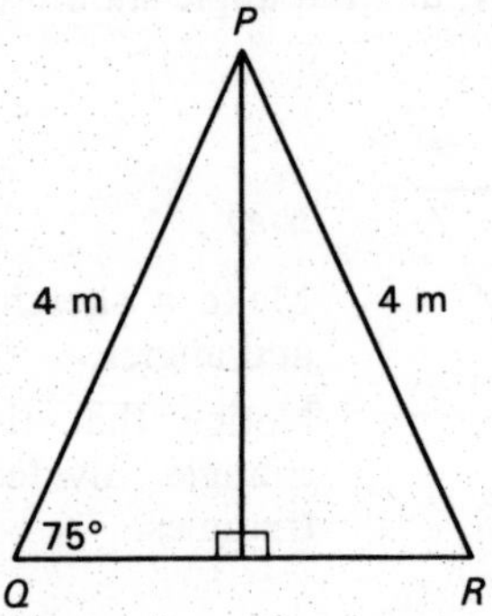

3 Find *YZ*.

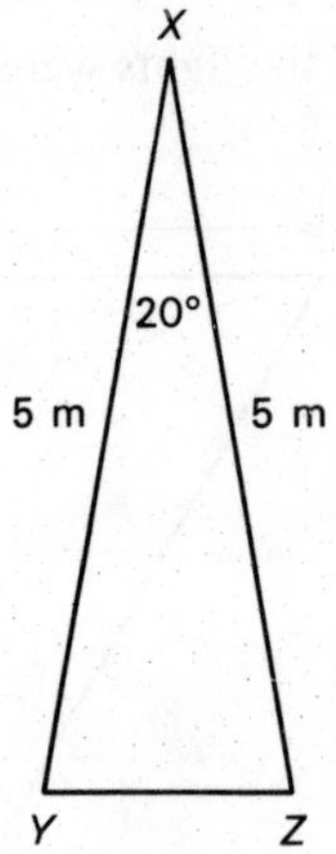

4 Triangle *STV* is isosceles with *ST* = *SV*.

Find the lengths of *ST* and *SV*.

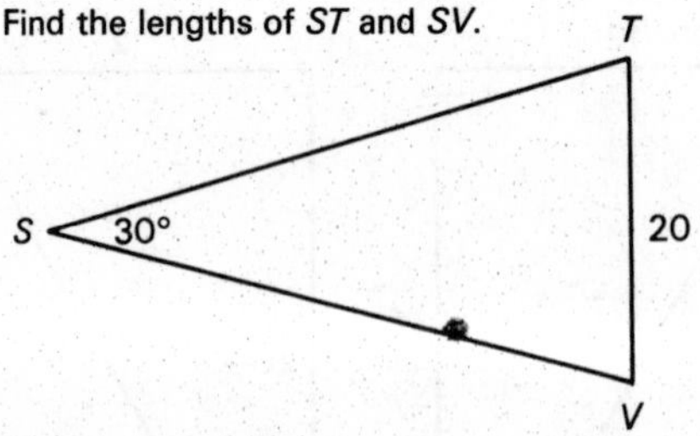

5 Find the length of *AB* and the length of the altitude of triangle *XAB* through *X*.

Hence find the area of triangle *XAB*.

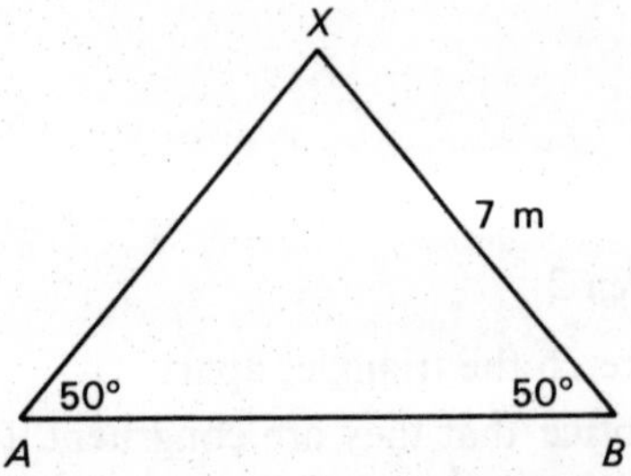

Continue with Section V

V Bearings

Example

A ship sails 30 km on a course of 030° and then sails due West until it is due North of its starting point.

What is the length of the second leg of its journey?

Step 1

Draw a sketch.

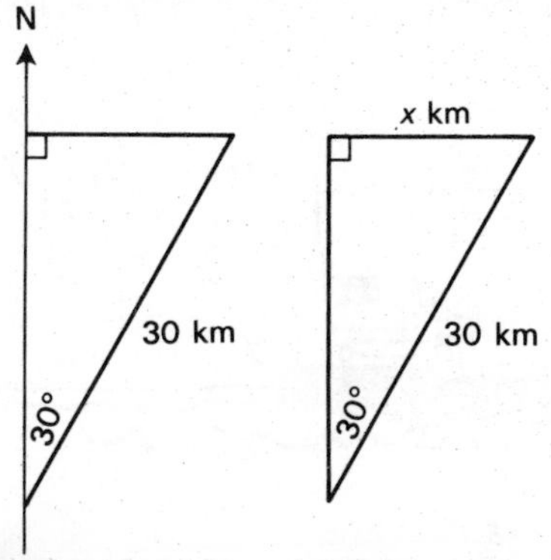

Step 2

Pick out the appropriate right-angled triangle and solve the problem.

Let length of the second leg = x km.

Hypotenuse known and opposite side wanted; so **sine** is used.

$$\frac{x}{30} = \sin 30°$$

$$\frac{x}{30} = 0.500$$

$$x = 30 \times 0.500$$
$$= 15$$

Length of second leg = 15 km.

Exercise

1 A ship sails 40 km on a course of 040° and then sails due West until it is due North of its starting point. What is the length of the second leg of its journey?

2 A ship sails 50 km on a course of 230°, and then due North until it is due West of its starting point.

What is the length of the second leg of its journey?

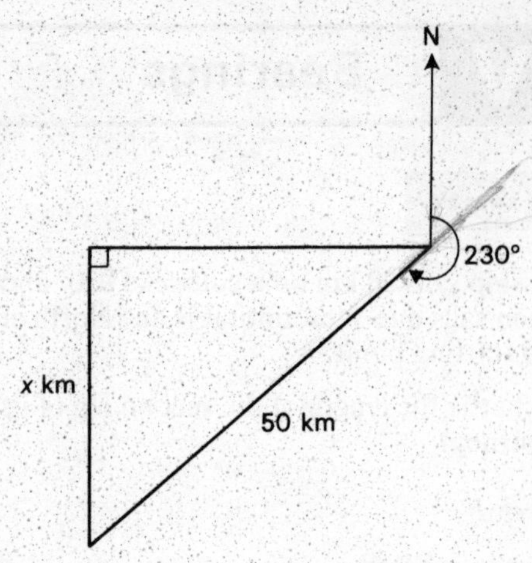

3 A ship sails 60 km on a course of 200° and then due North until it is due West of its starting point. What is the length of the second leg of its journey?

4 *A* and *B* are points on a coast and *B* is 6.5 km due North of *A*. If an oil rig is due East of *B* and 8 km from *A*, what is its bearing from *A*?

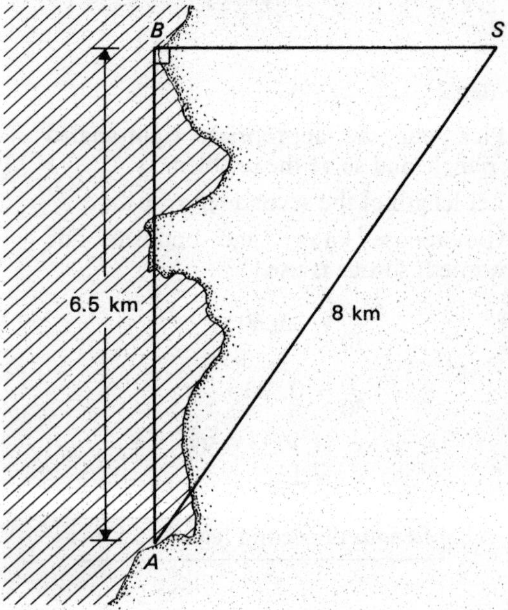

Continue with Section W

W Progress check

Exercise

Find the length of the hypotenuse in each of the following right-angled triangles.

1

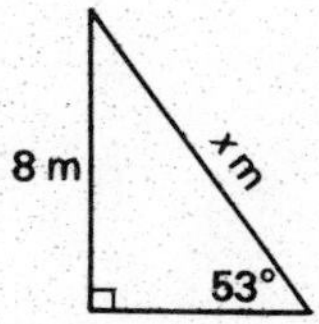

2

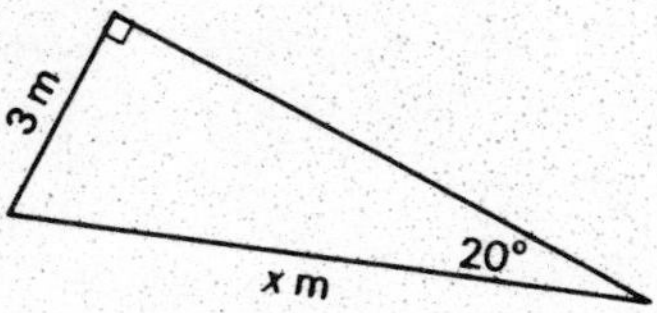

3

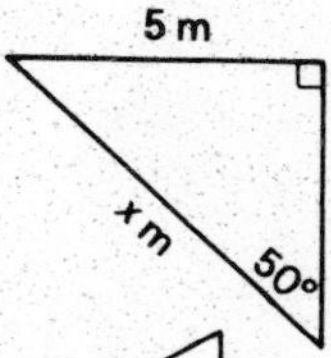

4

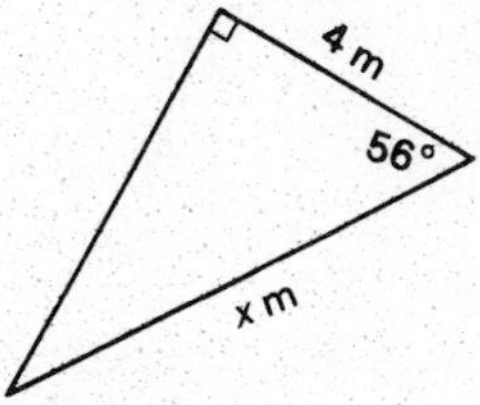

5

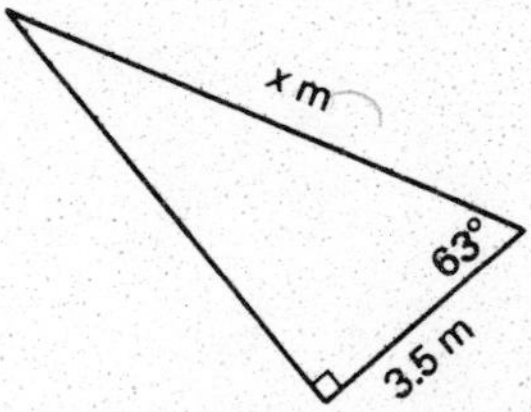

6

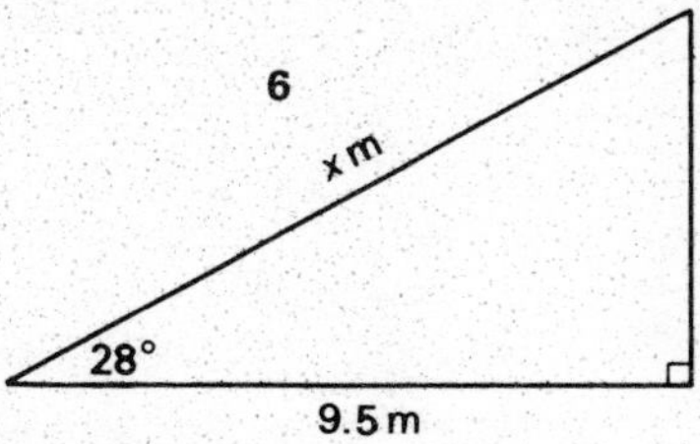

For each of the following triangles, draw a rough diagram and then calculate the required length.

7 $A\hat{B}C = 90°$, $A\hat{C}B = 68°$, and $BC = 7$ cm. Find the length of AC.

8 $P\hat{Q}R = 90°$, $Q\hat{P}R = 31°$, and $RQ = 10.5$ cm. Find the length of PR.

9 A ladder 3 m long rests with one end on a vertical wall and the other on horizontal ground. If the ladder is inclined at 69° to the horizontal, to what height up the wall does it reach?

10 An aircraft takes off at an angle of 38° to the horizontal. When it has travelled 1200 m along its flight path, what height has it reached?

11 Find the length of *UT*

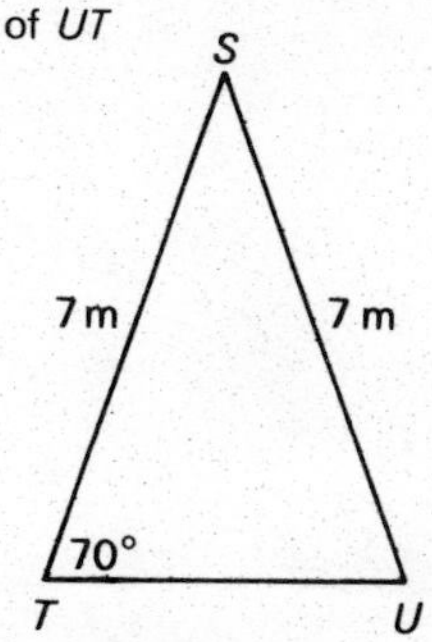

12 Find the length of *PQ*.

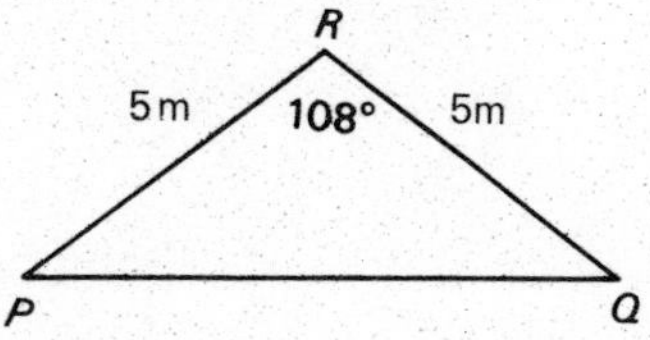

13 Triangle *CDE* is isosceles with $CD = DE$. Find the lengths of *CD* and *DE*.

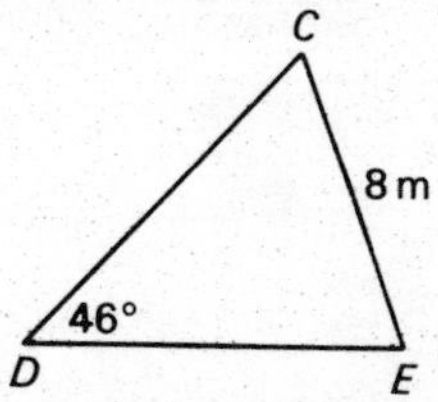

14 Find the length of *KL* and the length of the altitude of triangle *KLM* through *M*. Hence find the area of the triangle.

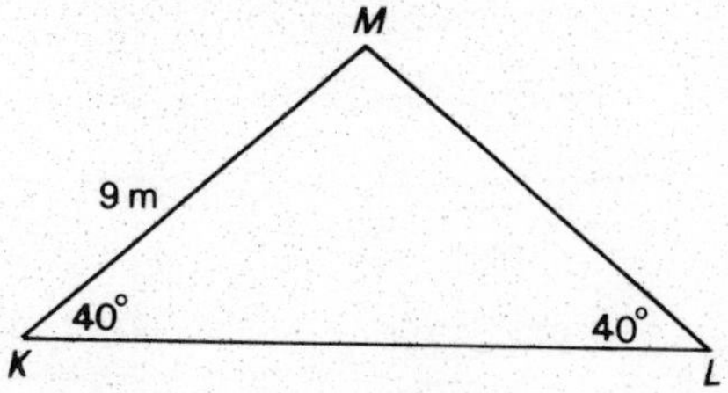

UNIT M5
Simple Functions and their Graphs

A The function machine

In many butchers' shops there is a machine whose function is to produce sausages. It works something like this:

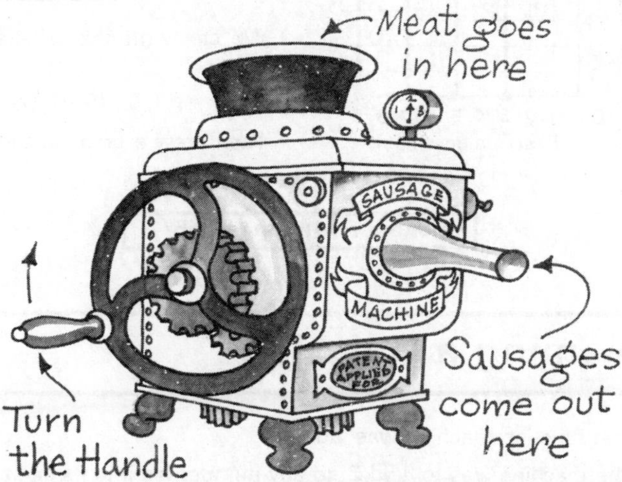

We can imagine a machine whose function is to produce 'Mathematical Sausages'. We could call it a **function machine**. It might work like this:

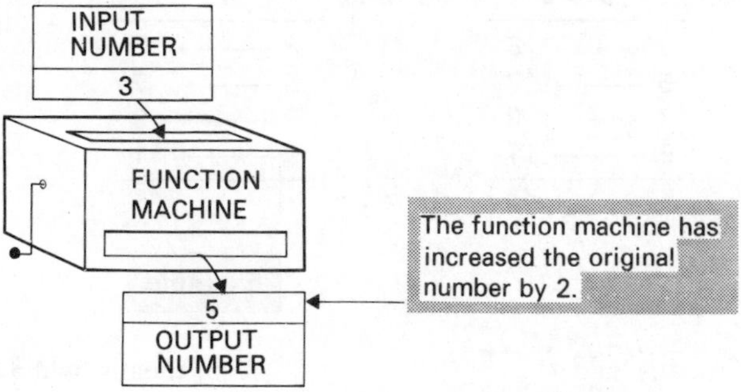

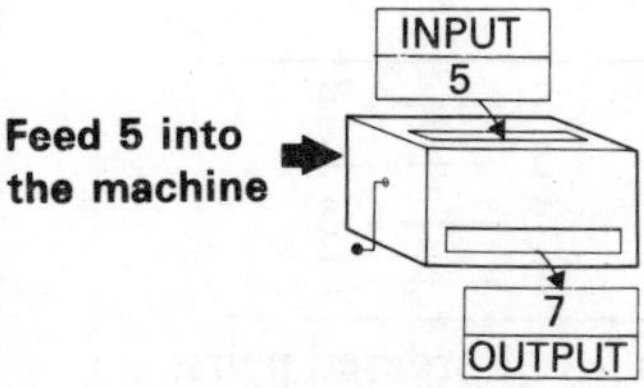

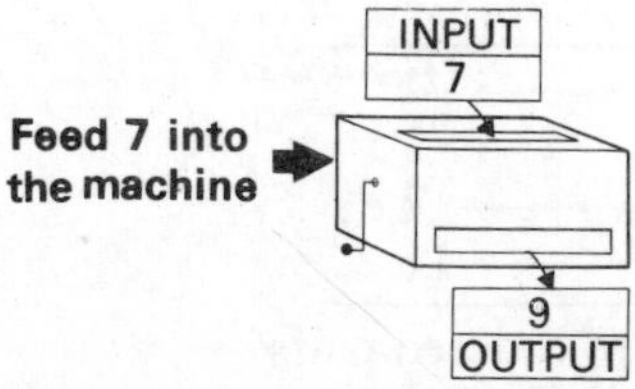

Each time a number is fed into the function machine the output is that number increased by 2.

The **rule** for this machine would be, **'add 2'**.

If we feed 9 into the machine the output would be 11.

The input and output numbers form pairs which are related to each other by the rule of the machine.

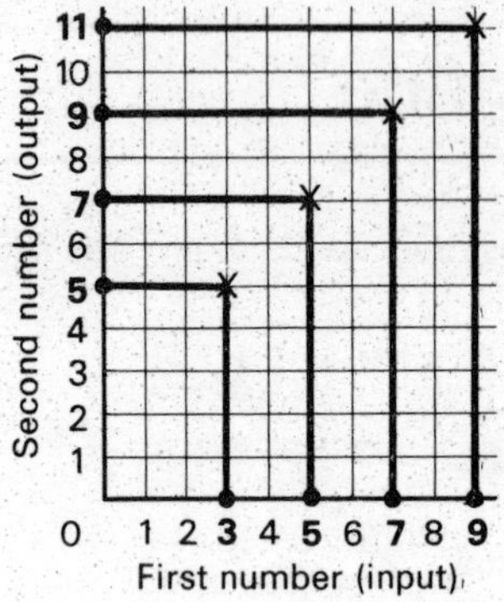

To show this relationship we write them in a table with the rule written at the top:

add 2
3 ⟶ 5
5 ⟶ 7
7 ⟶ 9
9 ⟶ 11

We can write this table as a set of ordered pairs:

{(3, 5), (5, 7), (7, 9), (9, 11)}

Then draw a graph to show the relationship.

Continue with Sheet M5/1

B Naming a function

The rule of the first function machine was **'add 2'**.

The function of the machine was to 'add 2' to any number fed into its input.

To describe the function of this machine we use the letter *f* and let *f* stand for the rule of the machine.

Instead of

add 2
3 ⟶ 5
5 ⟶ 7
7 ⟶ 9
9 ⟶ 11

we write

f
3 ⟶ 5
5 ⟶ 7
7 ⟶ 9
9 ⟶ 11

where *f* means **'add 2'**.

Example

f means **'add 4'**

f
0 ⟶ 4
1 ⟶ 5
3 ⟶ 7
7 ⟶ 11

Written as a set of ordered pairs:
{(0, 4), (1, 5), (3, 7), (7, 11)}

Example

f means **'add 3 then divide by 2'**

f
3 ⟶ 3
5 ⟶ 4
7 ⟶ 5
11 ⟶ 7

Written as a set of ordered pairs:
{(3, 3), (5, 4), (7, 5), (11, 7)}

Exercise

Copy and complete the following, writing the set of ordered pairs beneath each table.

1 *f* means **'multiply by 3'**

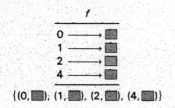

f
0 → □
1 → □
2 → □
4 → □

{(0, □), (1, □), (2, □), (4, □)}

2 *f* means **'divide by 2'**

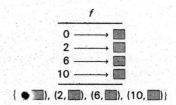

f
0 → □
2 → □
6 → □
10 → □

{(0, □), (2, □), (6, □), (10, □)}

3 *f* means **'multiply by 2 and add 1'**

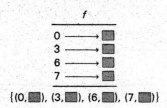

f
0 → □
3 → □
6 → □
7 → □

{(0, □), (3, □), (6, □), (7, □)}

4 *f* means **'add 6 then divide by 3'**

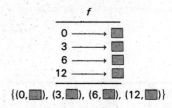

f
0 → □
3 → □
6 → □
12 → □

{(0, □), (3, □), (6, □), (12, □)}

You will notice that a function is a set of ordered pairs which can then be used to draw a graph of the function.

> A function acts on a given set of numbers and produces a different set of numbers.

Example

A function machine has a rule 'add 10'. It acts on the given set {1, 2, 3, 4}. What different set of numbers does the machine produce?

f means 'add 10'. To produce the new set, we have to 'add 10' to each member of the given set.

Given set   *Set produced*

$$\{1, 2, 3, 4\} \xrightarrow{f} \{11, 12, 13, 14\}$$

Example

A machine has the rule 'subtract 4'. It acts on the given set {9, 14, 17}. What set of numbers is produced by the machine?

Given set   *Set produced*

$$\{9, 14, 17\} \xrightarrow{f} \{5, 10, 13\}$$

Exercise

Write answers to the following in the same way as above.

5 A function machine has a rule 'add 8'. It acts on {2, 9, 13, 17}. What is the new set produced by the machine?

6 The rule of a function machine is 'subtract 6'. It acts on {10, 24, 32, 70}. What is the new set produced by the machine?

7 For a function machine *f* means 'multiply by 3'. *f* acts on {2, 8, 10, 14}. What is the new set produced by the machine?

8 A machine has the rule 'divide by 4'. What is the new set produced by the machine when it acts on {0, 8, 24, 36, 40}?

9 A machine has the rule 'divide by 2'. The *new* set produced by the machine is {0, 8, 12, 13}. What was the *original* set that was fed into the machine?

Continue with Section C

C Applying the rule

A function *f* acts upon the set {6, 7, 8, 9} according to the rule 'subtract 6'.

The table shows the effect of *f* on the given set:

$$\begin{array}{c} f \\ \hline 6 \longrightarrow 0 \\ 7 \longrightarrow 1 \\ 8 \longrightarrow 2 \\ 9 \longrightarrow 3 \\ \hline \end{array}$$

We write $f(8)$ to mean the result of applying *f* to 8,

$$\text{so } f(8) = 8 - 6 \qquad (f \text{ means 'subtract 6'})$$
$$= 2$$

$$\boxed{f(8) = 2}$$

Example

f acts upon {1, 4, 6, 8} according to the rule 'multiply by 2 and add 3'.

Calculate $f(1)$, $f(4)$, $f(6)$, $f(8)$.

$f(1)$ means the result of applying *f* to 1:

$$f(1) = (2 \times 1) + 3$$
$$= 2 + 3$$
$$= 5$$

Hence $f(1) = 5$

$f(4)$ means the result of applying *f* to 4:

$$f(4) = (2 \times 4) + 3$$
$$= 8 + 3$$
$$= 11$$

Hence $f(4) = 11$

Similarly:

$f(6) = (2 \times 6) + 3$
$= 15$

$f(6) = 15$

$f(8) = (2 \times 8) + 3$
$= 19$

$f(8) = 19$

Continue with Sheet M5/2

D The $f(x)$ notation

Example

f acts on $\{3, 4, 7\}$ according to the rule **'double the number and add 1'**. We can restate this as:

f acts on $\{3, 4, 7\}$ according to the rule $f(x) = 2x + 1$, where x can be replaced by 3, 4, or 7.

(a) Replace x by 3

$f(x) = 2x + 1$
So $f(3) = (2 \times 3) + 1$
$= 6 + 1$
$= 7$

(b) Replace x by 4

$f(x) = 2x + 1$
So $f(4) = (2 \times 4) + 1$
$= 8 + 1$
$= 9$

(c) Replace x by 7

$f(x) = 2x + 1$
So $f(7) = (2 \times 7) + 1$
$= 14 + 1$
$= 15$

So '$f(x) = 2x + 1$' is a convenient way of defining a function. To show that x may be replaced by 3, 4, or 7, we write $x \in \{3, 4, 7\}$, and read it as 'x is a member of $\{3, 4, 7\}$'.

Exercise

Write answers to the following, setting down your working as in the example above.

1 A function is defined by the rule $f(x) = x + 2$, $x \in \{0, 1, 2, 3\}$.
Calculate $f(0)$, $f(1)$, $f(2)$, $f(3)$.

2 A function is defined by the rule $f(x) = 3x$, $x \in \{4, 7, 9\}$.
Calculate $f(4)$, $f(7)$, $f(9)$.

3 A function is defined by the rule $f(x) = 4x - 2$, $x \in \{3, 9, 12\}$.
Calculate $f(3)$, $f(9)$, $f(12)$.

4 A function is defined by the rule $f(x) = 15 - 2x$, $x \in \{0, 2, 3, 5\}$.
Calculate $f(0)$, $f(2)$, $f(3)$, $f(5)$.

5 Restate the following in the form used above. A function acts upon $\{3, 9, 12\}$ according to the rule 'multiply by 5 and add 6'.

Example

A function is defined by the rule $f(x) = 3x + 2$ where $x \epsilon \{-2, 0, 2\}$.

Calculate $f(-2)$, $f(0)$, $f(2)$. Write the function as a set of ordered pairs and draw the graph.

$$f(x) = 3x + 2$$

$$\begin{aligned} f(-2) &= 3 \times (-2) + 2 \\ &= -6 + 2 \\ &= -4 \end{aligned} \qquad \begin{aligned} f(0) &= 3 \times 0 + 2 \\ &= 0 + 2 \\ &= 2 \end{aligned} \qquad \begin{aligned} f(2) &= 3 \times 2 + 2 \\ &= 6 + 2 \\ &= 8 \end{aligned}$$

f	
−2 →	−4
0 →	2
2 →	8

Note: the vertical axis is labelled *f* (*x*)

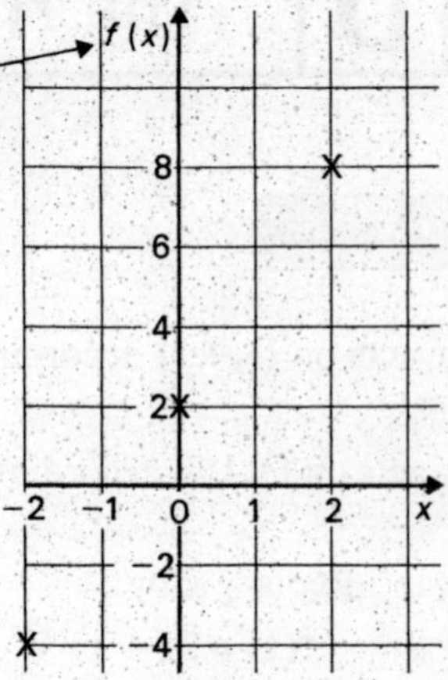

Set of ordered pairs:
$\{(-2, -4), (0, 2), (2, 8)\}$

Continue with Sheet M5/4

E Domain and range

A function is defined by $f(x) = 3x$ where $x \in \{1, 2, 3, 4\}$

So $f(1) = 3$; $f(2) = 6$;
$f(3) = 9$; $f(4) = 12$.

The set of values, $\{3, 6, 9, 12\}$, of the function is called the **range**.

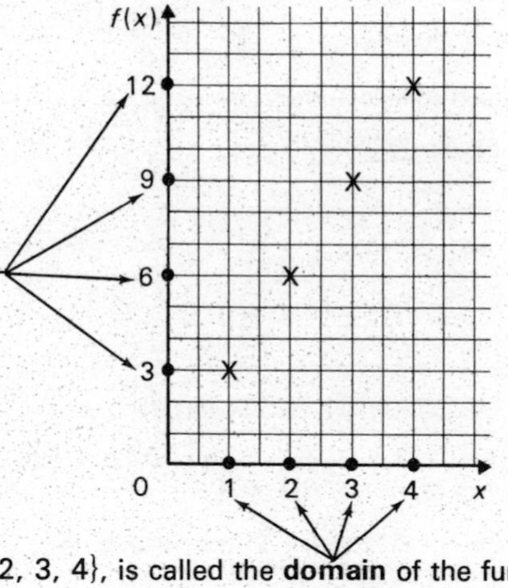

The given set, $\{1, 2, 3, 4\}$, is called the **domain** of the function.

If a function is defined by $f(x)$:

> The domain of the function is the set of replacements for x.
> The range of the function is the set of values of $f(x)$.

Example

$f(x) = 2x$.

Domain is $\{-1, 0, 1, 2, 3\}$
Range is $\{-2, 0, 2, 4, 6\}$

f		
-1	$\longrightarrow$	-2
0	$\longrightarrow$	0
1	$\longrightarrow$	2
2	$\longrightarrow$	4
3	$\longrightarrow$	6

Exercise

Copy and complete the following.

1 $f(x) = 4x$

f		
-2	$\longrightarrow$	□
-1	$\longrightarrow$	□
0	$\longrightarrow$	□
1	$\longrightarrow$	□
2	$\longrightarrow$	□

Domain is {□, □, □, □, □}
Range is {□, □, □, □, □}

2 $f(x) = 2x + 2$

f		
-2	$\longrightarrow$	□
-1	$\longrightarrow$	□
0	$\longrightarrow$	□
1	$\longrightarrow$	□

Domain is {□, □, □, □}
Range is {□, □, □, □}

3 $f(x) = x - 1$

f		
1	$\longrightarrow$	□
2	$\longrightarrow$	□
3	$\longrightarrow$	□
4	$\longrightarrow$	□

Domain is:
Range is:

Continue with Section F

F Progress check

Exercise

1 Copy and complete the following tables, writing the ordered pairs beneath each table.

(a) f means 'multiply by 2'

	f	
0	$\longrightarrow$	□
2	$\longrightarrow$	□
4	$\longrightarrow$	□
6	$\longrightarrow$	□

{(0, □), (2, □), (4, □), (6, □)}

(b) f means 'add 1 and multiply by 3'

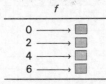

	f	
0	$\longrightarrow$	□
1	$\longrightarrow$	□
2	$\longrightarrow$	□
3	$\longrightarrow$	□

{(0, □), (1, □), (2, □), (3, □)}

2 f acts on $\{1, 3, 5, 7\}$ according to the rule 'add 3 and divide by 2'.
Calculate $f(1)$, $f(3)$, $f(5)$, $f(7)$.

3 f acts on $\{-2, -1, 0, 1, 2\}$ according to the rule 'add 4'.
Calculate $f(-2)$, $f(-1)$, $f(0)$, $f(1)$, $f(2)$.

4 A function is defined by the rule $f(x) = 4x - 1$, $x \in \{2, 4, 6\}$.
Calculate $f(2)$, $f(4)$, $f(6)$.

5 A function f is defined by the rule $f(x) = 2x + 1$ for $x \in \{-2, -1, 0, 1, 2\}$.
Calculate $f(-2)$, $f(-1)$, $f(0)$, $f(1)$, $f(2)$.
Write the function as a set of ordered pairs and draw its graph on 1 cm squared paper.

6 Copy and complete the following:

(a) $f(x) = 3x + 5$

	f	
−2	$\longrightarrow$	−1
−1	$\longrightarrow$	□
0	$\longrightarrow$	□
1	$\longrightarrow$	□

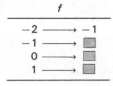

Domain is $\{-2, -1, 0, 1\}$
Range is {−1, □, □, □}

(b) $f(x) = x - 3$

	f	
−1	$\longrightarrow$	□
0	$\longrightarrow$	□
1	$\longrightarrow$	□
2	$\longrightarrow$	□

Domain is {□, □, □, □}
Range is {□, □, □, □}

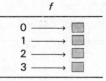

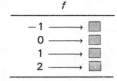

Ask your teacher what to do next

G Real numbers

So far, the domain and range of the functions whose graphs we have drawn have all been members of either the set of whole numbers (W) or the set of integers (Z).

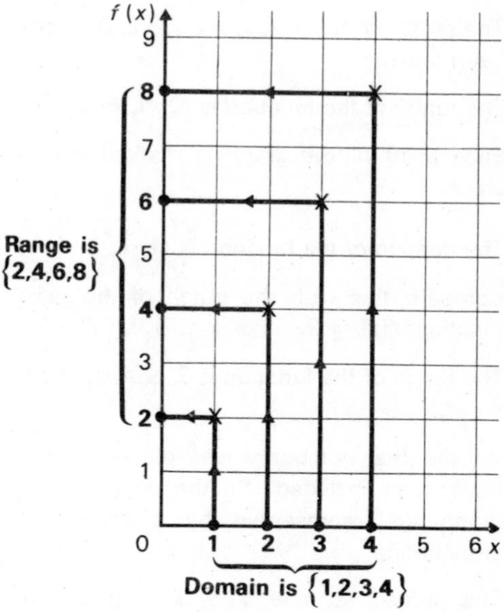

Example

$f(x) = 2x$ where $x \in \{1, 2, 3, 4\}$.

We can draw the domain on a number line:

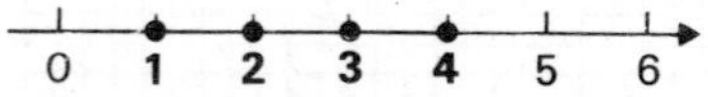

Each member is marked with a dot.

When we wish to include in the domain **all** the real number values from 1 to 4 (for instance 1, 2.35, 3.0, 3.99, etc.) then the number line is marked like this:

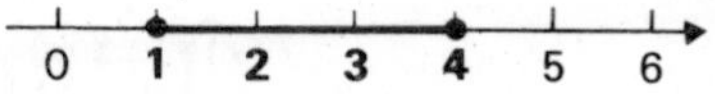

The dots (•) marking 1 and 4 and the heavy line joining these dots means that all possible number values from 1 to 4 are included.
If we let x stand for any number in the domain, then we write

$$1 \leq x \leq 4;\ x \in R$$

(R stands for the set of real numbers.)

The statement '$1 \leq x \leq 4;\ x \in R$' means that '$x$ may have any real value from 1 to 4 (including 1 and 4)'.

If we do **not** wish to include 1 or 4 then an open circle is drawn round 1 and 4 like this:

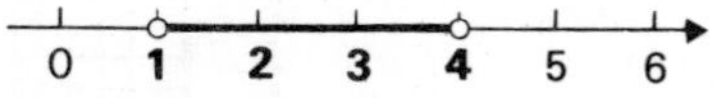

We write this as '$1 < x < 4;\ x \in R$' which means that 'x may have any real number value **greater** than 1 and **less** than 4' (1 and 4 are **not** included).

Continue with Sheet M5/5

H Graphs of functions

The graph of $f(x) = 2x$, $x \in \{1, 2, 3, 4\}$ has been drawn.

The range of the function is $\{2, 4, 6, 8\}$.

Each point of the graph is marked with a cross.

The domain of the function is $\{1, 2, 3, 4\}$.

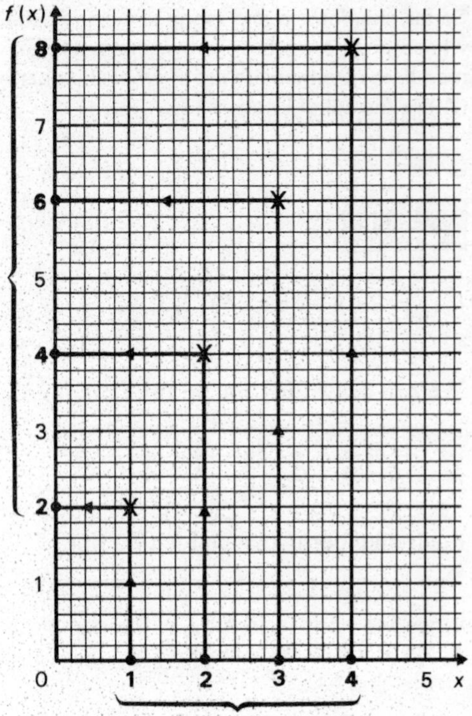

Compare this with the graph of the same function, $f(x) = 2x$, $1 \leq x \leq 4$, $x \in R$.

The range of the function is $2 \leq f(x) \leq 8$; $x \in R$.

All the real number values of the domain have been included. So the points of the graph are represented by a continuous straight line.

The domain is now $1 \leq x \leq 4$; $x \in R$. (It includes all the real numbers from 1 to 4.)

Example

Find $f(3.2)$ from the graph.

$f(3.2) = 6.4$

Check: $f(x) = 2x$

$f(3.2) = 2 \times 3.2$

$= 6.4$

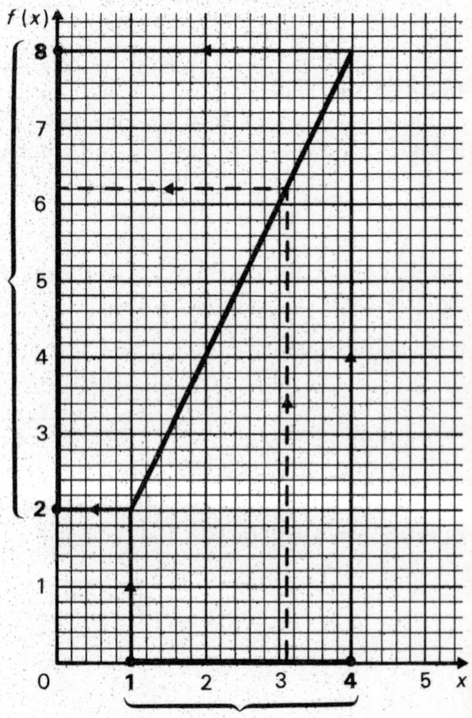

Exercise

1 From the graph find $f(1.8)$, $f(2.4)$, $f(3.8)$, →

Check your answers by calculation.

Complete sheet M5/5 (reverse)

Finding the input

Here is a function machine that has the rule, $f(x) = x + 3;\ x \in W$.

The number on the output card is 10.

What number was fed into the machine?

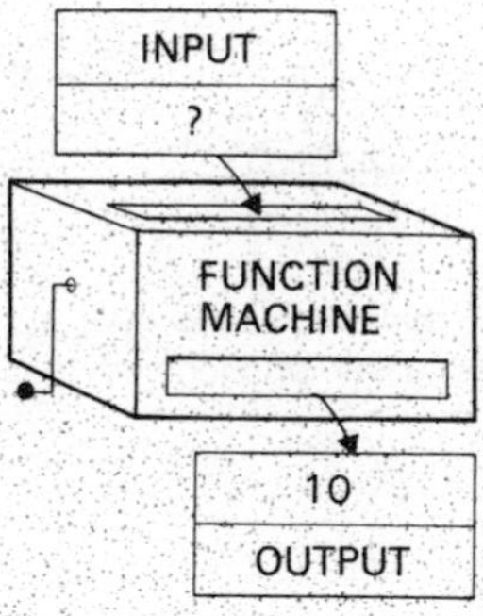

Rule: $f(x) = x + 3$

Output $= 10$

But $7 + 3 = 10$

So the **input** number is 7.

Exercise

1 The rule for this machine is $f(x) = x + 4;\ x \in W$. The output numbers are as shown. What numbers were fed into the machine? (The first one has been done for you.)

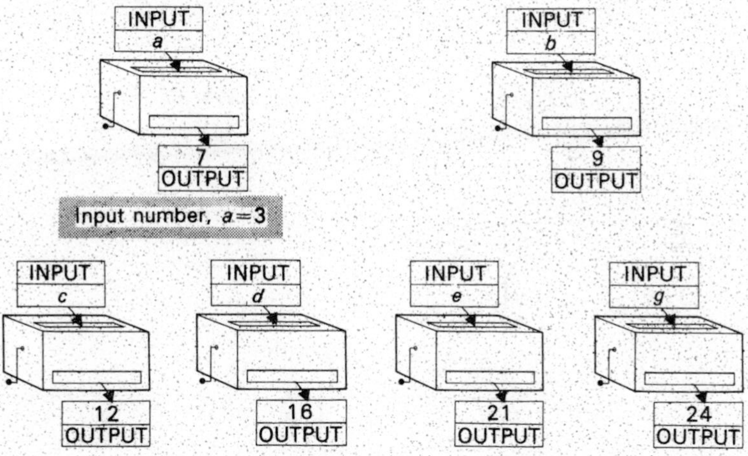

2 The rule for this machine is $f(x) = x - 3;\ x \in W$. What are the input numbers?

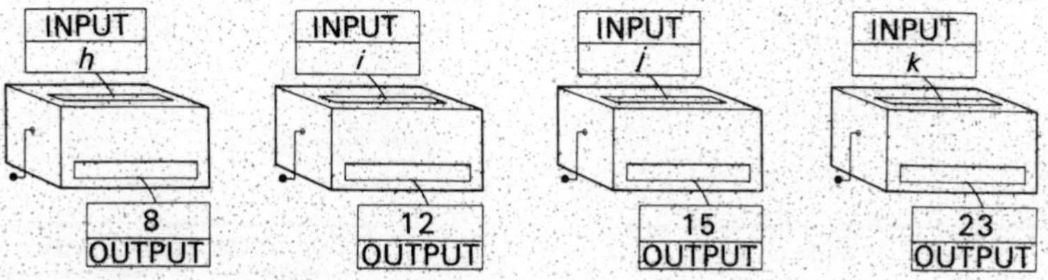

3 The rule for this machine is $f(x) = 2x + 1;\ x \in W$. What are the input numbers?

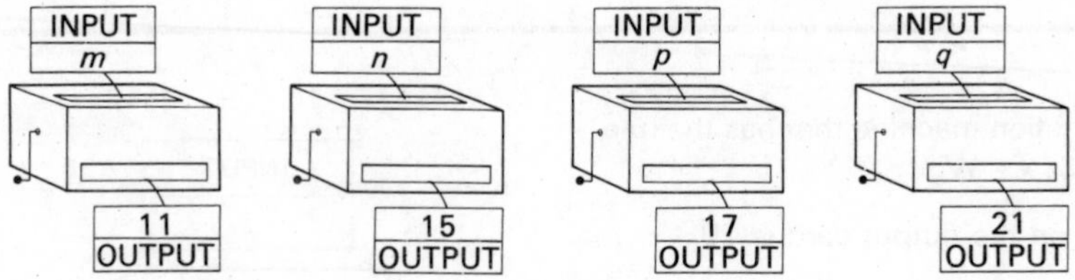

4 The rule for this machine is $f(x) = x - 2;\ x \in W$. Find the members of the domain that correspond to the values of the function shown in the sketch graphs below.

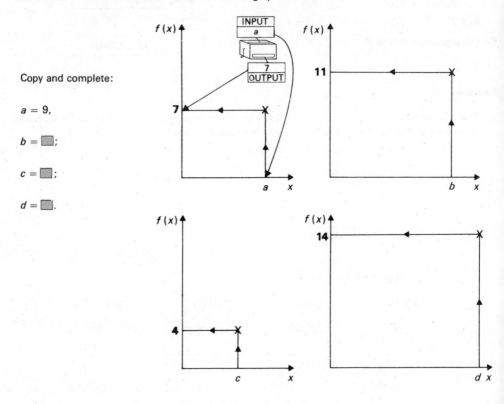

Copy and complete:

$a = 9$,

$b = $ ■;

$c = $ ■;

$d = $ ■.

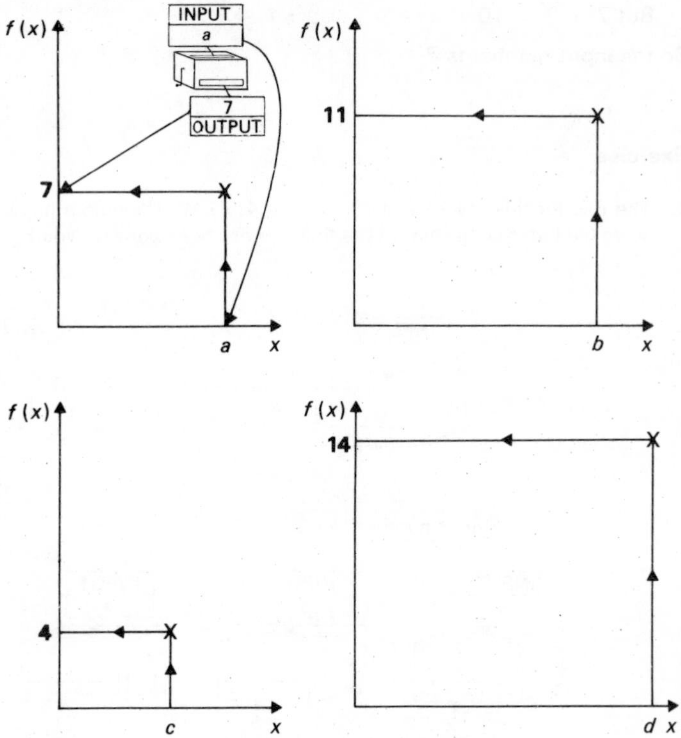

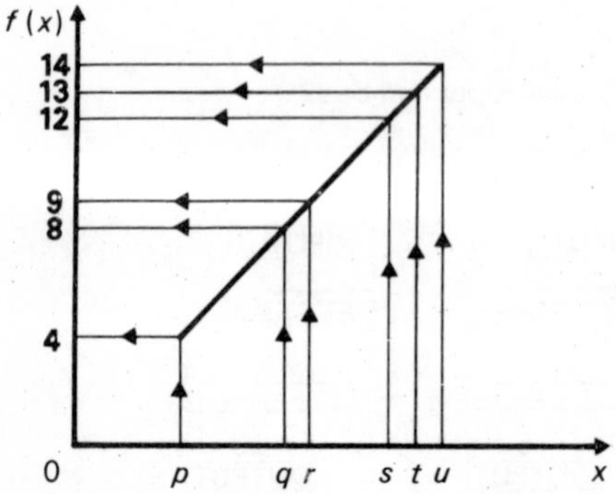

5 A graph of the function $f(x) = 2x$ is shown here. Its domain is $2 \le x \le 7;\ x \in R$.

Find replacements for $p, q, r, s, t,$ and u that correspond to the values of the function.

Example

$p = 2,\ u = 7.$

Continue with Section J

J Domain values

A function f is given by $f(x) = x + 3$; $x \in W$.

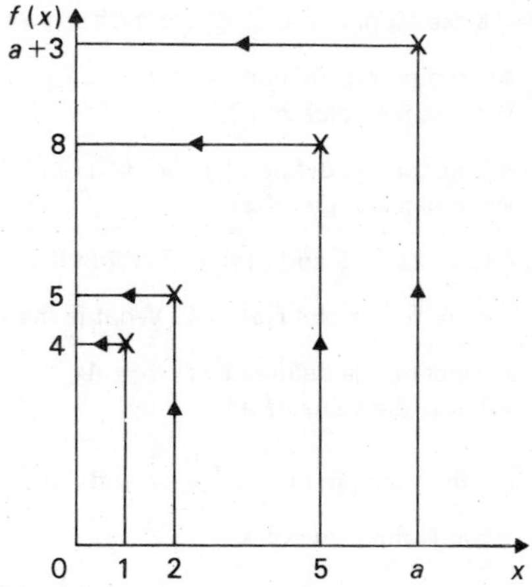

$f(x) = x + 3$
So $f(1) = 1 + 3 = 4$
$f(2) = 2 + 3 = 5$
$f(5) = 5 + 3 = 8$
$f(a) = a + 3$ (where a is any number in the domain)

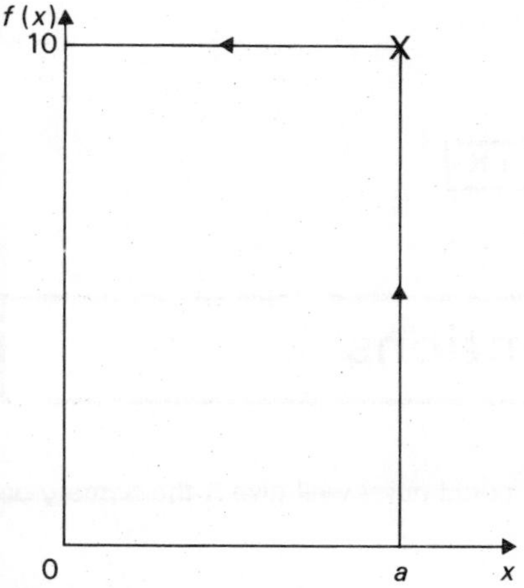

Now suppose that $f(a)$ has the value 10.
What is the value of a?

$f(a) = a + 3$
but $f(a) = 10$
so $a + 3 = 10$

$a = 7$

Example

A function f is given by $f(x) = 2x - 3$, $x \in W$, and $f(a) = 13$. What is the value of a?

$f(x) = 2x - 3$
so $f(a) = 2a - 3$
but $f(a) = 13$
so $2a - 3 = 13$
$2a = 16$

$a = 8$

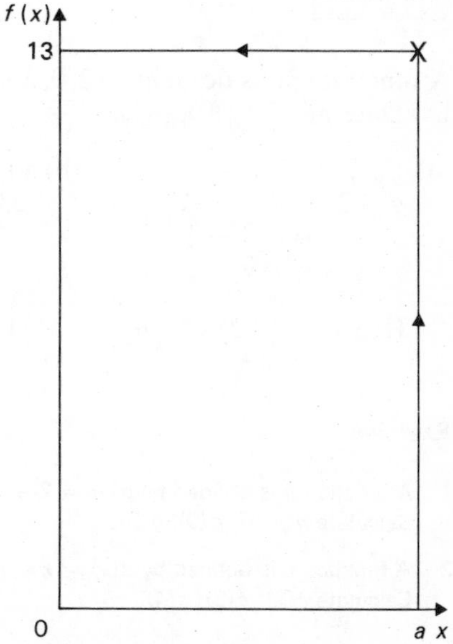

Exercise

Write answers for the following in the same way as in the example. The domain of each function is the set of whole numbers.

Draw a sketch graph to illustrate each answer as in the example.

1 A function f is defined by $f(x) = 2x + 1$ and $f(a) = 13$.
What is the value of a?

2 A function f is defined by $f(x) = 3x$ and $f(a) = 15$.
What is the value of a?

3 $f(x) = 2x - 5$ and $f(a) = 7$. What is the value of a?

4 $f(x) = 5 - x$ and $f(a) = 2$. What is the value of a?

5 A function f is defined by $f(x) = 4x - 2$ and $f(a) = 10$.
What is the value of a?

6 f is the function $f(x) = \frac{x+1}{2}$ and $f(a) = 5$.

What is the value of a?

Continue with Section K

K Other names for functions

So far we have always given a function the name f. We could quite well give it the name g or any other convenient letter.

Example

A function g has domain $\{-2, 0, 2\}$ and is defined by $g(x) = 4x - 1$.
Evaluate $g(-2)$, $g(0)$, $g(2)$.

(a)
$$\begin{aligned} g(x) &= 4x - 1 \\ g(-2) &= 4 \times (-2) - 1 \\ &= -8 - 1 \\ &= -9 \end{aligned}$$

Hence $g(-2) = -9$

(b)
$$\begin{aligned} g(x) &= 4x - 1 \\ g(0) &= 4 \times (0) - 1 \\ &= 0 - 1 \\ &= -1 \end{aligned}$$

Hence $g(0) = -1$

(c)
$$\begin{aligned} g(x) &= 4x - 1 \\ g(2) &= 4 \times (2) - 1 \\ &= 8 - 1 \\ &= 7 \end{aligned}$$

Hence $g(2) = 7$

Exercise

1 A function g is defined by $g(x) = 2 + 3x$ and its domain is $\{-3, 0, 3\}$.
Calculate $g(-3)$, $g(0)$, $g(3)$.

2 A function c is defined by $c(x) = \pi x$, $x \in \{2, 3, 4\}$, $\pi = 3.14$.
Calculate $c(2)$, $c(3)$, $c(4)$.

Example

A function k is defined by $k(x) = 2x - 1$. The domain is $-2 \leq x \leq 2; x \in R$.

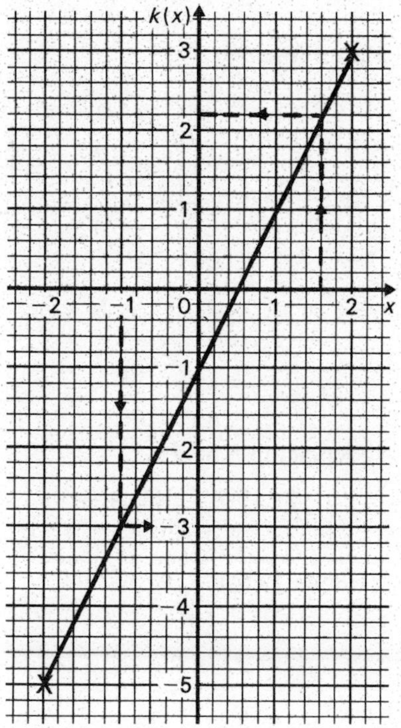

Step 1

Calculate $k(-2)$, $k(2)$.

$$k(x) = 2x - 1$$

$$k(-2) = 2(-2) - 1 = -4 - 1 = -5 \qquad k(2) = 2(2) - 1 = 4 - 1 = 3$$

Step 2

What is the range of the function?

Range: $-5 \leq k(x) \leq 3$

Step 3

Draw a graph of the function on 2 mm graph paper.

(The coordinates of the end points of the line are $(-2, -5)$ and $(2, 3)$.)

Step 4

From the graph, find the elements of the domain when the value of the function is (a) -3; (b) 2.2.

Elements of domain are (a) -1; (b) 1.6.

Exercise

3 $h(x) = 3x - 3$ with domain $-2 \leq x \leq 2$, $x \in R$.
(a) Calculate $h(-2)$, $h(2)$. (b) What is the range?
(c) Draw the graph of the function on 2 mm graph paper.
(d) From the graph, find the elements of the domain when the value of the function is (i) -6, (ii) 0.

4 A function is defined by $g(x) = 4 - x$, domain $-2 \leq x \leq 6$, $x \in R$.
(a) Calculate $g(-2)$, $g(6)$. (b) What is the range?
(c) Draw the graph of the function on 2 mm graph paper.
(d) From the graph what are the elements of the domain when the value of the function is (i) 2.6, (ii) -1.4?

Continue with Section L

L Find the function

Example

A function g is defined by $g(x) = px + 1$ (p is an integer).
(a) Given that $g(3) = 7$ find p.
(b) Calculate $g(2)$, $g(4)$.

(a)

$$g(x) = px + 1$$

So $g(3) = (p \times 3) + 1$ (replacing x by 3)

$$= 3p + 1$$

But $g(3) = 7$

So $3p + 1 = 7$

$$3p = 6$$

$$p = 2$$

(b) We write the function g as: $g(x) = 2x + 1$, replacing p by 2.

$$g(2) = 2(2) + 1 = 5$$

Hence $g(2) = 5$

$$g(4) = 2(4) + 1 = 9$$

Hence $g(4) = 9$

Exercise

Setting your work out as above, do the following questions:

1 A function g is defined by $g(x) = mx + 3$ (m is an integer). Given that $g(2) = 9$ find m. Calculate $g(6)$, $g(0)$.

2 A function is defined by $f(x) = 2x + q$ (q is an integer). Given that $f(4) = 10$ find q. Calculate $f(6)$, $f(-2)$.

3 A function h is defined by $h(x) = dx - 3$ (d is an integer). Given that $h(2) = 1$ find d. Find the values of $h(0)$, $h(3)$, $h(-3)$.

4 A function g is defined by $g(x) = r(2x + 1)$ (r is an integer). Given that $g(3) = 14$, find r. Calculate $g(5)$, $g(-4)$.

Continue with Section M

M The function game

Play this game with a neighbour. Make up a set of cards as shown on Sheet M5/6. You have to make up ordered pairs as defined by a function card.

1 Lay out the **domain** card, pack of **function** cards, and the **range** card as shown below:

Domain	**Function cards**	**Range**

The top function card is turned up to reveal the first function.

2 The dealer shuffles the pack of **value** cards and deals five cards each to his neighbour and himself. He then places the remainder of the **value** cards face down on the table turning up the top card and placing it alongside to start a discard pile.

Value cards	**Discard pile**

Domain	$f(x) = 2x$, $x \in \{1,2,3\}$	**Range**

3 The dealer looks at the function and its domain printed on the **function** card. **His neighbour** starts, if he can, by placing in the **domain** column a card which has any value in the domain of the function, say 3.

Domain	$f(x) = 2x$, $x \in \{1,2,3\}$	**Range**
3		

4 The function is defined by $f(x) = 2x; x \in \{1, 2, 3\}$.
So the correct response is 6 (because $f(3) = 2 \times 3 = 6$).

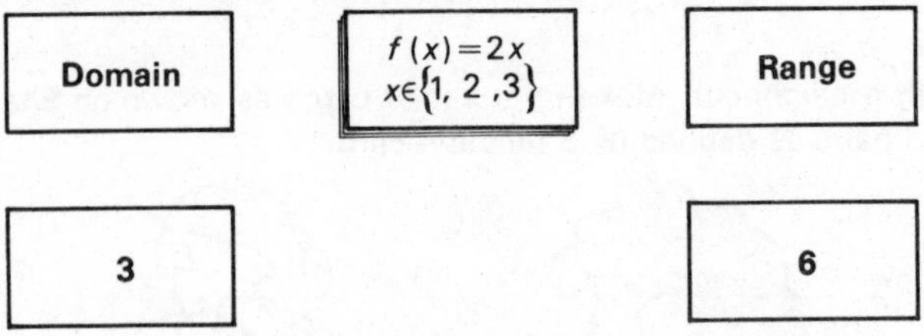

The dealer then places 6 in the **range** column, if he can.

5 After the dealer has laid aside this ordered pair he plays again in the **domain** column. He must again select a card which has a value within the domain of the function. If this is not possible he must pick up a value card and discard one but now the play goes to his neighbour. Continue to make ordered pairs in this way.

6 If a player cannot play, he picks up a **value** card and discards one. That is the finish of his turn.

7 The joker may replace any **stated** number.

8 The player who places all his cards first is the winner.
(You can check your responses by plotting the 'ordered pairs'. They should be on a straight line.)

9 Change the **function** card and play another game.

Continue with Section N

N Progress check

Exercise

1 Write symbols to describe the sets of numbers marked on the following number lines.

(a)
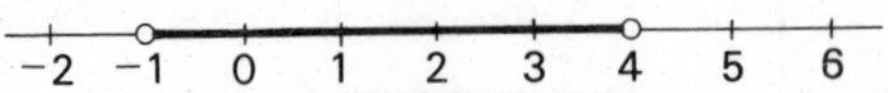

(b)
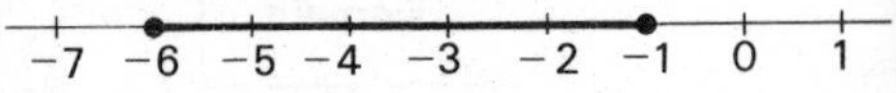

(c)
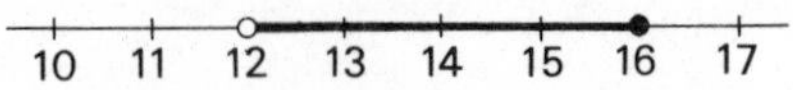

2 $f(x) = 8x + 4$ and $f(p) = 28$. What is the value of p?

3 $g(x) = \dfrac{x+2}{3}$ and $g(a) = 3$. What is the value of a?

4 A function f is defined by $f(x) = 2x - 4$ with domain $-2 \leq x \leq 2, x \in R$.
(a) Calculate $f(-2)$, $f(2)$.
(b) What is the range of the function?
(c) Draw the graph of the function on 2mm squared graph paper.

5 A function h is defined by $h(x) = kx - 5$ (k is an integer). Given that $h(4) = 7$, find k and calculate $h(2)$ and $h(-1)$.

Tell your teacher you have finished this Unit

UNIT M6
Periodicity and the Sine Function

A Repeating patterns

You need tracing paper

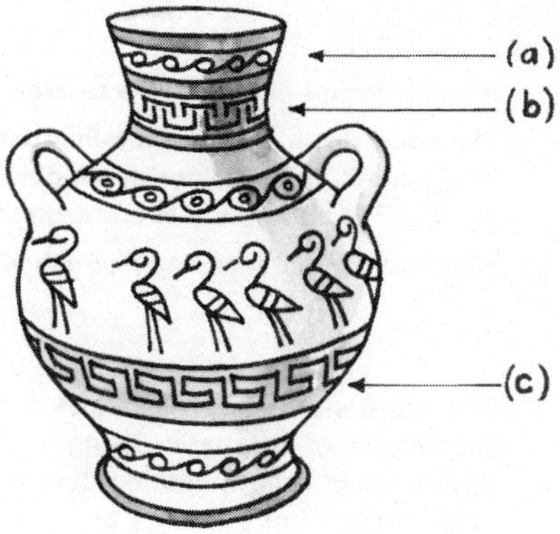

The diagram shows a Greek vase decorated with bands of different designs.

Each band has one basic design which is repeated over and over again to form the pattern.

Exercise

1 Here is band (a) drawn full size.

Check that the basic design measures 4 centimetres.

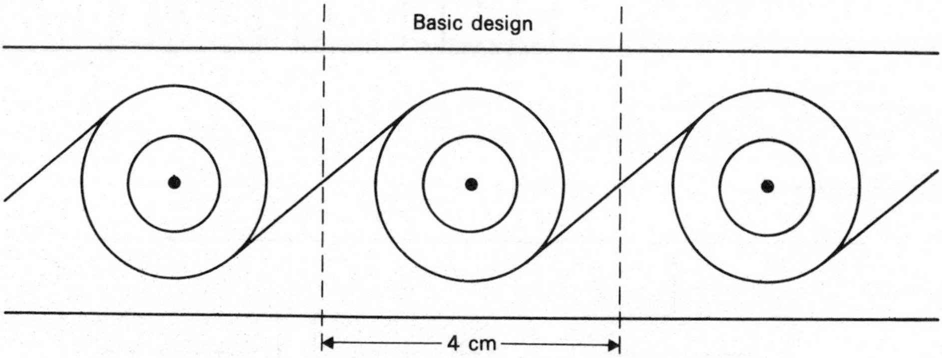

Using tracing paper, copy this basic design.

Move your tracing along band (a) until it matches the design again. You should find that you have moved the tracing 4 centimetres.

Move your tracing 8 centimetres along the band in the opposite direction. You should find that your tracing matches the design again.

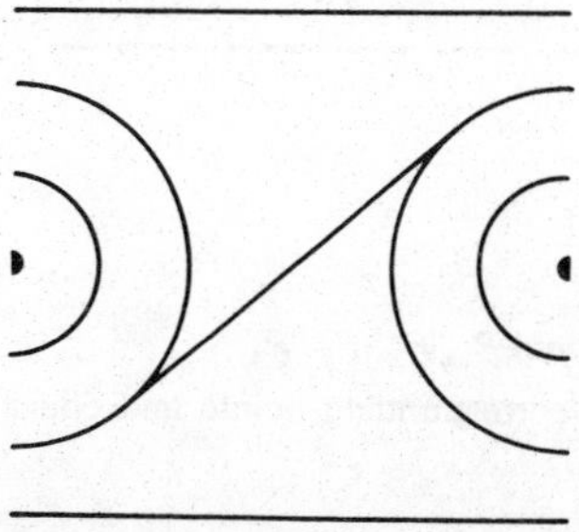

2 Copy this design onto tracing paper. Move your tracing paper along 4 cm to the left so that the ends of the diagrams match, and copy it again.
Repeat this twice.
Your pattern will be the same as band (a).

> **Any** length of four centimetres can be taken as the basic design.

3 Here is band (b).

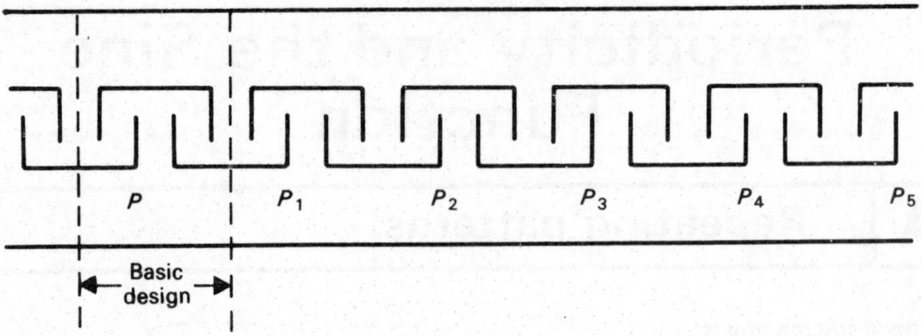

A basic design of band (b) is marked above. Check that it measures 2 centimetres.

The point P is marked on the first design.
The point P_1 is at the **corresponding point** on the next design.
P_2, P_3, P_4, and P_5 are at corresponding points on the designs which follow.
Measure the distance between P and P_1, P_1 and P_2, P_2 and P_3, P_3 and P_4, P_4 and P_5.

These distances should all equal the length of the basic design, so we could have measured the basic design from P to P_1 as in the diagram.

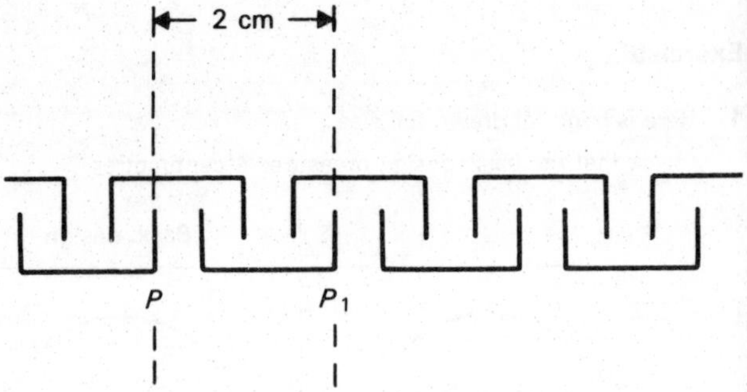

4 Here is band (c).

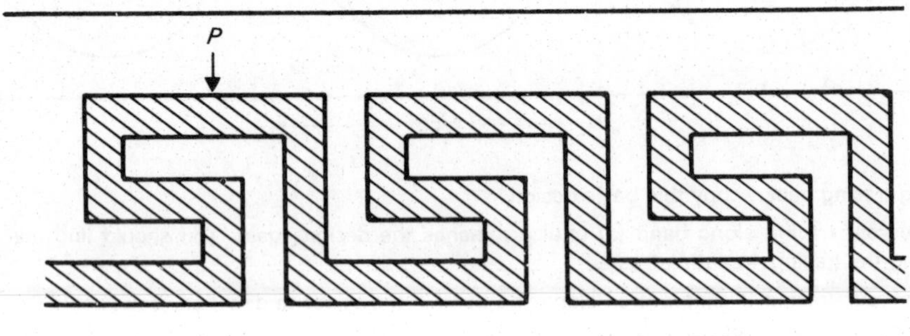

Copy band (c) onto tracing paper.

On your tracing paper extend the pattern.

(a) mark a basic design and measure its length.

(b) mark **four** points corresponding to the point P and label them P_1, P_2, P_3, P_4.

(c) measure the distance between any neighbouring pair of corresponding points and check that it is equal to the length of the basic design.

In any repeating pattern the length of the basic design is called the **period** of the pattern. In question 4 the period of the pattern is 3.5 cm. This means that the basic design is repeated every 3.5 cm.

5 What is the period of the pattern in question 1, 2, and 3?

In each of the following, identify the basic design, measure the period and note your answer.

6

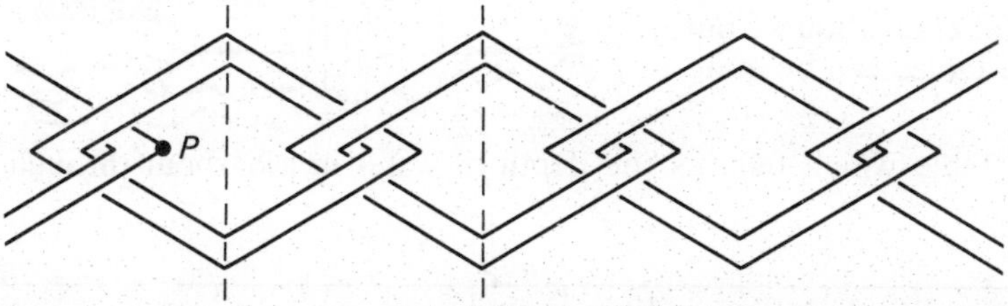

Period = ▭

7

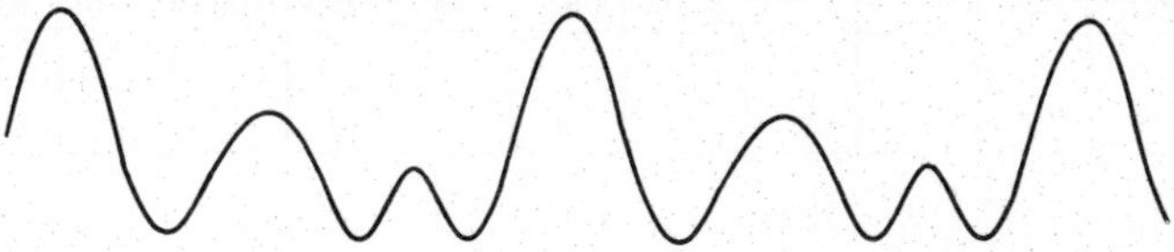

Period = ▭

Continue with Section B

B Patterns in nature

We have considered patterns which were repeated after a certain distance. Sometimes we are interested in events which are repeated after a certain **interval of time**.

Example

The phases of the moon are repeated at regular intervals of time.

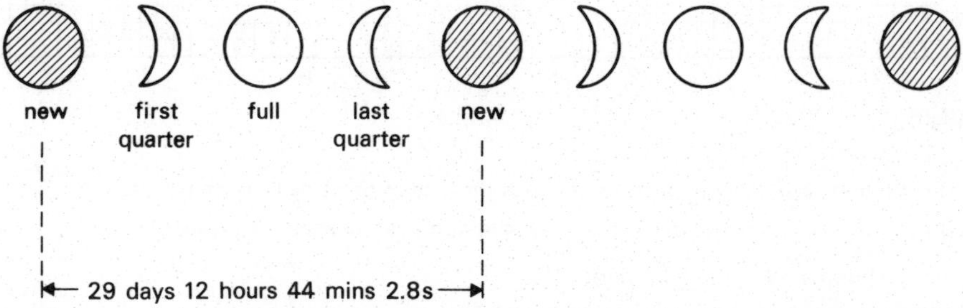

The **period** of the pattern is 29 days, 12 hours, 44 minutes, and 2.8 seconds.

Example

A harbour marker measures the depth of water in a harbour throughout the day.

We obtain information about tides and depths of water in different harbours from tide tables but these tables can be quite complicated.

Here is a simplified table which tells us the depth of water in a harbour throughout a 24 hour period.

Time	mid-night	0200	0400	0600	0800	1000	1200 noon	1400	1600	1800	2000	2200	mid-night
Depth of water in m	4.2	7.6	9.0	7.6	4.2	3.0	4.2	7.6	9.0	7.6	4.2	3.0	4.2

Exercise

1 Use the above table to answer the following questions.

(a) At approximately what times during the day was high tide?

(b) At approximately what times during the day was low tide?

We can 'picture' the tidal pattern by drawing a graph.

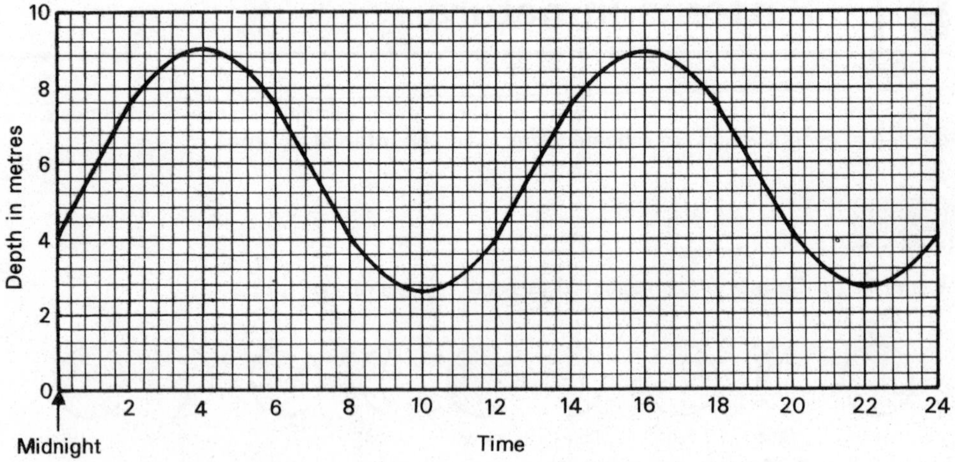

2 (a) On the 'time' axis, how many minutes does the side of one small square represent?

(b) On the 'depth' axis, what depth does the side of one small square represent?

3 Use the graph to answer the following:

(a) At what times during the day was the water 6 m deep?

(b) A ship needing at least a depth of 8 m of water wants to enter the harbour. Between what times can it enter?

(c) What is the period of the tide pattern?

A tide-level recorder is an instrument which automatically draws a graph to represent the changes in water level in a harbour. A float on the water moves a pen up and down over the surface of a paper-covered rotating cylinder.

The tide-level recorder draws a graph showing the level of water above or below a **mean level**, called a 'datum'.

Taken over a few days the recorder will draw a graph like this:

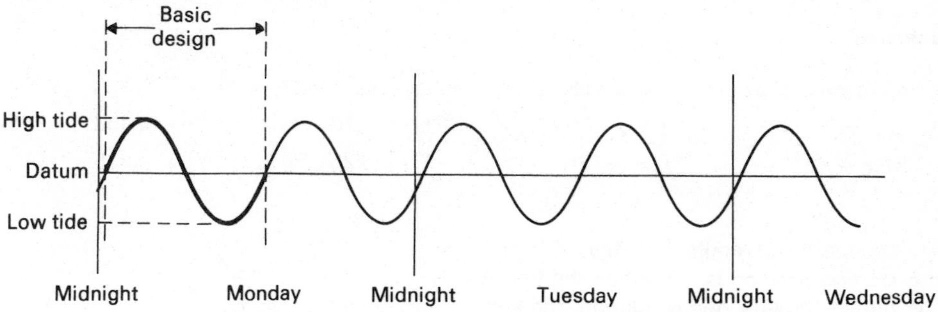

In this pattern the 'basic design' includes one high and one low tide.

Continue with Section C

C Going round in a circle

Imagine that you are on a chair *P* on a fair-ground wheel.

At the start the angle between *OP* and the starting position is 0°.

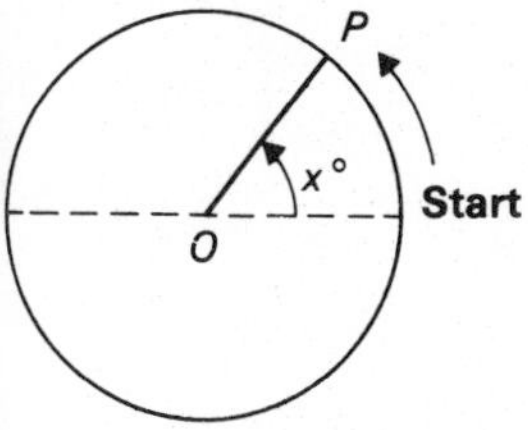

As the wheel rotates, the angle $x°$ between the arm *OP* and the starting position will increase.

Example

When $x = 120$ the chair P will be here:

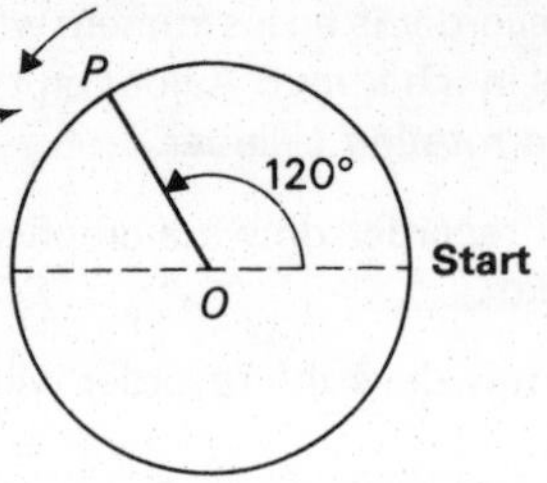

Exercise

1 Make sketches as in the example above to show the position of OP when

(a) $x = 90$ (b) $x = 180$ (c) $x = 270$ (d) $x = 360$

(e) $x = 45$ (f) $x = 135$ (g) $x = 225$ (h) $x = 315$

At the start the angle between OP and the starting position is 0°. When the wheel has turned through one revolution, the arm OP will have turned through 360° to bring OP back to its starting position.

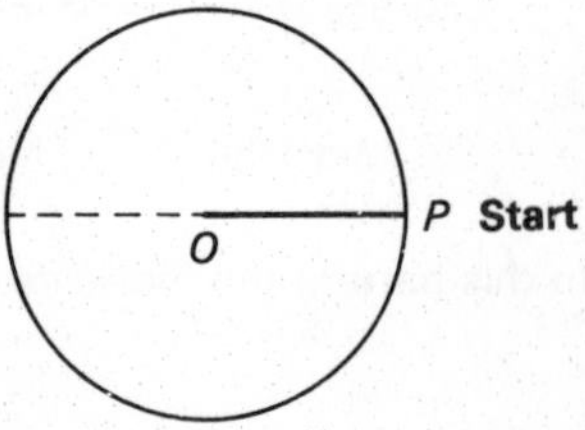

As the wheel continues to rotate, the angle increases still further and becomes greater than 360°.

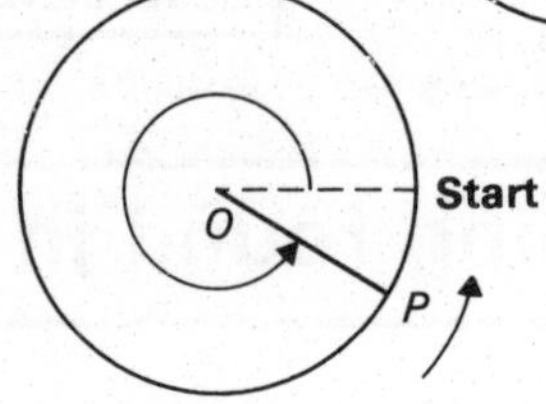

For example, in this diagram the arm OP has rotated through 500°.

It has turned through one revolution (360°) and then gone a further 140°.

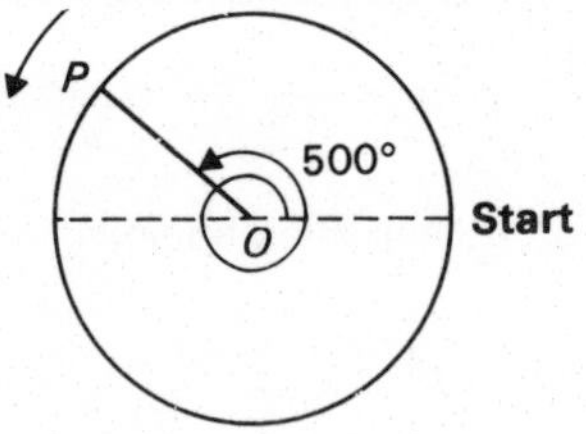

Example

Sketch an angle of 400°.

$400° = 360° + 40°$

one revolution

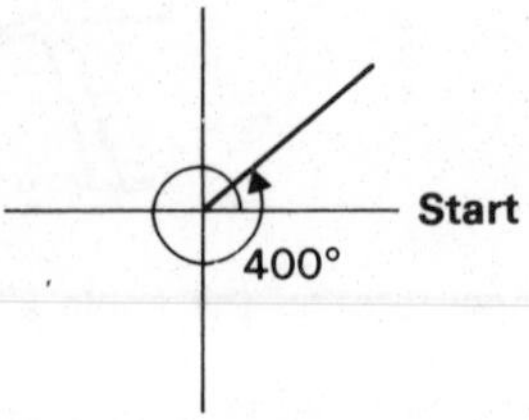

Exercise

2 Make sketches as in the example above to show the following angles.

Notice that the **start** must always be at the right-hand side as shown above.

(a) 120° (b) 300° (c) 370° (d) 450° (e) 540°

(f) 630° (g) 720° (h) 570° (i) 650° (j) 800°

3 In each of the following diagrams find the value of *x*.

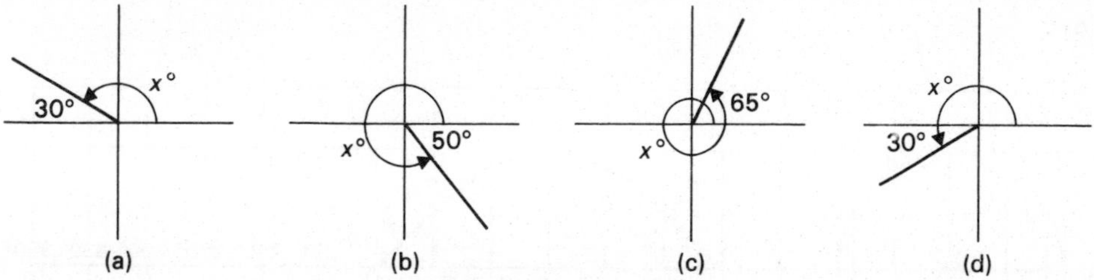

Continue with Section D

D How high?

The length of the vertical line *NP* in this diagram gives the distance of *P* from the starting level. As the fairground wheel rotates the distance of *P* from the starting level changes and the angle between *OP* and the starting position increases. This effect is shown in the following series of diagrams. At the start *N* and *P* coincide so $NP = 0$.

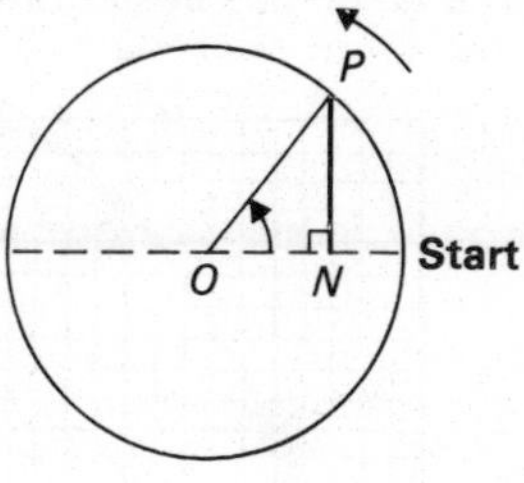

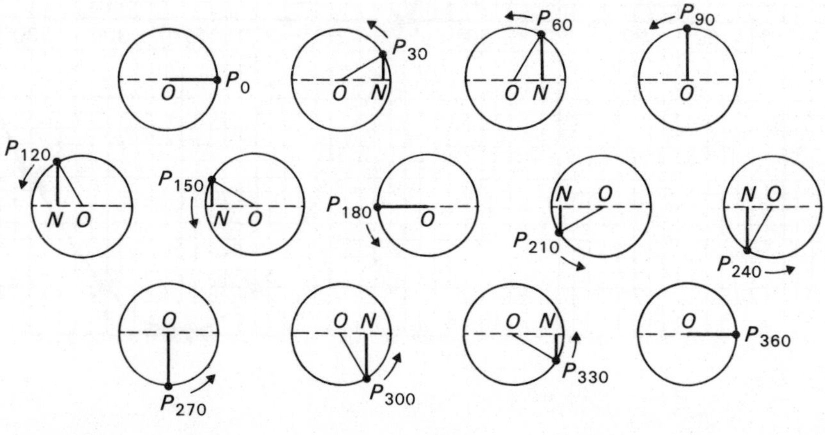

The circles have radius 1 cm, so *P* is never more than 1 cm above or below the starting level.

If the length of *NP* is measured in each diagram then we can draw a graph showing the **distance of *P* from the starting level** plotted against **the angle of rotation of *OP***. This graph is shown below.

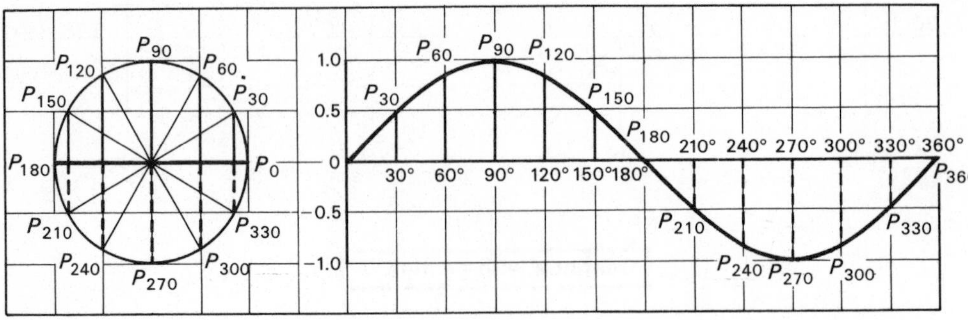

OP_0 corresponds to the starting level, OP_{30} indicates a rotation of 30°, OP_{60} a rotation of 60°, and so on.

The distance of *P* **above** the starting level is shown by a **positive** value on the graph (unbroken lines).

The distance of *P* **below** the starting level is shown by a **negative** value on the graph (broken lines).

The graph has been drawn to a larger scale below.

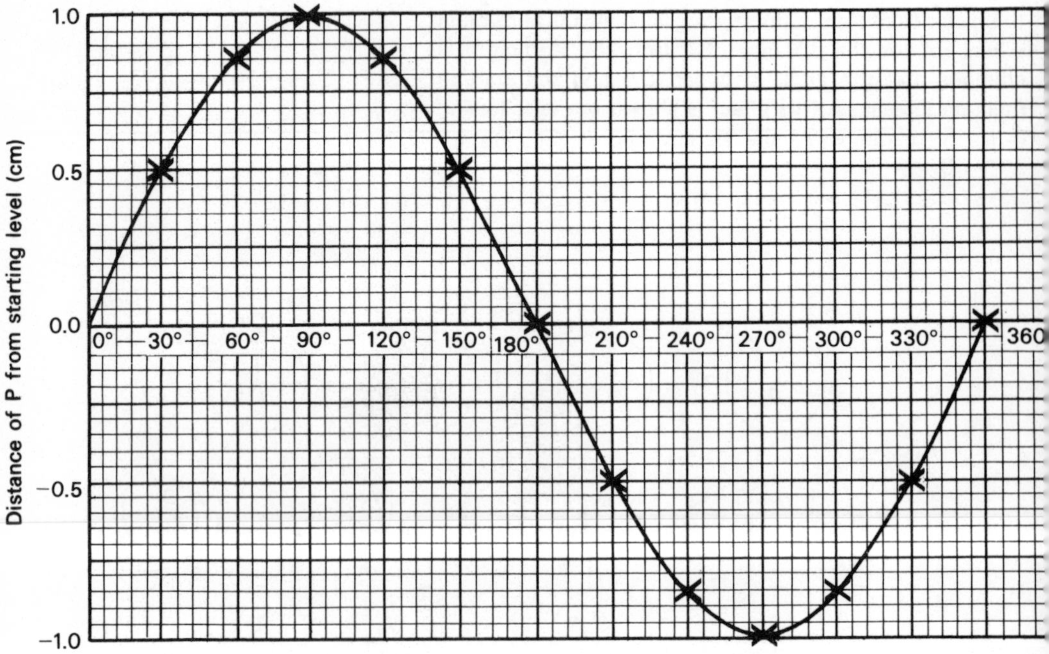

Example

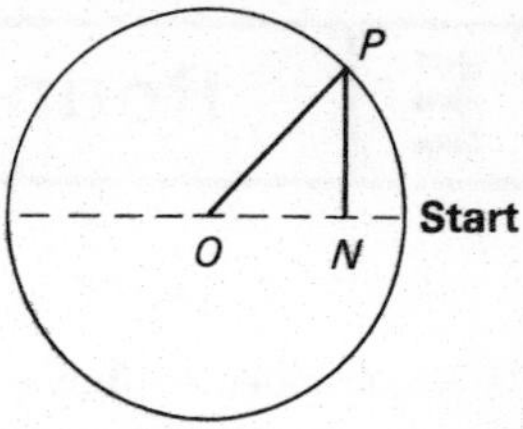

When OP has rotated through an angle of 48°, what is the distance of P from the starting level?

Use the graph on page 164 to find the distance when the angle of rotation is 48°.

(Along the horizontal axis the side of each small square represents 6°.)

You should find that the distance is about 0.74 cm.

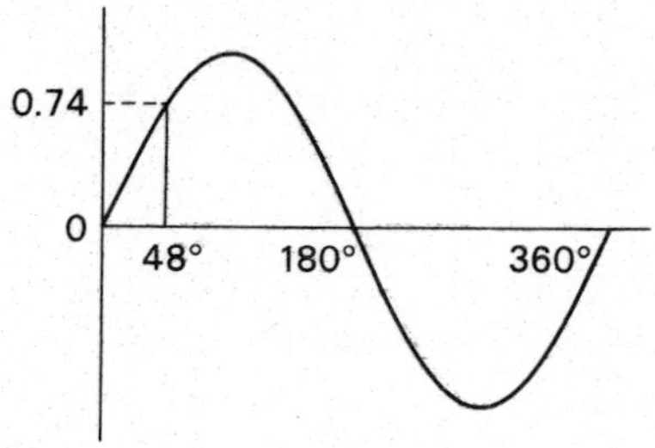

Exercise

Use the graph on page 164 for the following questions.

1 In the same way, find the distance of P from the starting level when the angle of rotation is

(a) 24° (b) 66° (c) 90° (d) 102° (e) 132°
(f) 180° (g) 192° (h) 234° (i) 270° (j) 330°

2 (a) What is the distance of P **above** the starting level for angles of 60° and 120°?
(b) What is the distance of P **below** the starting level for angles of 240° and 300°?

3 Find **two** angles for which P is
(a) 0.5 cm **above** the starting level;
(b) 0.5 cm **below** the starting level.

4 Find another angle for which P is the same distance **above** the starting level as for
(a) 18° (b) 72° (c) 126°.

5 Find another angle for which P is the same distance **below** the starting level as for
(a) 336° (b) 228° (c) 306°

6 For what angle is P at
(a) its greatest distance **above** the starting level?
(b) its greatest distance **below** the starting level?

7 For what angles is P **on** the starting level?

Continue with Section E

E Round and round and round

As *P* continues to move round the circle after one complete revolution, all the distances of *P* from the starting level are repeated.
We can show this on a graph.

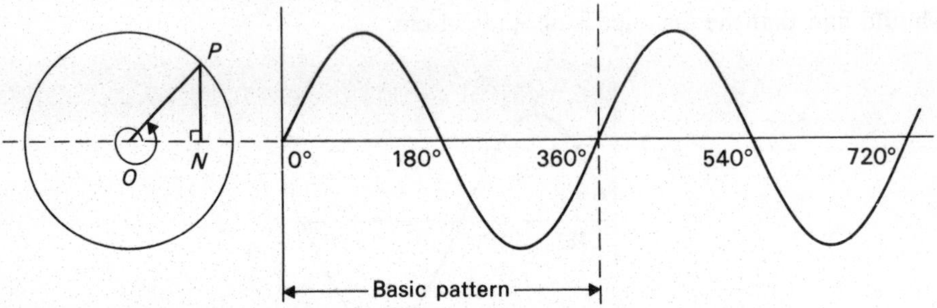

We have a basic pattern which is repeated over and over again.

The **period** of the pattern is 360°, that is, the pattern is repeated after 360°.

Example

When the arm *OP* has rotated through an angle of 780° is *P* above or below the starting level, and at what distance?

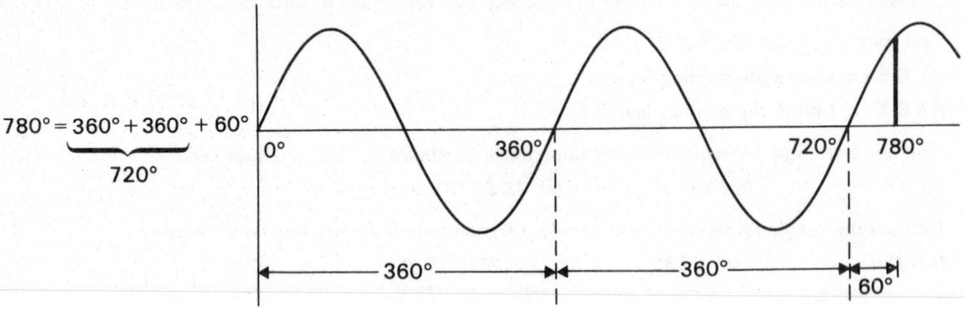

So *P* is above the starting level.

After a rotation of 780° the distance of *P* from the starting level is the same as after a rotation of 60°.

Read this distance from the graph on page 164.

You should find it to be 0.86 cm above the starting level.

Exercise

1 Find the distance of P from the starting level after a rotation of

(a) 732° (b) 810° (c) 948°

2 If P is 0.5 cm above the starting level, find all the angles between 0° and 720° which correspond to this distance.

3 If P is 0.5 cm below the starting level, find all the angles between 0° and 720°, which correspond to this distance.

Continue with Section F

F Sine graph

Look again at the circle round which OP rotates.

In a right-angled triangle the fraction

$$\frac{\text{opposite}}{\text{hypotenuse}}$$

is called the sine of the angle.

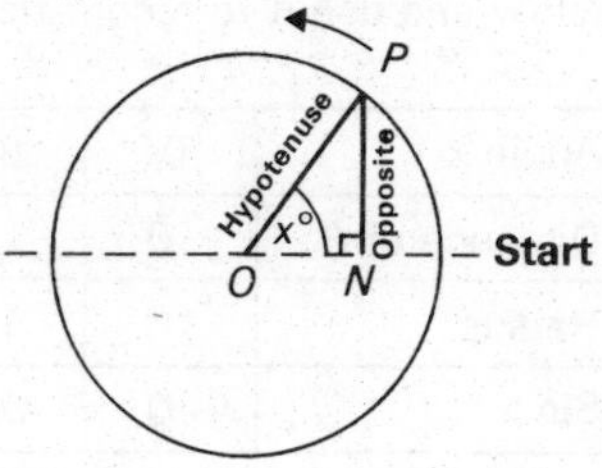

In the diagram,

$$\sin x^\circ = \frac{\text{distance of } P \text{ from starting point}}{\text{radius of circle}}$$

$$= \frac{NP}{OP}$$

The diagram below shows the position of OP after it has rotated through 30°.

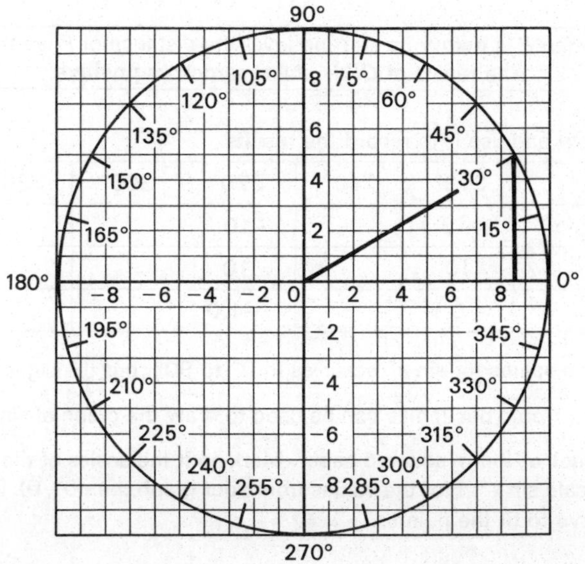

Read off the distance of *P* from its starting level, copy and complete:

Distance of $P = \square$

Radius of circle $= \square$

$$\sin 30° = \frac{\text{distance of } P \text{ from start}}{\text{radius of circle}}$$

$$= \frac{\square}{10}$$

$$= 0.5$$

In the same way copy and complete:

$$\sin 60° = \frac{\text{distance of } P \text{ from start}}{\text{radius}}$$

$$= \frac{\square}{10}$$

$$= \square$$

Continue in this way and calculate sin 90°, sin 120°, sin 150°, and sin 180°. Make a copy of the table below and use it to record the results.

Angle *x*	0°	30°	60°	90°	120°	150°	180°
Distance of *P*	0	5					
Radius	10	10					
Sin *x*	0	0.5					

0°–90° section   90°–180° section

Check the 0°–90° values using tables of sines. The values above should be close to the values in the tables.

Notice that the values in the 90°–180° section are the same as those in the 0°–90° section.

Continue in the same way and find values of sin 210°, sin 240°, and so on up to sin 360°.

Remember that when *P* is **below** its starting level the distance of *P* is taken to be **negative**. The radius of *OP* is still regarded as **positive**.

Copy the table below and use it to record the results.

Angle *x*	210°	240°	270°	300°	330°	360°
Distance of *P*	−5		−10			
Radius	10		10			10
Sin *x*	−0.5		−1.0			0

Notice that the same values for sin *x*° occur as in 0° to 90°, but the signs are **negative**.

The values of sin *x*° from your tables can be used to draw the graph of sin *x*° from 0° to 360°.

You will need a sheet of 2 mm squared paper. Mark on it the scales of the graph on page 164. Label the vertical scale sin *x*°. Plot the values from your graph, i.e. (0°, 0), (30°, 0.5), and so on. Draw a smooth curve to fit the points.

Compare your graph with that on page 164. You should find that the two curves match so the graph on page 164 is also the graph of sin $x°$.

The sine curve is the basic shape of all waves. It occurs often in mathematics. The graph of tide levels in Section B has this shape.

Exercise

From your graph of sin $x°$ find the value of each of the following:

1 sin 54° **2** sin 144° **3** sin 198°

4 sin 228° **5** sin 306° **6** sin 348°

Continue with Section G

G Sines to angles

From the sine curve you have drawn you will find that there are **two** angles which have a sine of 0.5; these are 30° and 150°.

There are also **two** angles which have a sine of −0.5; these are 210° and 310°.

This is shown in the diagram.

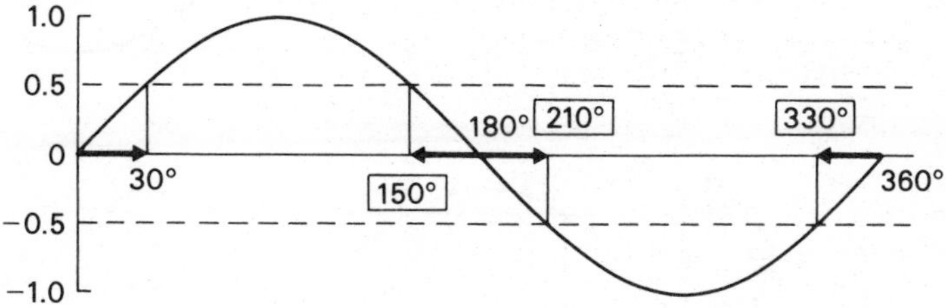

Notice that
150° is **30° less than** 180°; 210° is **30° greater than** 180°; 330° is **30° less than** 360°.

Example

Find what angles should be marked in the boxes on the following sine curve.

The dotted lines are equal distances from the horizontal axis.

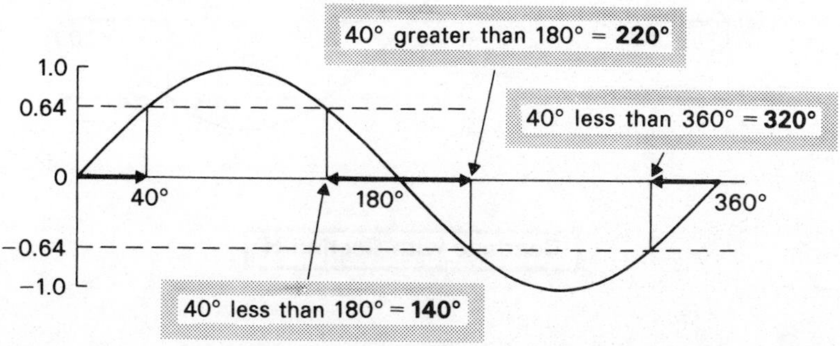

Exercise

In each diagram the dotted lines are equal distances from the horizontal axis.

In the same way as in the example, find what angles should be marked in the boxes (a), (b), and (c) on the following sine curves.

1

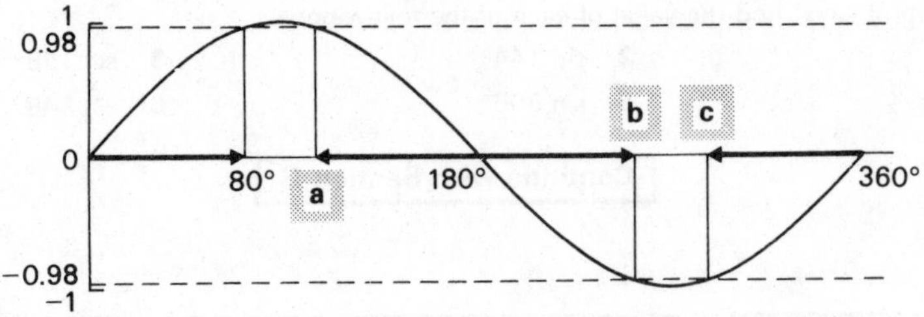

2

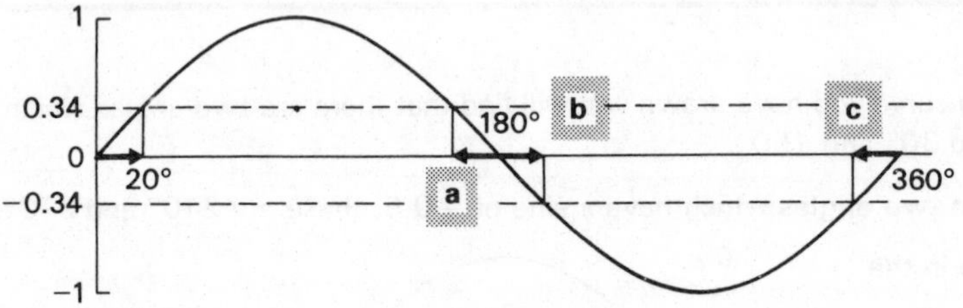

3

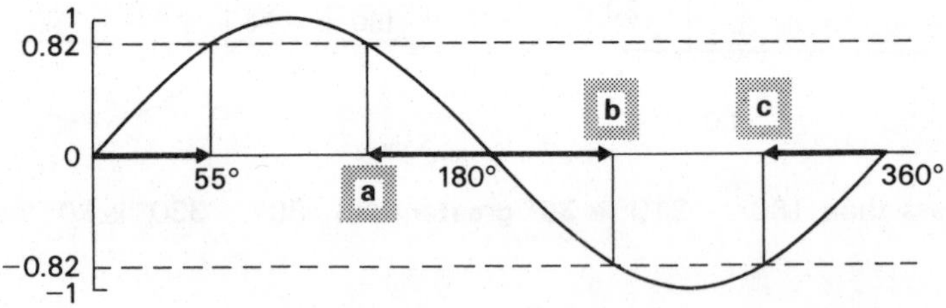

4

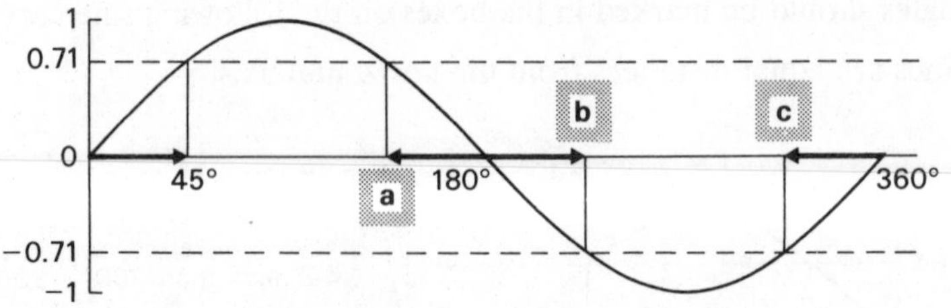

Continue with Section H

H Angles to sines

You need tables of sines.

Example

To find sin 150°.

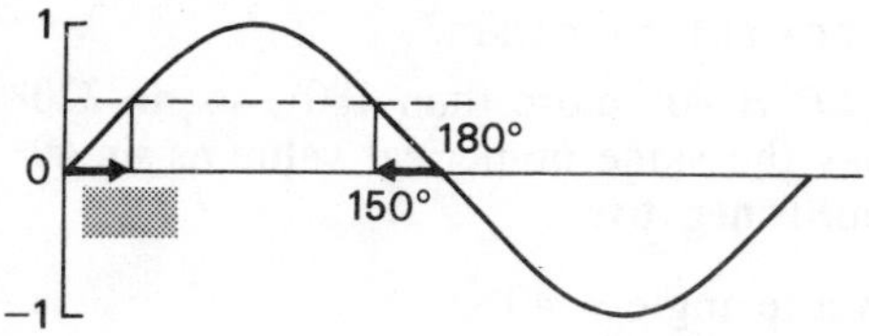

Look at the diagram.
150° is 30° less than 180°, so the angle which should be marked in the box is 30°.

We set out the working like this:

Acute angle = 30°
So sin 150° = sin 30° = 0.5

Use your table of sines to check that sin 30° = 0.5

Exercise

In each question find (a) the appropriate acute angle;
(b) the sine of this angle from your table.

For each question copy and complete the working.

1 Find sin 160°.

Acute angle = ▢
So sin 160° = sin ▢ = ▢

Use table of sines

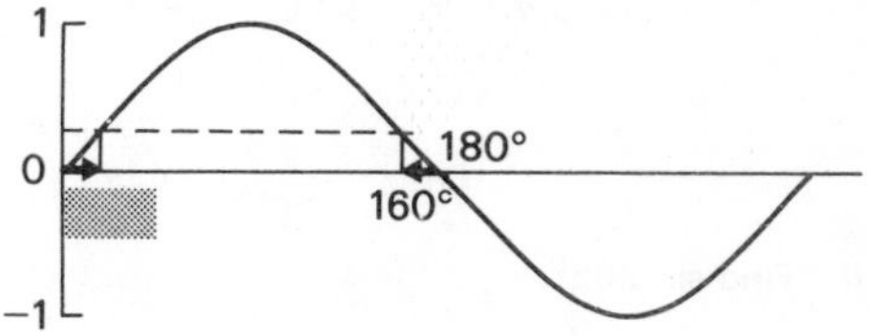

2 Find sin 145°.

Acute angle = ▢
So sin 145° = sin ▢ = ▢

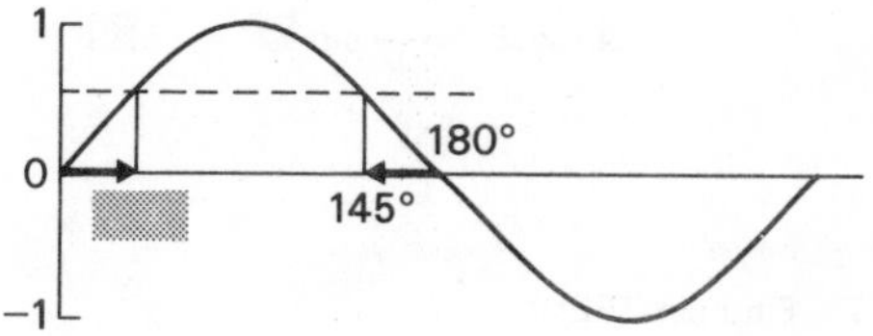

3 Find sin 132°.

Acute angle = ▢
So sin 132° = sin ▢ = ▢

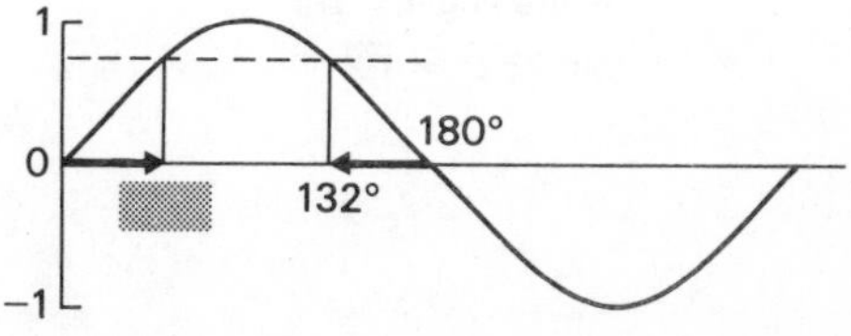

4 Find sin 109°.

Acute angle = ▢
So sin 109° = sin ▢ = ▢

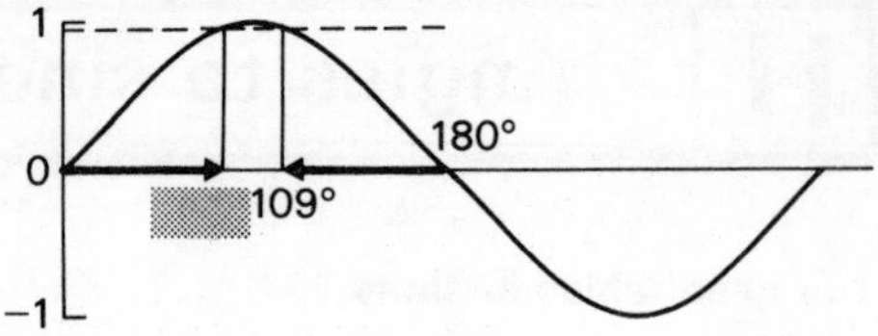

Example

To find sin 220°.

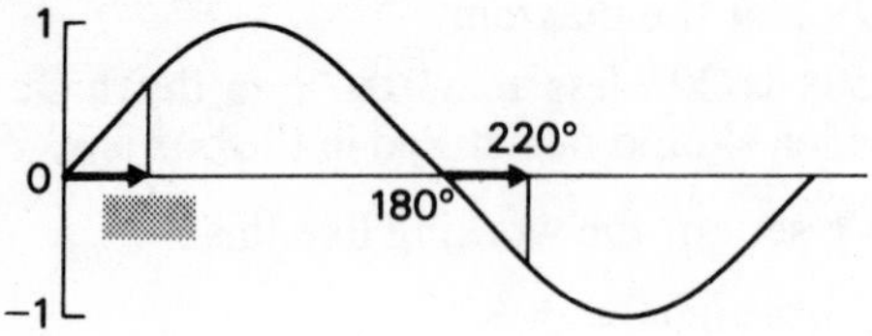

Look at the diagram.
220° is 40° more than 180°, so **sin 220°** has the same numerical value as **sin 40°** but is **negative**.

Acute angle = 40°
So sin 220° = −sin 40°
= −0.643 (from tables)

Exercise

For each question copy and complete the working:

5 Find sin 240°.

Acute angle = ▢
Sin 240° = −sin ▢ = − ▢

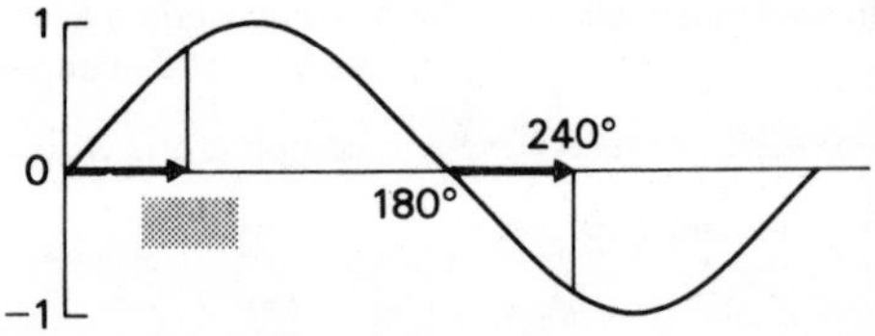

6 Find sin 205°.

Acute angle = ▢
Sin 205° = −sin ▢ = − ▢

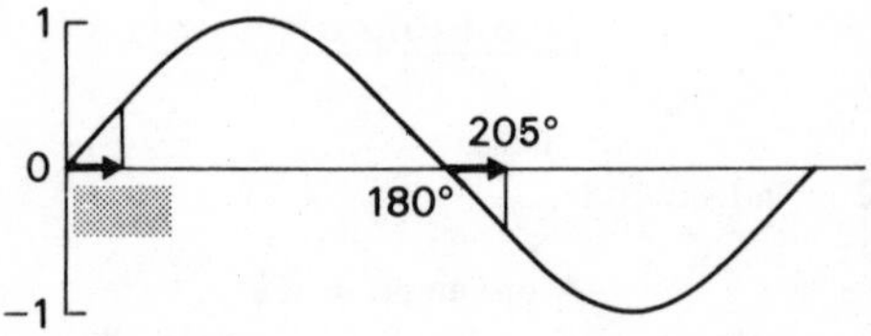

7 Find sin 252°.

Acute angle = ▢
Sin 252° = ▢

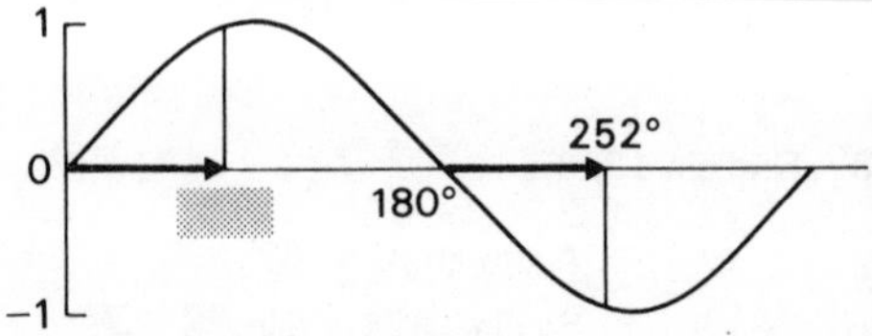

8 Find sin 219°.

Acute angle = □

Sin 219° = □

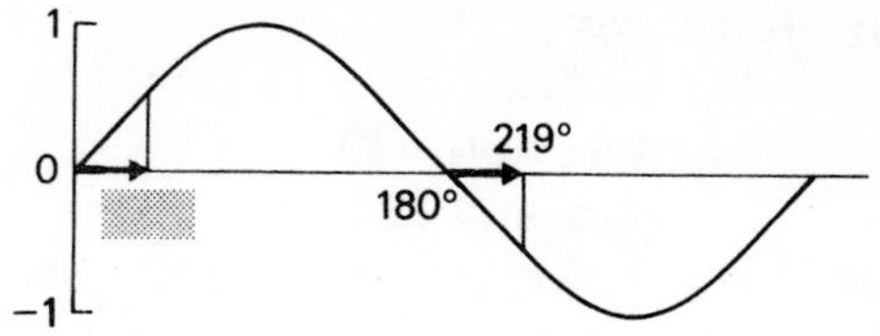

Example

To find sin 300°.

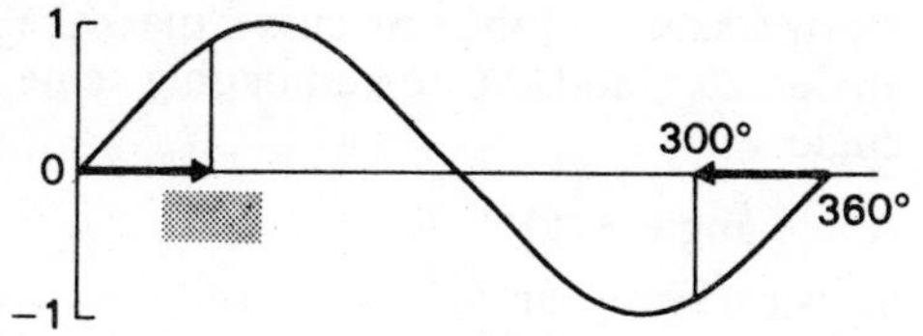

Look at the diagram.

300° is 60° less than 360°, so **sin 300°** has the same numerical value as **sin 60°** but is **negative**.

Acute angle = 60°

So sin 300° = −sin 60°

= −0.866

Exercise

For each question copy and complete the working:

9 Find sin 340°.

Acute angle = □

Sin 340° = −sin □ = □

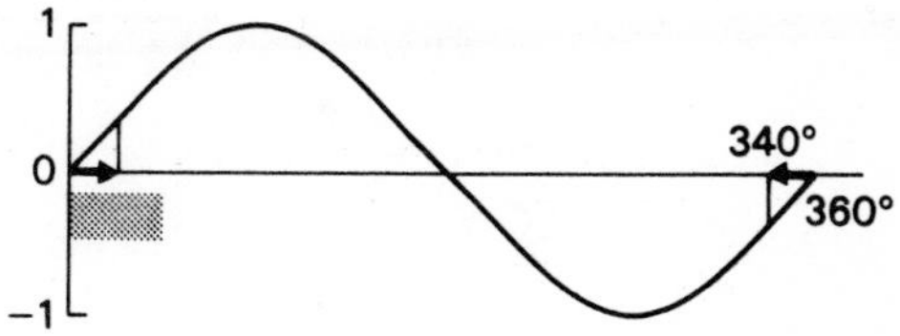

10 Find sin 315°.

Acute angle = □

Sin 315° = □

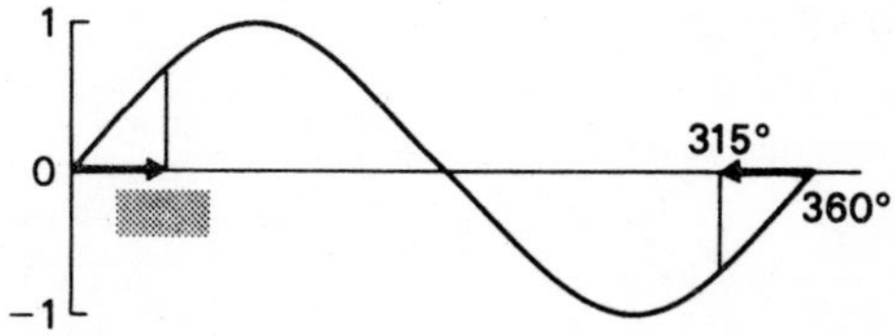

11 Find sin 282°.

Acute angle = □

Sin 282° = □

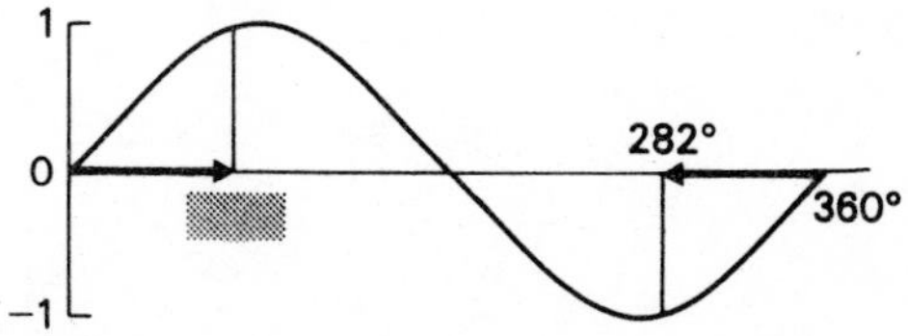

12 Find sin 308°.

Acute angle = ▢

Sin 308° = ▢

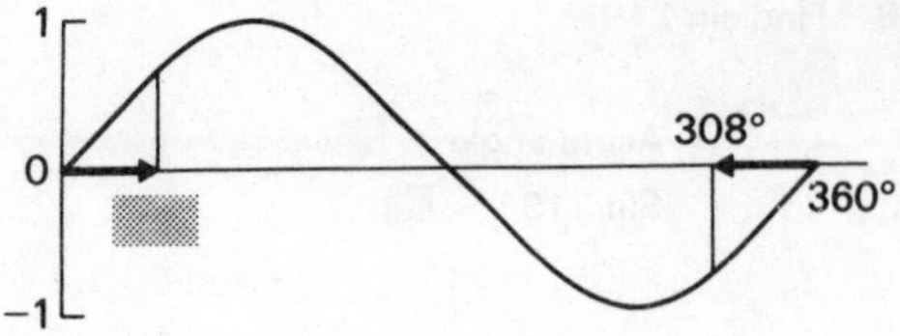

Example

To find sin 129°.

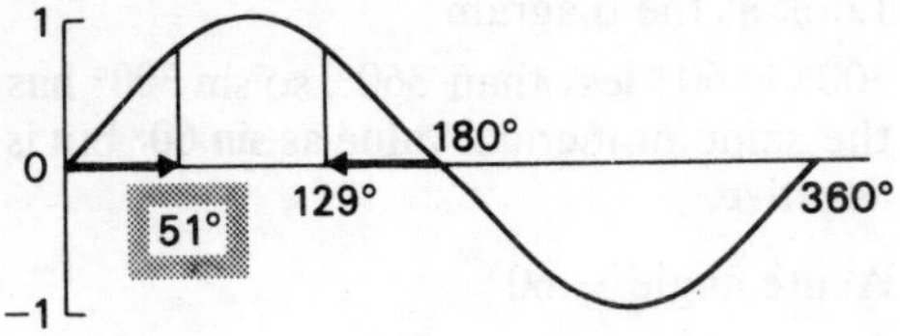

Draw a sketch of the sine curve, mark the angle 129°, and the corresponding acute angle.

Acute angle = 51°

So sin 129° = sin 51°
= 0.777.

Exercise

For each of the following, draw a sketch and then find the value as shown above.

13 sin 103° **14** sin 241° **15** sin 327°

Continue with Section I

I Progress check

Exercise

1

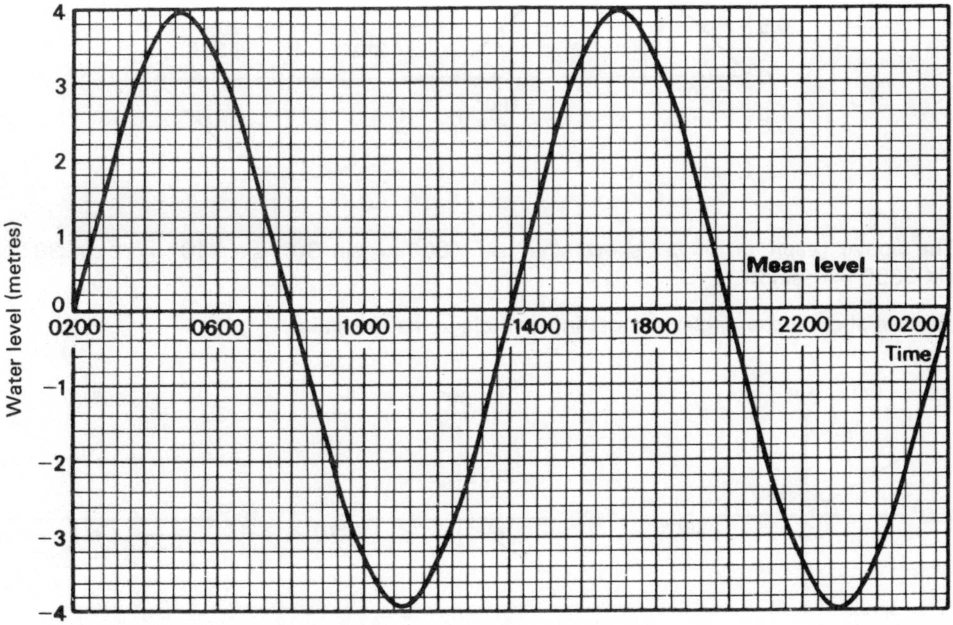

The graph shows how the water level in a channel rises and falls throughout a 24 hour period.

(a) What are the times of high water?

(b) What are the times of low water?

(c) At 1800 hours how far is the water level above mean level?

(d) At 1000 hours how far is the water level below mean level?

(e) At what times is the water level 2 m above mean level?

(f) At what times is the level at mean level?

(g) What is the period of this wave pattern?

2 In each diagram the dotted lines are equal distances from the horizontal axis. Find what angles should be marked in the boxes on the following sine curves.

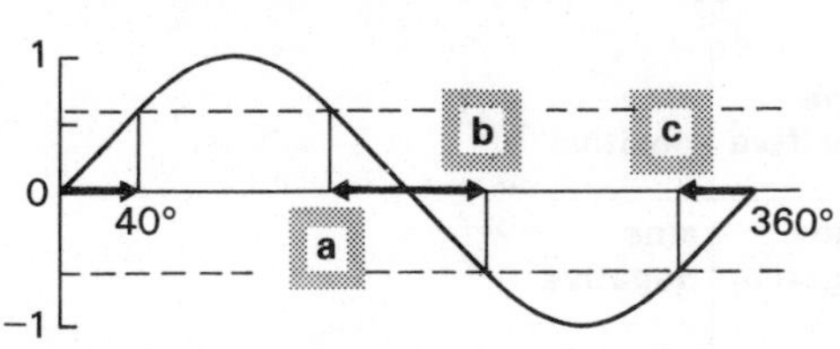

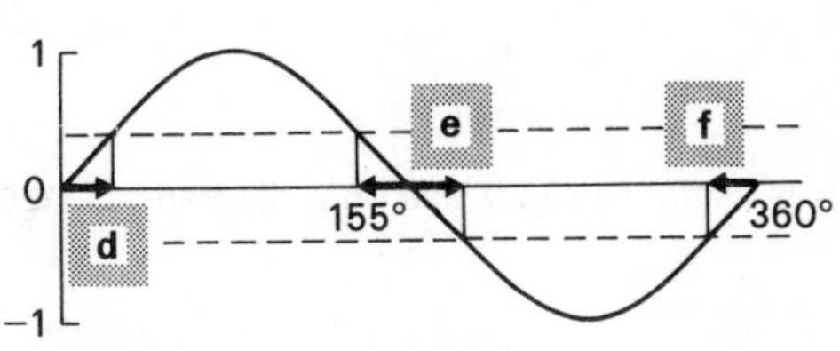

3 For each of the following, draw a sketch and then find the value.

(a) sin 145° (b) sin 214° (c) sin 105° (d) sin 317°

Ask your teacher what to do next

J Rotating arms

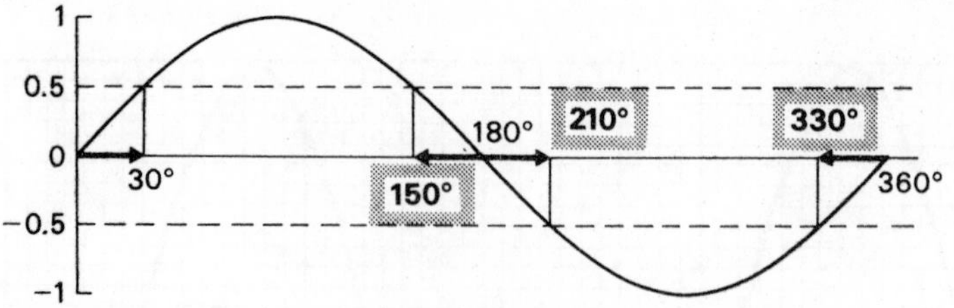

The above graph of sin $x°$ shows that sin 150° = sin 30°, sin 210° = −sin 30°, and sin 330° = −sin 30°.

We can show these angles on rotating-arm diagrams like this:

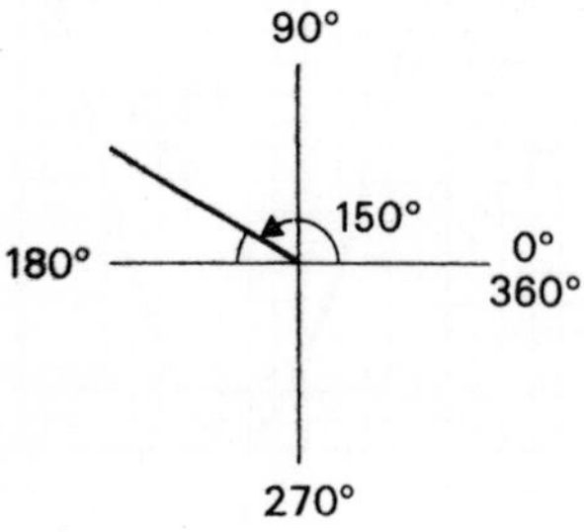

150° is 30° less than 180°

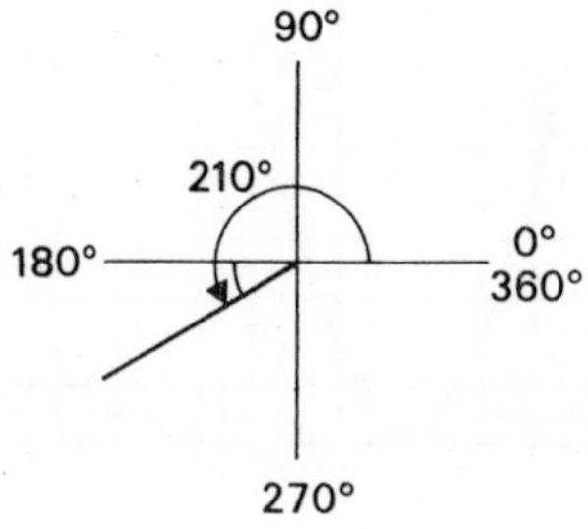

210° is 30° greater than 180°

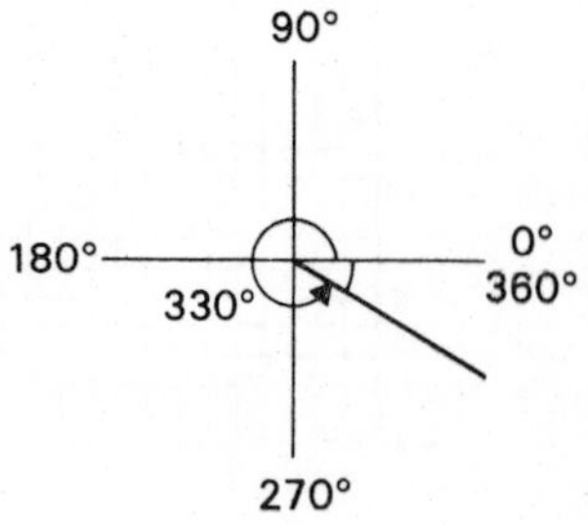

330° is 30° less than 360°

In each case notice that the **acute angle** between the rotating arm and the *horizontal* axis is the angle we would look up in sine tables in order to find the sines of 150°, 210°, and 330°.

Look at the graph of sin $x°$ again.

If x is between 0 and 180 then sin $x°$ is **positive**.

If x is between 180 and 360 then sin $x°$ is **negative**.

It is useful to show this on a diagram:

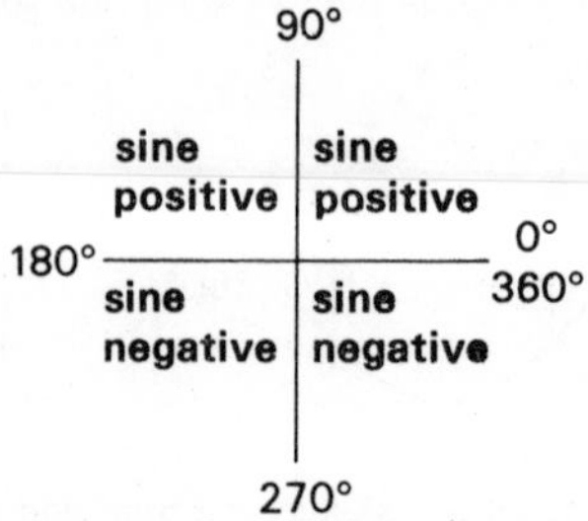

We are now ready to find the sines of angles using this diagram.

Example

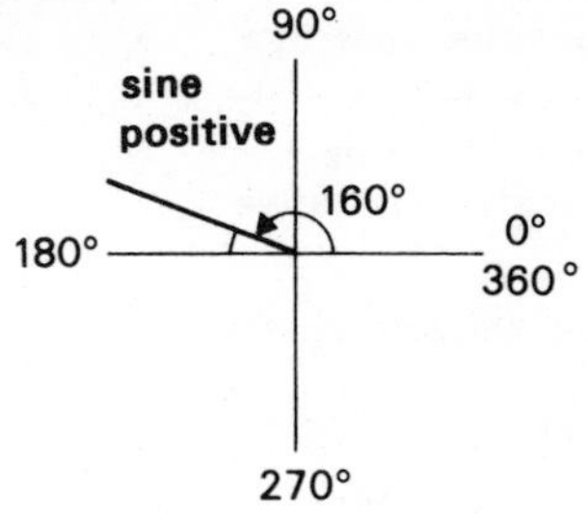

To find sin 160°

Draw a rotating-arm diagram for 160°.

Beside the rotating arm write whether the sine is **positive** or **negative** in this position.

Write down the acute angle between the arm and the horizontal:

acute angle = 20°

so sin 160° = sin 20° = 0.342

Exercise

1 Find sin 235°. Copy the diagram. Copy and complete the working.

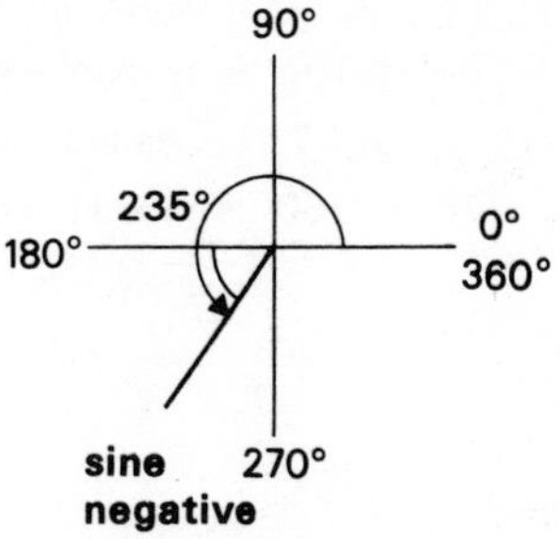

Acute angle = ▢

So sin 235° = − sin ▢ = − ▢

For each of the following draw a diagram and write the working as above, to find the value of the sine of the angle.

2 290°	**3** 133°	**4** 242°	**5** 103°
6 250°	**7** 135°	**8** 320°	**9** 350°

From the graph of sin x° we can read off some 'special' angles.

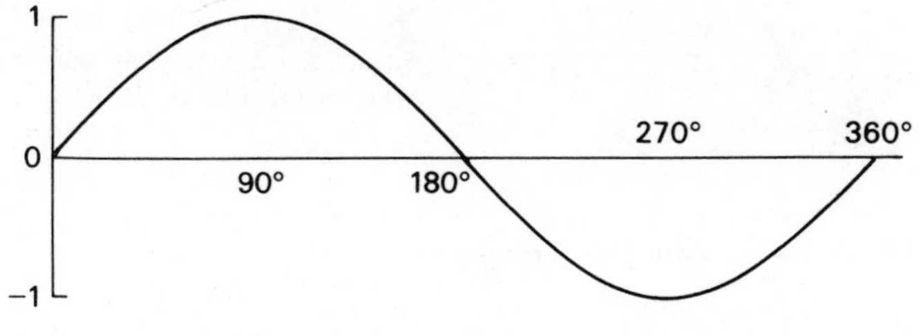

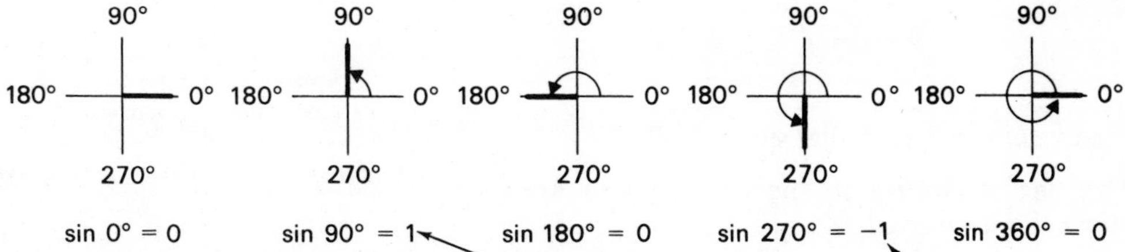

Notice that **the greatest value of sin x° is 1 and the least value is −1.**

We can summarize all this in a diagram:

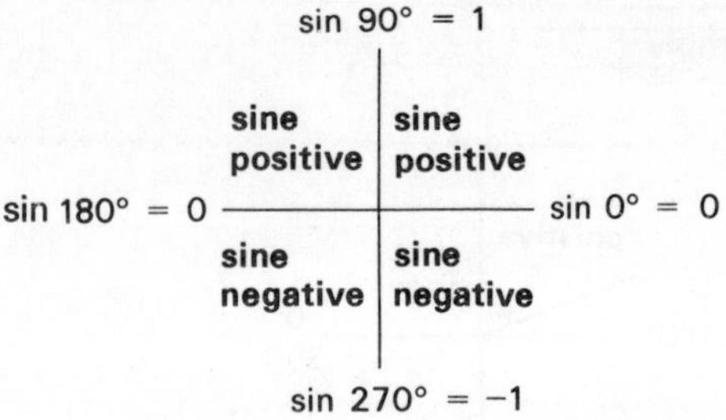

> Note: In a rotating-arm diagram,
>
> 0° to 90° is called the **first quadrant**
>
> 90° to 180° is called the **second quadrant**
>
> 180° to 270° is called the **third quadrant**
>
> 270° to 360° is called the **fourth quadrant**

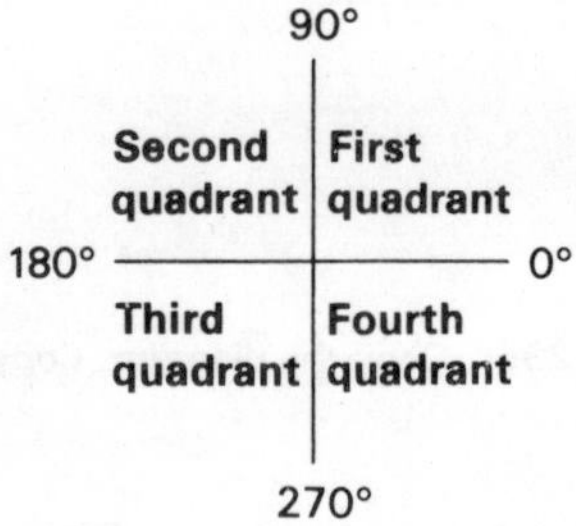

Continue with Section K

K Sign of the sine

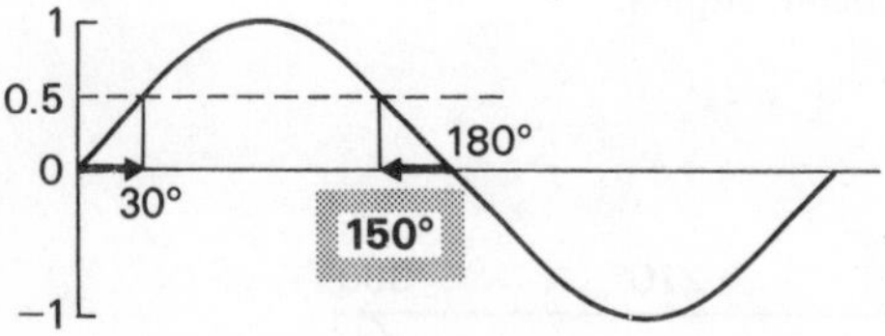

If we have to find values of x for which $\sin x° = 0.5$, we can use the graph of $\sin x°$ to show that $x = 30$ or $x = 150$.

Another method is to use a rotating-arm diagram.

Example

Find values of x such that $\sin x° = 0.5$.

The sine is **positive** so the rotating arm must lie above the horizontal axis.

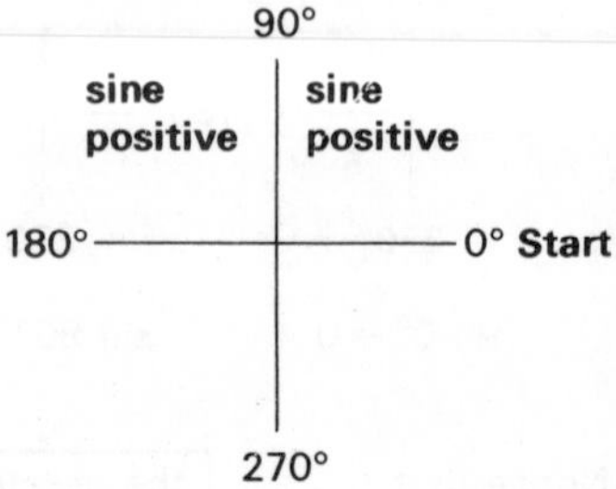

From tables of sines, the acute angle whose sine is 0.5 is 30°. Mark two positions of the arm which make angles of 30° with the horizontal.

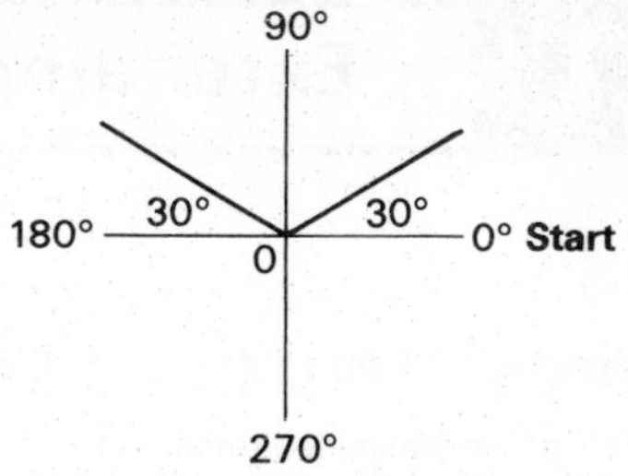

The rotating arm has turned through either 30° or (180 − 30)°, i.e. 30° or 150°. So the values of x such that $\sin x° = 0.5$ are 30 and 150.

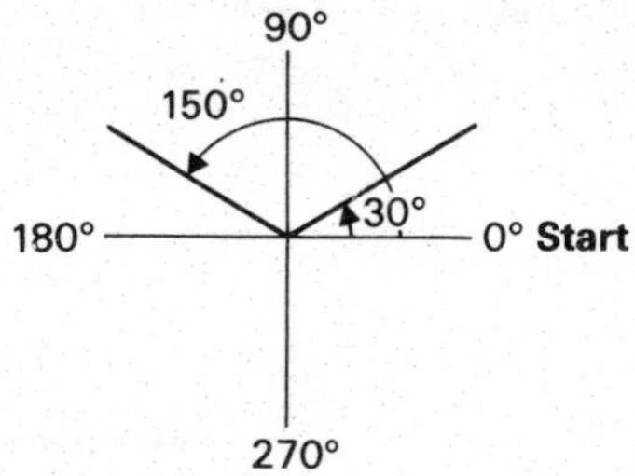

Exercise

1 Find values of x such that $\sin x° = -0.574$. Copy the diagram.

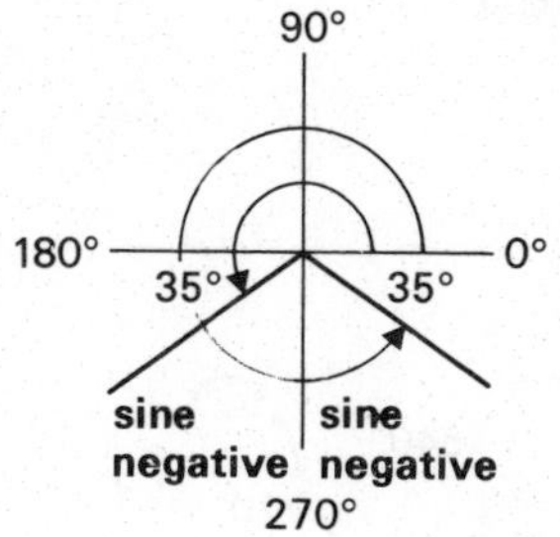

Copy and complete the working.

$\sin x° = -0.574$

Acute angle = 35° ← from tables

So $x = (180 + □)$ or $(360 - □)$

$= □$ or □

For each of the following draw a diagram and write the working as above.

2 $\sin x° = 0.643$	**3** $\sin x° = -0.866$	**4** $\sin x° = -0.766$
5 $\sin x° = 0.777$	**6** $\sin x° = -0.259$	**7** $\sin x° = 0.974$
8 $\sin x° = -0.5$	**9** $\sin x° = -0.156$	**10** $\sin x° = 0.910$

Continue with Section L

L Extending the graph

The graph of sin $x°$ from $x = 0$ to $x = 360$ looks like this ⟶

This is the 'basic design' of sin $x°$.

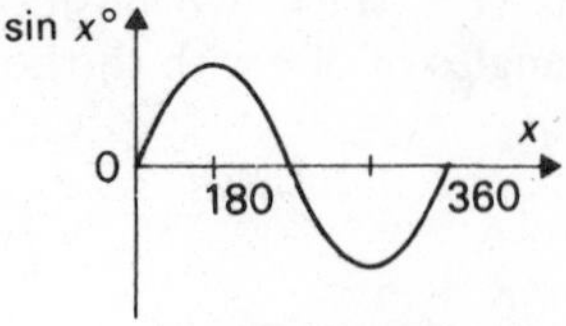

The **period** is 360°

The graph can be extended as shown below.

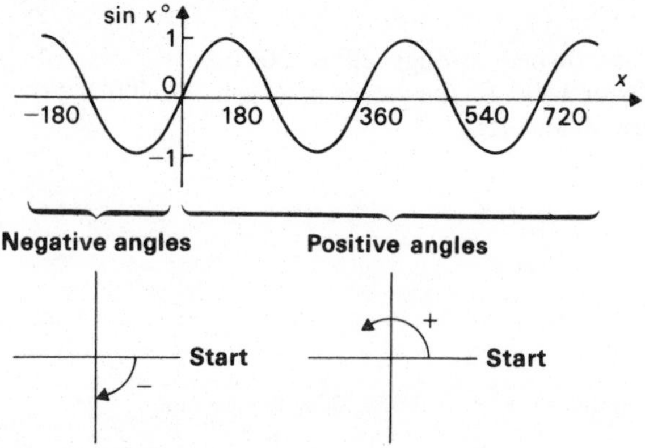

Negative angles are drawn CLOCKWISE from the **Start**

Positive angles are drawn ANTICLOCKWISE from the **Start**

We can use the graph to help us find the value of sin 410°.

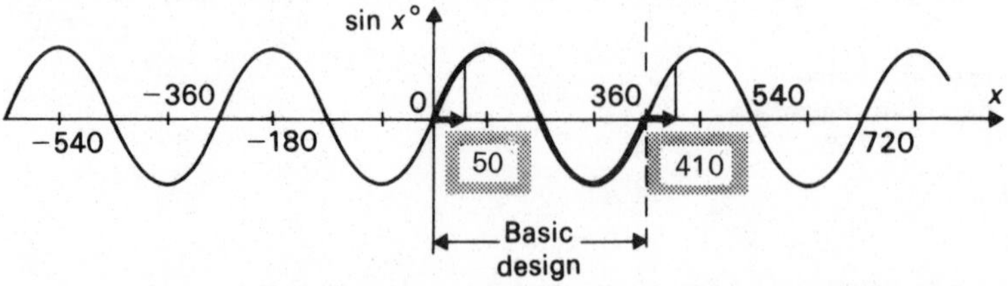

From the graph, we see that 410° is 50° greater than 360°, and so is 50° into the next repeat of the basic design.

So sin 410° = sin 50° = 0.766   (from tables)

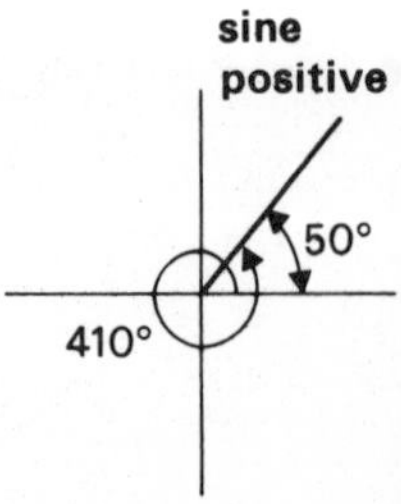

Another method is to use a rotating-arm diagram.

410° is 50° greater than 360°, and so lies where the sine is positive.

Acute angle = 50°

So sin 410° = sin 50° = 0.766

In the same way

sin 50° = sin 410° = sin 770° = sin 1130° = sin 1490°, etc.

sin 410° → (50° + 360°)

sin 770° → (50° + 2 × 360°)

sin 1130° → (50° + 3 × 360°)

sin 1490° → (50° + 4 × 360°)

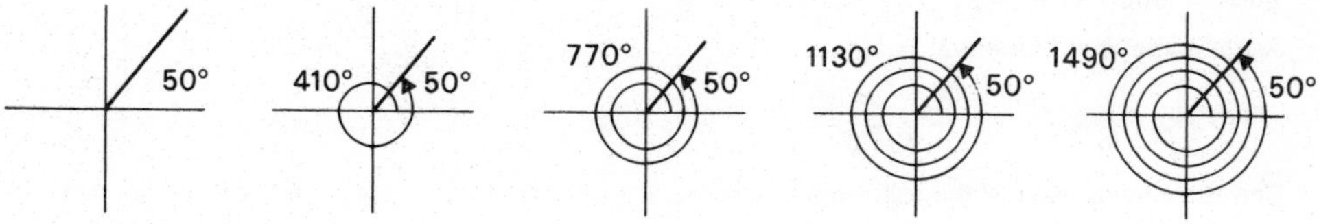

Also

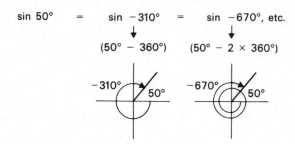

sin 50° = sin −310° = sin −670°, etc.

sin −310° → (50° − 360°)

sin −670° → (50° − 2 × 360°)

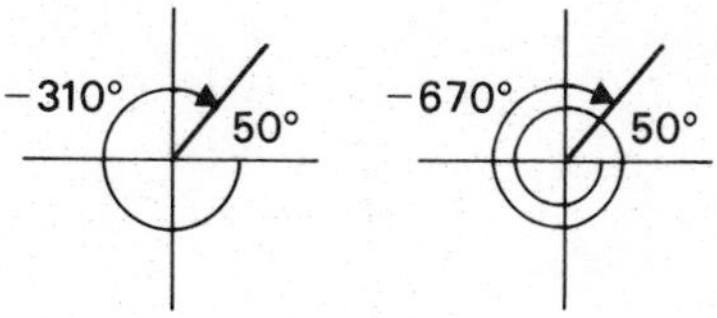

Some of these angles are shown on the graph below.

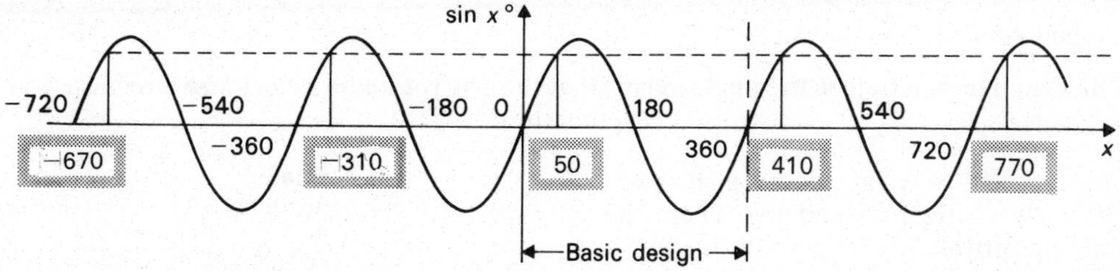

To find the sine of an angle which is not between 0° and 360° add or subtract suitable multiples of 360° until you obtain an angle between 0° and 360°. The sine of this angle may be calculated in the usual way.

Example

Find a point on the basic design between 0° and 360° which corresponds to
(a) sin 750° (b) sin −890°

(a) $750° = 360° + 390°$
$= 360° + 360° + 30°$

$\boxed{\sin 750° = \sin 30°}$

(b) $890° = 360° + 530°$
$= 360° + 360° + 170°$

$\boxed{\sin (-890)° = \sin (-170)°}$

Exercise

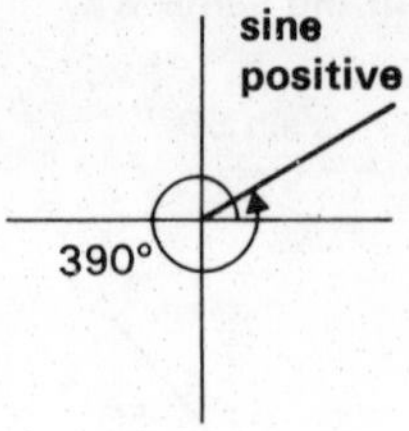

1 Find sin 390°.
Copy the diagram.
Copy and complete the working.

390° = 360° + 30°

Acute angle with horizontal = □

sin 390° = sin □

= □

2 Find the sine of each of the following angles.

(a) 420° (b) 480° (c) 530° (d) 900°

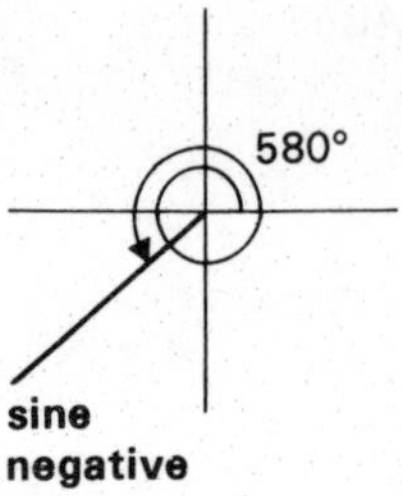

3 Find sin 580°.
Copy the diagram and working.

580° = 360° + 220°

Acute angle with horizontal = □

sin 580° = − sin □

= − □

4 Find the sine of each of the following:

(a) 600° (b) 585° (c) 645° (d) 630°

Example

To find sin (−585)°

The negative sign before the **angle** means that the arm rotates in a **clockwise** direction from the start.

585° = 360° + 225° so the arm is 45° **above** the horizontal and lies where the sine is **positive**.

Acute angle with horizontal = 45°

sin (−585)° = sin 45°

= 0.707

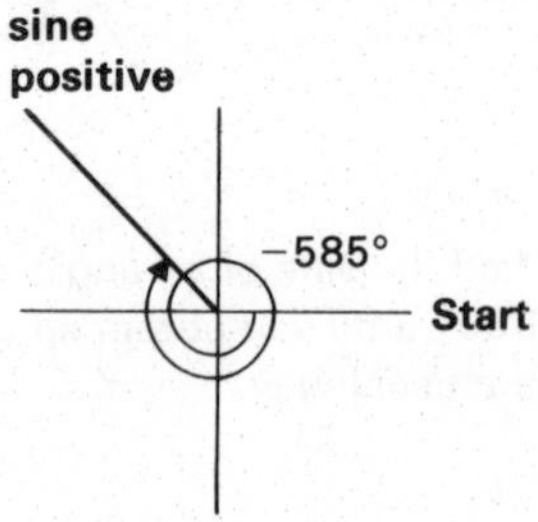

Exercise

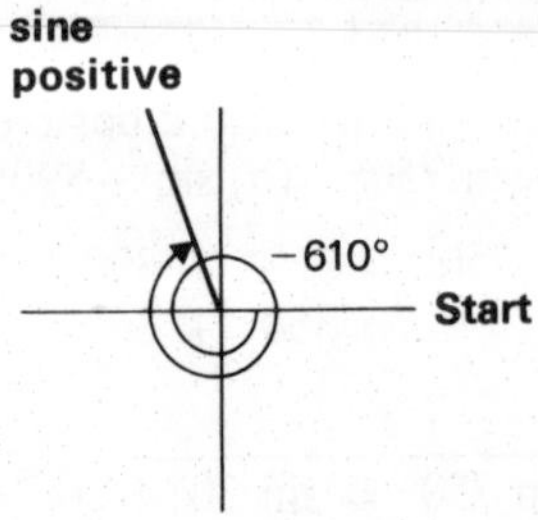

5 Find sin (− 610)°

Copy and complete:

610° = 360° + 250°

Acute angle with horizontal = □

sin (−610)° = sin □

= □

6 Find the sine of each of the following:

(a) $-575°$ (b) $-648°$ (c) $-702°$ (d) $-630°$

Example

Find $\sin(-500)°$.

$500° = 360° + 90° + 50°$

So the arm is 40° **below the horizontal** and lies where the sine is **negative.**

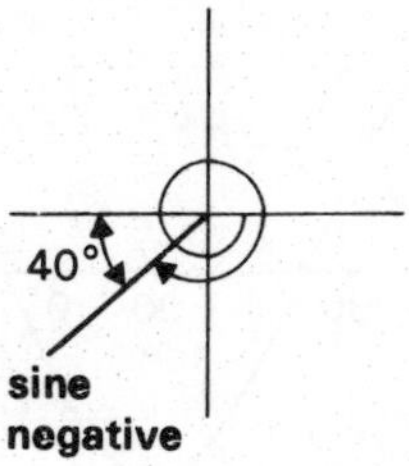

Acute angle $= 40°$

$\sin(-500)° = -\sin 40°$

$= -0.643$

$\sin(-500)° = -0.643$

Exercise

7 Find $\sin(-510)°$. Copy and complete:

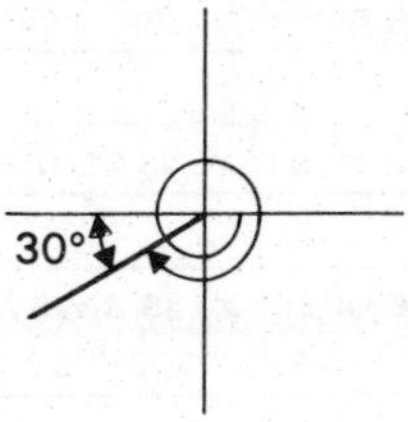

$510° = 360° + 90° + 60°$

Acute angle $= \square$

$\sin(-510)° = -\sin \square$

$= -\square$

$\sin(-510)° = \square$

8 Find the sine of each of the following angles:

(a) $-513°$ (b) $-477°$ (c) $-394°$ (d) $-418°$

Continue with Section M

M Related graphs

The basic pattern of the function $\sin x°$ is drawn below.

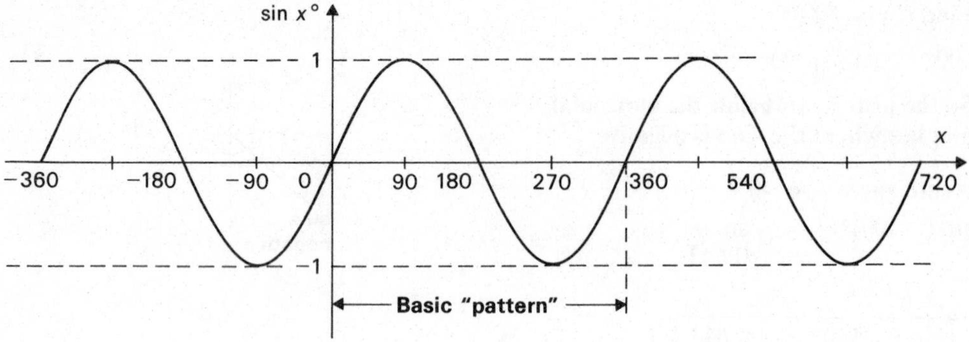

Important points to know are:

(a) The value of $\sin x°$ can never be greater than 1 or less than -1.

(b) The value of $\sin x°$ is zero at 0°, 180°, and 360°.

(c) The value of $\sin x°$ is always positive between 0° and 180° and always negative between 180° and 360°.

(d) The function repeats every 360°, so the period of the function is 360°.

In this section we shall investigate some of the possible variations to the basic pattern.

Exercise

Use 2 mm squared paper for each of the following exercises.

1 (a) Use the following table of values to draw the graph of $y = \sin x°$.
Scales: horizontal 1 cm = 30°; vertical 4 cm = 1 unit.

$x°$	0	30	60	90	120	150	180	210	240	270	300	330	360
$\sin x°$	0	0.5	0.87	1.0	0.87	0.5	0	−0.5	−0.87	−1.0	−0.87	−0.5	0

(b) Now copy and complete the following table and use the values to draw the graph of $y = 2 \sin x°$ on the same axes.

$x°$	0	30	60	90	120	150	180	210	240	270	300	330	360
$\sin x°$	0	0.5	0.87	1.0	0.87		0	−0.5	−0.87	−1.0			
$2 \sin x°$	0	1.0	1.74	2.0				−1.0	−1.74				

Compare the graphs of $\sin x°$ and $2 \sin x°$.

(i) What do you notice about the greatest and least values of $y = 2 \sin x°$?

(ii) What is the period of $\sin x°$, $2 \sin x°$?

(c) Draw the graph of $y = \frac{1}{2} \sin x°$ on the same axes.

(i) What are the greatest and least values of $y = \frac{1}{2} \sin x°$?

(ii) What is the period of $y = \frac{1}{2} \sin x°$?

2 Copy and complete the table.

Function	Period	Greatest value	Least value
$\sin x°$	360°	1	−1
$2 \sin x°$	360°		
$\frac{1}{2} \sin x°$	360°		

Compared with the graph of $y = \sin x°$ we see that

(a) the values of **2** $\sin x°$ are **twice** the corresponding values of $y = \sin x°$;

(b) the values of $y = \frac{1}{2} \sin x°$ are **half** the corresponding values of $y = \sin x°$;

(c) the period is the same for each function.

In general, if $y = p \sin x°$ then each value of $\sin x°$ is multiplied by p. The greatest value is p and the least value is $-p$. The period is the same as that for $y = \sin x°$.

3 Write down the greatest and least values for

(a) $y = 5 \sin x°$ (b) $y = 0.8 \sin x°$ (c) $y = b \sin x°$

4 The following diagrams represent the graphs of $y = a \sin x°$. What is the value of a in each?

(a)

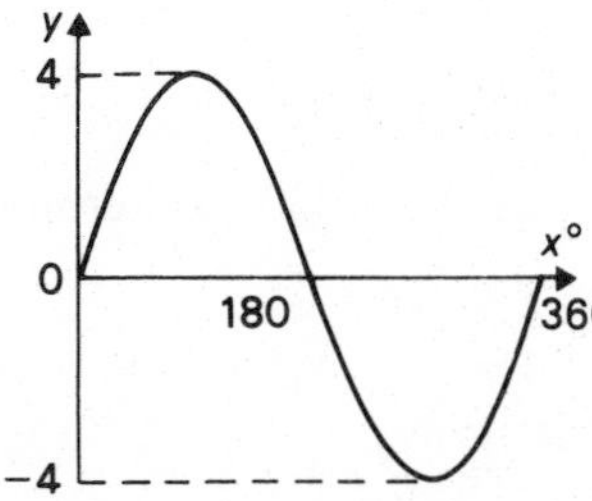

(b)

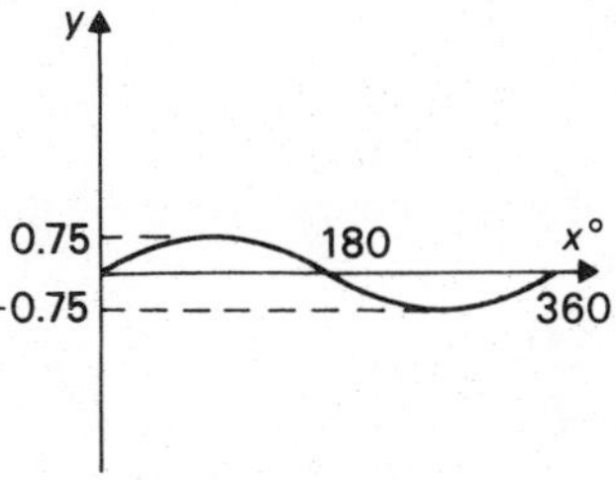

(c)

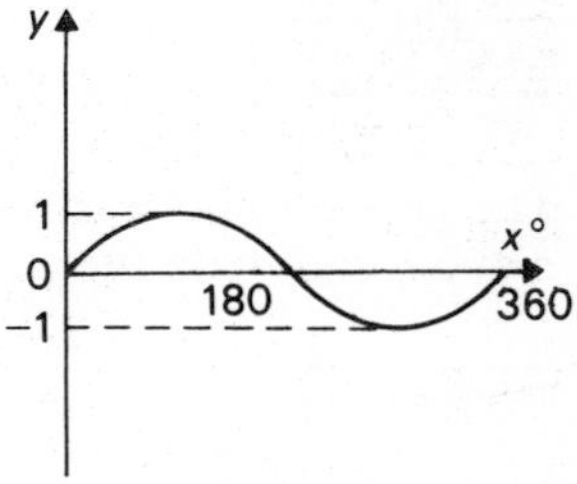

For the next question you will need a sheet of 2 mm squared paper.
Scales: horizontal, 1 cm = 30°; vertical, 4 cm = 1 unit.

5 (a) Use this table to draw the graph of $y = \sin 2x°$; $0 \leq x \leq 180$.

x	0	15	30	45	60	75	90	105	120	135	150	165	180
$2x$	0	30	60	90	120	150	180	210	240	270	300	330	360
$y = \sin 2x°$	0	0.5	0.87	1.0	0.87	0.5	0	−0.5	−0.87	−1.0	−0.87	−0.5	0

(b) Make up a table of values for $y = \sin \frac{1}{2}x°$; $0 \leq x \leq 720$, and draw the curve on the same axes.

Copy and complete the table.

Function	Period	Greatest value	Least value
$\sin x°$	360°	1	−1
$\sin 2x°$			
$\sin \frac{1}{2}x°$			

When we compare the graphs of $y = \sin 2x°$ and $y = \sin \frac{1}{2}x°$ with the graph of $y = \sin x°$ we see that

(a) the period of $y = \sin 2x°$ is 180° (i.e. $360 \div 2 = 180$) which is half the period of $y = \sin x°$;
(b) the period of $y = \sin \frac{1}{2}x°$ is 720° (i.e. $360 \div \frac{1}{2} = 720$) which is twice the period of $y = \sin x°$;
(c) the greatest and least values are the same for each (i.e. ±1).

So if $y = \sin qx°$ the period of the function is $(360 \div q)°$, and the greatest and least values of the function are ±1.

Exercise

6 What is the period of each of the following?

(a) $y = \sin x°$ (b) $y = \sin 3x°$ (c) $y = \sin 5x°$
(d) $y = \sin \frac{3}{4}x°$ (e) $y = \sin 0.8x°$ (f) $y = \sin 1.2x°$

In general, if $y = p \sin qx$

p determines the greatest and least values

$360° \div q$ determines the period

Example

The greatest and least values of $y = p \sin qx°$ are ±2.8 and the period is 450°. Determine *p* and *q* and write the equation.

(a) $p = 2.8$

(b) $\dfrac{360}{q} = 450$

$q = \dfrac{360}{450}$

$= \dfrac{4}{5}$

The equation is $y = 2.8 \sin \frac{4}{5}x° = 2.8 \sin 0.8x°$.

Exercise

7 The table lists various values for a function of the form $y = p \sin qx°$. Determine *p* and *q* and write the appropriate equation for each.

Greatest and least values	Period
(a) ±2	360°
(b) $\pm\frac{1}{2}$	180°
(c) ±1	240°
(d) ±10	540°
(e) ±0.7	225°

8 The diagrams represent graphs of $y = p \sin qx°$.

(a)

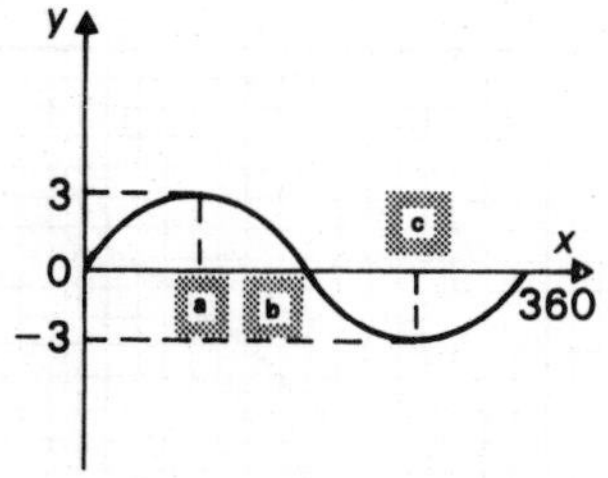

(b)

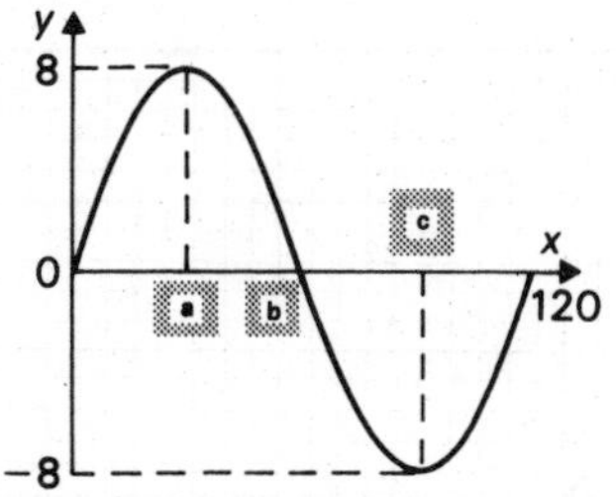

(c)

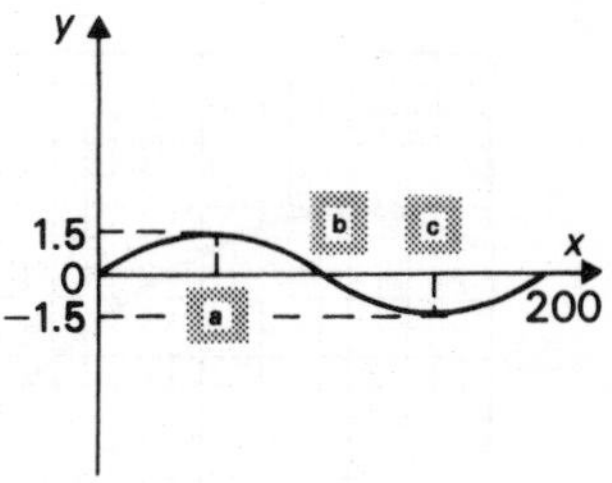

(i) Determine p and q and write the equation for each graph.

(ii) Write the angles indicated by the letters a, b, and c on each axis.

Example

To draw the graph of $y = \sin x°$ and, on the same axes, the graph of $y = \sin (30 + x)°$, make up a table of values:

x	0	30	60	90	120	150	180	210	240	270	300	330	360
$\sin x°$	0	0.5	0.87	1.0	0.87	0.5	0	−0.5	−0.87	−1.0	−0.87	−0.5	0
$30 + x$	30	60	90	120	150	180	210	240	270	300	330	360	390
$\sin (30 + x)°$	0.5	0.87	1.0	0.87	0.5	0	−0.5	−0.87	−1.0	−0.87	−0.5	0	0.5

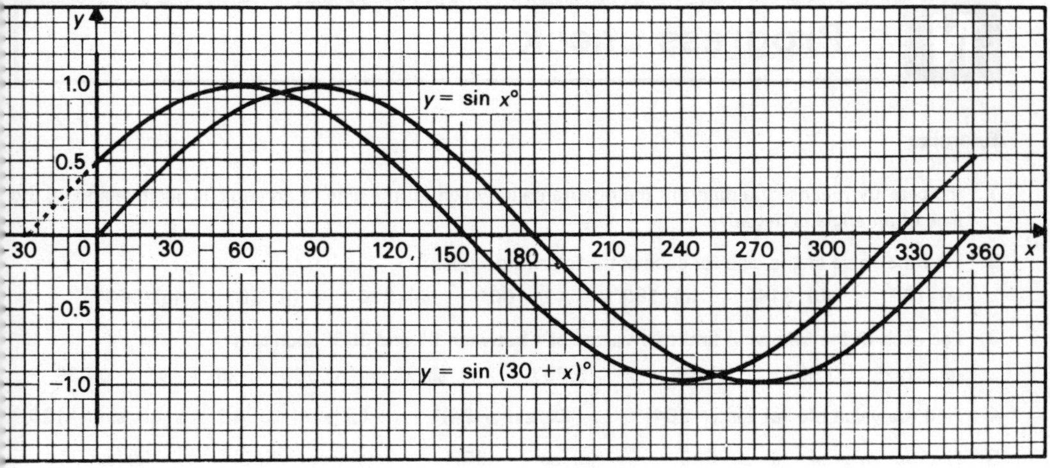

By comparing the two graphs we see that the graph of $y = \sin (30 + x)°$ is the same shape as the graph of $y = \sin x°$, but has been displaced to the left by 30°.

Exercise

9 What is the equation of the graph below? What is the period of the curve?

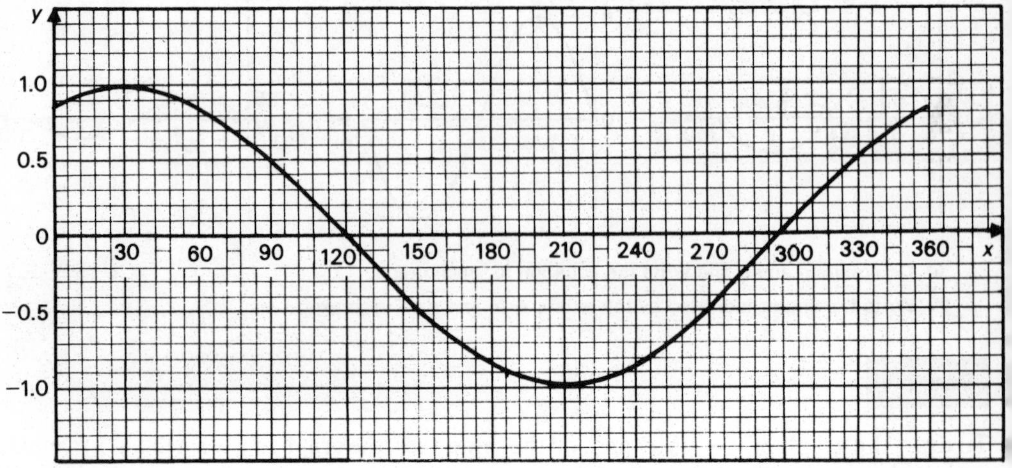

10 Make up a table of values for $y = \sin (x - 30)°$ and draw the graph. What effect does subtracting 30 from x have on the position of the graph? What is its period?

11 Draw the graph of $y = \sin (90 + x)°$. (This is the graph of the cosine function which you will meet in a later Unit.)

Continue with Section N

N Progress check

Exercise

1 Indicate by means of a diagram the quadrants in which (a) the sine of an angle is positive and (b) the sine of an angle is negative.

2 Find the value of the sine for each of the following angles:

(a) 168° (b) 314° (c) 180° (d) 100° (e) 230° (f) 90° (g) 360°

3 For each of the following find two values of x between 0° and 360° such that:

(a) $\sin x° = 0.584$ (b) $\sin x° = -0.857$ (c) $\sin x° = -0.669$ (d) $\sin x° = 0.939$.

4 Find the value of: (a) $\sin (-204)°$ (b) $\sin (-24)°$ (c) $\sin (-304)°$ (d) $\sin (-120)°$

5 Find the value of: (a) $\sin 680°$ (b) $\sin (-490)°$ (c) $\sin (-560)°$ (d) $\sin 740°$

6 What are the greatest and least values of: (a) $y = 7 \sin x$ (b) $y = \frac{3}{4} \sin x$.

7 What is the period of: (a) $y = 2 \sin 3x$ (b) $y = \frac{2}{3} \sin \frac{3}{2} x$.

8 Draw the graphs of (a) $y = \sin (x + 40)°$ and (b) $y = \sin (x - 40)°$ for $0 \leq x \leq 360$.

Tell your teacher that you have finished this Unit

UNIT M7

Equations of Straight Lines

A Gradient

The picture shows an aeroplane climbing after take-off.

We measure the **steepness** of the slope of its path like this:

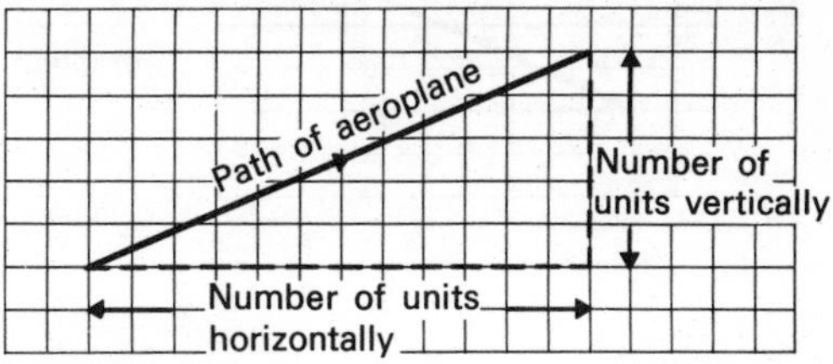

$$\text{Steepness} = \frac{\text{Number of units vertically}}{\text{Number of units horizontally}} = \frac{5}{12}$$

Exercise

1 Here is another aeroplane climbing after take-off. Its flight path has been drawn on the grid beside it.

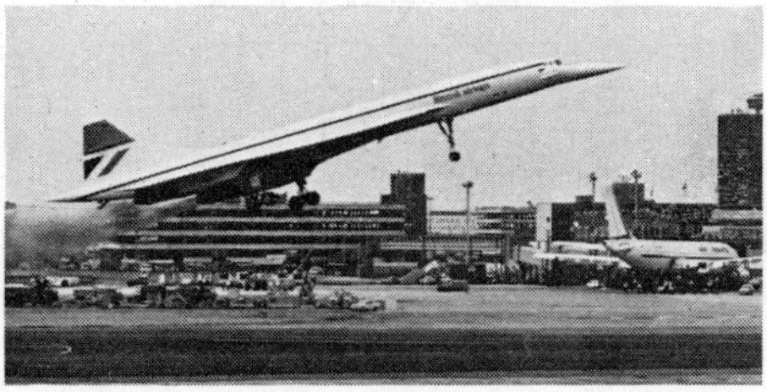

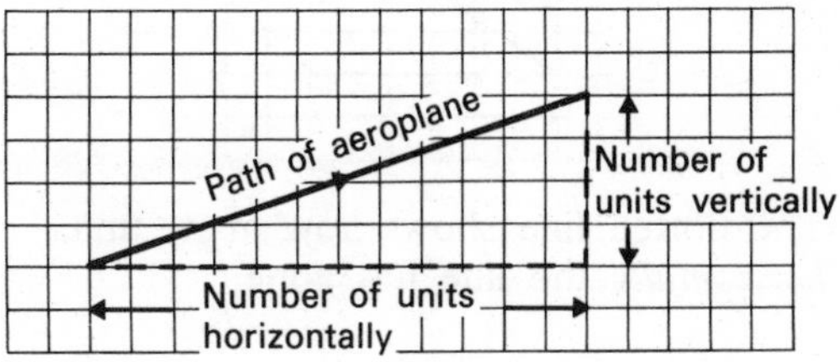

Copy and complete: $\text{steepness} = \dfrac{\text{number of units vertically}}{\text{number of units horizontally}} = \dfrac{\square}{\square}$

It is usual to call the steepness of the aeroplane's path the **gradient** of its path.

In this case the gradient is $\dfrac{4}{12} = \dfrac{1}{3}$.

2 This picture shows a skier being taken by chair-lift to the top of a ski-slope.

We can measure the gradient of the chairlift wire by drawing it on a grid.

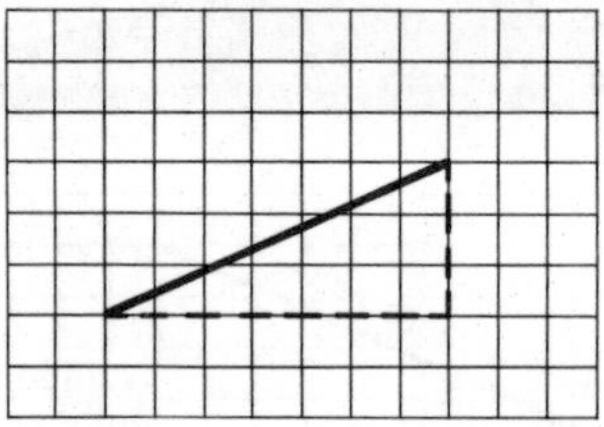

Copy and complete:

$$\text{gradient} = \frac{\text{number of units vertically}}{\text{number of units horizontally}}$$

$$= \frac{\square}{\square}$$

Example

This is how we calculate the gradient of this straight line drawn on a grid.

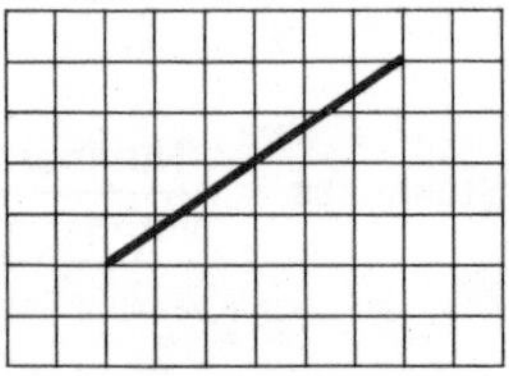

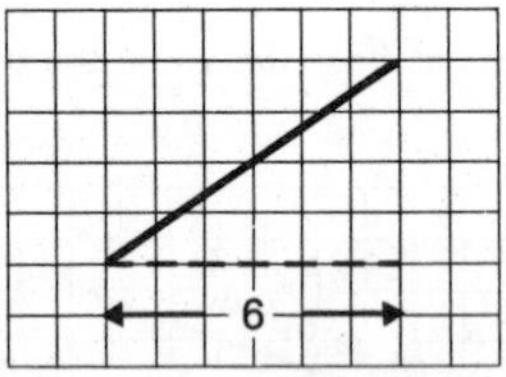

The dotted line shows how many units *horizontally* the line has gone.

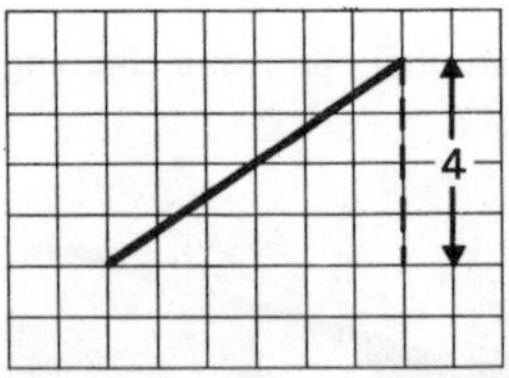

The dotted line shows how many units *vertically* the line has gone.

$$\text{gradient} = \frac{\text{number of units vertically}}{\text{number of units horizontally}}$$

$$= \frac{4}{6}$$

$$= \frac{2}{3}$$

Exercise

3 Find the gradient of the line in this diagram.

Copy and complete:

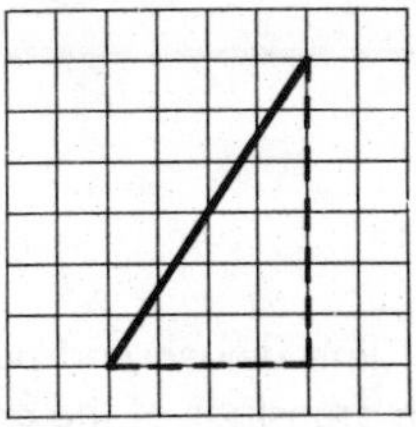

Number of units horizontally $= 4$

Number of units vertically $= \square$

$$\text{Gradient} = \frac{\text{number of units vertically}}{\text{number of units horizontally}}$$

$$= \frac{\square}{4} = \frac{\square}{\square}$$

In the same way, find the gradient of each of the lines below:

4

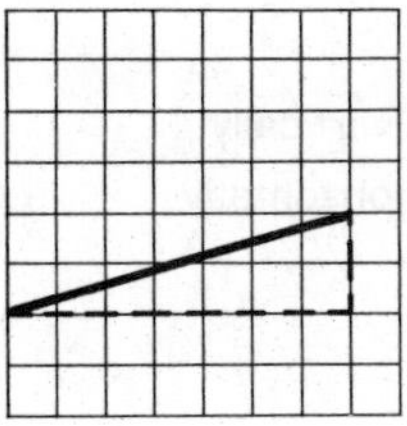

5

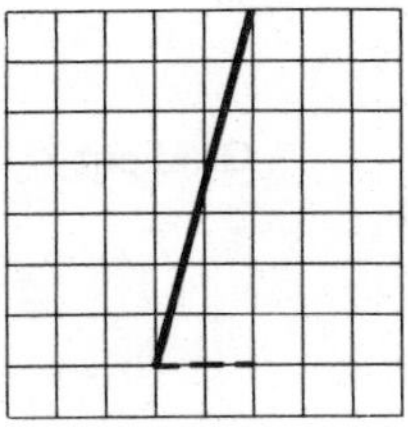

6

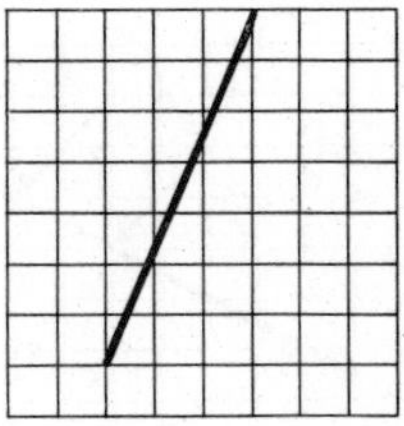

7

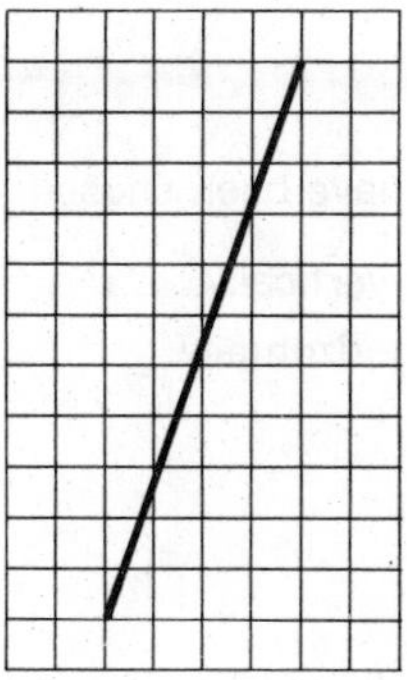

8

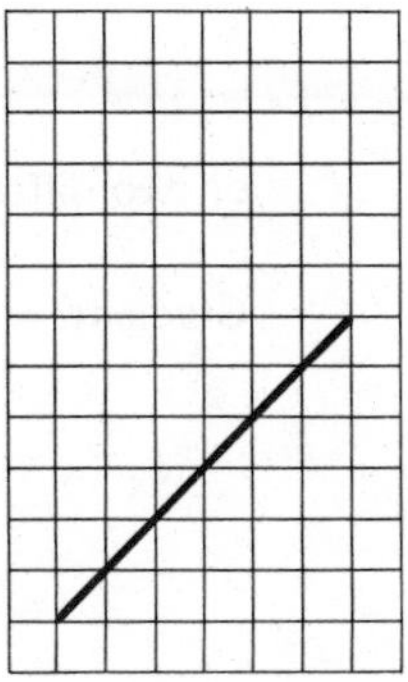

9

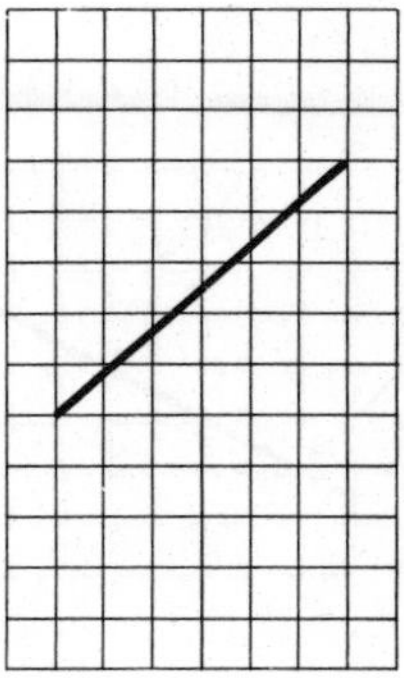

Continue with Section B

B Finding gradients

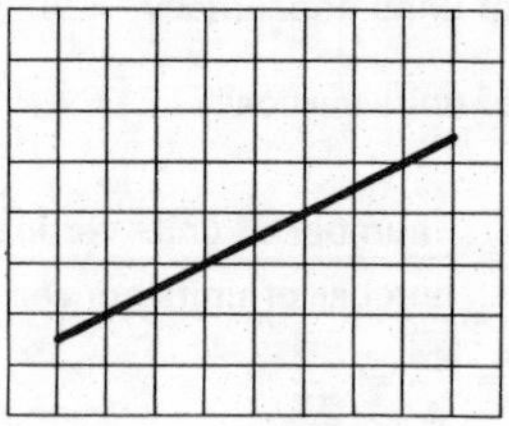

Here is a straight line whose end points are not exactly at the crossings of the grid lines.

To find its gradient two suitable points are chosen on the line and dotted lines are drawn.

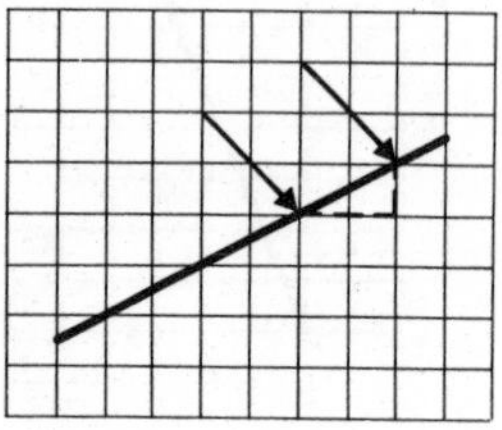

$$\text{Gradient} = \frac{\text{number of units vertically}}{\text{number of units horizontally}}$$

$$= \frac{1}{2}$$

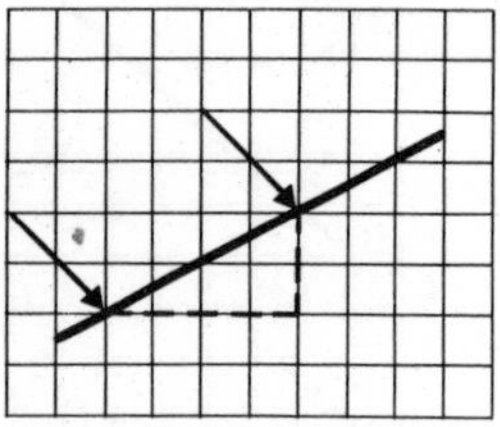

or two different points could have been chosen:

$$\text{Gradient} = \frac{\text{number of units vertically}}{\text{number of units horizontally}}$$

$$= \frac{2}{4}$$

$$= \frac{1}{2}$$

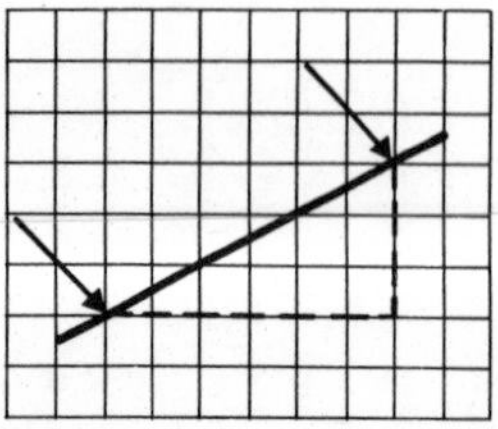

or another two points could have been chosen:

$$\text{Gradient} = \frac{\text{number of units vertically}}{\text{number of units horizontally}}$$

$$= \frac{3}{6}$$

$$= \frac{1}{2}$$

This shows that the gradient of a line is the same no matter which two suitable points are chosen.

Exercise

1

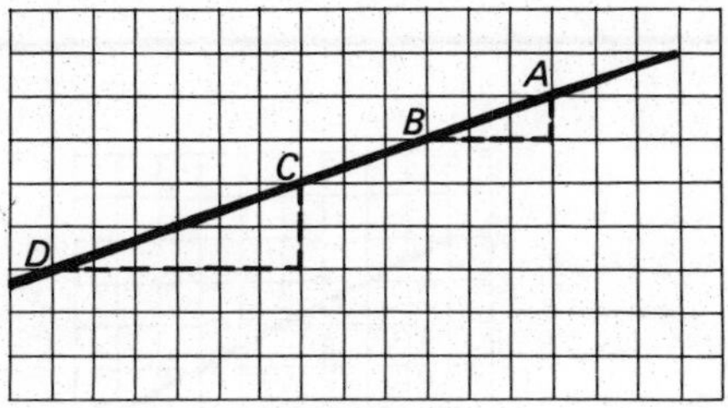

Copy and complete:
Using the points *A* and *B*,
the gradient of the line = ▭/▭

Using the points *C* and *D*,
the gradient of the line = ▭/▭
= ▭/▭

2

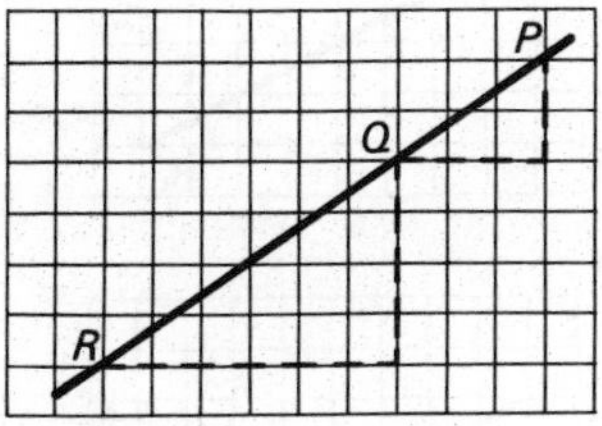

Copy and complete:
Using the points *P* and *Q*,
the gradient of the line = ▭/▭

Using the points *R* and *Q*,
the gradient of the line = ▭/▭
= ▭/▭

Take *two* suitable points on each of the following lines (that is, where the line passes through crossings of the grid) and find the gradient of each line.

3

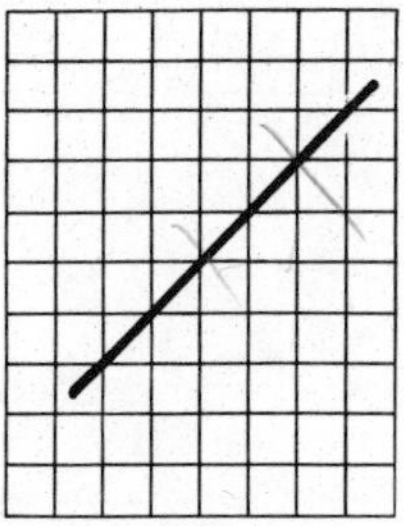

4

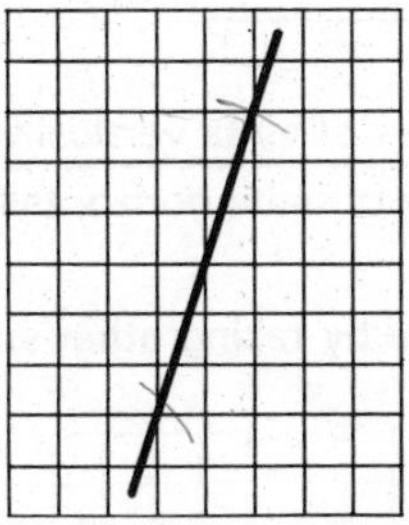

5

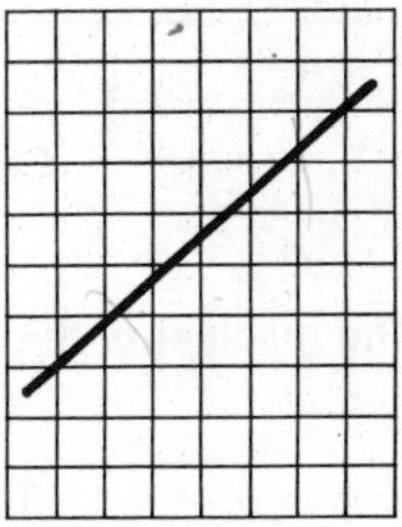

6

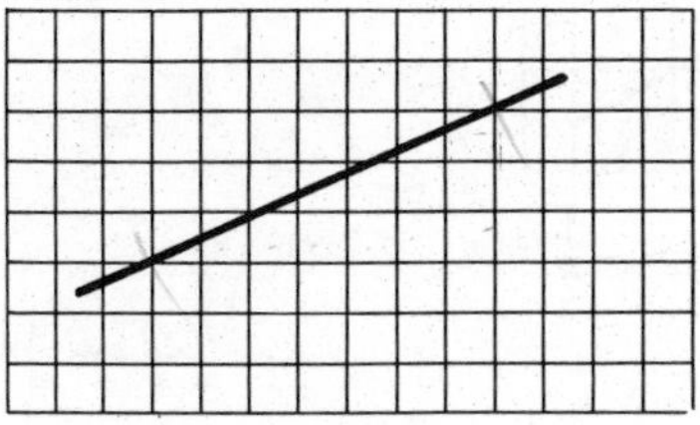

7

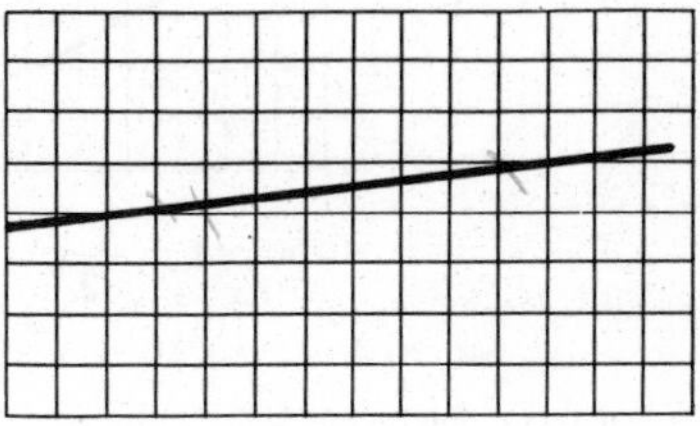

Continue with Section C

C Negative gradients

A straight line is drawn in the grid opposite. Notice that the line is sloping *downwards* from left to right.

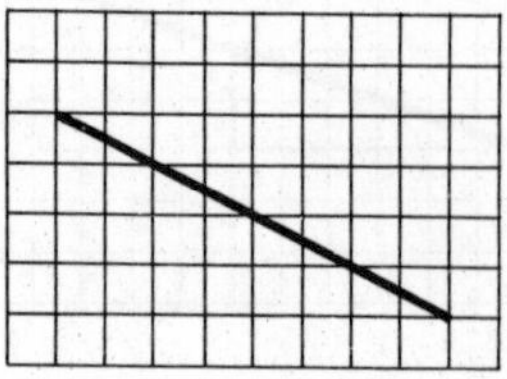

The dotted line shows how many units horizontally the line has gone.

Number of units horizontally = 8

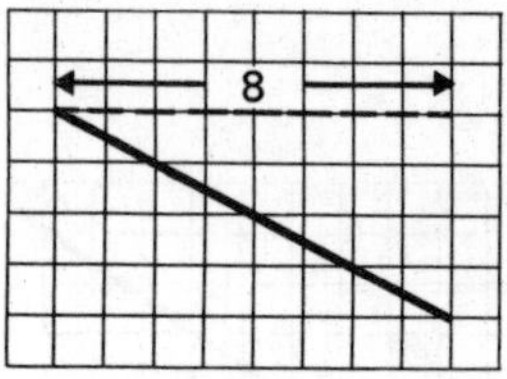

This dotted line shows how many units vertically the line has gone. The line has gone *down* 4 units.

Number of units vertically = −4

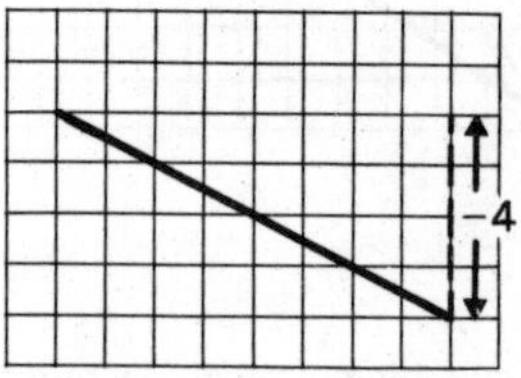

The negative sign indicates a *downwards* direction.

$$\text{Gradient} = \frac{\text{number of units vertically}}{\text{number of units horizontally}} = \frac{-4}{8} = -\frac{1}{2}$$

The gradient of the line may be found by taking other suitable points.

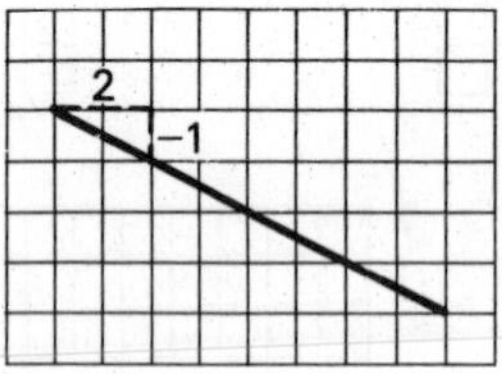

or

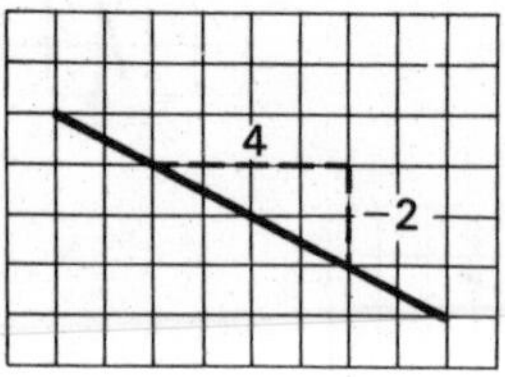

$\text{Gradient} = \frac{-1}{2} = -\frac{1}{2}$ $\text{Gradient} = \frac{-2}{4} = -\frac{1}{2}$

Lines sloping *upwards* from left to right have a positive gradient:

Lines sloping *downwards* from left to right have a negative gradient:

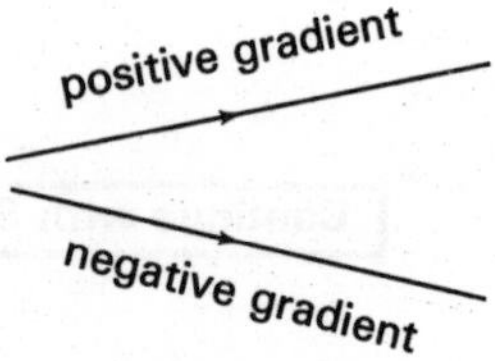

Exercise

1

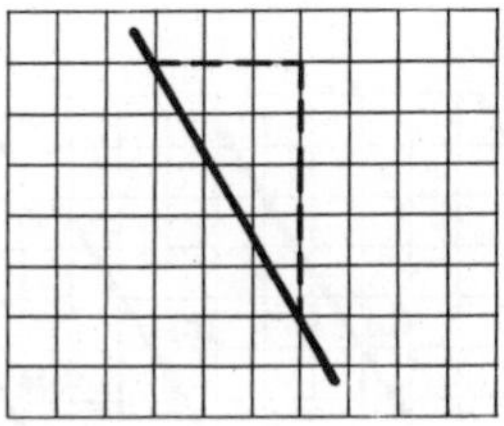

Copy and complete:

Number of units horizontally = ▒

Number of units vertically = −5

Gradient = $\frac{-5}{▒} = -\frac{▒}{▒}$

In the same way find the gradient of each of the following lines:

2

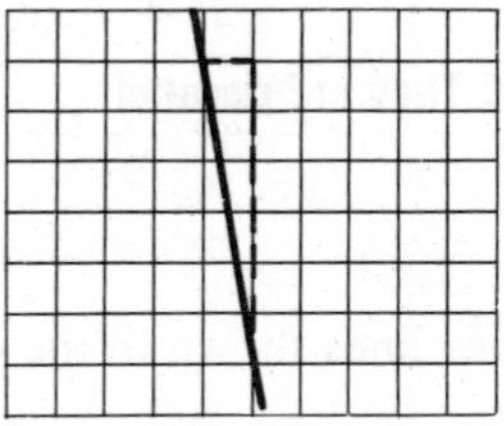

3

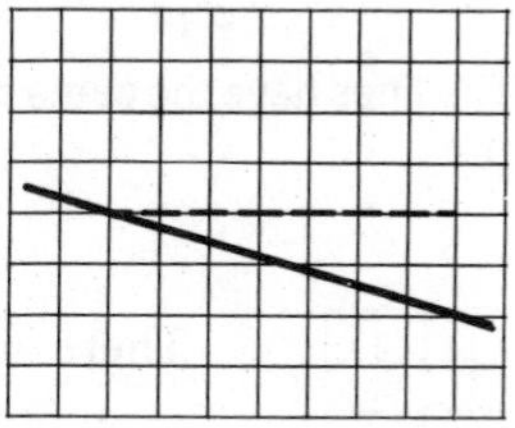

4

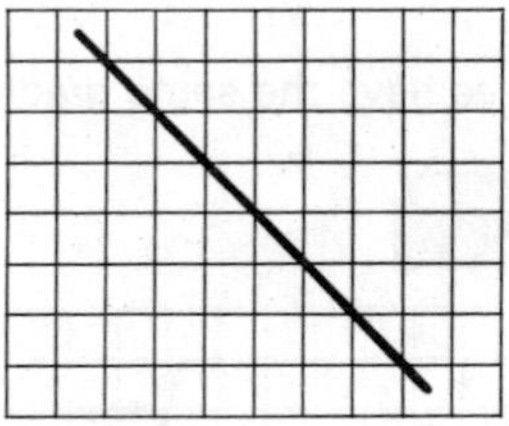

5

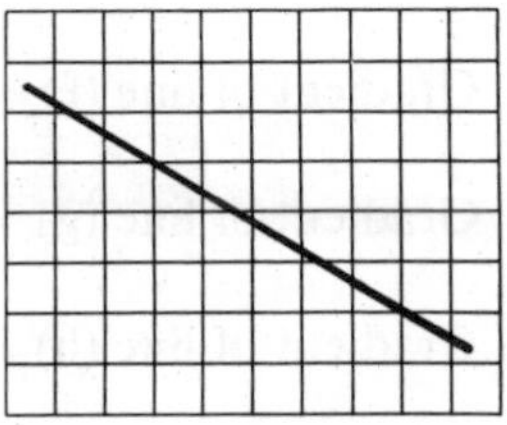

6

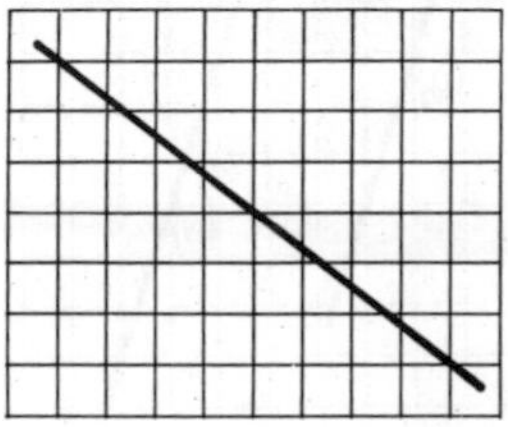

7 Find the gradient of each of the following lines:

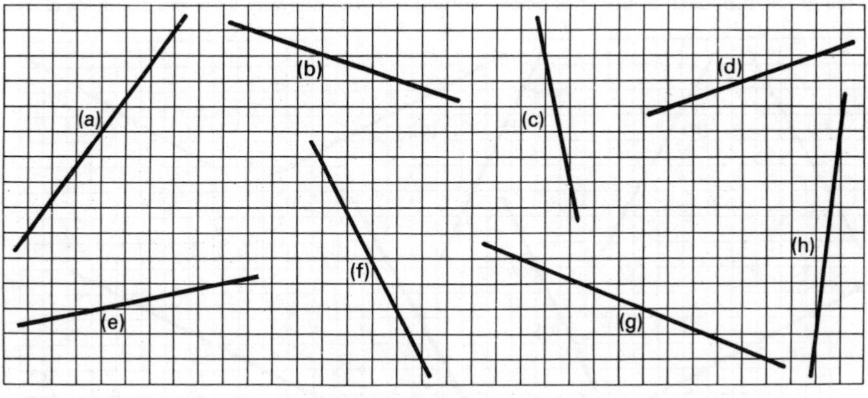

Continue with Section D

D Parallel lines

A set of four lines is shown on the grid.

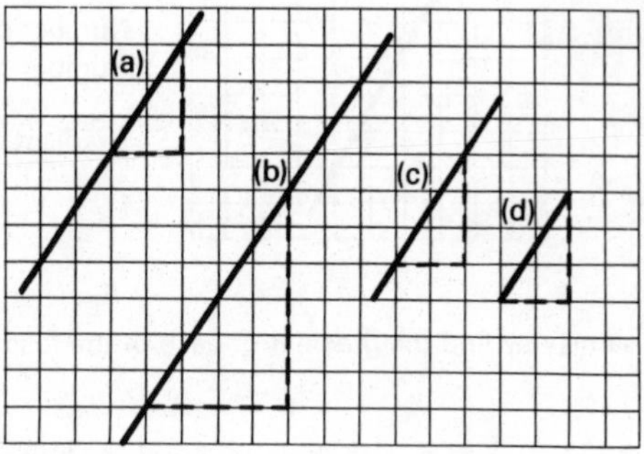

Gradient of line (a) $= \frac{3}{2}$

Gradient of line (b) $= \frac{6}{4} = \frac{3}{2}$

Gradient of line (c) $= \frac{3}{2}$

Gradient of line (d) $= \frac{3}{2}$

The lines have the same gradient. The lines have the same slope. They are **parallel.**

Example

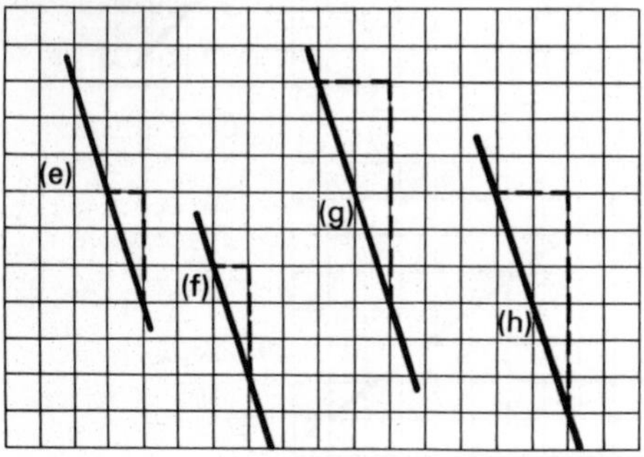

There are four lines shown in the grid.

Gradient of line (e) $= \frac{-3}{1} = -3$

Gradient of line (f) $= \frac{-3}{1} = -3$

Gradient of line (g) $= \frac{-6}{2} = -3$

Gradient of line (h) $= \frac{-6}{2} = -3$

The lines have the same gradient. They have the same slope. They are **parallel**.

Exercise

1 Find the gradient of each of the lines below, setting out your answers as in the examples above.

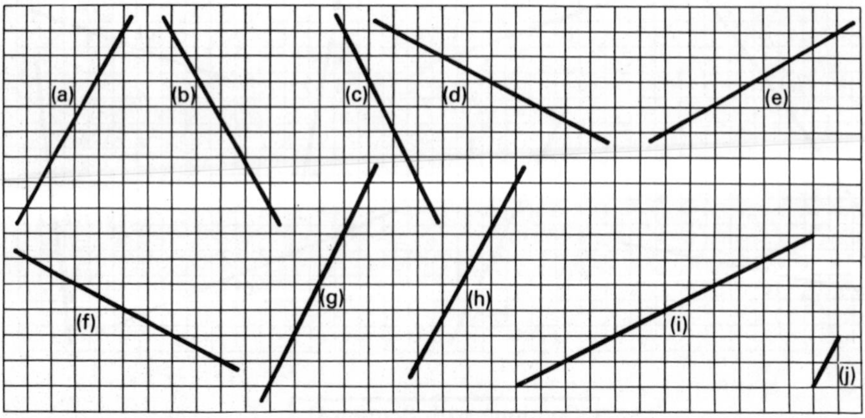

2 Which pairs of lines are parallel?

Continue with Section E

E Drawing lines of given gradient

Example

Draw a line of gradient 2 on squared paper.

$$\text{Gradient of line} = \frac{2}{1} = \frac{4}{2} = \boxed{\frac{8}{4}} = \frac{16}{8} = \ldots = \frac{\text{number of units vertically}}{\text{number of units horizontally}}$$

Step 1

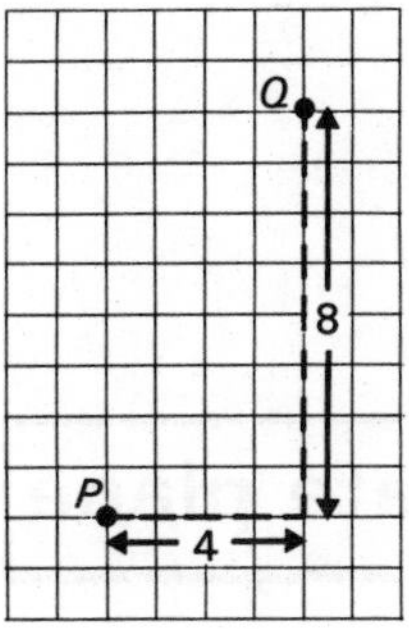

Mark a point *P* on the grid.

Go along a reasonable number of units, horizontally, say 4.

Now go up 8 units vertically.

Mark this second point *Q*.

Step 2

Join *P* to *Q*.

Extend the line both ways. ⟶

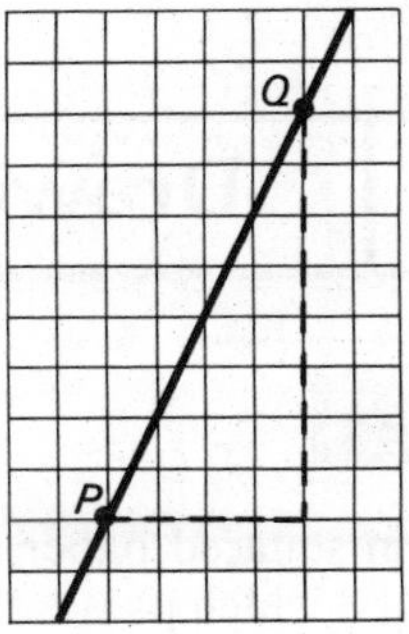

Exercise

1 Draw lines with the following gradients on $\frac{1}{2}$ cm squared paper.

(a) 3 (b) $\frac{3}{2}$ (c) $\frac{2}{3}$ (d) $\frac{5}{2}$ (e) $\frac{2}{5}$

Example

Draw a line of gradient $-\frac{2}{3}$ on squared paper.

$$\text{Gradient of line} = -\frac{2}{3} = \frac{-2}{3} = \boxed{\frac{-4}{6}} = \frac{-6}{9} = \ldots = \frac{\text{Number of units vertically}}{\text{Number of units horizontally}}$$

Step 1

Mark a point on the grid.

Go along a reasonable number of units horizontally, say 6.

Now go *down* 4 units vertically.

Mark this second point

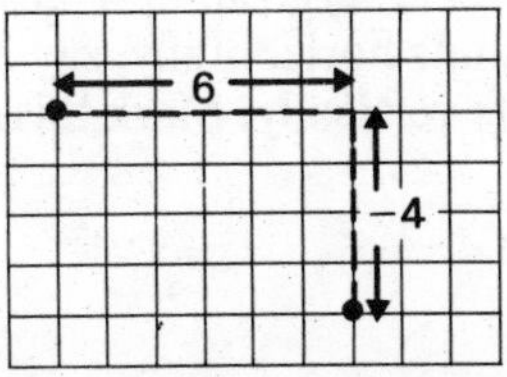

Step 2

Join the two points and extend the line both ways.

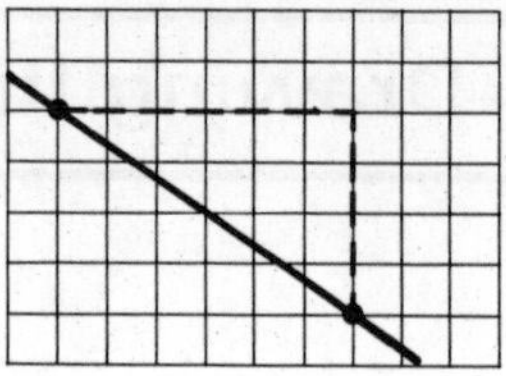

Exercise

2 Draw lines with the following gradients on $\frac{1}{2}$ cm squared paper.

(a) -2 (b) -3 (c) $-\frac{3}{2}$ (d) -5 (e) $-\frac{9}{7}$

Continue with Section F

F Drawing lines on the coordinate plane

Example

On $\frac{1}{2}$ cm squared paper draw a line with gradient 3 which passes through the point (2, 1).

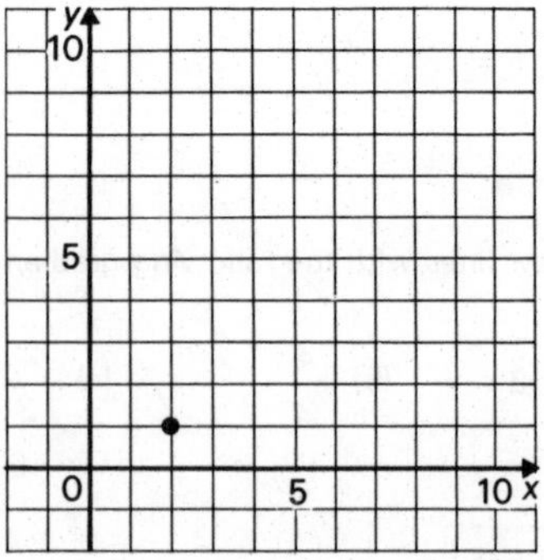

Step 1

Draw a set of axes.

Label them O, x, y and mark arrow heads as shown.

Plot the point (2, 1).

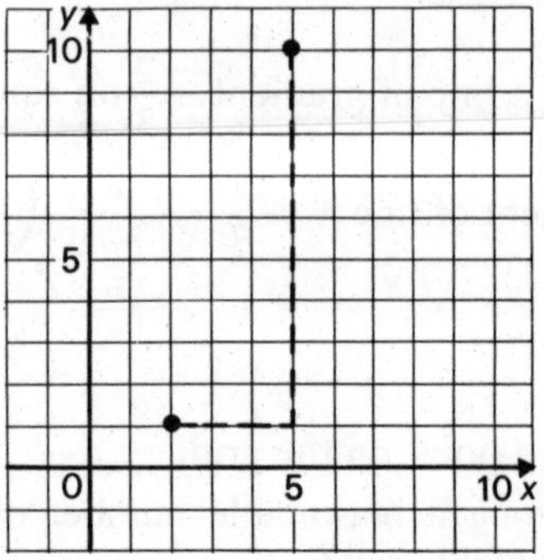

Step 2

$$\text{Gradient} = \frac{3}{1} = \frac{6}{2} = \boxed{\frac{9}{3}} = \frac{12}{4} = \ldots$$

$$= \frac{\text{number of units vertically}}{\text{number of units horizontally}}$$

From the point (2, 1) go along a reasonable number of units horizontally, say 3. Then go up 9 units vertically. Mark this second point.

Step 3

Join the two points and extend the line both ways.

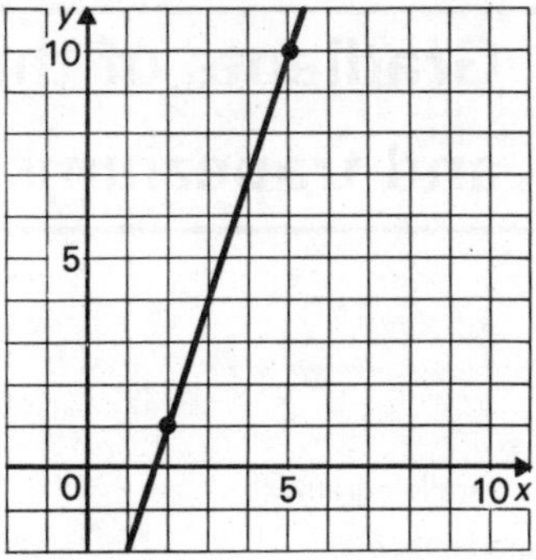

Exercise

1 (a) Copy this diagram on $\frac{1}{2}$ cm squared paper.

(b) Draw a line with gradient 2 which passes through the origin.

(c) Draw a line with gradient 2 which passes through (5, 2).

(d) Draw a line parallel to the lines already drawn and which passes through (10, 5).

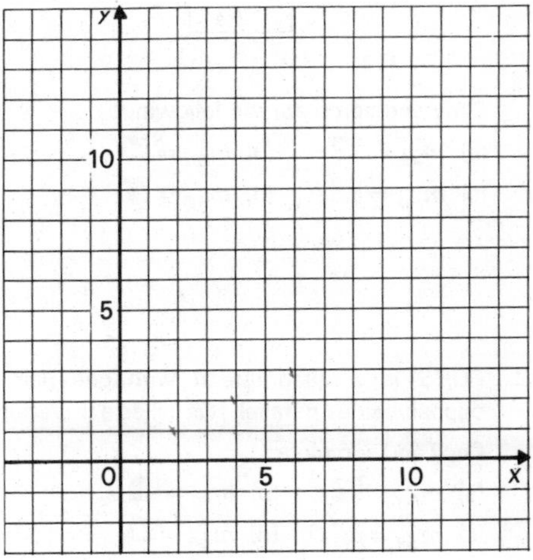

2 (a) Copy this diagram on $\frac{1}{2}$ cm squared paper.

(b) Draw a line with gradient -1 which passes through the origin.

(c) Draw a line with gradient -1 which passes through (7, 2).

(d) Draw a line parallel to the lines already drawn which passes through (3, -11).

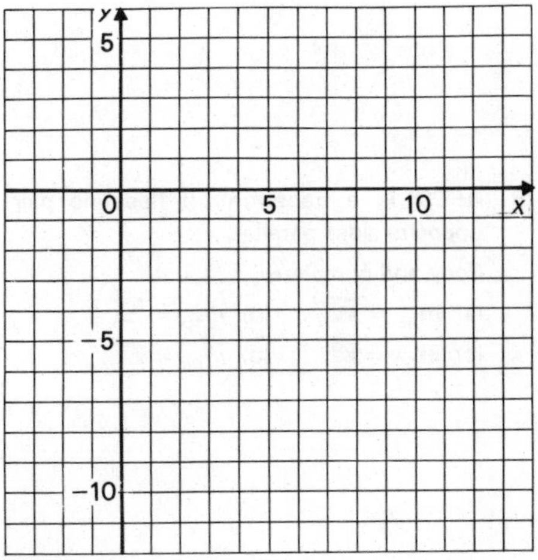

Continue with Section G

G Gradients of the sides of parallelograms and trapeziums

Exercise

1 *ABCD* is a parallelogram.

Find the gradients of:

(i) *AB* (ii) *DC* (iii) *AD* (iv) *BC*.

A shorthand way of writing the gradient of *AB* is m_{AB}

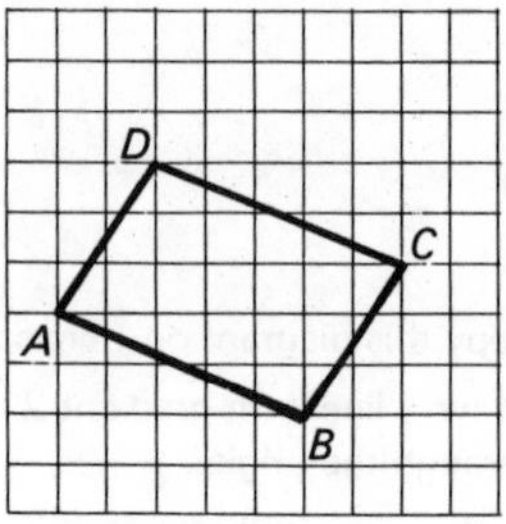

Copy and complete the following:

(a) $m_{AB} = \blacksquare$ (b) $m_{DC} = \blacksquare$

(c) $m_{AD} = \blacksquare$ (d) $m_{BC} = \blacksquare$

2 *PQRS* is a quadrilateral with one pair of opposite sides parallel. It is called a trapezium.

Copy and complete:

(a) $m_{PQ} = \blacksquare$ (b) $m_{PS} = \blacksquare$

(c) $m_{SR} = \blacksquare$ (d) $m_{QR} = \blacksquare$

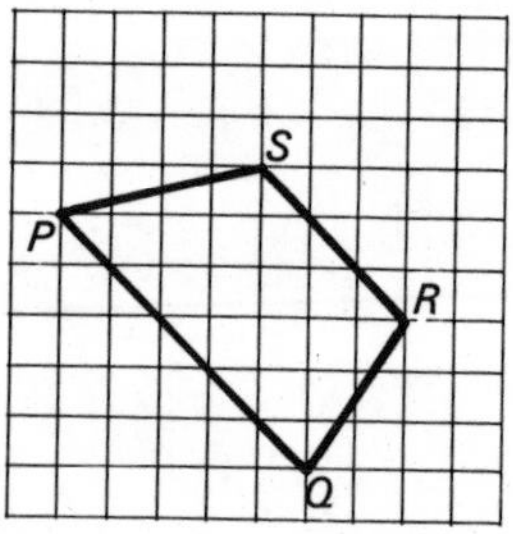

3 *ABCD* is a trapezium. It has one pair of opposite sides parallel.

Copy and complete:

(a) $m_{AB} = \blacksquare$ (b) $m_{AD} = \blacksquare$

(c) $m_{DC} = \blacksquare$ (d) $m_{CB} = \blacksquare$

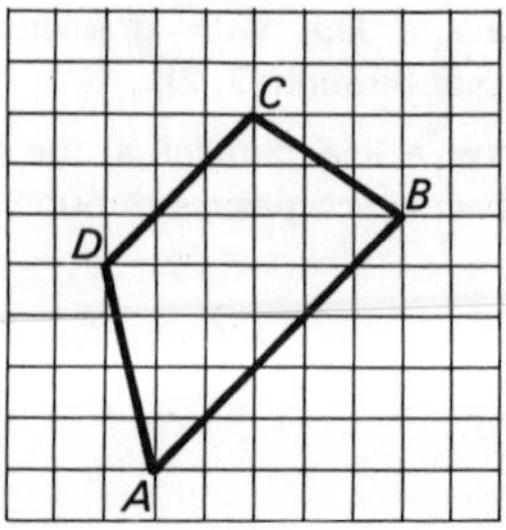

Continue with Section H

H Graph of $y = mx$

Exercise

1 The equation $y = 2x$ describes a set of points. Any point which is a member of this set has

y-coordinate equal to twice x-coordinate

So, if $x = 0$, then $y = 2 \times 0 = 0$, and (0, 0) is a member of the set.
if $x = 1$, then $y = 2 \times 1 = 2$, and (1, 2) is a member of the set.

(a) Copy and complete:
If $x = 2$, then $y = \square \times \square = \square$, and (2, $\square$) is a member of the set.
If $x = 3$, then $y = \square \times \square = \square$, and (3, $\square$) is a member of the set.
Other members of the set are (4, $\square$), (5, $\square$), (6, $\square$).

(b) Copy the grid on $\frac{1}{2}$ cm squared paper and plot the points from (a) on the grid.

Draw a straight line through the points and label the line $y = 2x$.

Check that the gradient of the line $y = 2x$ is $\frac{2}{1} = 2$

Using m as shorthand for gradient, we can write

$m = 2$

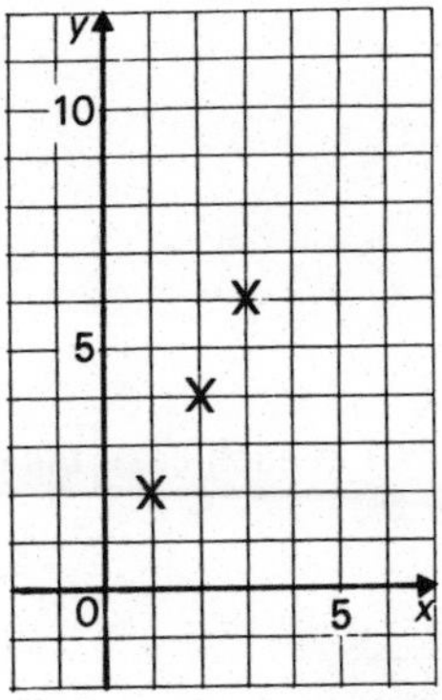

2 The equation $y = \frac{1}{2}x$ describes another set of points. Any point which is a member of this set has

y-coordinate equal to half of x-coordinate

So, if $x = 0$, then $y = \frac{1}{2}$ of $0 = 0$, and (0, 0) is a member of the set;
if $x = 2$, then $y = \frac{1}{2}$ of $2 = 1$, and (2, 1) is a member of the set.

(a) Copy and complete:
If $x = 4$, then $y = \frac{1}{2}$ of $\square = \square$ and (4, $\square$) is a member of the set.
Other members of the set are (6, $\square$), (8, $\square$), (10, $\square$).

(b) Copy the grid on $\frac{1}{2}$ cm squared paper and plot the points from (a).

Draw a straight line through the points and label the line

$$y = \tfrac{1}{2}x$$

Copy and complete:
The gradient of the line $y = \frac{1}{2}x$ is $m = \square$.

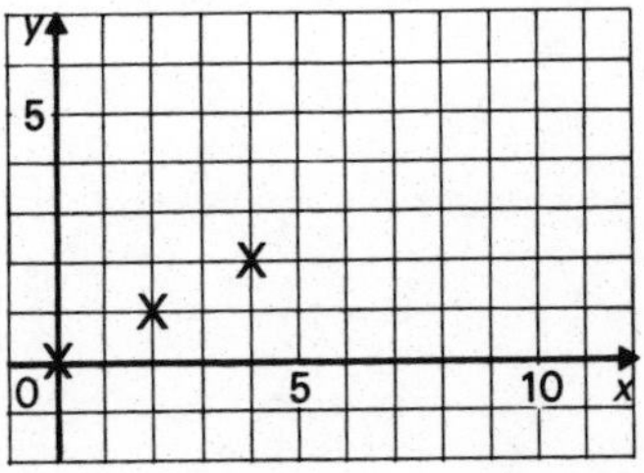

3 The equation $y = -3x$ describes another set of points.

If $x = 0$, then $y = -3 \times 0 = 0$, so (0, 0) is in the set.
If $x = 1$, then $y = -3 \times 1 = -3$, so (1, −3) is in the set.
If $x = -1$, then $y = -3 \times -1 = 3$, so (−1, 3) is in the set.

Copy and complete:

Other members of the set are

(−2, ■), (−3, ■), (2, ■).

Plot these points on a $\frac{1}{2}$ cm squared grid.

Draw a line through the points and label it

$$y = -3x$$

Copy and complete:

The gradient of the line $y = -3x$ is $m =$ ■.

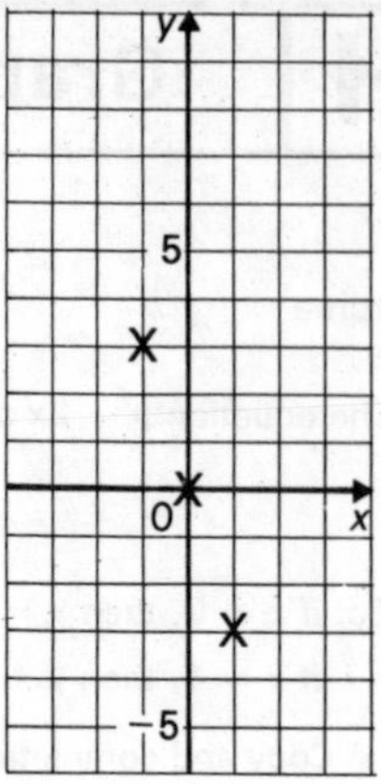

From questions 1, 2, and 3 we have the results in the table:

Equation of line	Gradient
$y = 2x$	2
$y = \frac{1}{2}x$	$\frac{1}{2}$
$y = -3x$	−3

Notice that in each case the coefficient of x is the same as the gradient.

Example

What is the gradient of the line $y = x$?

The equation may be written as $y = 1x$ (since $1 \times x = x$)

So, $m = 1$

Exercise

Write down the gradient of each of the following lines:

4 $y = 4x$ **5** $y = 5x$ **6** $y = \frac{1}{4}x$ **7** $y = -\frac{1}{3}x$

8 $y = -2x$ **9** $y = -4x$ **10** $y = -x$ **11** $y = 7x$

Continue with Section I

I Graph of $y = mx + c$

Exercise

1 The equation $y = 2x + 1$ describes a set of points.

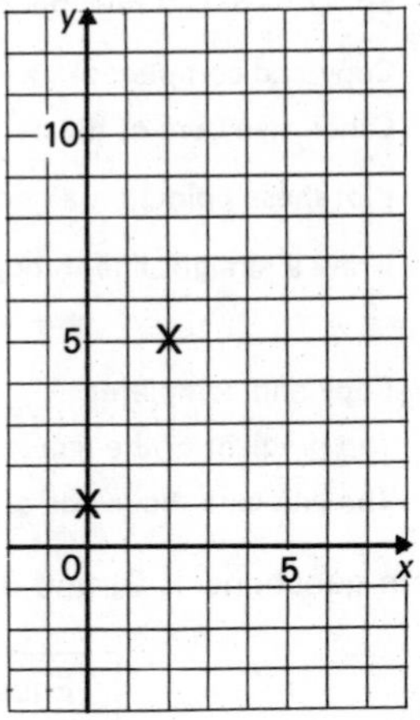

If $x = 0$, then $y = (2 \times 0) + 1$
$= 0 \quad + 1$
$= 1$

So, (0, 1) is a member of the set.
If $x = 2$, then $y = (2 \times 2) + 1$
$= 4 \quad + 1$
$= 5$

So, (2, 5) is a member of the set.

Copy and complete:

Other members of the set are (3, ■), (4, ■) (−2, ■).

Plot these points on a $\frac{1}{2}$ cm squared grid.

Draw a straight line through the points and label the line

$$y = 2x + 1$$

Copy and complete:

The gradient of the line $y = 2x + 1$ is $m =$ ■.

The line cuts the y-axis at (0, ■).

2 The equation $y = 3x + 4$ describes a set of points.

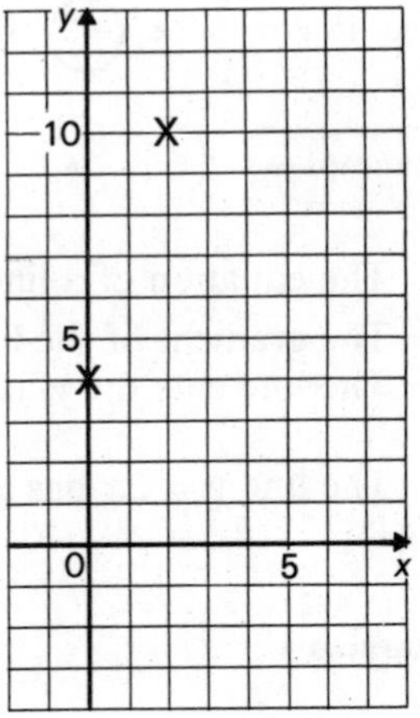

If $x = 0$, then $y = (3 \times 0) + 4$
$= 0 \quad + 4$
$= 4$

So, (0, 4) is a member of the set.

If $x = 2$, then $y = (3 \times 2) + 4$
$= 6 \quad + 4$
$= 10$

So, (2, 10) is a member of the set.

Copy and complete:

Other members of the set are (3, ■), (1, ■), (−2, ■).

Plot these points on a grid.

Draw a straight line through the points and label it

$$y = 3x + 4$$

Copy and complete:

The gradient of the line $y = 3x + 4$ is $m =$ ■.

The line cuts the y-axis at (0, ■).

3 The equation $y = -3x - 2$ describes a set of points.

If $x = 0$, then $y = (-3 \times 0) - 2$
$= 0 - 2$
$= -2$

So, $(0, -2)$ is a member of the set.

If $x = 2$, then $y = (-3 \times 2) - 2$
$= -6 - 2$
$= -8$

So, $(2, -8)$ is a member of the set.

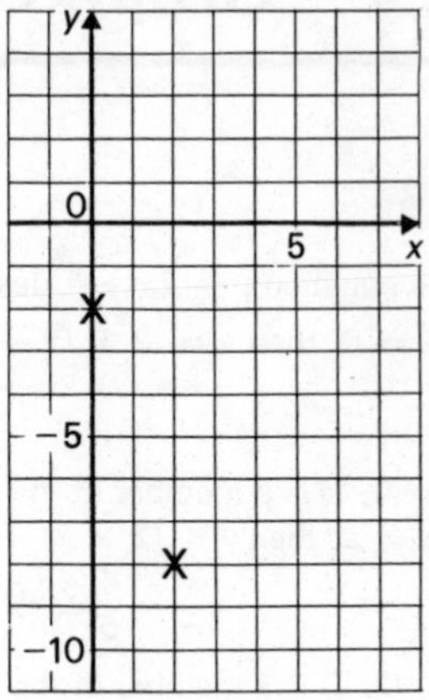

Copy and complete:

Other members of the set are (3,□), (−1,□), (−2,□).

Plot these points on a grid as in the diagram.

Draw a straight line through the points and label it

$$y = -3x - 2$$

Copy and complete:

The gradient of the line $y = -3x - 2$ is $m =$ □.

The line cuts the y-axis at (0,□).

From questions 1, 2, and 3 we have the results

Equation of line	Gradient	Cuts the y-axis at
$y = 2x + 1$	2	(0, 1)
$y = 3x + 4$	3	(0, 4)
$y = -3x - 2$	−3	(0, −2)

Notice that, in $y = (-3)x - 2$ the coefficient of x is -3 and the **gradient** of the line is (-3).

Also, in $y = -3x\ (-2)$ the constant term is -2 and the line **cuts the y-axis** at $(0, (-2))$.

Examples

1 The equation of a line is $y = 4x + 2$
The gradient of the line is $m = 4$.
The line cuts the y-axis at $(0, 2)$

2 The equation of a line is $y = \frac{1}{2}x - 4$
The gradient of this line is $m = \frac{1}{2}$.
The line cuts the y-axis at $(0, -4)$.

3 The line $y = 2x$ has gradient $m = 2$ and cuts the y-axis at $(0, 0)$.

Exercise

Write down the gradient m of each of the following lines and the point where it cuts the y-axis.

4 $y = 3x - 1$

5 $y = x + 2$

6 $y = 5x - 2$

7 $y = 3x$

8 $y = -2x + 5$

9 $y = -4x - 3$

10 $y = -\frac{1}{3}x + 1$

11 $y = -5x$

12 $y = 3x - 5$

Continue with Section J

J Finding equations of lines

Example

What is the equation of the line drawn on the grid?

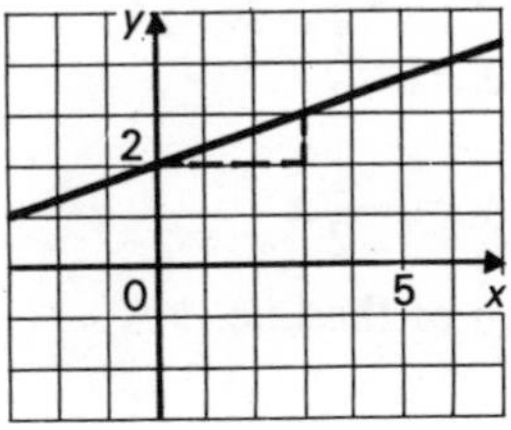

Gradient of line is $m = \frac{1}{3}$

Line cuts y-axis at $(0,2)$

So $y = \frac{1}{3}x + 2$

is the equation of the line.

Example

What is the equation of the line drawn on the grid?

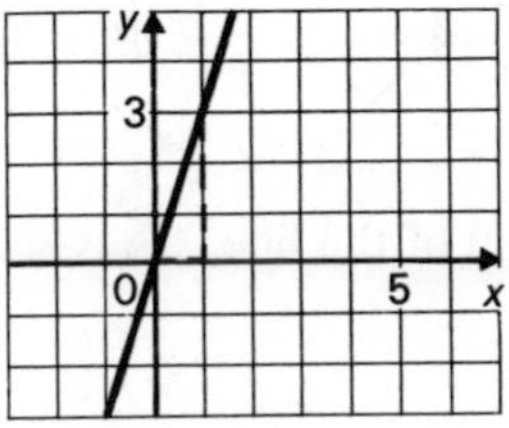

Gradient of line is $m = \frac{3}{1} = 3$

Line cuts y-axis at $(0,0)$

So $y = 3x + 0$

or $y = 3x$

is the equation of the line.

Exercise

Write down the equations of these straight lines.

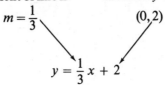

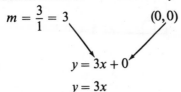

1 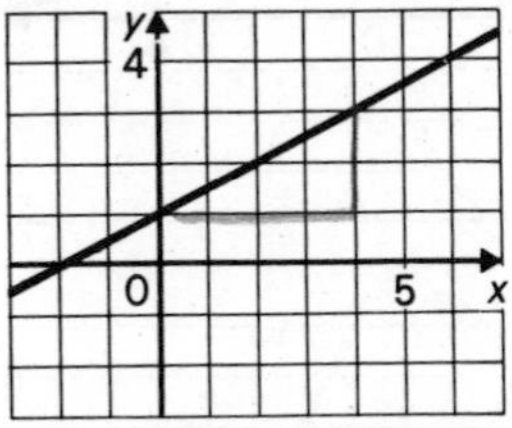

2 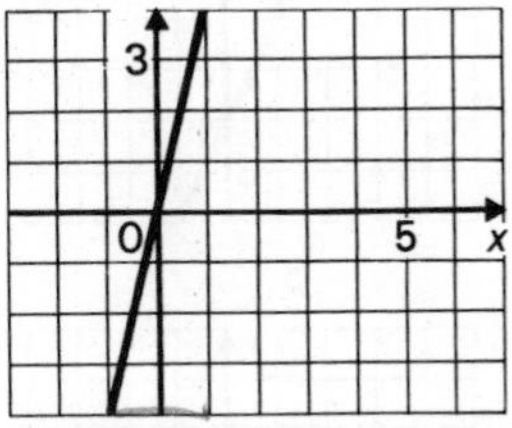

3 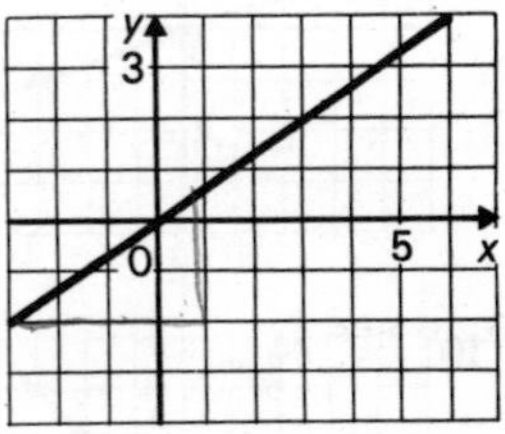

4 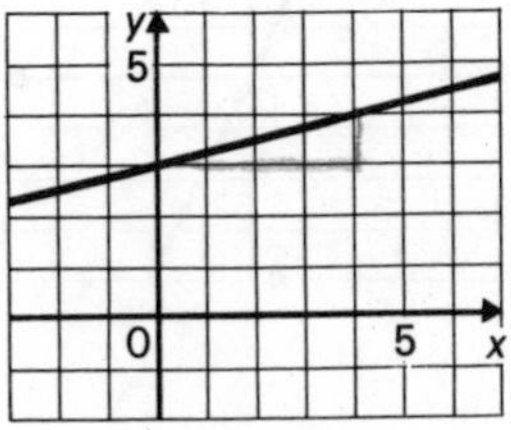

5 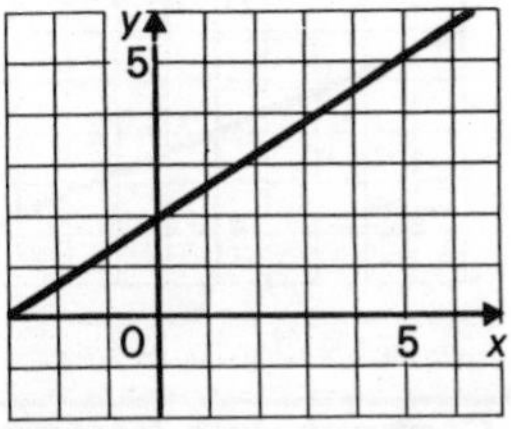

6 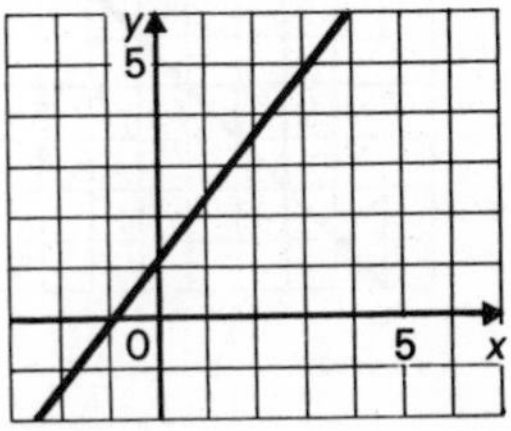

Example

What is the equation of the line drawn on the grid?

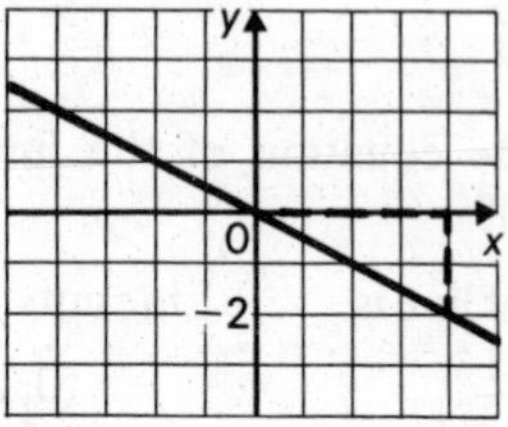

Gradient of line is $m = -\frac{2}{4} = -\frac{1}{2}$

Line cuts y-axis at (0, 0)

So $y = -\frac{1}{2}x + 0$

or $y = -\frac{1}{2}x$

is the equation of the line.

Example

What is the equation of the line drawn on the grid?

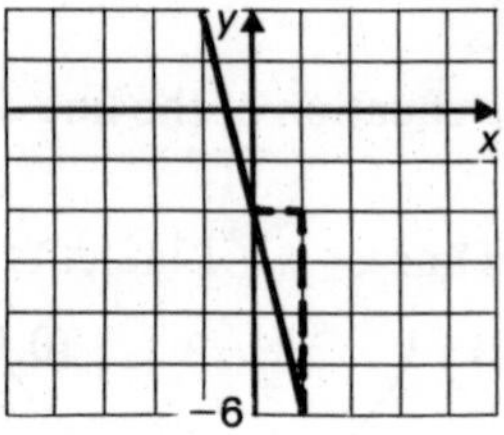

Gradient of line is $m = -\frac{4}{1} = -4$

Line cuts y-axis at (0, −2)

So $y = -4x - 2$

is the equation of the line.

Exercise

Write down the equations of these straight lines.

7 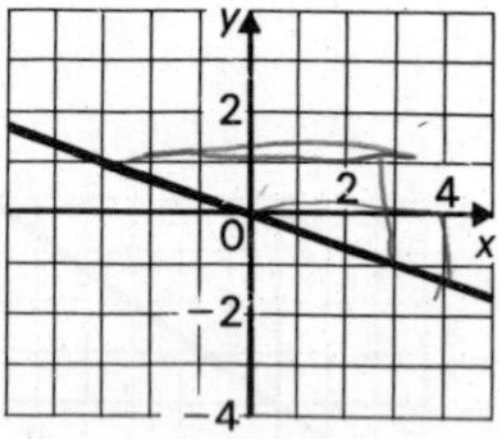

8 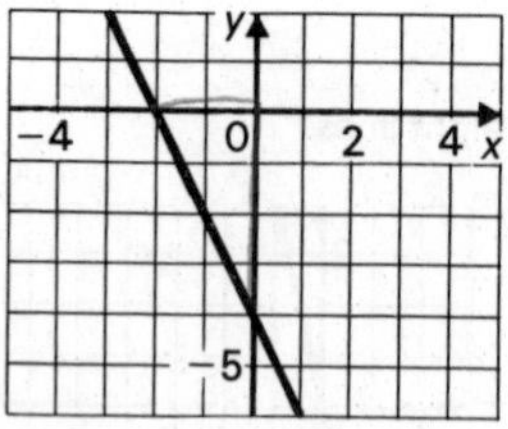

9 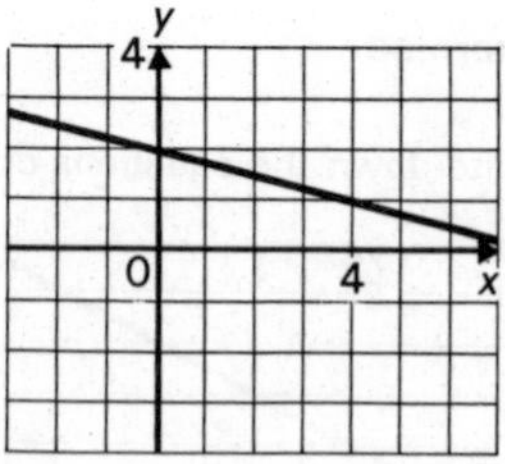

10 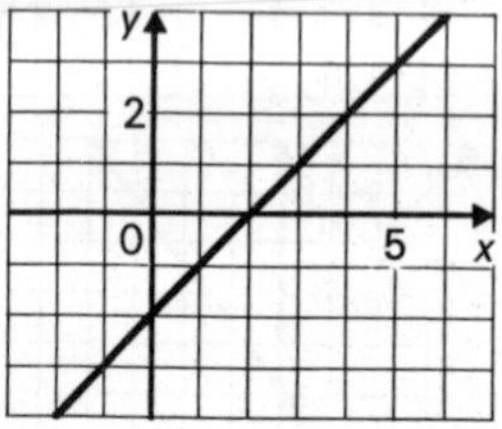

11 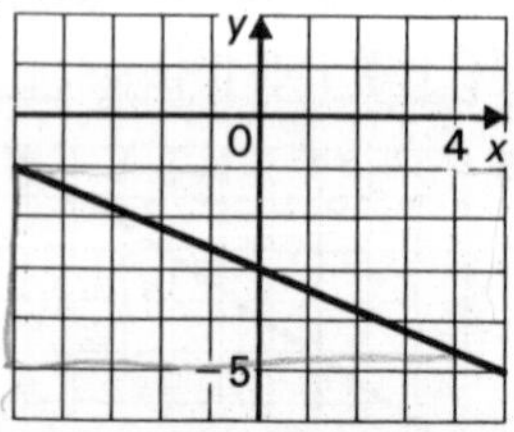

12 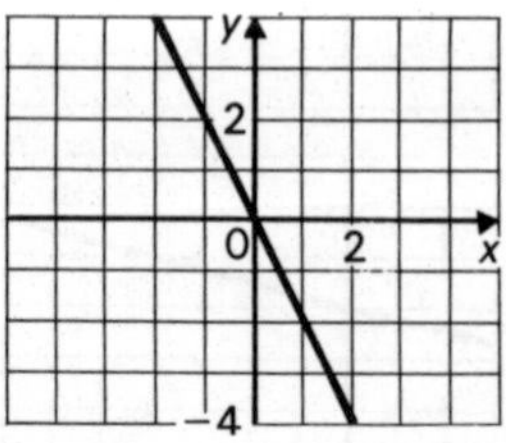

Continue with Section K

K Distance–time graphs

Exercise

1 The table shows the distances travelled by a snail.

Time in minutes	1	2	3	4	5	6
Distance (cm)	2	4	6	8	10	12

This can be shown on a graph as follows.

Draw two axes at right angles on $\frac{1}{2}$ cm squared paper.

Label the horizontal axis **time (minutes).**

Label the vertical axis **distance (cm).**

Plot a time of 1 minute and a distance of 2 cm as in the graph opposite.

Continue in this way to plot the remaining times and corresponding distances.

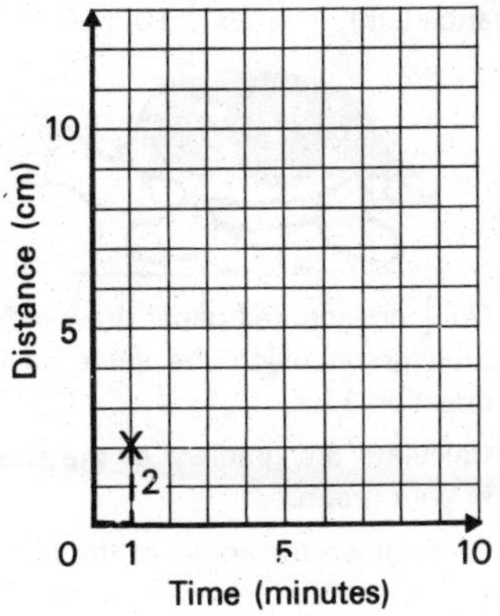

The points all lie on a straight line which has been drawn on the graph opposite.

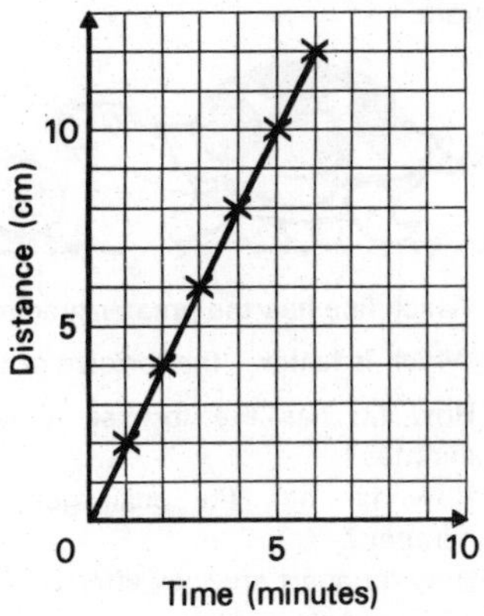

The graph is called a **distance–time graph.**

From the table, the snail moved 2 cm every minute.

Copy and complete:

The **speed** of the snail is ▒ cm per minute.

The **gradient** of the line in the graph $= \frac{6}{3} =$ ▒

Notice that the **gradient** of the line = the **speed** (in cm per minute) of the snail.

2 Write down the speeds represented in each of the following **distance–time** graphs:

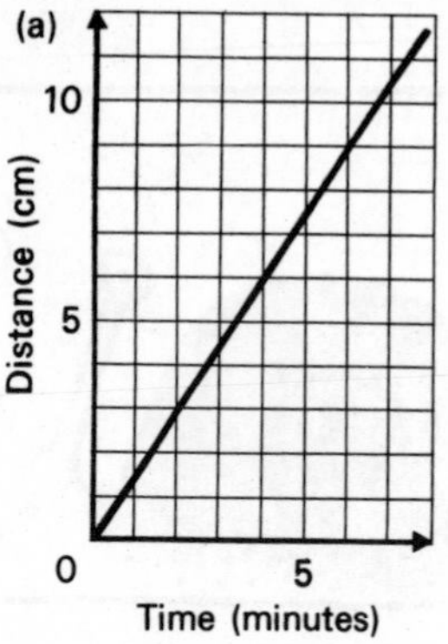

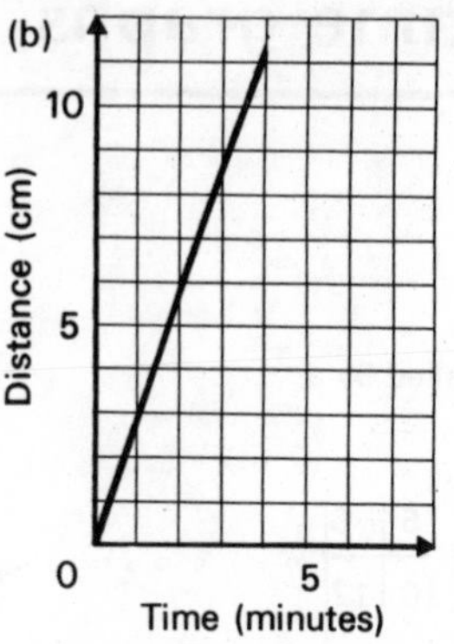

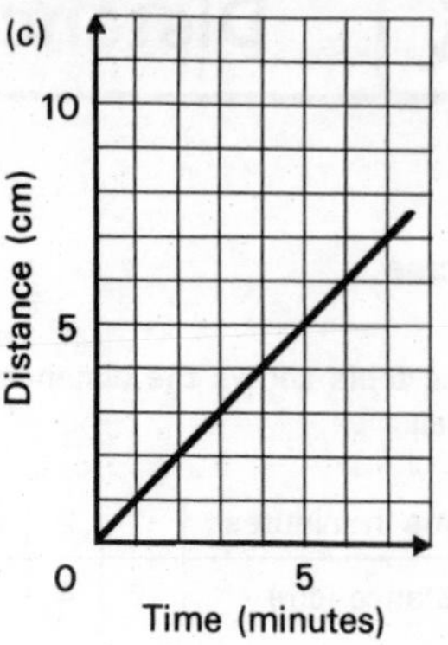

3 The following table shows the distances travelled by a tortoise.

Time in minutes	1	2	3	4	5	6
Distance (cm)	5	10	15	20	25	30

(a) On $\frac{1}{2}$ cm squared paper draw a distance–time graph using the same scales as in question 1.

(b) Calculate the gradient of the straight line in your graph.

(c) Write down the speed of the tortoise.

4 The graph on the right shows the distance–time graphs of the snail (in question 1) and the tortoise (in question 3) drawn on the same diagram.

(a) Which line has the greater gradient?

(b) Which is faster – the tortoise or the snail?

(c) How far has the tortoise gone after 2 minutes?
How far has the snail gone after 2 minutes?
How far apart are they after 2 minutes?

(d) How far apart are the snail and the tortoise after 3 minutes, after 5 minutes, and after 6 minutes?

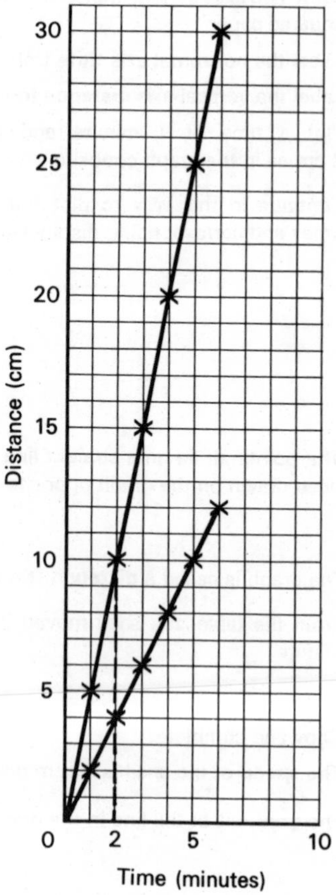

The line with the greater gradient represents the faster speed.

5 The diagram shows the distance–time graphs of a cyclist, a walker, and a car. Which line is most likely to represent the graph of each?

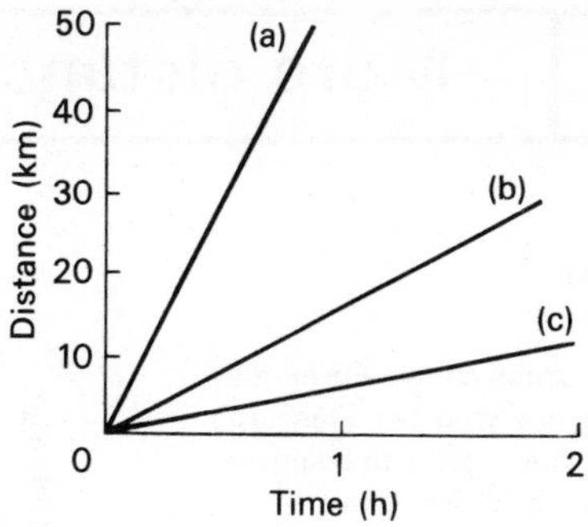

6 The graph below shows the speeds of (a) a bus, (b) a motor-scooter (c) a cyclist, and (d) a walker. Find the speed of each in kilometres per hour.

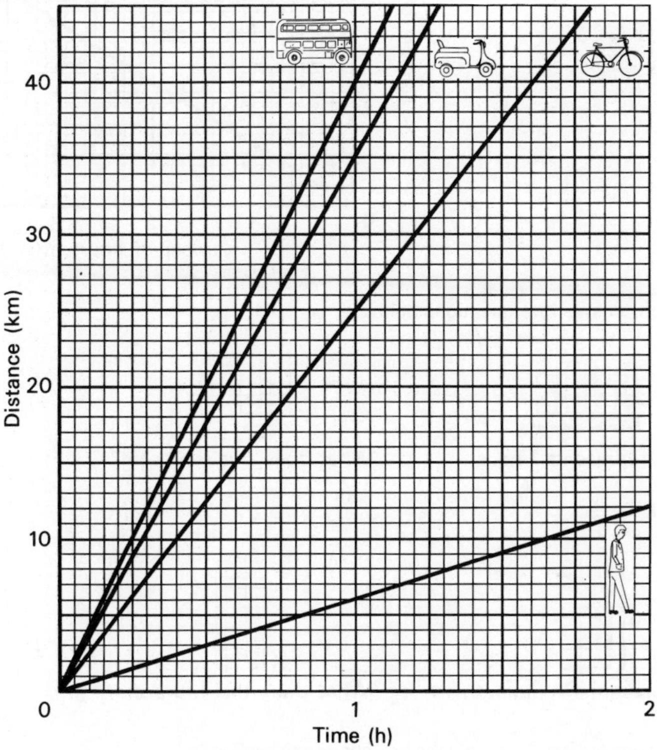

Continue with Section L

L More distance–time graphs

Exercise

1 This graph shows the journey of a boy who left Glasburgh at 9 a.m. to go to Edingow, which is 24 km away.

His journey was in two parts; the first part was covered on foot and the second on a bicycle.

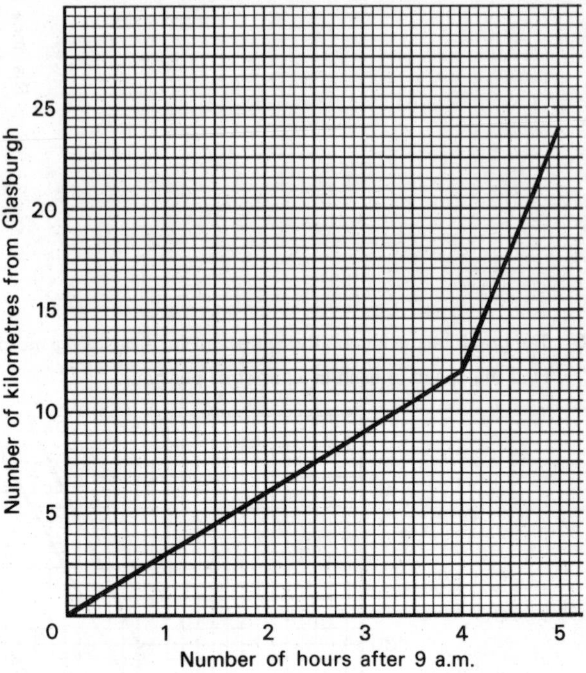

From the graph, answer the questions below:

(a)

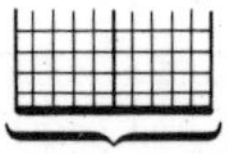

This represents 1 hour.

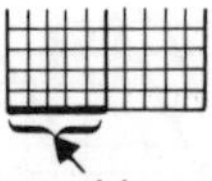

What does this represent?

(b)

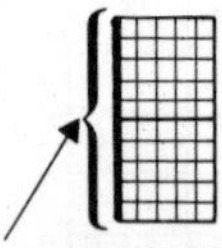

This represents 5 kilometres.

What does this represent?

(c) How many hours after 9 a.m. did the boy change to cycling?

(d) How many kilometres had he travelled when he began to cycle?

(e) How many kilometres did he walk every hour?

(f) What was his walking speed?

(g) For how long was the boy cycling?

(h) How many kilometres did he cover on the bicycle?

(i) What was his cycling speed?

(j) At what time did the boy reach Edingow?

2 The graph shows the journey of a boy who left Glasburgh at 9 a.m. to go to Edingow, 24 km away.

His journey was in two parts – the first part was covered by bicycle and the second, after a short rest, was covered on foot.

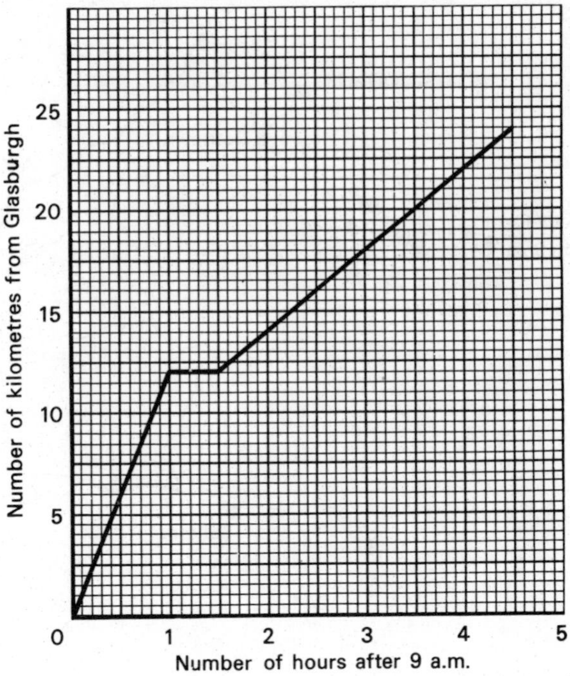

(a)

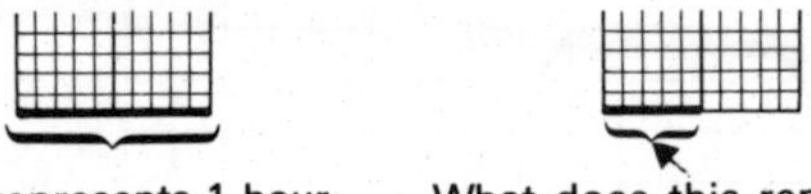

This represents 1 hour. What does this represent?

(b)

This represents 5 kilometres. What does this represent?

(c) For how many hours did the boy cycle?

(d) How many kilometres did he cover by bicycle?

(e) What was his cycling speed?

(f) How long did he rest?

(g) When did the boy begin his walk?

(h) For how many hours did he walk?

(i) How many kilometres did he walk?

(j) What was his walking speed?

(k) At what time did the boy reach Edingow?

3

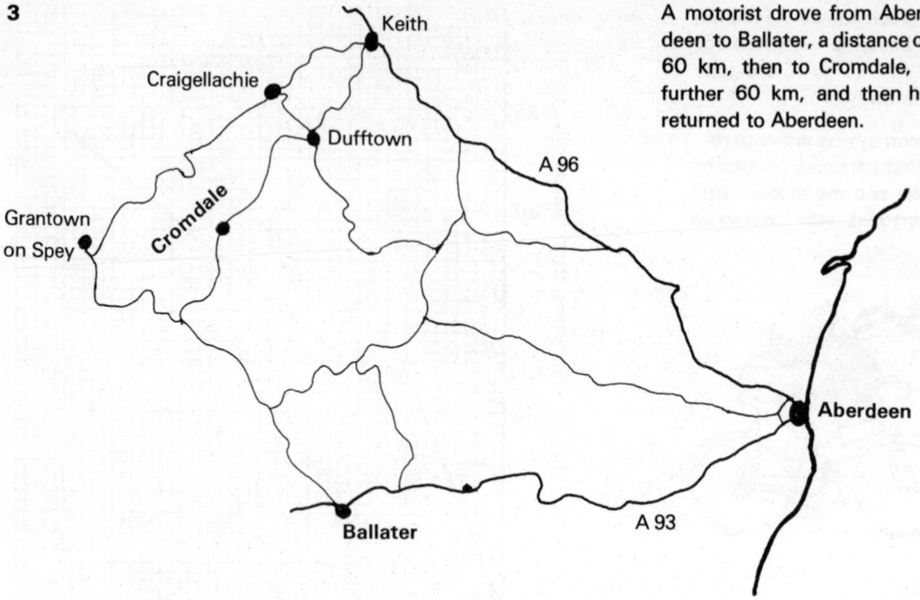

A motorist drove from Aberdeen to Ballater, a distance of 60 km, then to Cromdale, a further 60 km, and then he returned to Aberdeen.

The following is the distance–time graph of his journey.

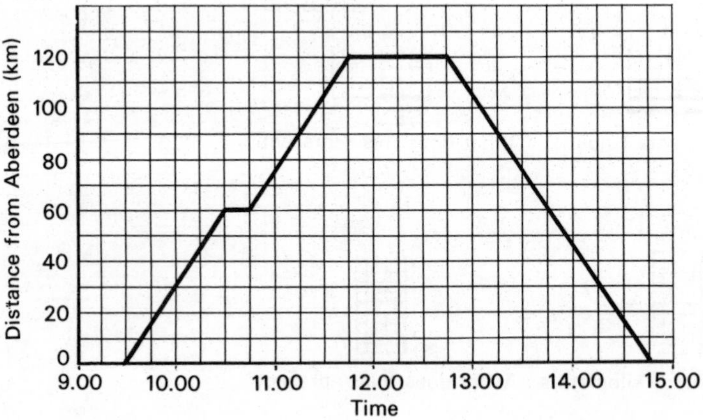

From the graph, answer the following questions:

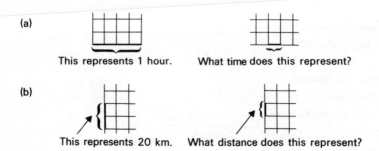

(a)

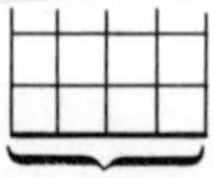

This represents 1 hour.

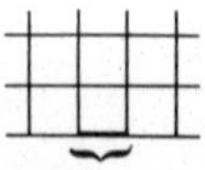

What time does this represent?

(b)

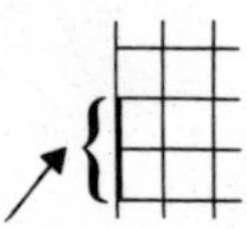

This represents 20 km.

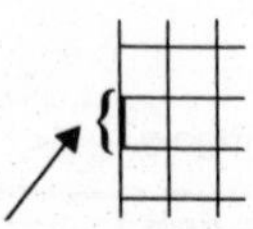

What distance does this represent?

(c) At what time did the motorist leave Aberdeen?

(d) How long did he take to go from Aberdeen to Ballater?

(e) What was his speed from Aberdeen to Ballater?

(f) How long did he stop at Ballater?

(g) How long did he take to go from Ballater to Cromdale?

(h) What was his speed from Ballater to Cromdale?

(i) How long did he stop at Cromdale?

(j) When did he leave Cromdale?

(k) How long did he take to go from Cromdale to Aberdeen?

(l) What was his speed from Cromdale to Aberdeen?

4 This is the distance–time graph of a motorist and a cyclist travelling from Cramond to Dalkeith, a distance of 30 kilometres.

(a) At what time did the *cyclist* leave Cramond?

(b) How far did he travel before resting?

(c) At what speed did he cycle?

(d) For how long did he rest?

(e) At what time did he start his journey again?

(f) Did he continue at the same speed as before?

(g) At what time did the *motorist* leave Cramond?

(h) What was his speed?

(i) How far had he gone after half an hour?

(j) At what time did the motorist overtake the cyclist?

(k) How far from Dalkeith was the cyclist when he was overtaken?

(l) At what time did the motorist arrive at Dalkeith?

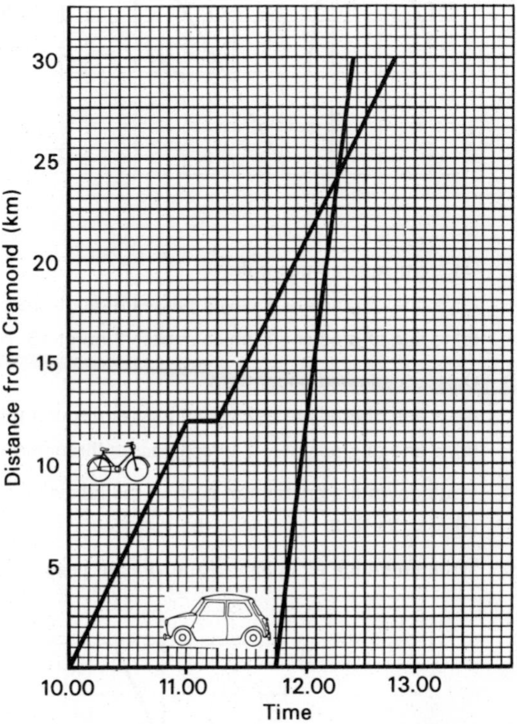

Continue with Section M

M Progress check

Exercise

1 Write down the gradients of the following lines.

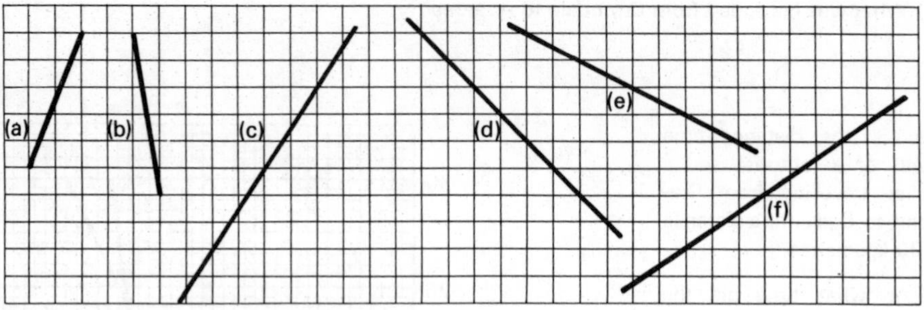

2 On $\frac{1}{2}$ cm squared paper draw

(a) a line of gradient 1 which passes through the origin;

(b) a line of gradient 1 which passes through (3, 5).

3 On $\frac{1}{2}$ cm squared paper draw

(a) a line of gradient -2 which passes through the origin;

(b) a line of gradient -2 which passes through $(-1, -3)$.

4 Write down the gradient of each of the following lines and the point where each cuts the y-axis.

(a) $y = 2x + 3$ (b) $y = \frac{1}{5}x$ (c) $y = -\frac{1}{2}x + 1$ (d) $y = x - 5$

5 Write down the equations of the straight lines drawn in the following diagrams.

(a)

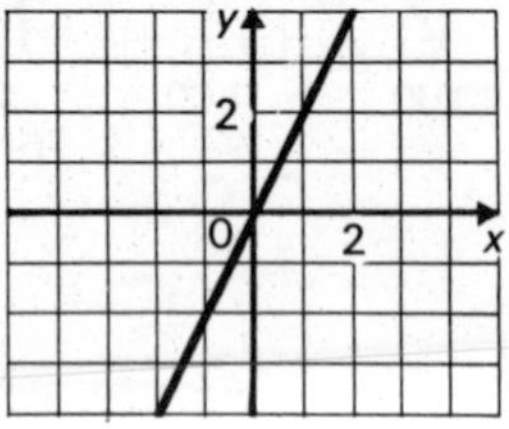

(b)

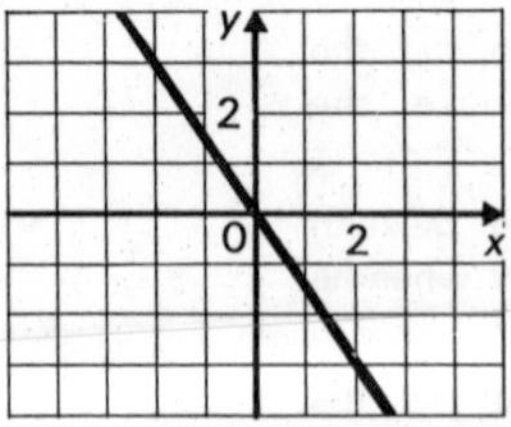

(c)

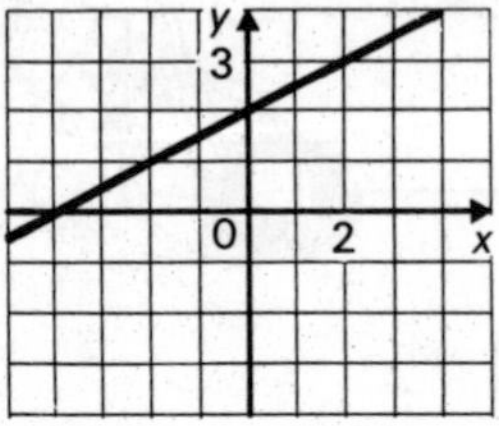

(d)

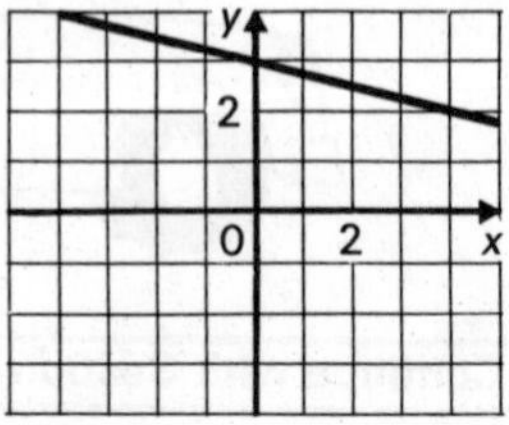

(e)

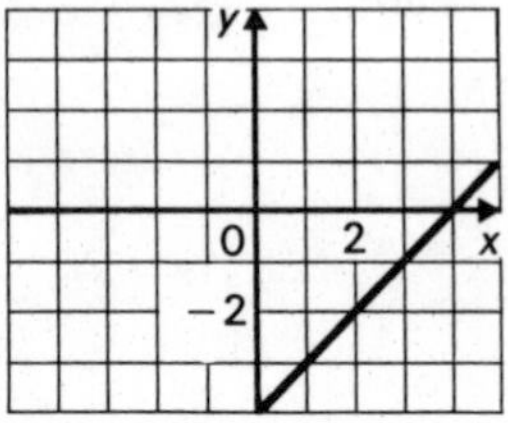

6 (a) In the distance–time graph on the right, which line represents the fastest speed? Which represents the slowest?

(b) Find the speed in *km per hour* represented by each line.

(c) Which line is most likely to represent the graph of

(i) a lorry?
(ii) a fast car?
(iii) a cyclist?

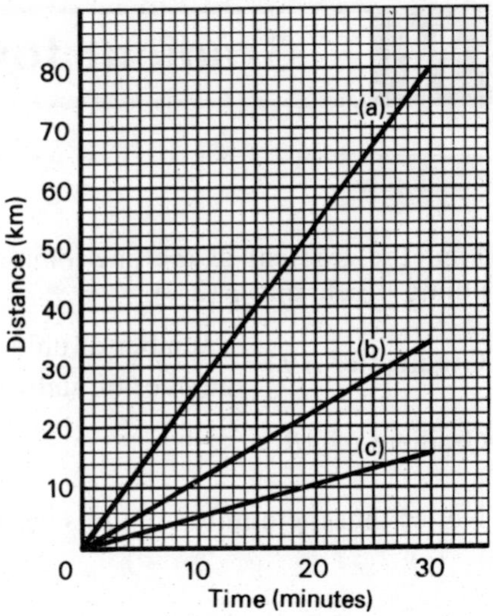

7 A boy set out on a 16 km journey. He walked the first 4 km, had a rest, and then completed the journey by bicycle. This distance–time graph shows his journey.

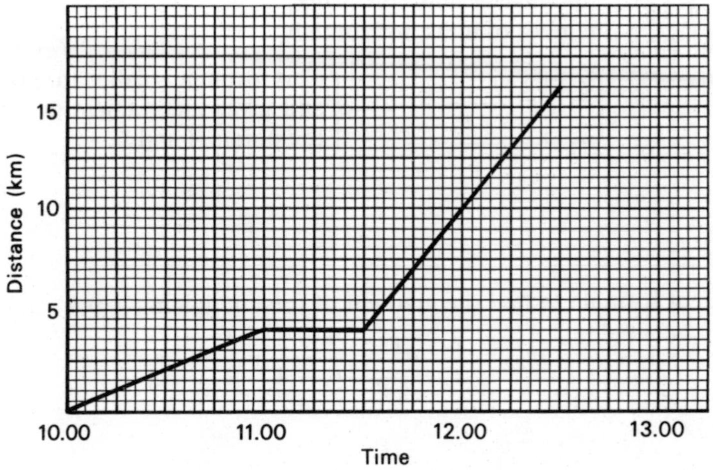

(a) For how long did the boy rest?

(b) What was the boy's walking speed?

(c) What was the boy's cycling speed?

(d) When did he reach his destination?

Ask your teacher what to do next

N Gradient formula

Example

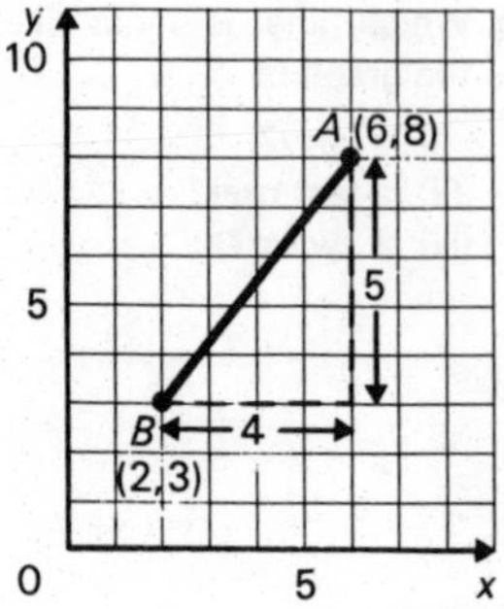

Find the gradient of the line joining the points $A(6, 8)$ and $B(2, 3)$.

$$\text{Gradient of } AB = \frac{\text{number of units vertically}}{\text{number of units horizontally}} = \frac{5}{4}.$$

$$\text{Gradient of } AB = \frac{5}{4}.$$

Notice that the number of units vertically $= 5$
$= 8 - 3$
$=$ (y coordinate of A) $-$ (y coordinate of B)
$= y_A - y_B$

and the number of units horizontally $= 4$
$= 6 - 2$
$=$ (x coordinate of A) $-$ (x coordinate of B)
$= x_A - x_B$

$$\text{So, gradient of } AB = \frac{\text{number of units vertically}}{\text{number of units horizontally}} = \frac{y_A - y_B}{x_A - x_B}$$

$$\boxed{m_{AB} = \frac{y_A - y_B}{x_A - x_B}}$$

This formula is called the **gradient formula** and gives the gradient of the line joining the points A and B.

Example

Use the gradient formula to find the gradient of the line joining $A(6, 9)$ and $B(4, 5)$.

$$m_{AB} = \frac{y_A - y_B}{x_A - x_B} = \frac{9 - 5}{6 - 4} = \frac{4}{2} = 2.$$

Exercise

Use the gradient formula to find the gradients of the lines joining the following pairs of points.

1 $A(5, 11)$ and $B(1, 3)$
2 $C(7, 4)$ and $D(5, 2)$
3 $E(6, 5)$ and $F(3, 4)$
4 $G(3, 7)$ and $H(1, 6)$
5 $J(4, 9)$ and $K(1, 1)$
6 $L(8, 7)$ and $M(4, 0)$
7 $M(10, 6)$ and $N(1, 3)$
8 $R(12, 7)$ and $S(2, 2)$
9 $V(2, 8)$ and $T(1, 7)$

Example

Use the gradient formula to find the gradient of the line joining $P(4, 5)$ to $Q(-1, 6)$.

$$m_{PQ} = \frac{y_P - y_Q}{x_P - x_Q} = \frac{5 - 6}{4 - (-1)} = \frac{5 - 6}{4 + 1} = \frac{-1}{5} = -\frac{1}{5}.$$

Exercise

Use the gradient formula to find the gradients of the lines joining the following pairs of points.

10 $A(5, -2)$ and $B(6, 6)$
11 $C(4, -1)$ and $D(1, 2)$
12 $E(-1, 5)$ and $F(6, 19)$
13 $G(-2, 3)$ and $H(1, 1)$
14 $J(-5, -2)$ and $K(-10, -3)$
15 $L(5, 2)$ and $M(7, 0)$
16 $N(2, -8)$ and $M(3, -6)$
17 $P(4, 0)$ and $Q(0, 3)$
18 $R(0, 4)$ and $S(3, 0)$

Continue with Section O

O Gradients of lines parallel to the axes

Example

Find the gradient of the line joining $A(6, 3)$ and $B(2, 3)$.

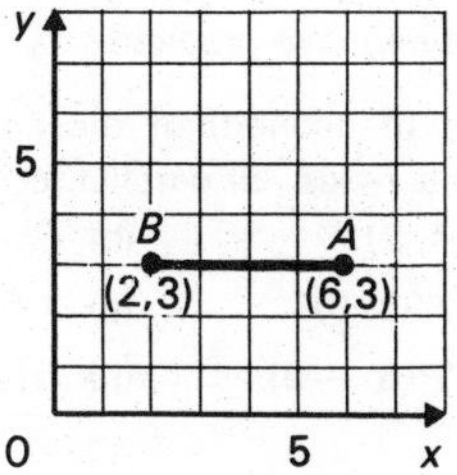

Notice that the line AB is parallel to the x-axis.

$$\text{Gradient of } AB = \frac{y_A - y_B}{x_A - x_B} = \frac{3-3}{6-2} = \frac{0}{4} = 0$$

AB is parallel to the x-axis and has gradient $m = 0$.

Any line parallel to the x-axis has gradient equal to zero.

Example

Find the gradient of the line joining $P(2, 6)$ and $Q(2, 2)$.

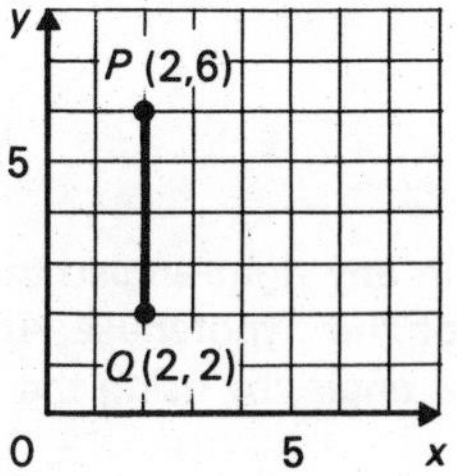

Notice that PQ is parallel to the y-axis.

$$\text{Gradient of } PQ = \frac{y_P - y_Q}{x_P - x_Q} = \frac{6-2}{2-2} = \frac{4}{0}$$

Division by 0 is not defined.

PQ is parallel to the y-axis and its gradient is not defined.

The gradient of any line parallel to the y-axis is not defined.

Exercise

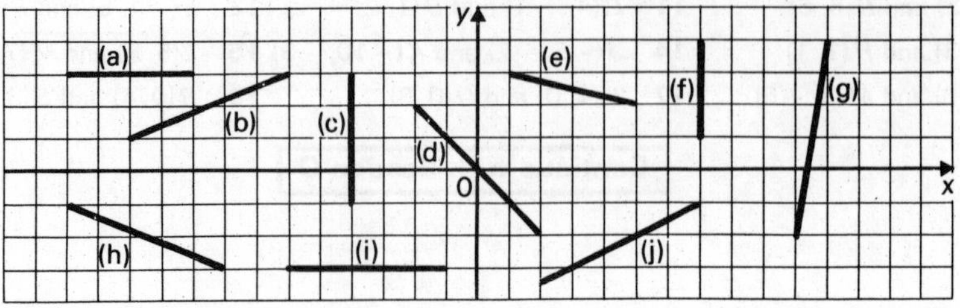

1 Which lines in the diagram have gradients equal to 0?

2 For which lines is the gradient not defined?

3 Which lines have a *positive* gradient?

4 Which lines have a *negative* gradient?

5 Find the gradients (if defined) of the lines joining the following pairs of points. Say which lines are (i) parallel to the x-axis, (ii) parallel to the y-axis.

(a) $A(6, 2)$ and $B(4, 2)$ (b) $C(-2, 6)$ and $D(-2, 4)$ (c) $E(3, 5)$ and $F(2, 4)$

(d) $G(3, -1)$ and $H(3, 8)$ (e) $J(5, -1)$ and $K(-1, -1)$ (f) $L(1, 2)$ and $M(-1, -2)$

(g) $N(7, -7)$ and $P(6, -6)$ (h) $Q(\frac{1}{2}, 8)$ and $R(\frac{1}{2}, 9)$ (j) $S(2, \frac{3}{4})$ and $T(3, \frac{3}{4})$

Continue with Section P

P Distance formula

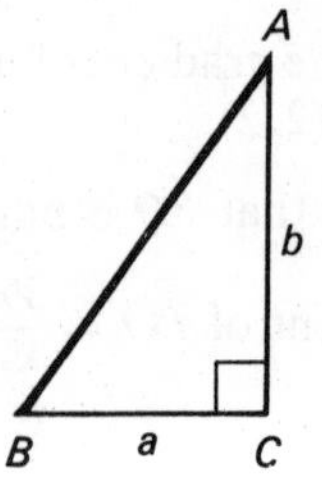

Remember that in any right-angled triangle ABC we can find the length of the hypotenuse AB, that is, the side opposite the right angle, by using the formula.

$$AB = \sqrt{a^2 + b^2} \ldots \text{Pythagoras' Theorem.}$$

Example

Find the length of the hypotenuse of the triangle *PQR*.

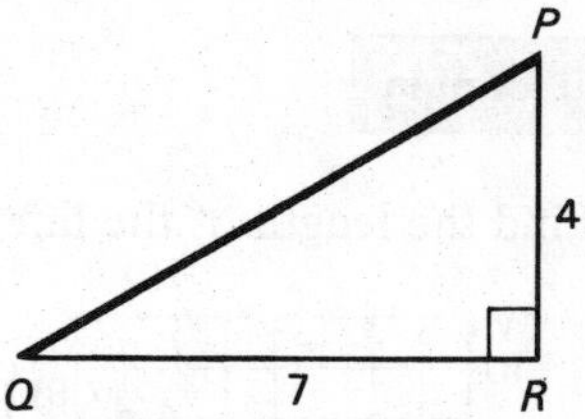

$$\text{Hypotenuse} = PQ = \sqrt{7^2 + 4^2}$$
$$= \sqrt{49 + 16}$$
$$= \sqrt{65}$$
$$= 8.06 \text{ (from square root tables)}$$

Exercise

Find the length of the hypotenuse in each of the following triangles.

1

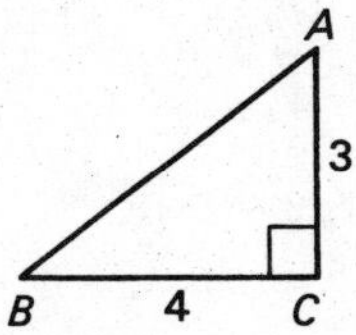

2

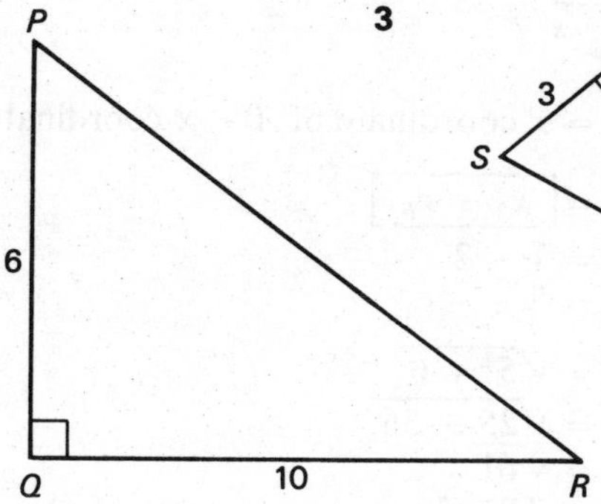

3

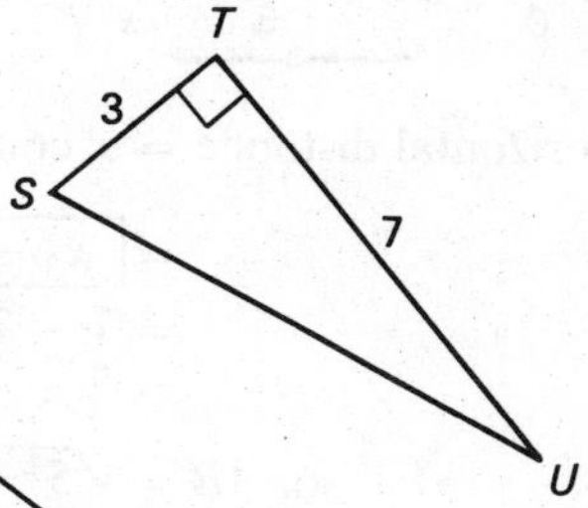

4

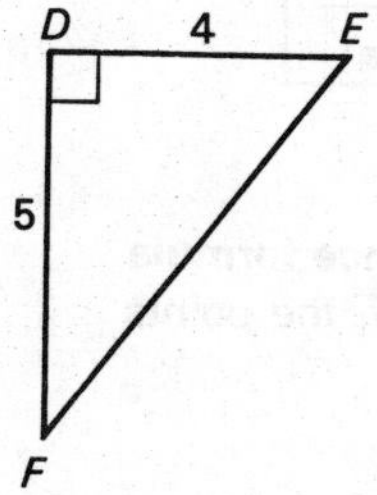

5

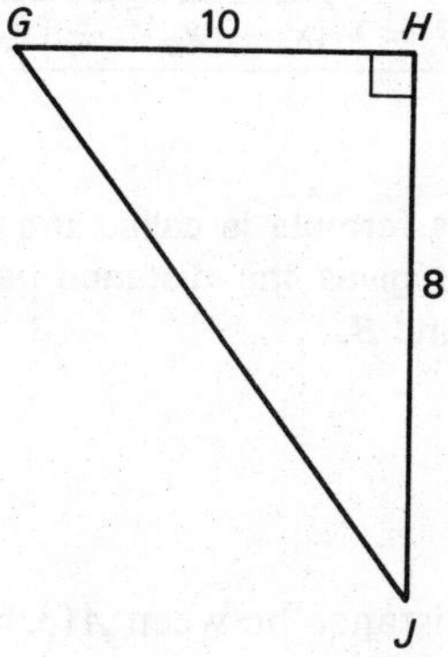

6

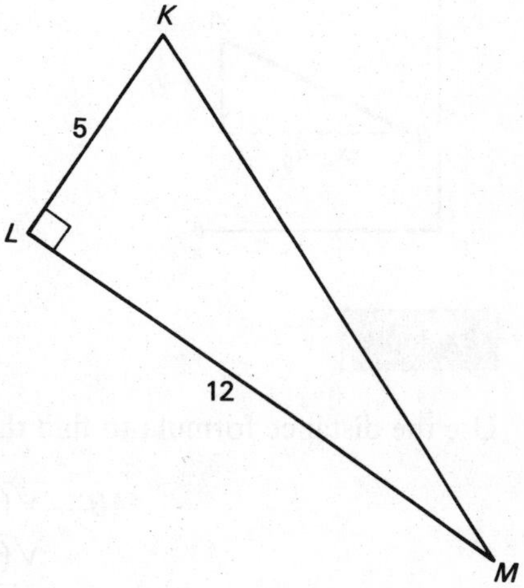

We can use Pythagoras' Theorem to calculate the length of the line joining two points whose coordinates are known.

Example

Find the length of the line joining $A(7,9)$ and $B(2,3)$.

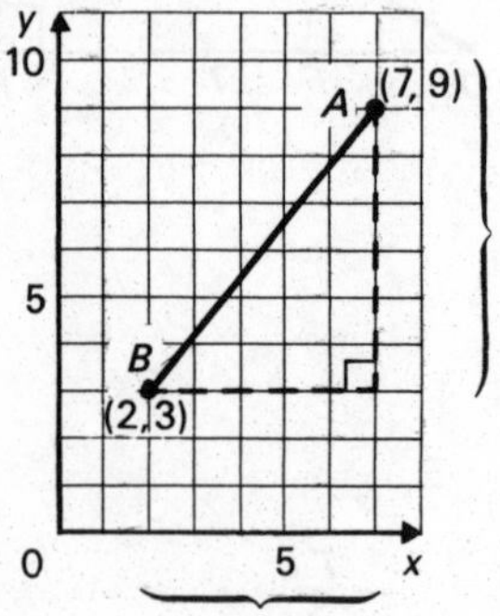

Vertical distance = y coordinate of A − y coordinate of B

$$= \boxed{y_A - y_B}$$
$$= 9 - 3$$
$$= 6$$

Horizontal distance = x coordinate of A − x coordinate of B

$$= \boxed{x_A - x_B}$$
$$= 7 - 2$$
$$= 5$$

$$\text{so, } AB = \sqrt{5^2 + 6^2}$$
$$= \sqrt{25 + 36}$$
$$= \sqrt{61}$$
$$= 7.81 \text{ (from square root-tables).}$$

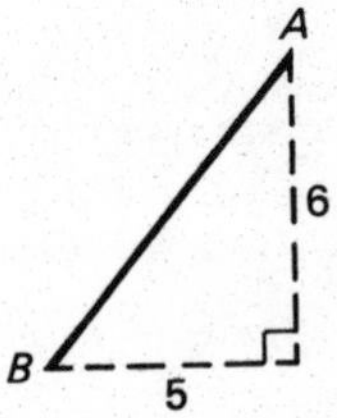

We see that

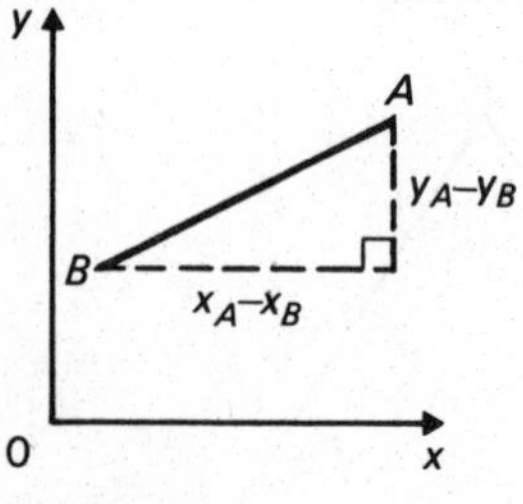

$$\boxed{AB = \sqrt{(x_A - x_B)^2 + (y_A - y_B)^2}}$$

This formula is called the **distance formula** and gives the distance between the points *A* and *B*.

Example

Use the distance formula to find the distance between $A(3,6)$ and $B(1,2)$.

$$AB = \sqrt{(x_A - x_B)^2 + (y_A - y_B)^2}$$
$$= \sqrt{(3-1)^2 + (6-2)^2}$$
$$= \sqrt{2^2 + 4^2}$$
$$= \sqrt{4 + 16}$$
$$= \sqrt{20}$$
$$= 4.47 \text{ (from square root tables)}$$

Example

Use the distance formula to find the distance between $P(3, 2)$ and $Q(7, -4)$.

$$\begin{aligned} PQ &= \sqrt{(x_P - x_Q)^2 + (y_P - y_Q)^2} \\ &= \sqrt{(3-7)^2 + (2-(-4))^2} \\ &= \sqrt{(3-7)^2 + (2+4)^2} \\ &= \sqrt{(-4)^2 + 6^2} \\ &= \sqrt{16 + 36} \\ &= \sqrt{52} \\ &= 7.21 \end{aligned}$$

Exercise

7 Copy and complete:

The distance between $A(9, 7)$ and $B(4, 3)$ is

$$\begin{aligned} AB &= \sqrt{(x_A - x_B)^2 + (y_A - y_B)^2} \\ &= \sqrt{(9-4)^2 + (\square - \square)^2} \\ &= \sqrt{\square^2 + \square^2} \\ &= \sqrt{\square + \square} \\ &= \sqrt{\square} \\ &= \square \end{aligned}$$

8 Copy and complete:

The distance between $P(5, 3)$ and $R(-2, 8)$ is

$$\begin{aligned} PR &= \sqrt{(x_P - x_Q)^2 + (y_P - y_Q)^2} \\ &= \sqrt{(5-(-2))^2 + (\square - \square)^2} \\ &= \sqrt{(\square + \square)^2 + \square^2} \\ &= \sqrt{\square^2 + \square^2} \\ &= \sqrt{\square + \square} \\ &= \sqrt{\square} \\ &= \square \end{aligned}$$

Use the distance formula to find the distance between the following pairs of points:

9 $A(4, 5)$ and $B(0, 3)$
10 $C(6, 13)$ and $D(1, 1)$
11 $K(4, 9)$ and $L(3, 8)$
12 $P(2, 8)$ and $Q(1, 5)$
13 $S(8, 2)$ and $R(5, 2)$
14 $J(5, 9)$ and $F(0, 3)$
15 $H(2, 5)$ and $F(7, 9)$
16 $J(6, 9)$ and $G(6, 1)$
17 $S(1, 0)$ and $C(4, 7)$
18 $D(1, -4)$ and $S(-5, 2)$
19 $J(0, 0)$ and $N(6, 10)$
20 $T(2, 2)$ and $V(-1, -7)$

Continue with Section Q

Q The equation $y=mx+c$

The following table was obtained in Section H.

Equation of line	Gradient (m)	Cuts the y-axis at
$y = \mathbf{2}x + \mathbf{1}$	**2**	(0, **1**)
$y = \mathbf{3}x + \mathbf{4}$	**3**	(0, **4**)
$y = \mathbf{-3}x \mathbf{- 2}$	**−3**	(0, **−2**)

Notice that all the graphs were straight lines with equations of the form

$$y = mx + c$$

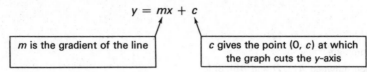

m is the gradient of the line

c gives the point (0, *c*) at which the graph cuts the *y*-axis

In general

$y = \boldsymbol{mx} + \boldsymbol{c}$ is the equation of a **straight line** with gradient $\boldsymbol{m}$, cutting the y-axis at (0, $\boldsymbol{c}$)

Example

The equation $y = 3x - 4$ may be written

$$y = 3x + (-4)$$

(m = 3, c = −4)

and so represents a straight line with **gradient 3** cutting the y-axis at **(0, −4)**.

Example

The equation $y = -7x$ may be written

$$y = -7x + 0$$

(m = −7, c = 0)

and so represents a straight line with **gradient** −**7** cutting the y-axis at **(0, 0)**.

Exercise

Copy and complete the following tables:

	Equation of line	Gradient	Cuts y-axis at
1	$y = 3x + 5$	3	0,5
2	$y = 6x - 1$	6	0,−1
3	$y = 5x$	5	0, 0
4	$y = x + 7$	1	0, 7
5	$y = -7x - 2$	−7	0, −2
6	$y = -\frac{3}{4}x + 3$	$-\frac{3}{4}$	0, 3

	Equation of line	Gradient	Cuts y-axis at
7	$y = \frac{1}{2}x - \frac{5}{2}$		
8	$y = 8$		
9	$y = -x + 1$		
10	$y = 4x - 4$		
11	$y = -5$		
12	$y = \frac{1}{3}x - \frac{2}{3}$		

Continue with Section R

R The equation $ax+by=c$

Is the graph of $3x + 4y = 12$ a straight line?

We can rearrange $3x + 4y = 12$ into the form $y = mx + c$ as follows:

Subtract $3x$ from both sides:

$$4y = -3x + 12$$

Divide both sides by 4:

$$y = -\tfrac{3}{4}x + 3$$

which is of the form

$$y = mx + c$$

So $3x + 4y = 12$ represents a straight line with gradient $-\frac{3}{4}$ cutting the y-axis at (0.3).

In general, **the equation $ax + by = c$ represents a straight line**

Exercise

1 Copy and complete:

The equation $2x + 3y = 6$ may be put in the form $y = mx + c$ as follows:

$$2x + 3y = 6$$

Subtract $2x$ from both sides: $\square = -2x + \square$

Divide both sides by $\square$: $y = \square x + \square$

This has the form $y = mx + c$

So, $2x + 3y = 6$ represents a straight line with gradient $\square$ cutting the y-axis at $(0, \square)$.

By rearranging the equation in the form $y = mx + c$, show that each of the following equations represents a straight line and state the gradient of each and the points where it cuts the y-axis.

2 $x + 4y = 8$
3 $7x - y = 14$
4 $x + y - 7 = 0$
5 $2x = y - 4$
6 $4x + 2y = 1$
7 $4x - 5y = 20$
8 $x = 2y - 6$
9 $2x + 5y + 10 = 0$
10 $3y + 6 = 2x$
11 $x + 8y + 16 = 0$
12 $5x - 4y - 2 = 0$
13 $10y - 2x = 15$
14 $x - y = 1$
15 $7x = 2y - 14$
16 $\frac{1}{2}y + 3x = 1$

Continue with Section S

S Drawing the graph of $ax+by=c$

We have seen that the equation $ax + by = c$ represents a straight line. Once we know by looking at an equation that it represents a straight line, we need only find and plot **two points** on the line in order to draw its graph. (A third point may be used as a 'check point'.)

Two suitable points on the line are usually

the point with x-coordinate equal to zero
the point with y-coordinate equal to zero.

Example

Draw the graph of $2x + 3y = 12$.

When $x = 0$ in $2x + 3y = 12$
then $0 + 3y = 12$

and $y = 4$

So, (0, 4) lies on the line.

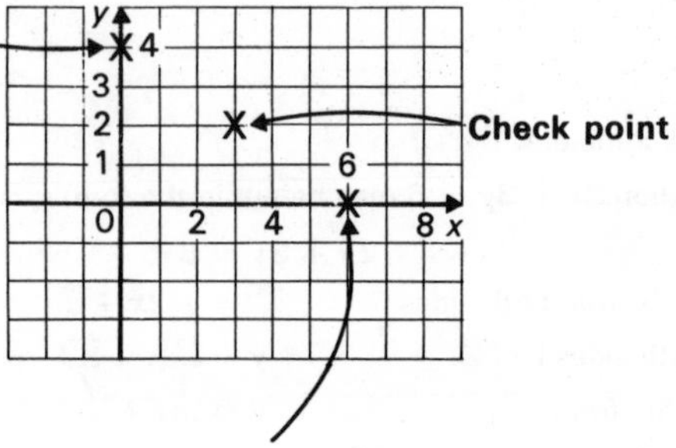

When $y = 0$ in $2x + 3y = 12$
then $2x + 0 = 12$

and $x = 6$ So, (6, 0) lies on the line.

As a check point, take $x = 3$, say.
When $x = 3$ in $2x + 3y = 12$
then $6 + 3y = 12$
Subtract 6 from both sides
$3y = 6$

$y = 2$

So (3, 2) lies on the line.

These three points are joined and the line extended both ways.

The equation of the line is written on the diagram as shown.

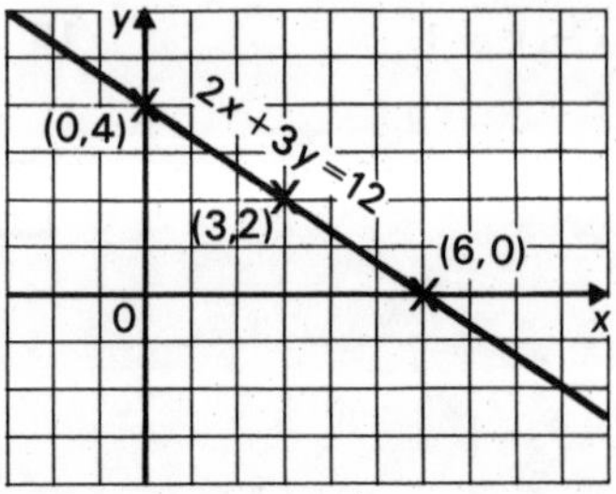

Exercise

1 Copy and complete:

The line with equation $3x + 7y = 21$ may be drawn as follows:

When $x = 0$ in $3x + 7y = 21$

then $0 + ▢ = ▢$

and $y = ▢$

So (0, ▢) lies on the line.

When $y = 0$ in $3x + 7y = 21$

then $▢ + 0 = ▢$

and $x = ▢$

So (▢, 0) lies on the line.

Plot these two points on $\frac{1}{2}$ cm squared paper and draw the line joining them.

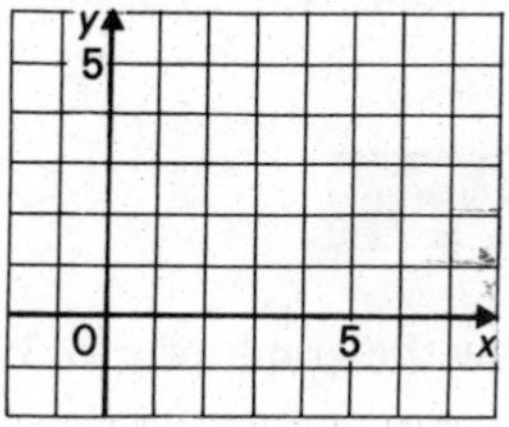

Draw graphs of the following lines on $\frac{1}{2}$ cm squared paper.

2 $2x - 5y = 10$
3 $3x + 2y = -6$
4 $x + 3y = 9$
5 $4x + 5y = 20$
6 $2x - 3y = 12$
7 $5x - 6y = 30$
8 $3x - 8y = 24$
9 $x + y = 1$
10 $x + y = 4$
11 $3x + 6y = 18$
12 $2x - y = -4$
13 $-x + 10y = 10$
14 $7x - y = 14$
15 $4x - y = 2$
16 $x - y = -1$

Continue with Section T

T Drawing the graph of $y = mx + c$

Example

Draw the graph of $y = 2x - 4$.

We can rearrange the equation into the form $ax + by = c$ as follows:

$$y = 2x - 4$$

Subtract $2x$ from both sides: $-2x + y = -4$

which is in the form $ax + by = c$

When $x = 0$ in $-2x + y = -4$

then $y = -4$

and so $(0, -4)$ lies on the line.

When $y = 0$ in $-2x + y = -4$

then $-2x = -4$

and $x = 2$

and so $(2, 0)$ lies on the line.

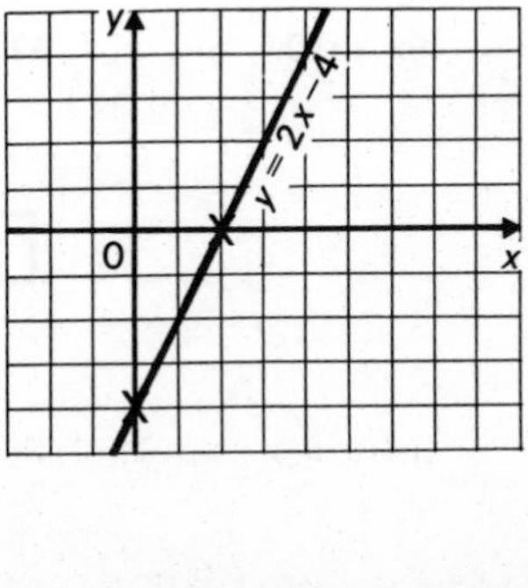

Plot the points (0, –4) and (2, 0) and draw the straight line joining them.

(As a check point):

When $x = 1$ in $-2x + y = -4$

then $-2 + y = -4$

and $y = -2$

The point (1, –2) lies on the line.

Example

Draw the graph of $y = 3x$.

When $x = 0$ in $y = 3x$,

then $y = 0$

So, (0, 0) lies on the line.

When $y = 0$ in $y = 3x$

then $3x = 0$

and $x = 0$

So, (0, 0) lies on the line.

But we need two **distinct** points in order to draw the line, so take another value of x, say $x = 1$.

When $x = 1$ in $y = 3x$

then $y = 3$

So (1, 3) lies on the line.

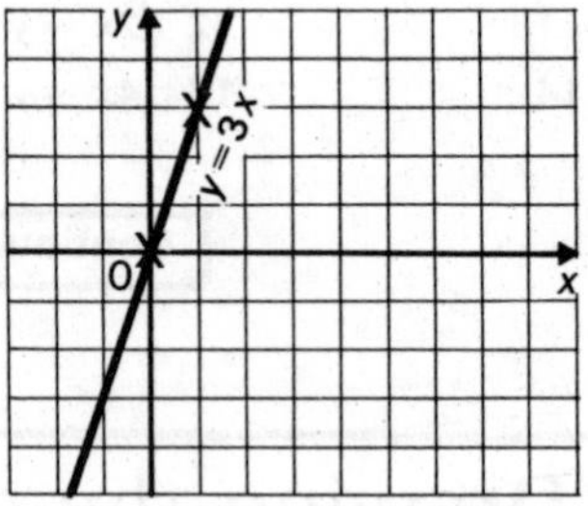

We can now draw the line passing through (0, 0) and (1, 3).

Exercise

Draw graphs of the following lines on $\frac{1}{2}$ cm squared paper.

1 $y = 3x - 5$	2 $y = -2x + 7$	3 $y = 6x$
4 $y = x + 3$	5 $y = 2x - 1$	6 $y = -2x + 3$
7 $y = -2x$	8 $y = x$	9 $y = -x - 4$
10 $y = -5x + 10$	11 $y = -x$	12 $y = 8x + 4$

Continue with Section U

U Progress check

Exercise

1 Use the gradient formula to find the gradients of the lines joining the following points:
(a) $(-1, 6)$ and $(-5, 3)$ (b) $(-4, -3)$ and $(-2, 7)$ (c) $(2, -1)$ and $(-6, 6)$

2

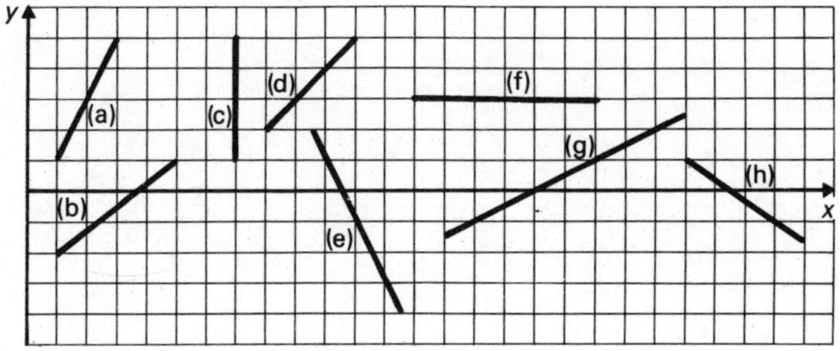

Which line in the diagram has a gradient equal to
(i) 1 (ii) $\frac{1}{2}$ (iii) -2 (iv) $\frac{3}{4}$ (v) 0 (vi) $-\frac{2}{3}$ (vii) 2?
For which line is the gradient not defined?

3 Use the distance formula to calculate the distance between the following points:
(a) $(5, 8)$ and $(1, 6)$ (b) $(3, 8)$ and $(6, -4)$ (c) $(4, 0)$ and $(0, 5)$

4 Rearrange each of the following lines in the form $y = mx + c$ and find (i) its gradient (ii) the point where it cuts the y-axis.
(a) $3y = 4x - 6$ (b) $5x + 2y = 4$ (c) $x - 4y + 12 = 0$.

5 Draw the graph of each of the following lines on $\frac{1}{2}$ cm squared paper
(a) $5x + 6y = 30$ (b) $2x - 3y = 18$ (c) $y = -3x + 7$ (d) $y = -5x$

Tell your teacher you have finished this Unit

UNIT M8
Quadratic Functions and their Graphs

A Functions

Earlier, you discovered that a function acted on a given set of numbers to produce a new set of numbers.

For example, a function f which changes a number x into a new number $2x + 1$ can be written as $f: x \rightarrow 2x + 1$.

We often write $f(x)$ to stand for the new number, called the **value of the function.**
So $f(x) = 2x + 1$.

Example

A function f is defined by the rule $f(x) = 2x + 1$, $x \in \{0, 1, 2, 3\}$. List the set of ordered pairs and draw the graph of the function.

	f	
x	$\longrightarrow$	$2x + 1$
0	$\longrightarrow$	1
1	$\longrightarrow$	3
2	$\longrightarrow$	5
3	$\longrightarrow$	7

We write this as a set of ordered pairs: $\{(0, 1), (1, 3), (2, 5), (3, 7)\}$ and plot the points on a grid.

The set of values $\{1, 3, 5, 7\}$ of the function is called the **range** of the function.

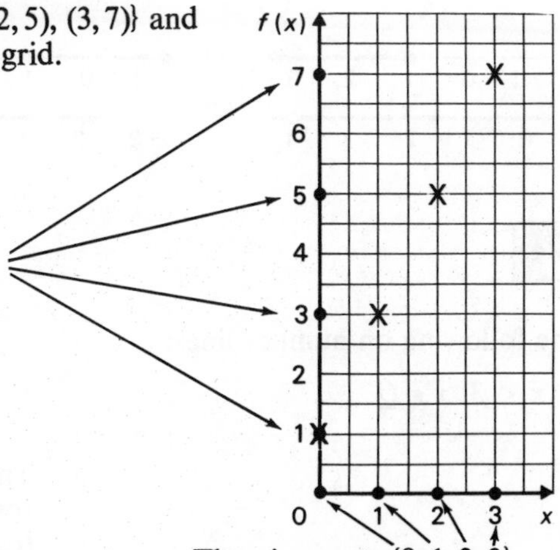

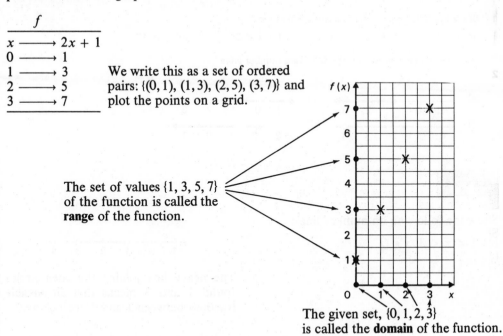

The given set, $\{0, 1, 2, 3\}$ is called the **domain** of the function.

> The **domain** of a function is the set of replacements for x.
> The **range** of a function is the set of values of $f(x)$.

Notice that since the **domain** has only four members the graph is **four crosses**. We must **not** draw a line through them.

Continue with Sheet M8/1

B Sets of numbers

Here are some sets of numbers you will be using in this Unit.

$W = \{0, 1, 2, 3, \ldots\}$ The set of whole numbers.

$Z = \{\ldots, -3, -2, -1, 0, 1, 2, 3, \ldots\}$ The set of integers.

$Q = \{\text{fractions}\}$; Q is made up of all numbers which can be expressed in fraction form – for example $\frac{7}{3}$, $-5\frac{1}{2}$, 36.97, $\frac{36}{1}$.

Example

Show the following on number lines:

(a) $x > 2$, $x \in Q$

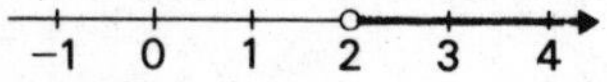

The open circle round 2 means that 2 is *not* included.

(b) $x \leq 2$, $x \in Q$

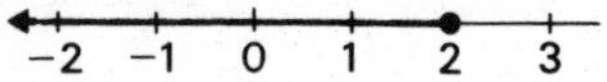

The dot (●) on 2 means that 2 *is* included.

Exercise

1 Show the following on number lines where $x \in Q$.

(a) $x > 0$ (b) $x \geq -1$ (c) $x < 3$ (d) $x \geq 16$

2 Describe the sets shown on the following number lines

(a)

(b)

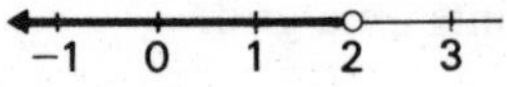

(c)

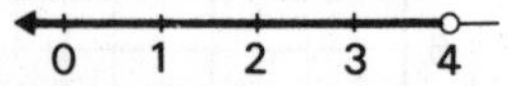

(d)

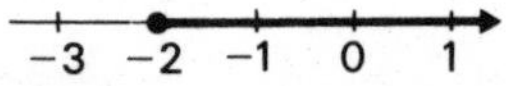

Example

Show the following on number lines:

(a) $1 < x < 3$; $x \in Q$.

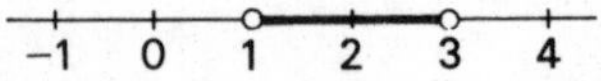

The heavy line joining the open circles round 1 and 3 means that **all possible fractions** between 1 and 3 are included.

(b) $1 \leq x \leq 3$; $x \in Q$.

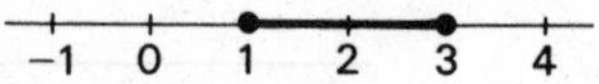

The dots marking 1 and 3 mean that the numbers 1 and 3 are included as well as **all** possible fractions between 1 and 3.

Exercise

3 Show the following on number lines, where $x \in Q$.

(a) $2 \leq x \leq 6$ (b) $1 < x \leq 4$ (c) $-2 < x < 3$ (d) $0 \leq x \leq 6$.

4 Describe the sets shown on the following number lines:

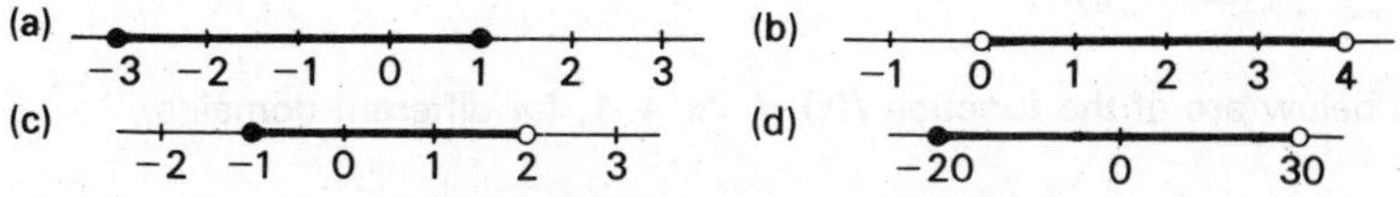

Continue with Section C

C Straight line graphs

Compare the graphs of $f(x) = 3x$ shown below:

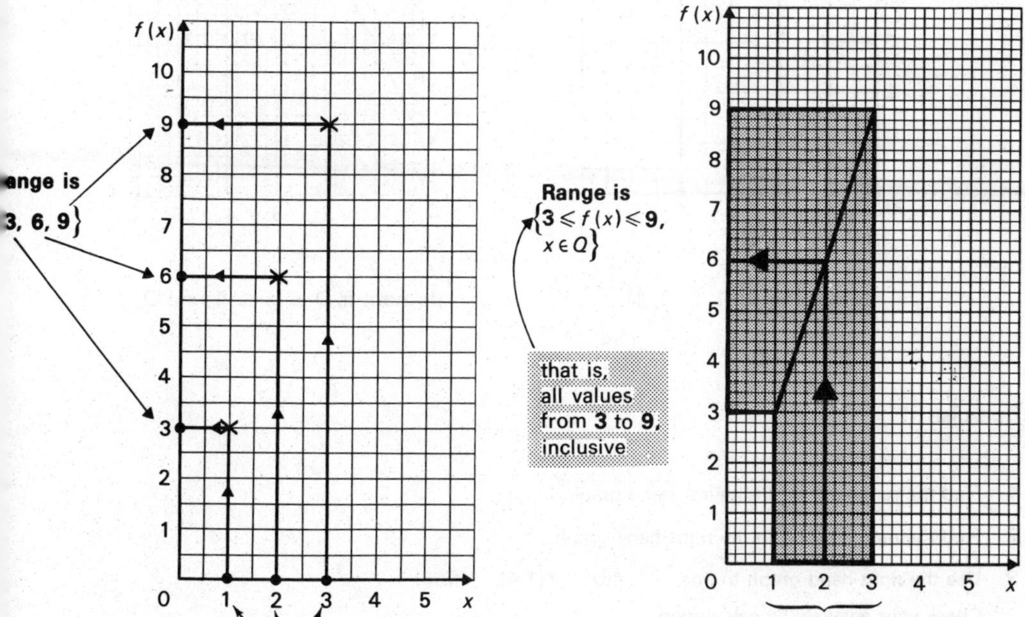

domain is {1, 2, 3} so each point is marked individually with a cross.

domain is $1 \leq x \leq 3$, $x \in Q$. The domain includes **all** the fraction values from 1 to 3. The points on the graph are represented by a continuous line.

Example

Use the graph on the right of the previous page to find $f(1.2)$

$f(1.2) = 3.6$

Check: $f(x) = 3x, x \in Q$
$f(1.2) = 3 \times 1.2$
$= 3.6$

The graphs below are of the function $f(x) = 2x + 1$, for different domains.

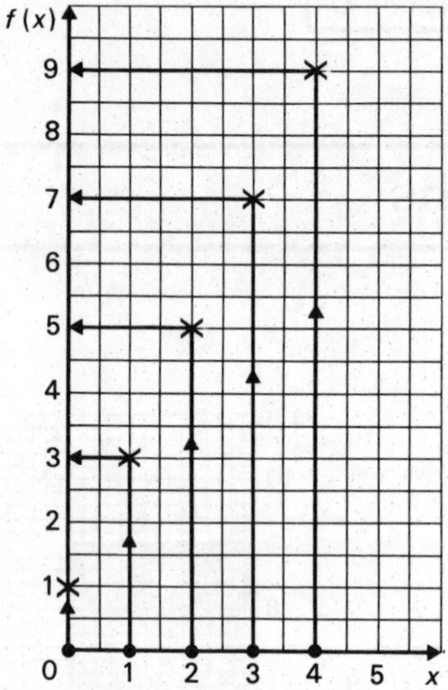

domain is $\{0, 1, 2, 3, 4\}$.

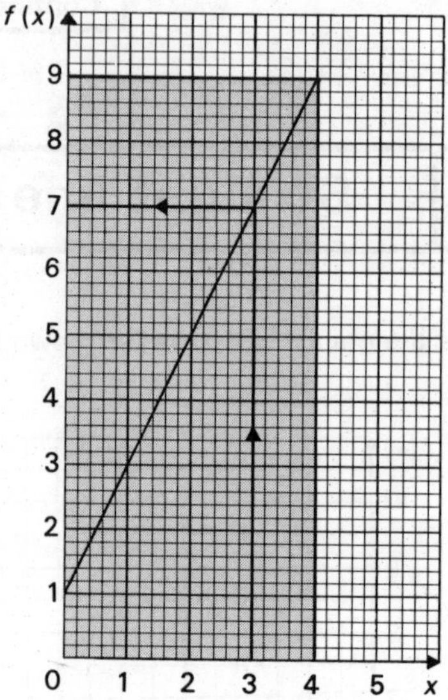

domain is $0 \leq x \leq 4; x \in Q$.

Exercise

1 Find the range of $f(x)$ in the left-hand graph.

2 Find the range of $f(x)$ in the right-hand graph.

3 Use the right-hand graph to find: $f(0)$, $f(1.4)$, $f(3.6)$
Check your answers by calculation.

Continue with Section D

D Tables of values

A function is defined by $f(x) = 2x + 1;\ -3 \leq x \leq 3,\ x \in Q$.

f		
x	$\longrightarrow$	$2x + 1$
-3	$\longrightarrow$	-5
-2	$\longrightarrow$	-3
-1	$\longrightarrow$	-1
0	$\longrightarrow$	1
1	$\longrightarrow$	3
2	$\longrightarrow$	5
3	$\longrightarrow$	7

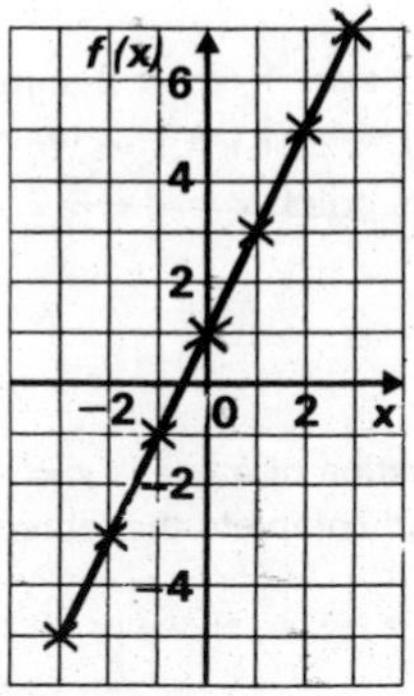

This function produces a set of ordered pairs, some of which are:

$$\{(-3, -5), (-2, -3), (-1, -1), (0, 1), (1, 3), (2, 5), (3, 7)\}$$

The graph of the function is shown above.

If (x, y) is a member of this set of ordered pairs then

second number = (2 × first number) + 1

that is $y = 2x + 1$

The table below is a convenient way of setting out the calculations.

x	-3	-2	-1	0	1	2	3
$2x$ $+1$	-6 $+1$	-4 $+1$	-2 $+1$	0 $+1$	2 $+1$	4 $+1$	6 $+1$
$y = 2x + 1$	-5	-3	-1	1	3	5	7

$-6 + 1 = -5$

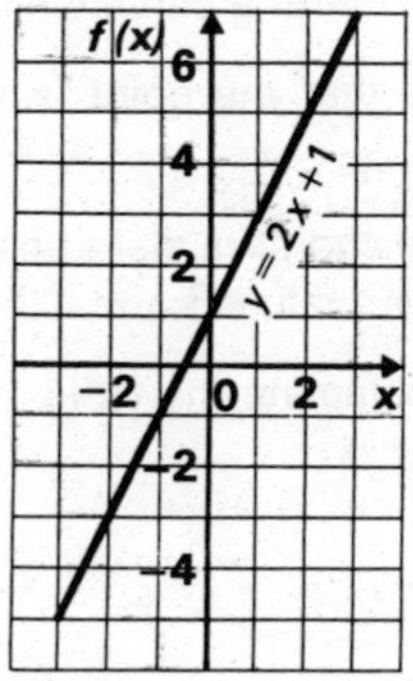

We can draw a graph showing all the points (x, y) like this:

Notice that we write the equation of this line as

$$y = 2x + 1$$

Exercise

1 The equation of a line is $y = 3x + 2; -3 \leq x \leq 2, x \in Q$.
Copy and complete the table; then draw the graph of $y = 3x + 2$ on $\frac{1}{2}$ cm squared paper.

Scales: x-axis, 1 cm = 2 units
y-axis, 1 cm = 2 units

Label the graph $y = 3x + 2$.

x	-3	-2	-1	0	1	2
$3x$ $+2$	-9 $+2$					
$y = 3x + 2$	-7					

$-9 + 2 = -7$

2 The equation of a line is $y = -4x - 3; -2 \leq x \leq 1, x \in Q$.
Copy and complete the table; then draw the graph of $y = 3x + 2$ on $\frac{1}{2}$ cm squared paper.

Scales: x-axis, 1 cm = 2 units
y-axis, 1 cm = 2 units

Label the graph.

x	-2	-1	0	1
$-4x$ -3	8 -3			
$y = -4x - 3$	5			

$8 - 3 = 5$

Continue with Section E

E Curves

So far the functions we have studied could be represented by straight line (or **linear**) graphs.

For the remainder of this Unit we are going to study functions that can be represented by curves (or **non-linear** graphs).

We will start with a curve which has the equation $y = x^2$.

This means that the point (x, y) will lie on the curve if the y coordinate is the square of the x coordinate.

To draw the curve we make up a table of values for $y = x^2; -3 \leq x \leq 3, x \in Q$. For convenience we select integer values from -3 to 3.

Copy and complete the table.

x	-3	-2	-1	0	1	2	3
$y = x^2$	9						

$(-3) \times (-3) = 9$

Remember: The product of two **negative** numbers is a **positive** number.

List the set of ordered pairs:
{(−3, 9), (−2, □), (−1, □), (0, □), (1, □), (2, □), (3, □)}

Plot these points on a grid like the one on the right and draw a smooth curve through them. Label the curve $y = x^2$.

A curve with this shape is called a **parabola.**

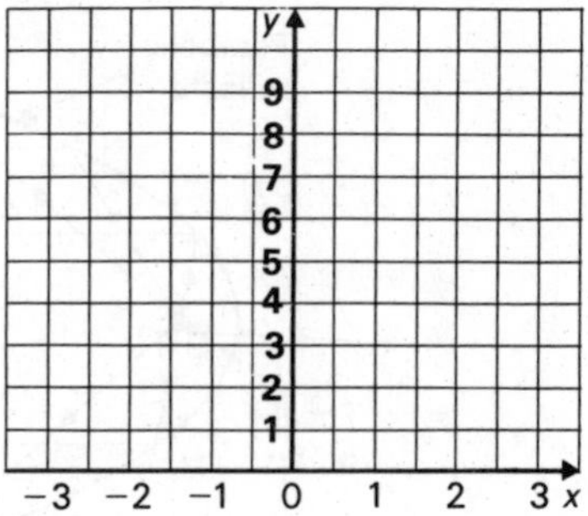

Continue with Section F

F The parabola

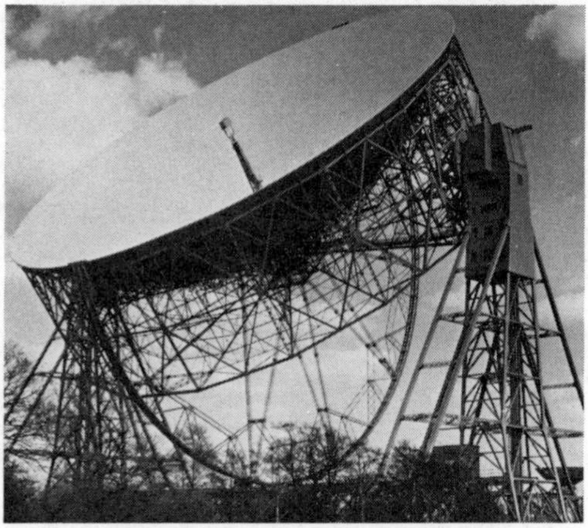

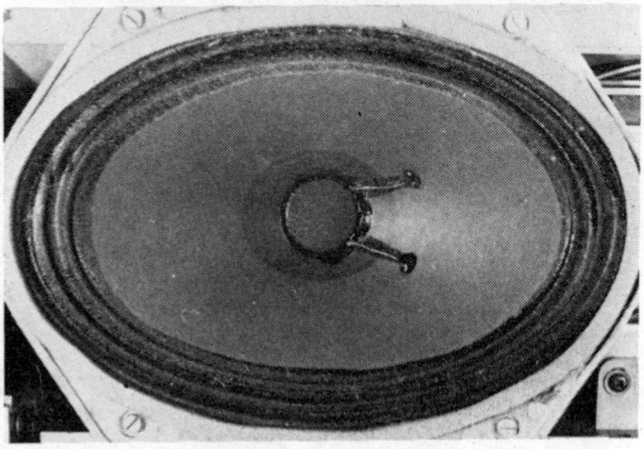

The cross-sections of torch reflectors, car headlamps, and radar aerials all have the shape of a parabola.

A light bulb placed at the focal point of a parabolic curve produces a beam of light rays which are parallel. Some of the rays have been drawn below.

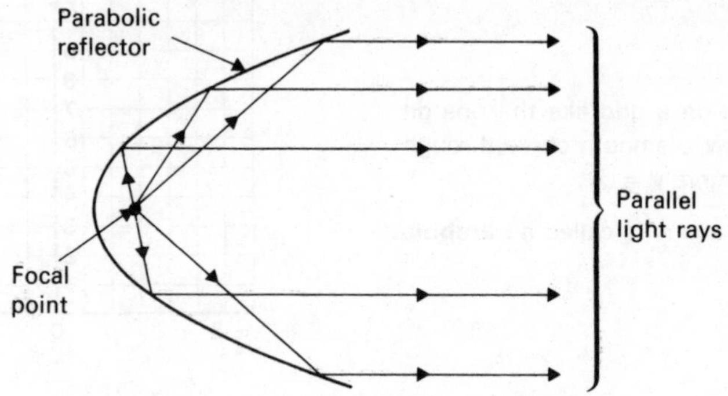

Step 1

Take a piece of tracing paper and a pencil.

Carefully trace the parabola shown here.

Label the tracing **A** as shown.

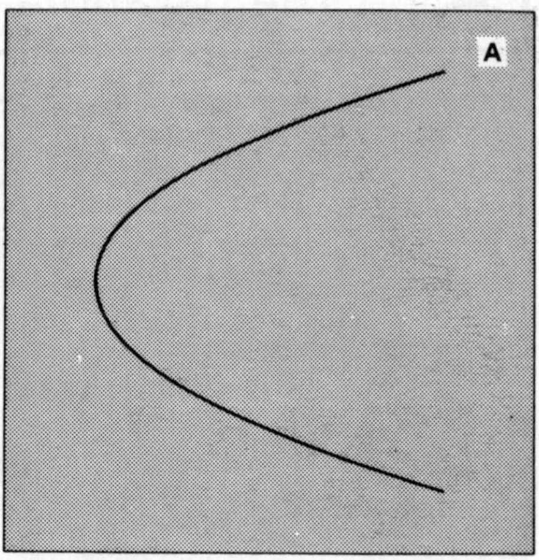

Step 2

Fold the tracing so that one half of the curve fits on the other half and make a crease along the fold.

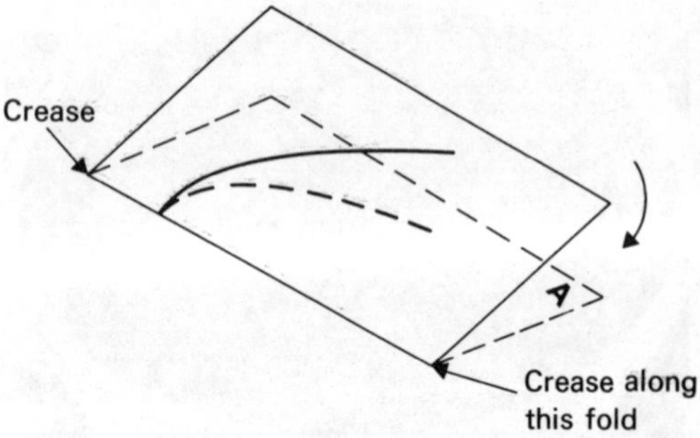

Step 3

Lay the tracing flat and draw a line along the crease. Label this line **'axis of symmetry'**.

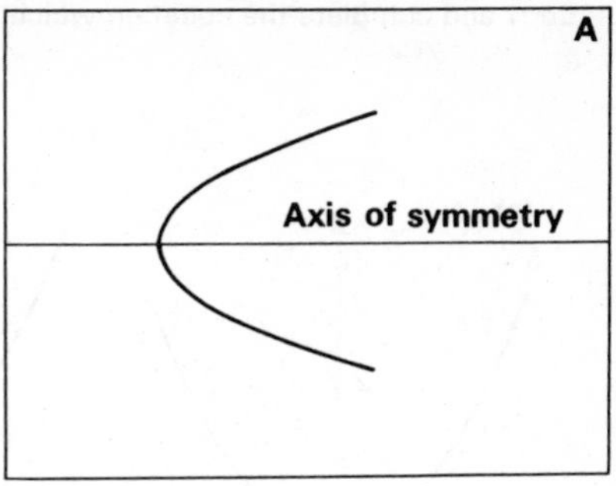

Keep your tracing

Exercise

The curve $y = x^2$, which you drew earlier, is shown again here.

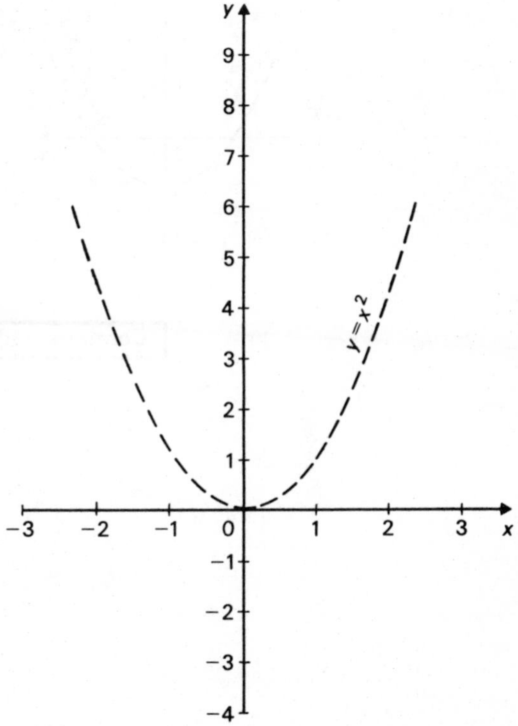

1 (a) Take your tracing and match it with this curve.

The axis of symmetry lies on the y-axis.

In this position the curve on your tracing has the equation $y = x^2$.

Which of the sketches shown in question 2 illustrates this?

(b) Move the curve on your tracing upwards to 1 on the y-axis, keeping the axis of symmetry along the y-axis.

Each value of x^2 has been increased by 1.

So in this position the equation of the curve is $y = x^2 + 1$.

Which of the sketches shown in question 2 illustrates this?

(c) Move the curve on your tracing up to 2 on the y-axis. The equation of the curve in this position is $y = x^2 + 2$.

Which of the sketches shown in question 2 illustrates this?

(d) Move the curve on your tracing so that its equation becomes $y = x^2 - 1$. Which of the sketches shown in question 2 illustrates this?

(e) Move the curve on your tracing so that its equation becomes $y = x^2 - 2$. Which of the sketches show in question 2 illustrates this?

2 Copy and complete the equation which appears on each curve.

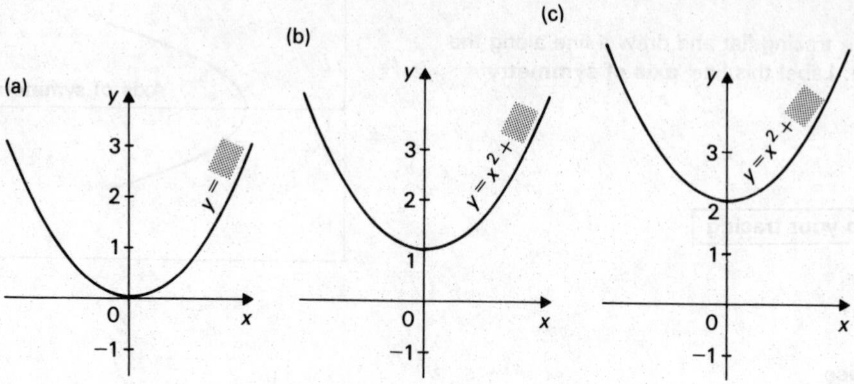

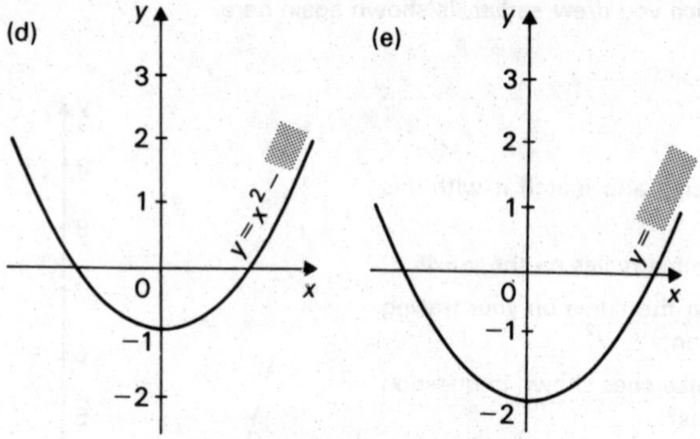

Continue with Section G

G $y=x^2+k$

Example

Draw the graph of $y = x^2 + 3$; $-3 \leq x \leq 3$, $x \in Q$ and state the equation of the axis of symmetry.

Make a table of values like this, choosing suitable values of x.

$(-3) \times (-3) = 9$ → 9; $(-2) \times (-2) = 4$ → 4

x	-3	-2	-1	0	1	2	3
x^2 $+3$	9 $+3$	4 $+3$	1 $+3$	0 $+3$	1 $+3$	4 $+3$	9 $+3$
$y = x^2 + 3$	12	7	4	3	4	7	12

$9 + 3 = 12$ → 12; $4 + 3 = 7$ → 7

List the set of ordered pairs:

$(-3, 12), (-2, 7), (-1, 4), (0, 3), (1, 4), (2, 7), (3, 12)$

Choose suitable scales.

The y-axis must extend from 0 to 12 and the x-axis must extend from -3 to 3.

Plot the points and draw a smooth curve through them.

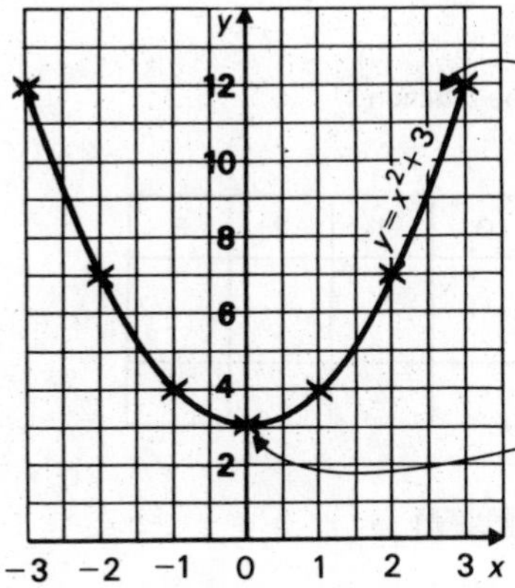

Label the curve $y = x^2 + 3$

Take care to make the curve smooth at the lowest point.

The axis of symmetry is the y-axis.

All points on the y-axis have their x coordinate equal to zero.

So the axis of symmetry is the line $x = 0$.

Exercise

Draw the following curves on $\frac{1}{2}$ cm squared paper, using the same scales for the axes as in the previous example.

1 The table below shows values of the function with equation
$y = x^2 + 4; -3 \leq x \leq 3, x \in Q$.

x	-3	-2	-1	0	1	2	3
x^2 $+4$	9 $+4$	4 $+4$	1 $+4$	0 $+4$	1 $+4$	4 $+4$	9 $+4$
$y = x^2 + 4$	13	8	5	4	5	8	13

Copy and complete the list of ordered pairs.

{(−3, 13), (−2, 8), (−1, ▢), (0, ▢), (1, ▢), (2, ▢), (3, ▢)}

Draw the curve and label it.

Use tracing A to check your graph.

State the equation of the axis of symmetry.

2 The table below shows values of the function with equation
$y = x^2 + 3; -3 \leq x \leq 3, x \in Q$.

x	-3	-2	-1	0	1	2	3
x^2 $+3$	9 $+3$	4 $+3$	1 $+3$	0 $+3$	1 $+3$	4 $+3$	9 $+3$
$y = x^2 + 3$	12	7	4	3	4	7	12

Copy and complete the list of ordered pairs.

{(−3, ▢), (−2, ▢), (−1, ▢), (0, ▢), (▢, ▢), (▢, ▢), (▢, ▢)}

Draw the curve and label it.

Use tracing A to check your graph.

State the equation of the axis of symmetry.

3 Copy and complete the table, which shows values of the function with equation $y = x^2 - 3; -3 \leq x \leq 3, x \in Q$.

x	-3	-2	-1	0	1	2	3
x^2 -3	9 -3	4 -3					
$y = x^2 - 3$	6	1					

Copy and complete the list of ordered pairs.

{(−3, 6), (−2, 1), (▢, ▢), (▢, ▢), (▢, ▢), (▢, ▢), (▢, ▢)}

Draw the curve and label it.

Use tracing A to check your graph.

State the equation of the axis of symmetry.

Continue with Section H

H $y = -x^2 + k$

Exercise

1 Draw the curve $y = -x^2$; $-3 \le x \le 3$, $x \in Q$.

Copy and complete the following table of values.

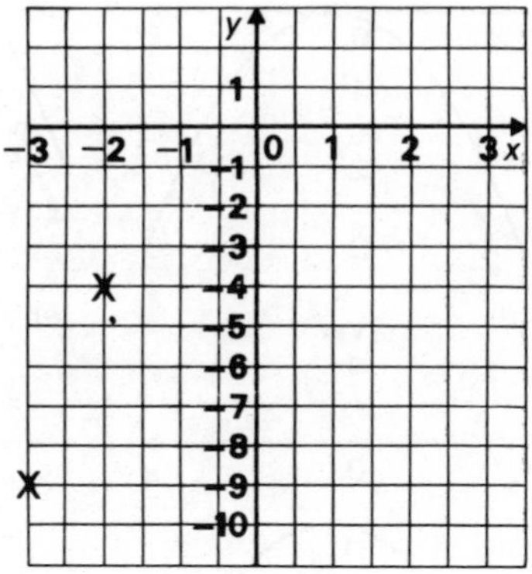

x	-3	-2	-1	0	1	2	3
x^2	9	4	1	0	1	4	9
$y = -x^2$	-9	-4					

List the set of ordered pairs

{(−3, −9), (−2, −4), (−1, □), (0, □), (1, −1), (2, □), (3, □)}

Plot these points on a grid like the one opposite and draw a smooth curve through them.

Label the curve $y = -x^2$. The curve is a **parabola.**

Note that the negative coefficient of x^2 reflects the graph of $y = x^2$ in the x-axis.

2 (a) As before, the axis of symmetry lies on the y-axis.

In this position the equation of the curve is $y = -x^2$.

Which of the sketches shown in question 3 illustrates this?

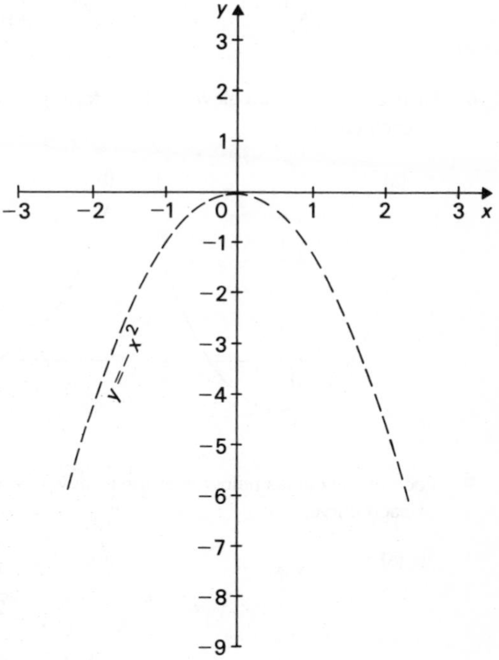

(b) Move the curve on your tracing upwards to 1 on the y-axis, keeping the axis of symmetry on the y-axis. Each value of $-x^2$ has been increased by 1.

So in this position the equation of the curve is $y = -x^2 + 1$.

Which of the sketches shown in question 3 illustrates this?

(c) Move the curve on your tracing so that its equation becomes $y = -x^2 + 2$.

Which of the sketches shown in question 3 illustrates this?

(d) Move the curve on your tracing so that its equation becomes $y = -x^2 - 1$.

Which of the sketches shown in question 3 illustrates this?

(e) Move the curve on your tracing so that its equation becomes $y = -x^2 - 2$. Which of the sketches shown in question 3 illustrates this?

(f) Move the curve on your tracing so that its equation becomes $y = -x^2 - 2\frac{1}{2}$. Which of the sketches shown in question 3 illustrates this?

3 Copy and complete the equation which appears on each curve.

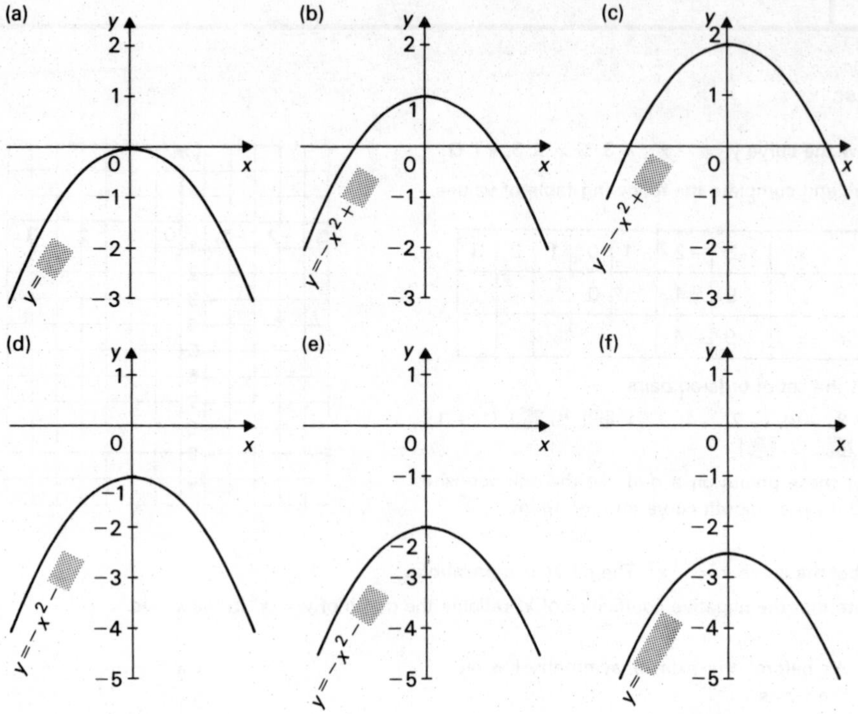

4 Each of the curves below is of the form $y = x^2 + k$, where k is an integer. Write down the equation of each curve.

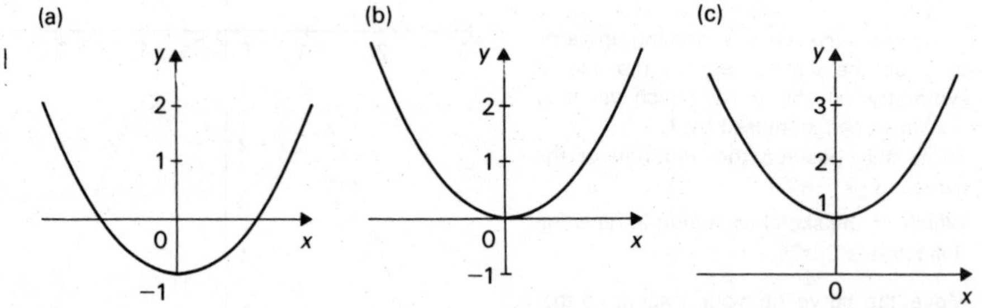

5 Each of the curves below is of the form $y = -x^2 + k$, where k is an integer. Write down the equation of each curve.

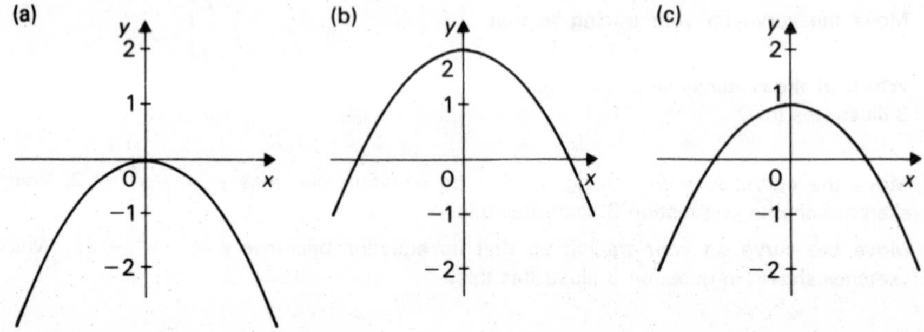

Example

Sketch the curve with equation $y = -x^2 + 1$, where the domain is $-2 \le x \le 2$, and state the equation of the axis of symmetry.

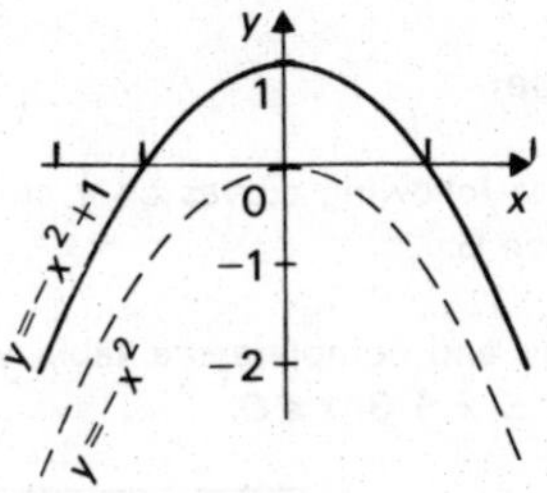

Axis of symmetry $x = 0$

Exercise

Copy each of the following diagrams and then sketch the curves with equations given below, where the domain is $-2 \le x \le 2$.

State the equation of the axis of symmetry in each case.

6 $y = -x^2 - 1$

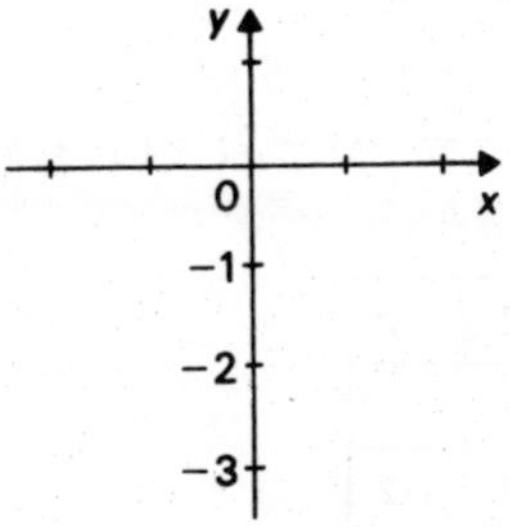

Axis of symmetry: $x =$

7 $y = -x^2 + 2$

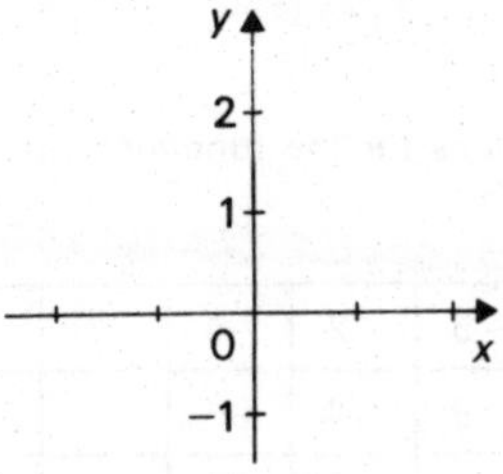

Axis of symmetry:

8 $y = -x^2 + 4$

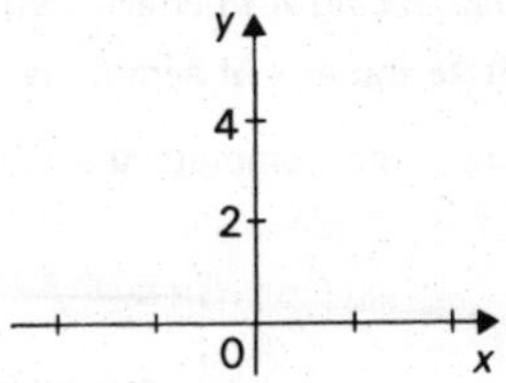

Axis of symmetry:

9 $y = x^2$

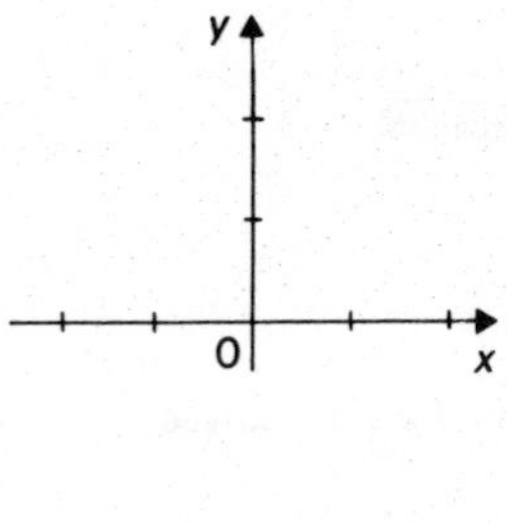

Axis of symmetry:

10 $y = x^2 - 3$

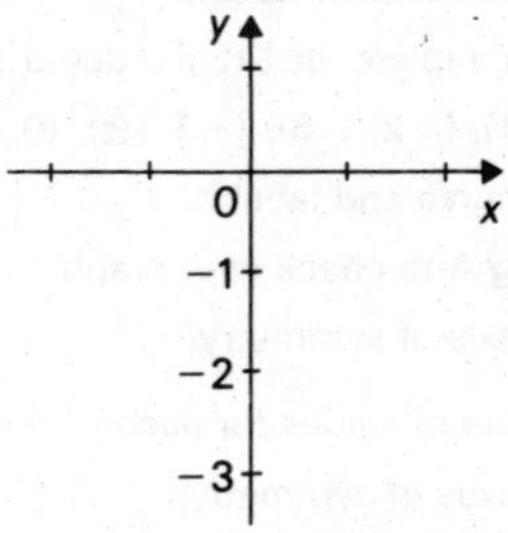

Axis of symmetry:

Continue with Section I

I More tables of values

Exercise

Draw the following curves on $\frac{1}{2}$ cm squared paper, using the same scales for the axes as in the example in Section G.

1 Copy and complete the table which shows values of the function with equation $y = -x^2 + 3$; $-3 \leq x \leq 3$, $x \in Q$.

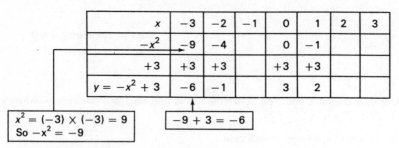

x	−3	−2	−1	0	1	2	3
$-x^2$	−9	−4		0	−1		
+3	+3	+3		+3	+3		
$y = -x^2 + 3$	−6	−1		3	2		

$x^2 = (-3) \times (-3) = 9$
So $-x^2 = -9$

$-9 + 3 = -6$

Copy and complete the list of ordered pairs.

{(−3, −6), (−2, −1), (−1, □), (0, □), (1, □), (2, □), (3, □)}

Draw the curve and label it.

Use tracing A to check your graph.

State the axis of symmetry.

2 Copy and complete the table of values for the function with equation $y = -x^2 - 2$; $-3 \leq x \leq 3$, $x \in Q$.

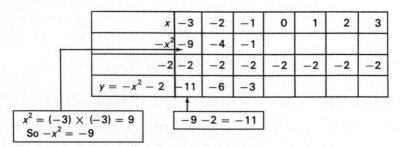

x	−3	−2	−1	0	1	2	3
$-x^2$	−9	−4	−1				
−2	−2	−2	−2	−2	−2	−2	−2
$y = -x^2 - 2$	−11	−6	−3				

$x^2 = (-3) \times (-3) = 9$
So $-x^2 = -9$

$-9 - 2 = -11$

Copy and complete the list of ordered pairs.

{(−3, −11), (−2, −6), (−1, □), (0, □), (□, □), (□, □), (□, □)}

Draw the curve and label it.

Use tracing A to check your graph.

State the axis of symmetry.

3 Make a table of values for each of the following equations and draw the curves.

State the axes of symmetry.

(a) $y = -x^2 + 1$; $-4 \leq x \leq 4$, $x \in Q$

(b) $y = -x^2 - 3$; $-3 \leq x \leq 3$, $x \in Q$

Continue with Section J

J Turning points

Look at the picture below. It represents a boy pulling a sledge up a hill and sledging down the other side.

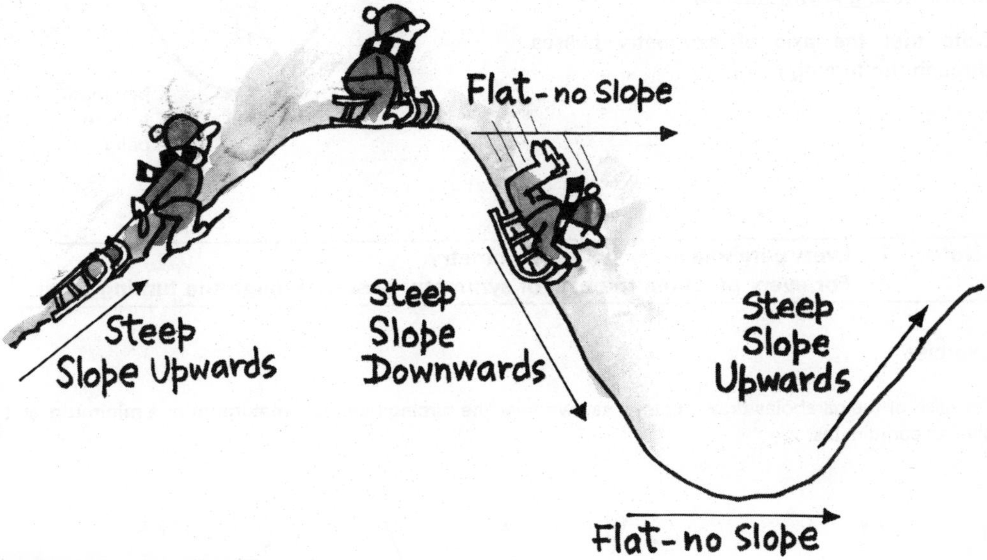

Going up the hill the slope is steep.

At the top of the hill there is **no** slope—the sledge is **horizontal**.

Going down the hill the slope is again steep.

The point at which the slope changes from steep upwards to steep downwards is called the **maximum turning point.**

In the valley the point at which the slope changes from steep downwards to steep upwards is called the **minimum turning point**.

The parabola with equation $y = -x^2 + 3$ is drawn here. The curve has a **maximum** turning point at $(0, 3)$. The maximum value is $y = 3$.

Take tracing A and match it with the curve.

Note that the turning point lies on the axis of symmetry.

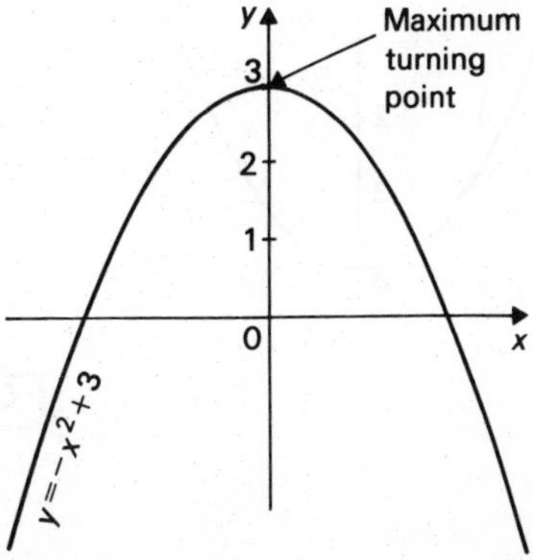

The parabola with equation $y = x^2 - 2$ is drawn here. The curve has a **minimum** turning point at (0, −2). The **minimum** value is $y = -2$.

Match tracing A with the curve.

Note that the axis of symmetry passes through the turning point.

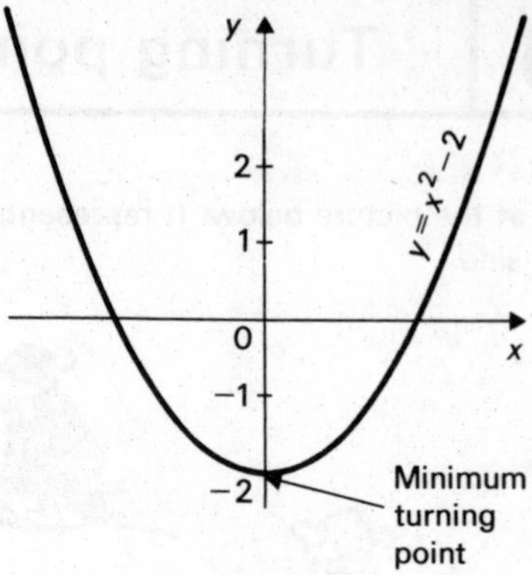

Note:	**1**	**Every parabola has an axis of symmetry.**
	2	**For every parabola the axis of symmetry passes through the turning point.**

Exercise

For each of the parabolas drawn below, say whether the turning point is a **maximum** or a **minimum**, and give its coordinates.

1

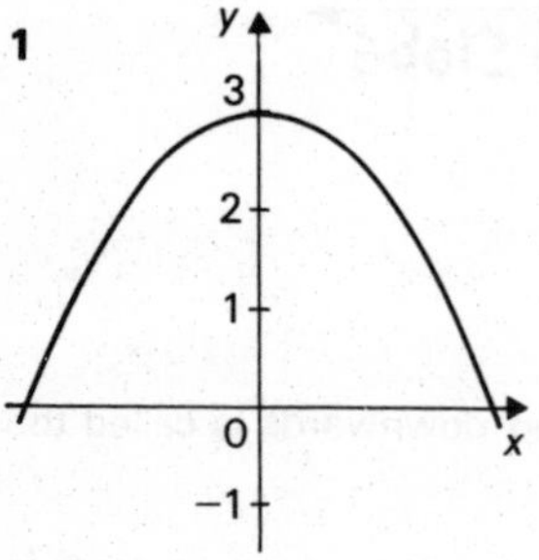

2

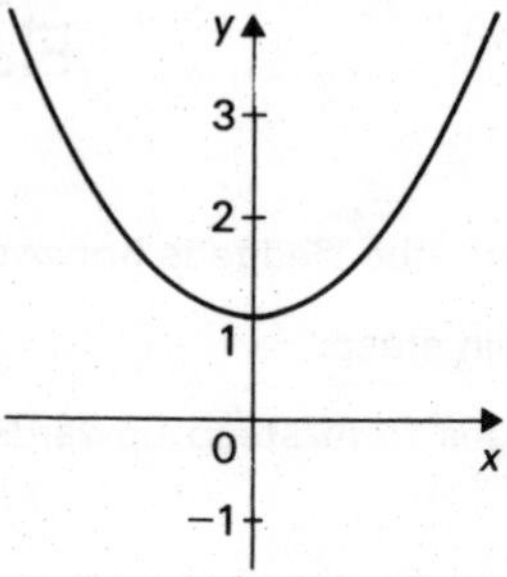

3

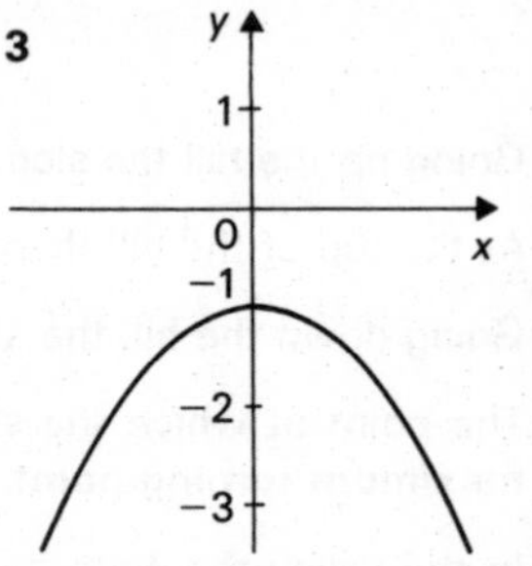

4

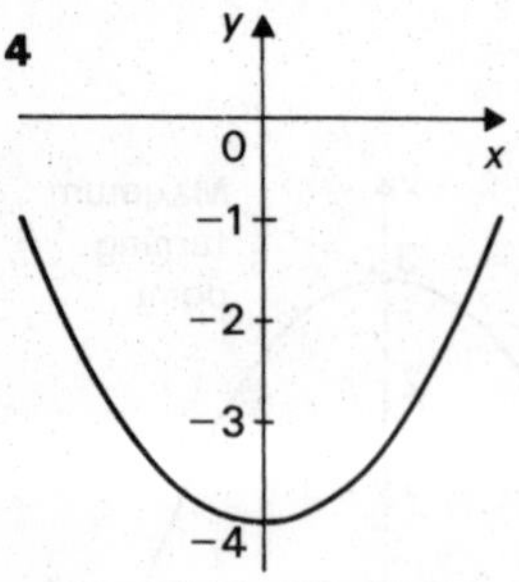

5

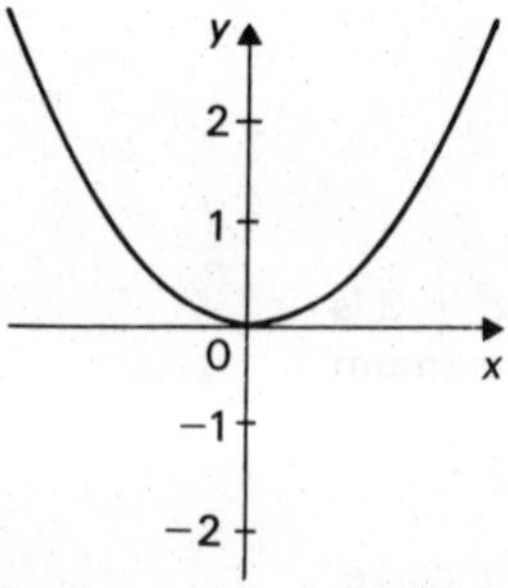

6

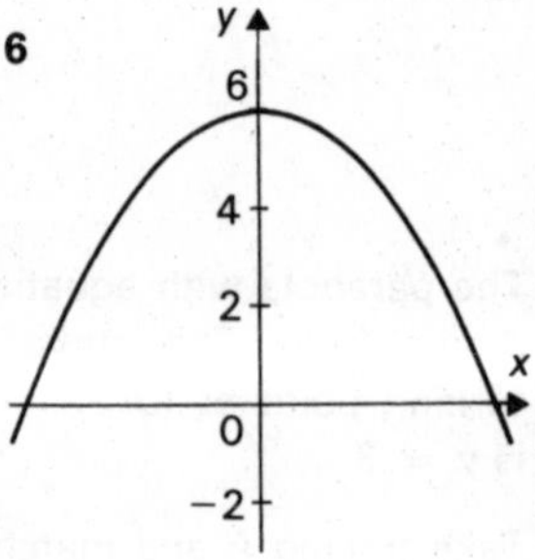

Continue with Section K

K $y = kx^2$

The graph of $y = x^2$, $x \in Q$ is drawn on the grid shown. Copy and complete the diagram.

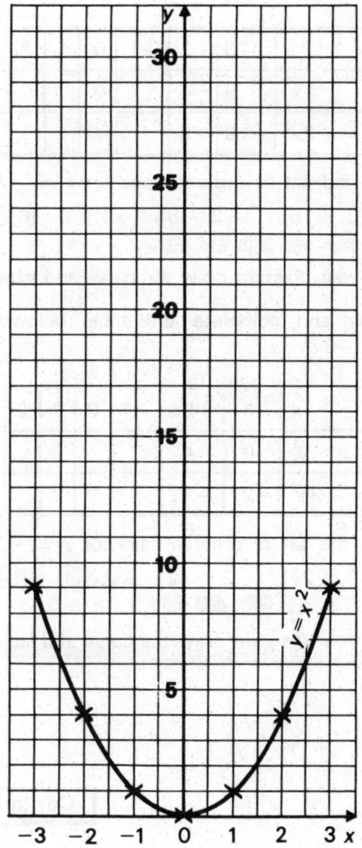

Exercise

1 Copy and complete the table below for $y = 2x^2$.

x	−3	−2	−1	0	1	2	3
x^2	9	4					
$y = 2x^2$	18	8					

List the set of ordered pairs for $y = 2x^2$.
{(−3, 18), (−2, 8), (−1, ▢), (0, ▢), (▢, ▢), (▢, ▢), (▢, ▢)}
On your diagram draw the curve and label it.

2 Copy and complete the table below for $y = 3x^2$.

x	−3	−2	−1	0	1	2	3
x^2	9	4					
$y = 3x^2$	27	12					

List the set of ordered pairs for $y = 3x^2$.
{(−3, 27), (−2, 12), (1, ▢), (▢, ▢), (▢, ▢), (▢, ▢), (▢, ▢)}.
On your diagram, draw the curve and label it.

The graph of $y = -x^2$, $x \in Q$ is drawn on the grid shown.
Copy and complete the diagram.

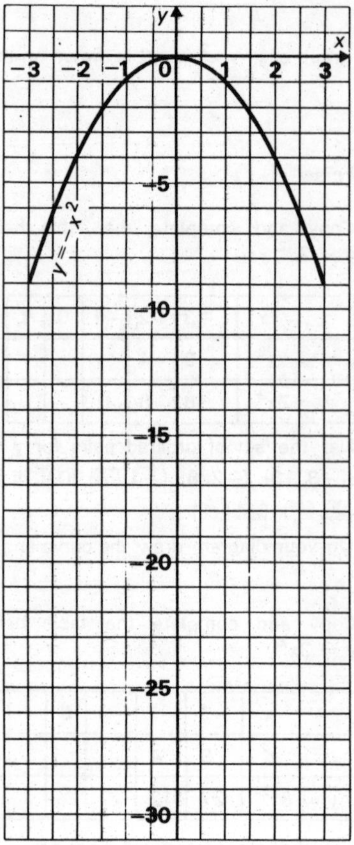

Exercise

3 Copy and complete the table below for $y = -2x^2$.

x	−3	−2	−1	0	1	2	3
x^2	9	4	1	0			
$y = -2x^2$	−18	−8					

List the set of ordered pairs for $y = -2x^2$.
{(−3, −18), (−2, −8), (−1, ▢), (0, ▢), (▢, ▢), (▢, ▢), (▢, ▢)}

On your diagram draw the curve and label it.

4 Copy and complete the table below for $y = -3x^2$.

x	−3	−2	−1	0	1	2	3
x^2	9	4					
$y = -3x^2$	−27	−12					

List the set of ordered pairs for $y = -3x^2$.
{(−3, −27), (−2, −12), (▢, ▢), (▢, ▢), (▢, ▢), (▢, ▢), (▢, ▢)}

On your diagram draw the curve and label it.

Continue with Section L

L $y = x^2 + ax + b$

So far the parabolas we have drawn have been symmetrical about the y-axis (equation of the axis of symmetry is $x = 0$). As we shall see, this is not always the case.

Example

Draw the curve with equation $y = x^2 + 2x + 1$; $-4 \leq x \leq 2$, $x \in Q$.

x	−4	−3	−2	−1	0	1	2
x^2	16	9	4	1	0	1	4
$+2x$	−8	−6	−4	−2	0	2	4
$+1$	+1	+1	+1	+1	+1	+1	+1
$y = x^2 + 2x + 1$	9	4	1	0	1	4	9

$16 - 8 + 1 = 9$

List the set of ordered pairs:

{(−4, 9), (−3, 4), (−2, 1), (−1, 0), (0, 1), (1, 4), (2, 9)}

Plot these points.

Because $x \in Q$ we can draw a smooth curve through the points.

Take tracing A and fit it over the curve.

As the tracing fits exactly the curve is a parabola but it is not symmetrical about the *y*-axis, unlike the previous curves.

The curve is symmetric about a line parallel to the *y*-axis and 1 unit to the left.

All points on this line have an *x* coordinate equal to −1, so the equation of the axis of symmetry is $x = -1$.

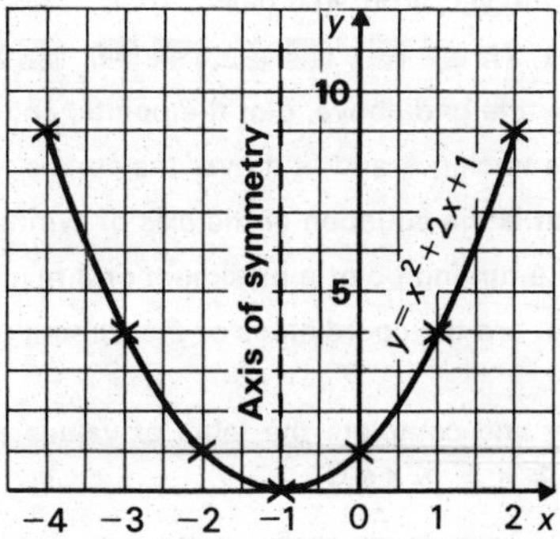

The curve has a minimum turning point with coordinates (−1, 0).

Note that the axis of symmetry passes through the minimum turning point.

Exercise

1 Draw the graph of $y = x^2 - 2x - 2$, $-2 \leq x \leq 4$, $x \in Q$

Copy and complete the table of values.

x	−2	−1	0	1	2	3	4
x^2	4	1	0				
$-2x$	4	2					
-2	−2	−2					
$y = x^2 - 2x - 2$	6	1					

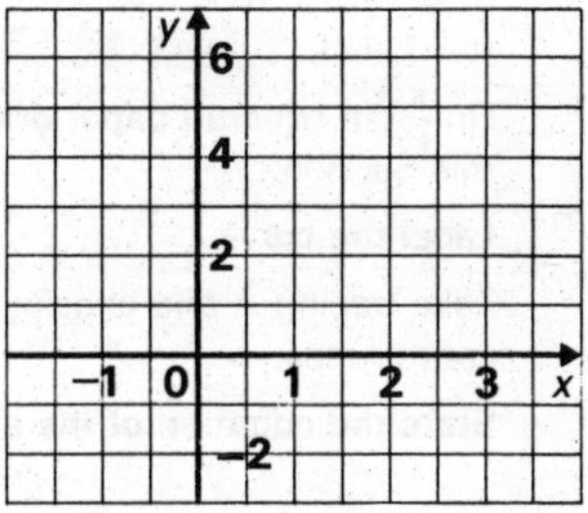

List the set of ordered pairs:

{(−2, 6), (−1, 1), (0, □), (1, □), (□, □), (□, □), (□, □)}

Copy the grid on the previous page. Plot the points and draw a smooth curve through them.

Take tracing A and fit it over the curve.

What is the equation of the axis of symmetry?

Is it a maximum or minimum turning point?

What are the coordinates of the turning point?

2 Draw the graph of $y = x^2 - 4x + 2$; $-1 \leq x \leq 5$, $x \in Q$,

Copy and complete the table of values.

x	−1	0	1	2	3	4	5
x^2	1	0	1				
$-4x$	4						
$+2$	+2						
$y = x^2 - 4x + 2$	7						

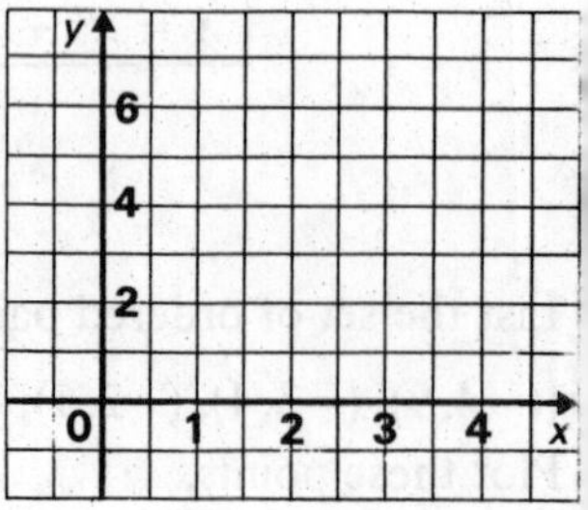

List the set of ordered pairs:

{(−1, 7), (□, □), (□, □), (□, □), (□, □), (□, □), (□, □)}

Copy the grid above, plot the points, and draw a smooth curve through them.

Take tracing A and fit it over the curve.

What is the equation of the axis of symmetry?

Is the turning point a maximum or a minimum?

What are the coordinates of the turning point?

3 Copy and complete the table of values and then draw the curve with equation $y = x^2 - 2x - 3$; $-3 \leq x \leq 5$, $x \in Q$.

x	−3	−2	−1	0	1	2	3	4	5
x^2	9								
$-2x$	6			0			−6		
-3	−3	−3	−3	−3	−3	−3	−3	−3	−3
$y = x^2 - 2x - 3$	12		0						2

Copy and complete the set of ordered pairs.

{(−3, 12), (□, □), (□, □), (□, □), (□, □), (□, □), (□, □), (□, □), (□, □)}

On $\frac{1}{2}$ cm squared paper draw axes with the same scales as in the worked example at the beginning of this Section.

Label the curve.

Take tracing A and check your graph. Say if it has a maximun or a minimum turning point and state its coordinates.

State the equation of the axis of symmetry.

Continue with Section M

M Progress check

Exercise

1 Draw number lines to show the following:

(a) $-2 \le x \le 3, x \in Q$ (b) $1 < x \le 5, \quad x \in Q$

2 Describe the intervals shown on the following number lines:

(a)

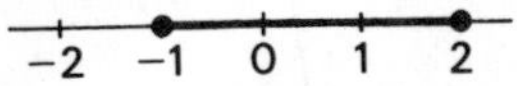

(b)

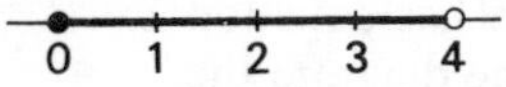

3 On $\frac{1}{2}$ cm squared paper draw the curve with equation $y = x^2 - 4$; $-4 \le x \le 4, x \in Q$. State the equation of the axis of symmetry.

4 For each of the following curves:

(a) Say whether it has a maximum or a minimum turning point and state its coordinates.

(b) State the equation of the axis of symmetry.

(i)

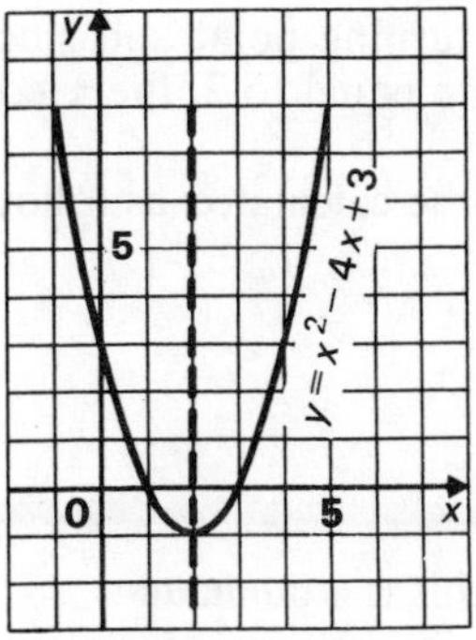

(ii)

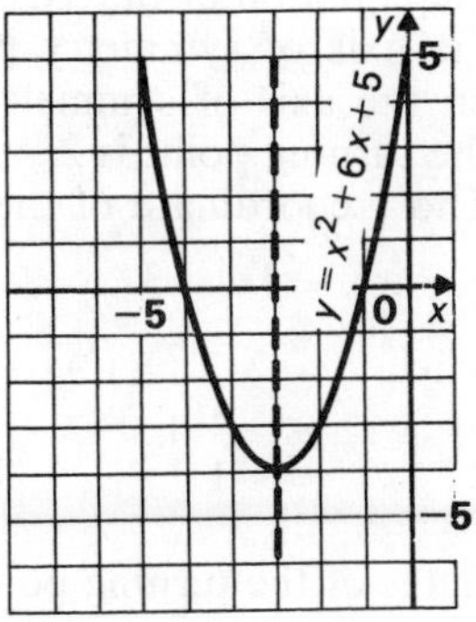

(iii)

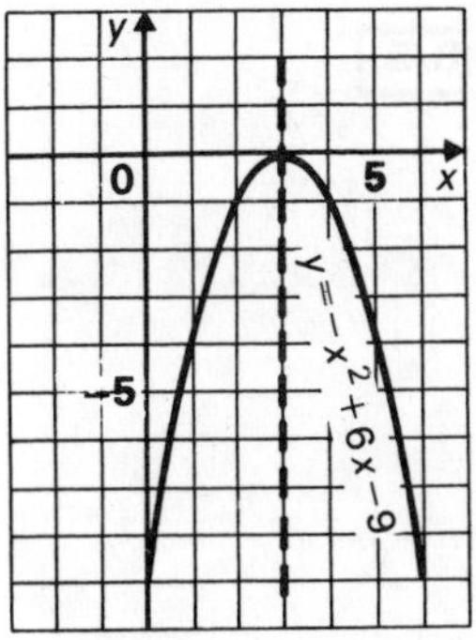

(iv)

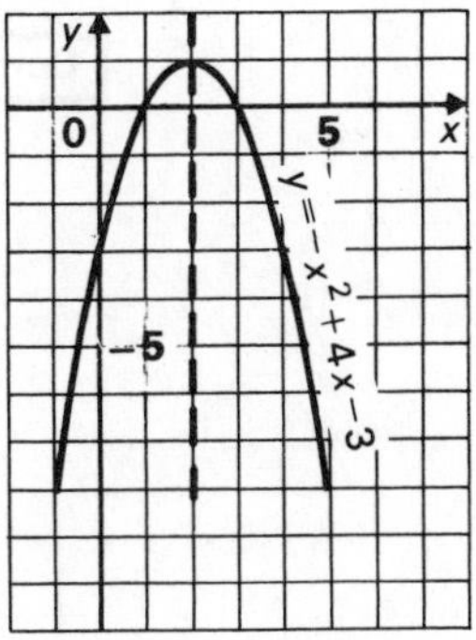

5 On $\frac{1}{2}$ cm squared paper draw the curve with equation $y = -x^2 + 2x + 3$; $-2 \le x \le 4, x \in Q$. Say whether it has a maximum or a minimum turning point and state its coordinates. State the axis of symmetry.

Ask your teacher what to do next

N Calculating turning values

When we know the equation of the axis of symmetry we can determine the coordinates of the maximum or minimum turning point.

Example

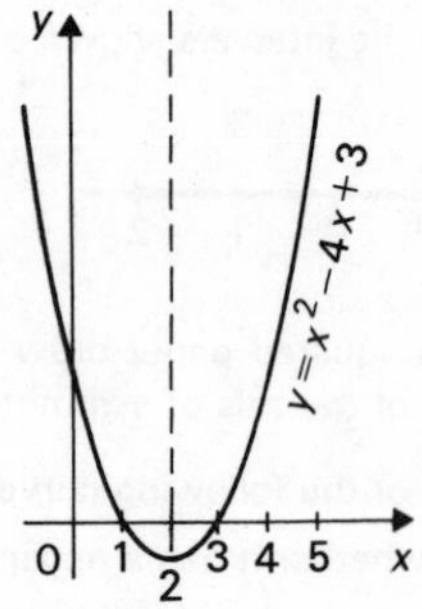

The curve shown opposite has equation $y = x^2 - 4x + 3$. From the diagram the axis of symmetry will be a line parallel to the y-axis passing half way between the points (1, 0) and (3, 0), that is, passing through the point (2, 0). So all points on the axis of symmetry will have x coordinate equal to 2.

Hence (i) the equation of the axis of symmetry is $x = 2$;

(ii) the axis of symmetry passes through the turning point and since all points on the axis of symmetry have x coordinate equal to 2, the x coordinate of the turning point is 2:

(iii) The y coordinate of the turning point can be calculated as follows

$$y = x^2 - 4x + 3$$

$$\text{when } x = 2,\ y = (2)^2 - 4(2) + 3 = 4 - 8 + 3$$
$$= -4 + 3$$
$$= -1$$

The coordinates of the turning point are (2, −1) and this is a **minimum**.

Continue with Sheet M8/2

O Recognizing quadratic functions

The curves we have drawn so far are all graphs of **quadratic** functions.

The following are examples of quadratic functions.

$f(x) = x^2$
$f(x) = x^2 - 4x + 3$
$f(x) = x^2 - 2x - 2$

They are called **quadratic** functions because the highest power of x is 2.

Towards the end of this unit we will work with functions like $f(x) = x^3 - 1$. This is **not** a quadratic function.

3 is the highest power of x

Sometimes quadratic functions are disguised

$f(x) = x(x - 3)$ is a quadratic function

since $f(x) = (x \times x) - (3 \times x)$

$= x^2 - 3x$

2 is the highest power of x.

$f(x) = x(5 - x)$ is a quadratic function

since $f(x) = (x \times 5) - (x \times x)$

$= 5x - x^2$ ← 2 is the highest power of x

So far we have used f for function and x for the variable. Sometimes in practical problems we will meet quadratic functions like the following:

$A(x) = x(6 - x)$ or $A = x(6 - x)$
$H(t) = 20t - 5t^2$ or $H = 20t - 5t^2$
$h(t) = 10t - 5t^2$ or $h = 10t - 5t^2$

Exercise

Which of the following functions are quadratic functions?

1 $f(x) = x^2 - 4x + 3$

2 $g(x) = x(x - 4)$

3 $S(t) = t^3 + t^2 - 6$

4 $h = 30t - 5t^2$

5 $A = x(25 - x)$

In the remaining sections we shall use the real number system which is the set of all numbers including W, Z, and Q and the irrationals. Examples of irrational numbers are $\sqrt{2}$ and π.

Continue with Section P

P Solving quadratic equations graphically

Let us look again at the graph of $f(x) = x^2 - 4x + 3;\ -1 \le x \le 5,\ x \in R$.

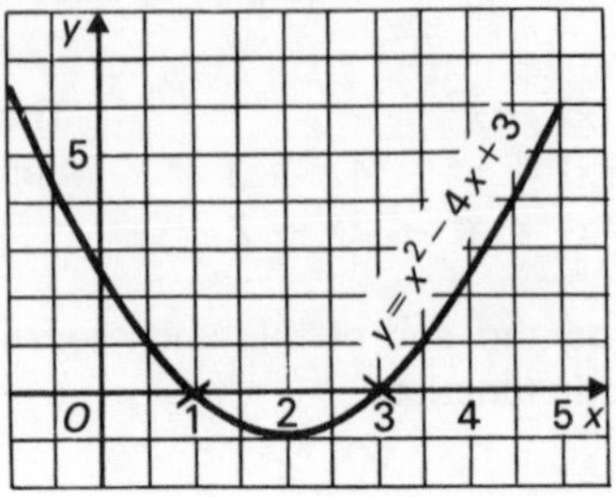

It is possible to solve the equation $x^2 - 4x + 3 = 0$ by using this graph.

The x-axis has equation $y = 0$.

At the points marked with a cross

$$y = 0$$

and also $$y = x^2 - 4x + 3$$

So $x^2 - 4x + 3 = 0$ at these points.

The solutions of the equation $x^2 - 4x + 3 = 0$ are $x = 1$ and $x = 3$.

Checks

When $x = 1$,

$$\begin{aligned} x^2 - 4x + 3 &= (1)^2 - 4(1) + 3 \\ &= 1 - 4 + 3 \\ &= 0 \end{aligned}$$

When $x = 3$,

$$\begin{aligned} x^2 - 4x + 3 &= (3)^2 - 4(3) + 3 \\ &= 9 - 12 + 3 \\ &= 0 \end{aligned}$$

$x = 1$ and $x = 3$ are solutions of the quadratic $x^2 - 4x + 3 = 0$.

Example

Use the graph of the function $f(x) = x^2 - 5x + 6$ to find the solutions of the equation $x^2 - 5x + 6 = 0$.

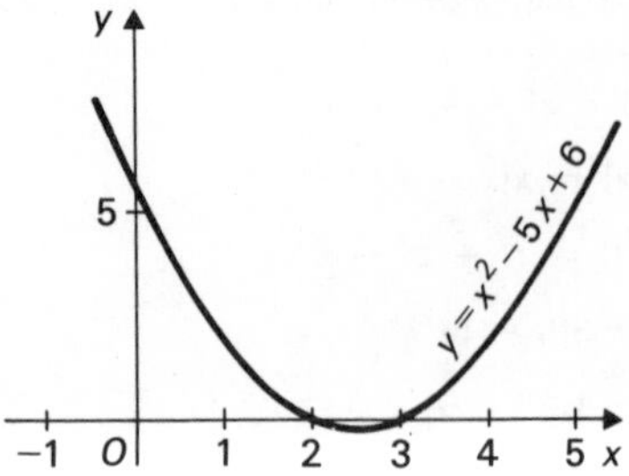

From the graph the curve crosses the x-axis when $x = 2$ and $x = 3$.

So the solutions of $x^2 - 5x + 6 = 0$ are $x = 2$ and $x = 3$.

Checks

When $x = 2$,

$$\begin{aligned} x^2 - 5x + 6 &= (2)^2 - 5(2) + 6 \\ &= 4 - 10 + 6 \\ &= 0 \end{aligned}$$

When $x = 3$,

$$\begin{aligned} x^2 - 5x + 6 &= (3)^2 - 5(3) + 6 \\ &= 9 - 15 + 6 \\ &= 0 \end{aligned}$$

Exercise

1 From each of the graphs shown below find the roots of the given equation.
Check your answers by substitution in the equation.

(a) $x^2 - 6x + 5 = 0$

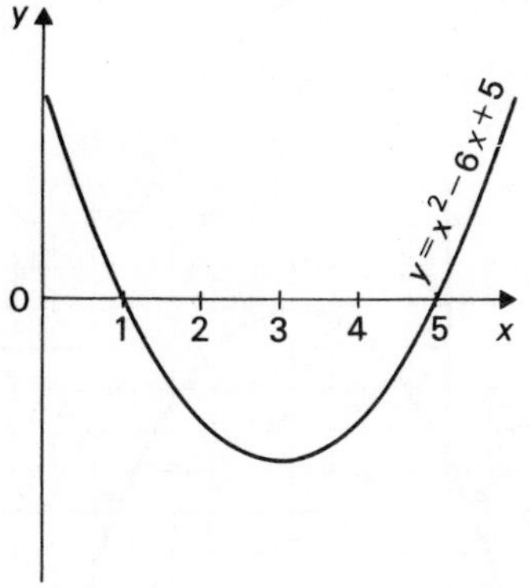

(b) $-x^2 + 3x = 0$

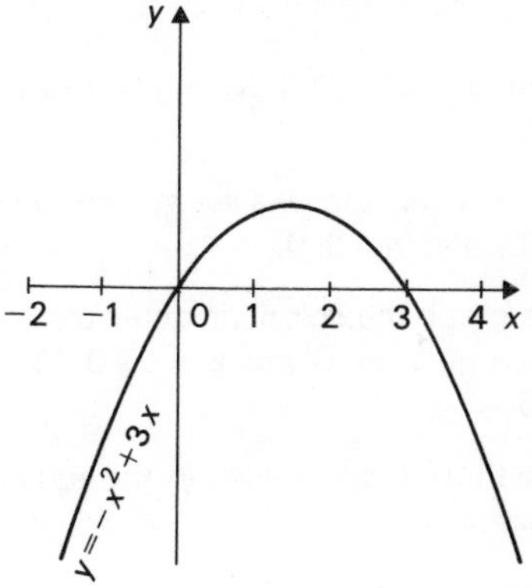

(c) $2x^2 - x - 10 = 0$

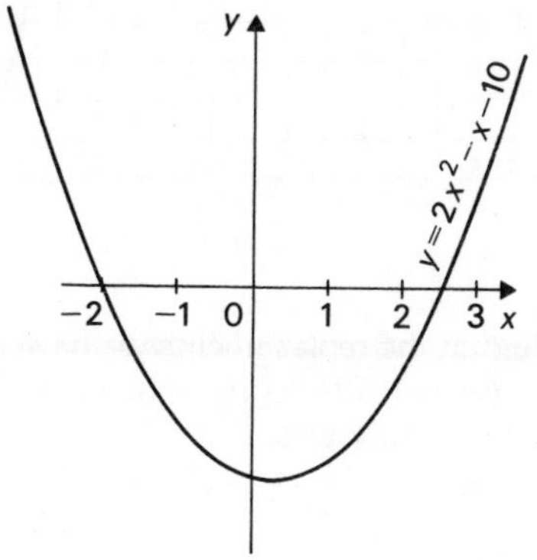

(d) $-x^2 + 2x + 3 = 0$

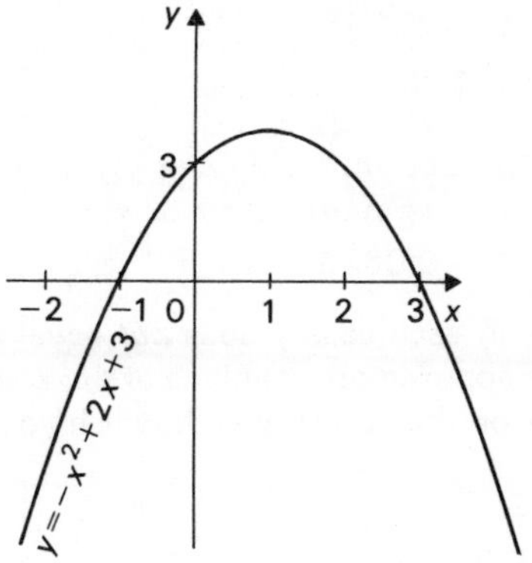

2 By drawing the curves on $\frac{1}{2}$ cm squared paper find the solutions of the following quadratic equations.

(a) $x^2 - 3x - 4 = 0; x \in R$

x	−2	−1	0	1	2	3	4	5
$y = x^2 - 3x - 4$	6	0	−4	−6	−6	−4	0	6

(b) $x^2 + 3x + 2 = 0; x \in R$

x	−4	−3	−2	−1	0	1
$y = x^2 + 3x + 2$	6	2	0	0	2	6

(c) $x^2 - 5x + 4 = 0, x \in R$

x	0	1	2	3	4	5
$y = x^2 - 5x + 4$	4	0	−2	−2	0	4

Continue with Section Q

Q Approximate solutions

The solutions of quadratic equations are not always integers.

The graph of $y = -x^2 + 4x + 1$ is drawn at the side.

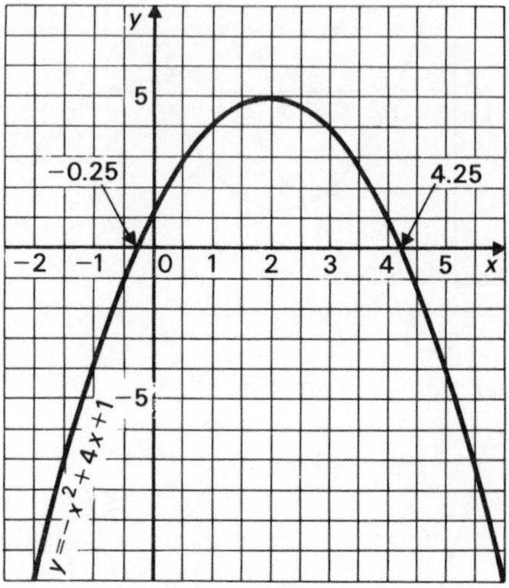

The curve cuts the x-axis at the points $(-0.25, 0)$ and $(4.25, 0)$.

From the graph the solutions of the equation $-x^2 + 4x + 1 = 0$ are $x = -0.25$ and $x = 4.25$.

Now substitute these values in the equation of the curve:

When $x = -0.25$

$$\begin{aligned} y &= -x^2 + 4x + 1 \\ &= -(-0.25)^2 + 4 \times (-0.25) + 1 \\ &= -0.0625 - 1 + 1 \\ &= -0.0625 \end{aligned}$$

When $x = 4.25$

$$\begin{aligned} y &= -x^2 + 4x + 1 \\ &= -(4.25)^2 + 4 \times (4.25) + 1 \\ &= -18.0625 + 17 + 1 \\ &= -0.0625 \end{aligned}$$

Because in each case y does *not* equal zero we conclude that the replacements we have used for x are approximate solutions of the equation $y = -x^2 + 4x + 1$. The degree of approximation depends on the accuracy with which you can read the scale of the x-axis.

Exercise

1 From each of the following graphs find approximate solutions for the given equations. (Do *not* work out checks.)

(a)

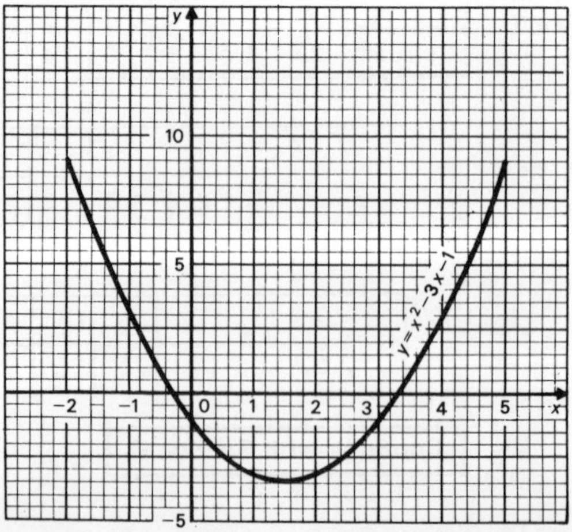

(b)

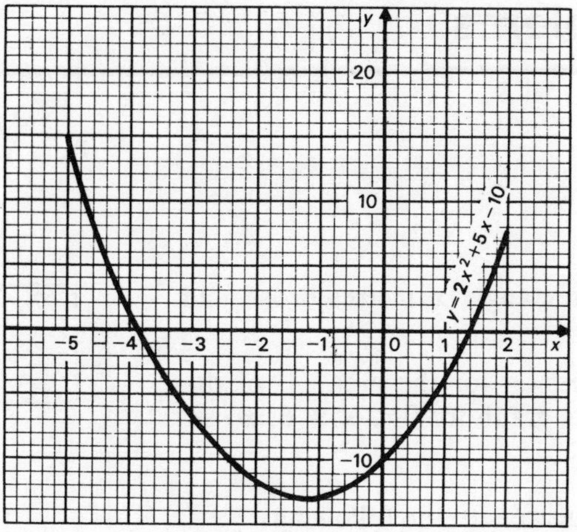

2 Draw the following curves and use them to find approximate solutions of the corresponding quadratic equations found by putting $y = 0$. $x \in R$ in each case. Use 2 mm squared paper.

(a)

x	0	1	2	3	4	5
x^2	0	1	4	9	16	25
$-5x$	0	−5	−10	−15	−20	−25
$+3$	3	3	3	3	3	3
$y = x^2 - 5x + 3$	3	−1	−3	−3	−1	3

(b)

x	−2	−1	0	1	2	3
$-x^2$	−4					
x	−2					
$+5$	5					
$y = -x^2 + x + 5$	−1					

Continue with Section R

R Problems

Example

The figure shows a rectangle x metres broad and $(6 - x)$ metres long.

Write down an expression for the area, A, of the rectangle and draw its graph for $0 \leq x \leq 6$; $x \in R$.

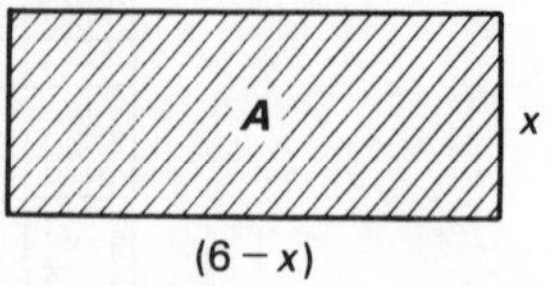

From the graph find answers to the following:

(a) What is the area of the rectangle when $x = 1.5$ m?

(b) What are the dimensions of the rectangle when its area $= 6$ m²?

(c) What is the maximum area of the rectangle, and what is the name of the figure with maximum area?

The area of the rectangle is given by the formula $A = x(6 - x)$.

This is a quadratic function.

x	0	1	2	3	4	5	6
x	0	1	2	3	4	5	6
$6 - x$	6	5	4	3	2	1	0
$A = x(6 - x)$	0	5	8	9	8	5	0

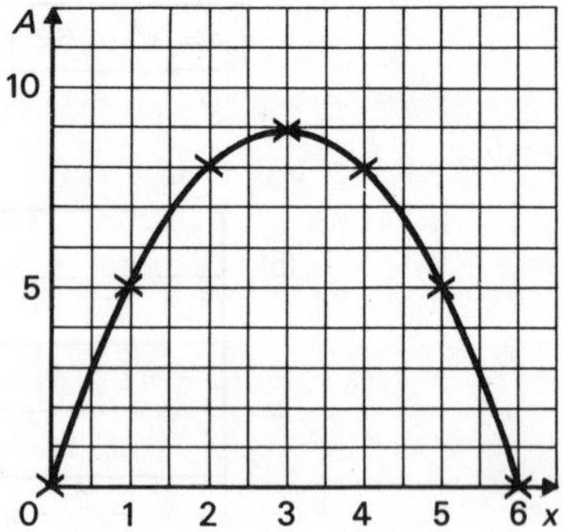

(a) When x is 1.5 m the area is about 6.8 m².

(b) When the area $= 6$ m², $x = 1.25$. The dimensions are 1.25 m and 4.75 m.

(c) Maximum area $= 9$ m². When the area is at a maximum the length and breadth are both 3 m long, so the figure is a square.

Exercise

1 A rectangle is x metres broad and $(8 - x)$ metres long.

Write down an expression for the area, A of the rectangle.

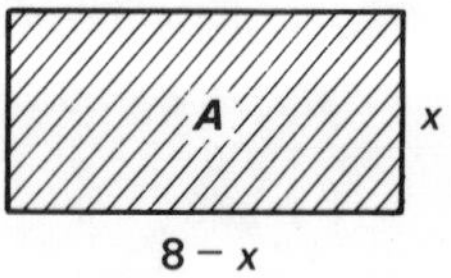

Copy and complete the table of values for the area when $0 \leq x \leq 8, x \in R$.

x	0	1	2	3	4	5	6	7	8
$8 - x$	8		6					1	
$A = x(8 - x)$	0		12					7	

$0 \times 8 = 0$

Draw the graph for $0 \leq x \leq 8, x \in R$, using 2 mm graph paper.

Vertical scale (A) : 1 cm = 2 units of area.

Horizontal scale (x) : 1 cm = 1 unit.

Use your graph to answer the following:

(a) What is the area of the rectangle when $x = 2.6$ metres?

(b) What are the possible dimensions of the rectangle when its area is $9.2\ m^2$?

(c) What is the maximum area of the rectangle, and, when the area is a maximum, what is the figure called?

2 A farmer has 20 metres of fencing. What is the maximum rectangular area he can enclose if he uses a boundary wall for one side of the enclosure?

Let the breadth of the enclosure be x metres

The length of the enclosure is $(20-2x)$ metres.

The area, $A = x(20 - 2x)$.

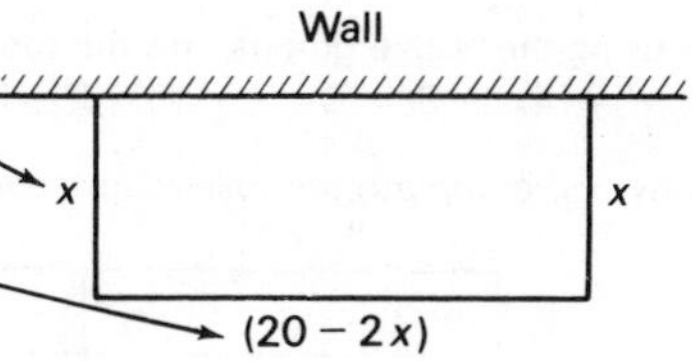

Copy and complete the table of values:

x	0	1	2	3	4	5	6	7	8	9	10
$20 - 2x$	20	18	16								
$A = x(20 - 2x)$	0	18									

Draw the graph on 2 mm graph paper.

Horizontal scale: 1 cm = 1 unit of length.

Vertical scale: 1 cm = 10 units of area.

What is the maximum area of the rectangular enclosure?

3 The height (H), of a projectile above its point of projection after t seconds is $H = 5t(4 - t)$.

Draw the graph of $H = 5t(4 - t)$ for $0 \leq t \leq 4$.

Use 2 mm graph paper and a scale of 2 cm per unit for t and 2 cm per 10 units for H.

From your graph find:

(a) The maximum height of the projectile.

(b) The time taken by the projectile to reach its maximum height.

(c) The time interval during which the projectile was over 10 metres above its starting point.

Continue with Section S

S Progress check

Exercise

1 (a) For each of the following graphs write down the equation of the axis of symmetry of the curve. Find the coordinates of the turning point and state whether this is a maximum or a minimum.

(i)

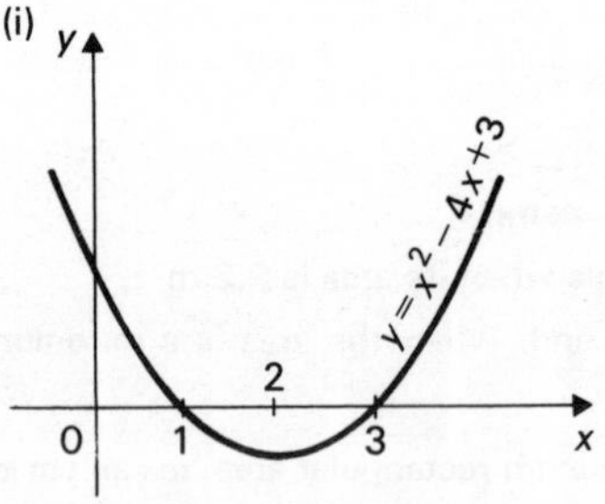

(ii)

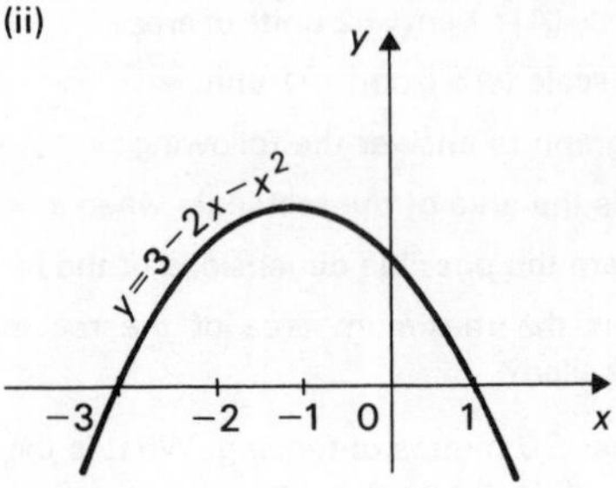

(b) By using the above graphs find the roots of the following equations.
(i) $x^2 - 4x + 3 = 0$ (ii) $3 - 2x - x^2 = 0$

2 (a) Copy and complete the following table for the curve $y = x^2 - 3x + 1$.

x	−2	−1	0	1	2	3	4	5
x^2	4							
$-3x$	6							
$+1$	+1							
$y = x^2 - 3x + 1$	11							

(b) On 2 mm graph paper draw the graph of $y = x^2 - 3x + 1$; $-2 \le x \le 5$, $x \in R$.

(c) Use the graph to find the approximate solutions of the equation $x^2 - 3x + 1 = 0$.

3 A rectangle *KLMN* is 8 m long and 4 m broad. A quadrilateral *PQRS* is formed as shown with $KP = NQ = LS = x$ metres, and $NR = 2x$ metres.

It can be shown that the area A m^2 of the quadrilateral is given by $A = 16 + 2x - x^2$.

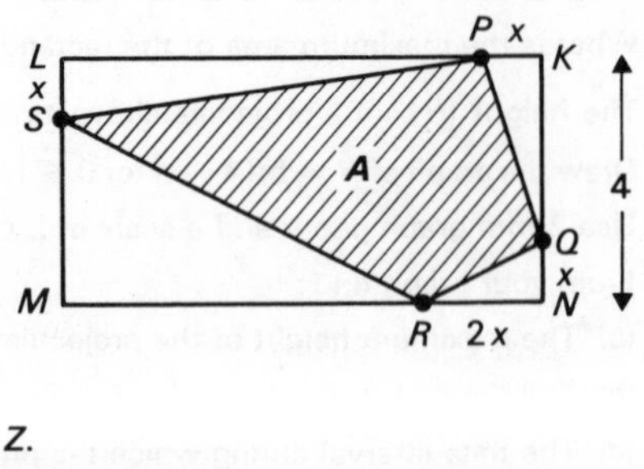

(a) Complete a table of values for A, $-3 \le x \le 5$, $x \in Z$.

(b) On 2 mm graph paper draw a graph of A, $-3 \le x \le 5$, $x \in R$.

(c) What is the maximum area of the quadrilateral?

Tell your teacher you have finished this Unit

UNIT M9
Transformations

A | Translations

This photograph shows a movement called a **translation**.

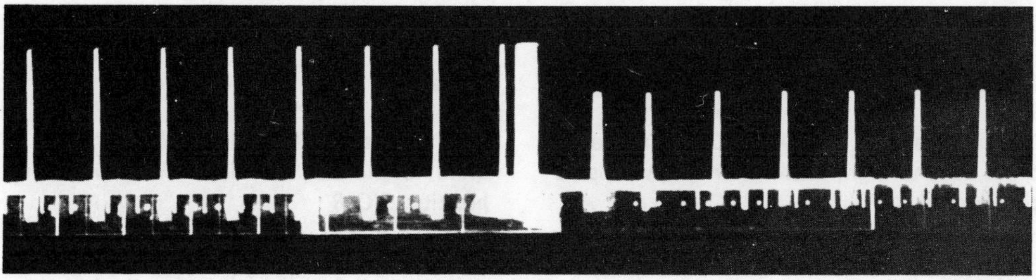

The diagrams below show examples of movements called **translations**.

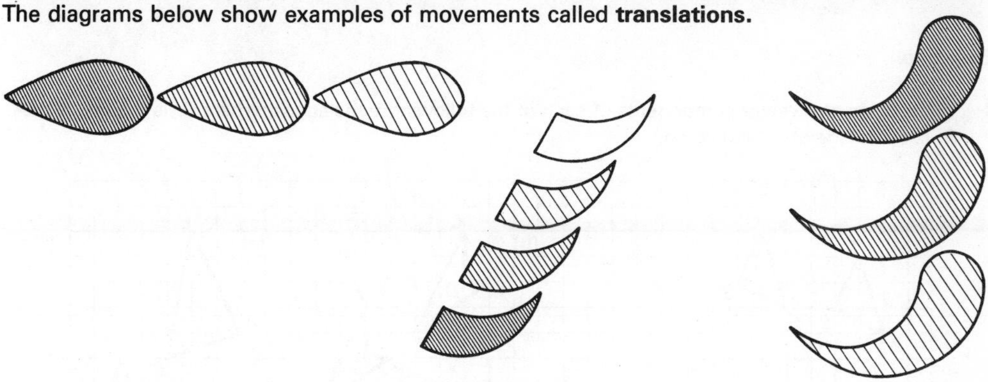

The shaded figure in each diagram can be moved *without turning* to take the place of the one next to it.

Exercise

1 Take a stencil and trace out all four shapes.

Now place a ruler against the stencil, slide the stencil along the ruler and redraw the four shapes. This movement is called a **translation**.

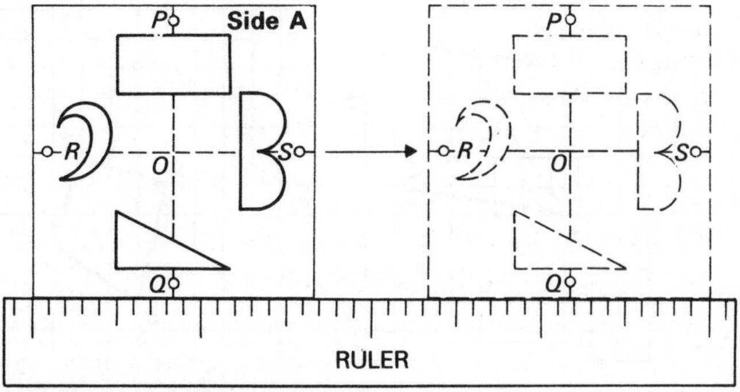

Continue with Sheet M9/1

B Vector components

The translations shown in the diagrams below can be described using vector components.

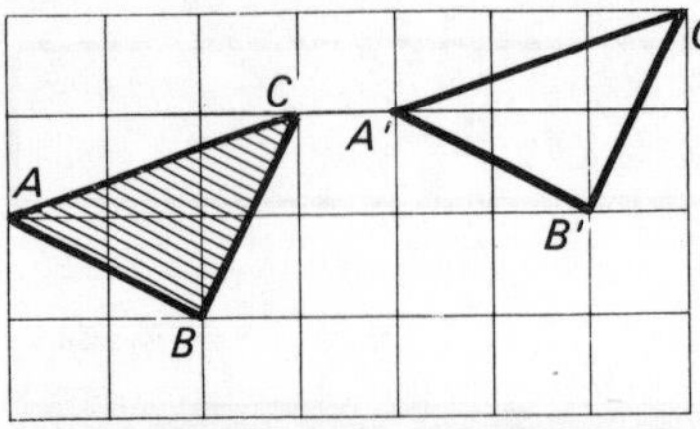

Translation $\begin{pmatrix} 4 \\ 1 \end{pmatrix}$

This means that triangle *ABC* has moved 4 units to the right and 1 unit upwards to positions *A′B′C′*.

Triangle *A′B′C′* is the image of triangle *ABC* under translation $\begin{pmatrix} 4 \\ 1 \end{pmatrix}$.

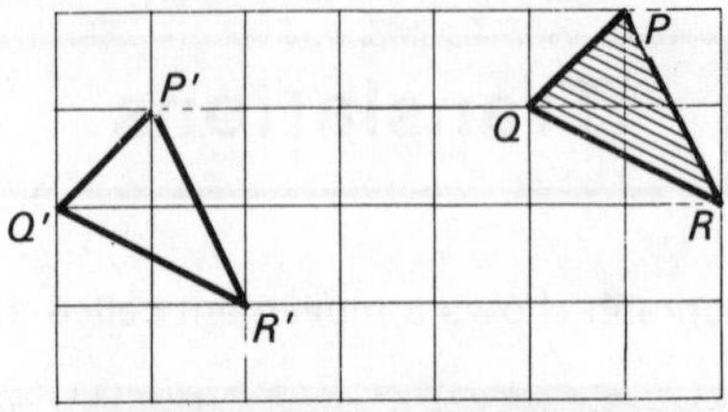

Translation $\begin{pmatrix} -5 \\ -1 \end{pmatrix}$

This means that triangle *PQR* has moved 5 units to the left and 1 unit downwards to position *P′Q′R′*.

Triangle *P′Q′R′* is the image of triangle *PQR* under translation $\begin{pmatrix} -5 \\ -1 \end{pmatrix}$.

Exercise

1 Write down the vector components of each of the following translations, where *A′* is the image of *A*, *B′* is the image of *B*, and so on.

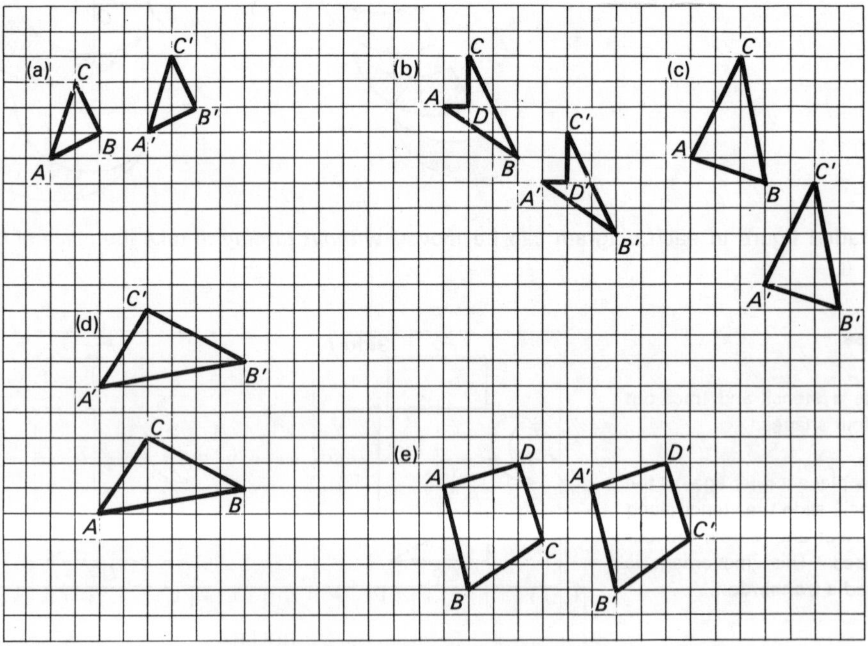

Continue with Section C

C Drawing images

Given a diagram and a translation we can show an image diagram.

Example

Show the image of triangle *ABC* under the translation $\begin{pmatrix}4\\2\end{pmatrix}$.

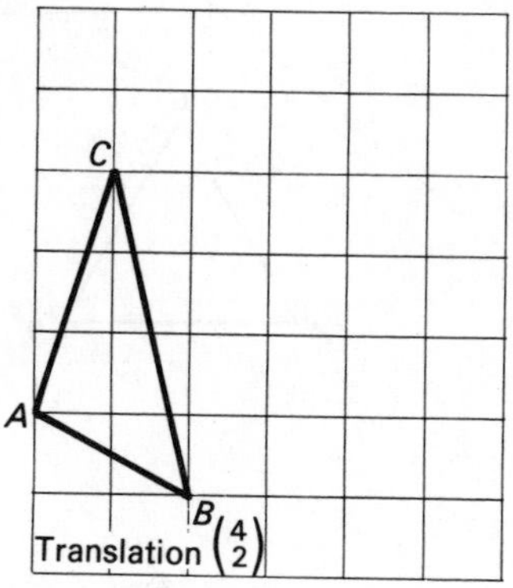

Mark the image points *A′*, *B′* and *C′*, and join them up, thus →

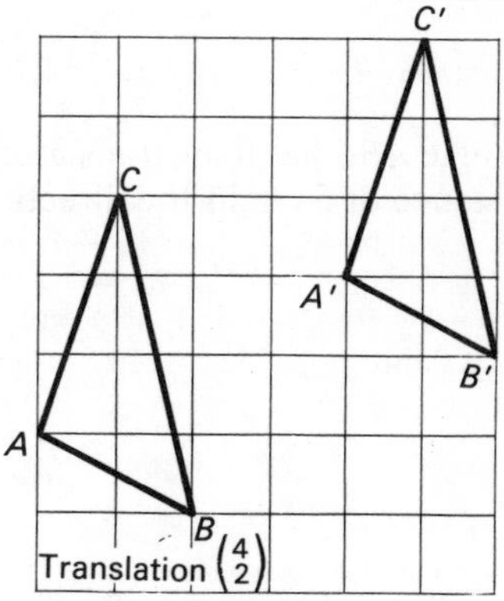

Exercise

1 Copy the following figures and draw their images under the given translations.

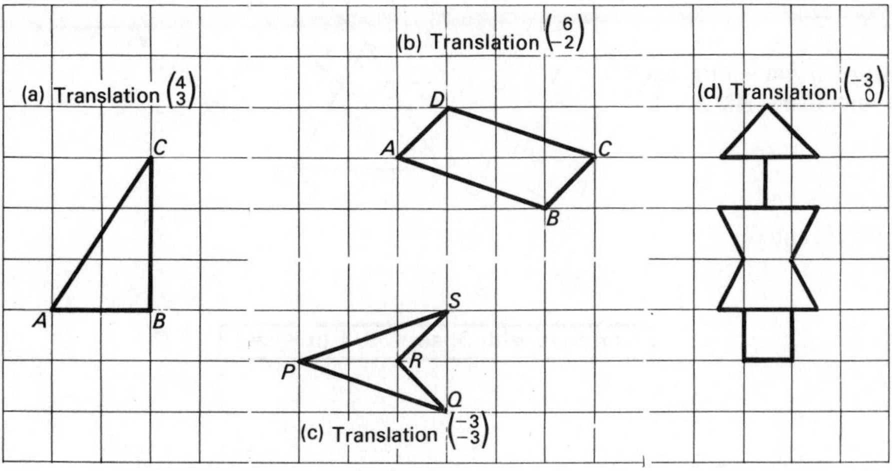

Continue with Section D

D Translations using instruments

A translation may be specified by using a distance and a direction.

Example

Triangle ABC has to be translated through a distance of 5 cm in the direction XY.

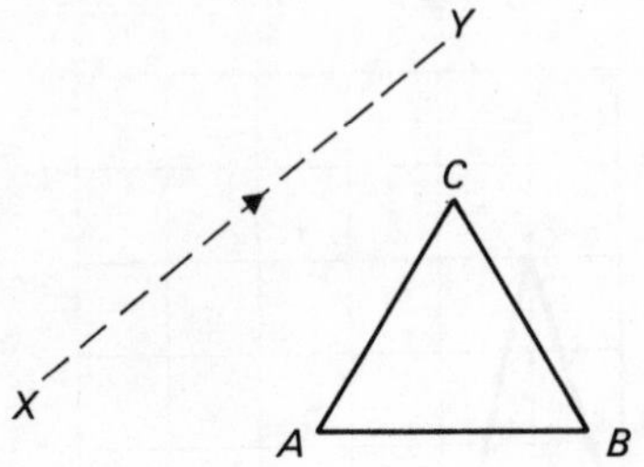

Step 1

Draw lines through A, B, and C parallel to XY.
(If you have forgotten how to draw parallel lines see the Appendix at the end of the Unit.)

Step 2

Measure 5 cm along each line and mark A', B', and C'.

Step 3

Join A', B', and C'.

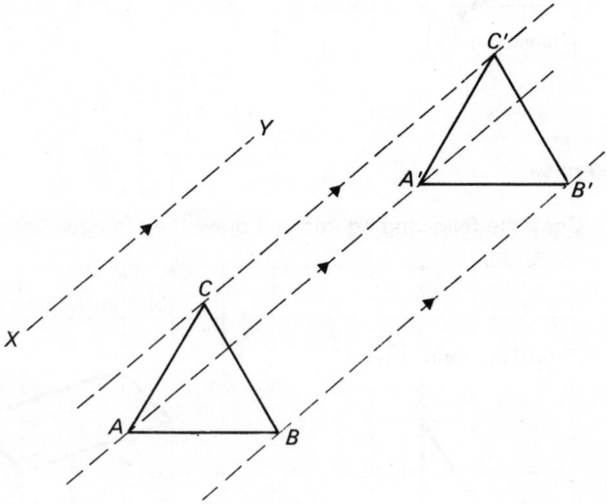

Continue with Sheet M9/1 (reverse)

E Reflections

This photograph shows a **reflection.**

In diagram 1 below, if a mirror is placed along *ZZ′*, we obtain diagram 2.

The line *ZZ′* is called an **axis of reflection.**

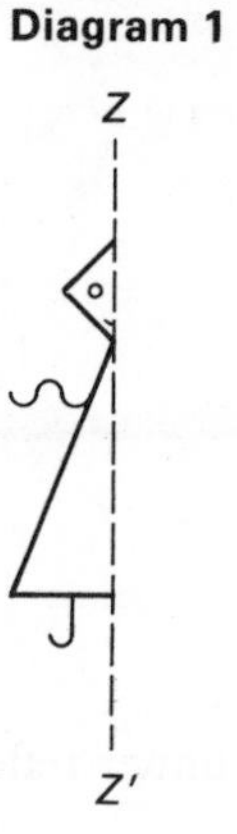

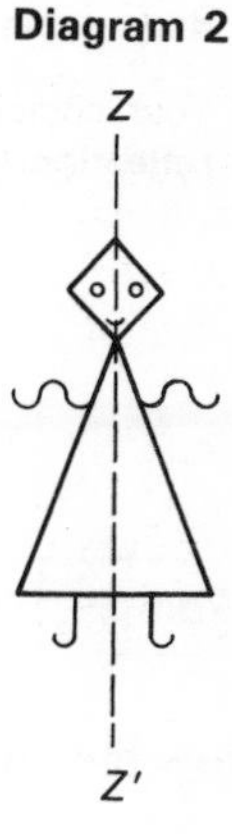

In this figure, the triangles are images of each other under reflection in the dotted line.

The dotted line is the axis of reflection, sometimes called the *axis of symmetry.*

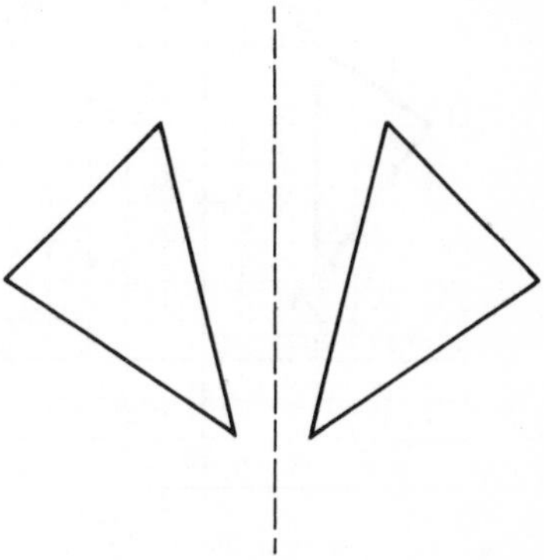

Exercise

1 Draw a dotted line ZZ', 10 cm long, and place your stencil on top of your line so that the holes P and Q are on the line ZZ' as shown.

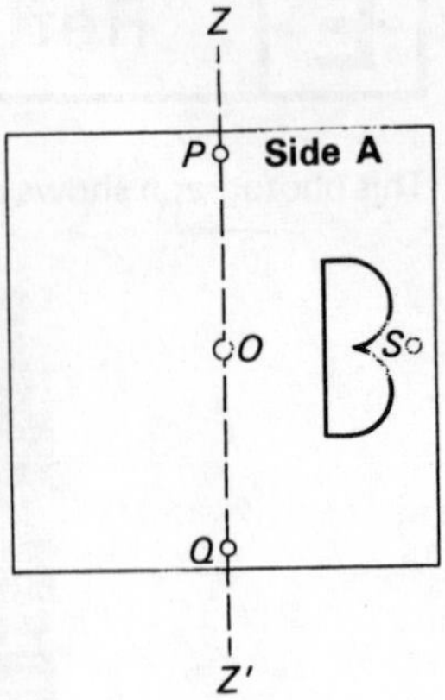

Trace out the shape nearest S.

Mark the points P and Q through the holes on your stencil.

Now turn the stencil over so that side B is uppermost, and points P and Q are in the same position as before.

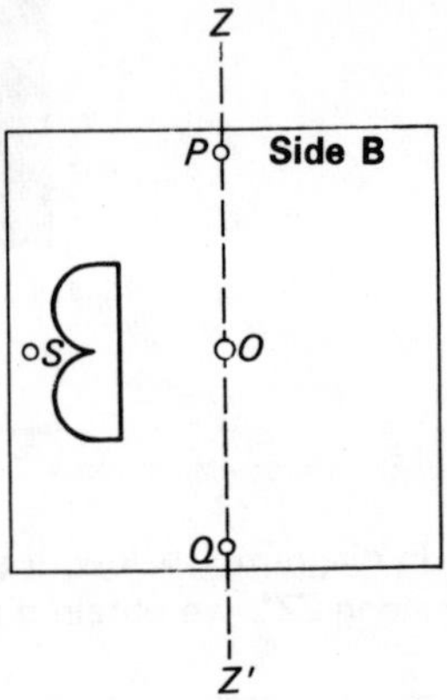

Redraw the shape.

Your completed drawing is an example of a **reflection**.

Example

Show the image of triangle ABC under reflection in YY'.

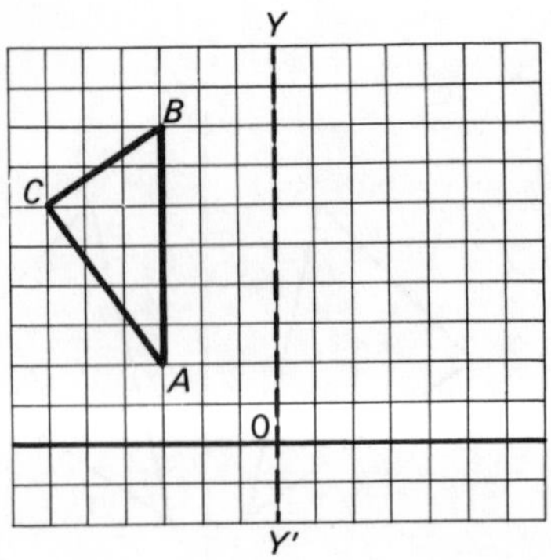

Mark the image points A', B', C' and join them up, thus

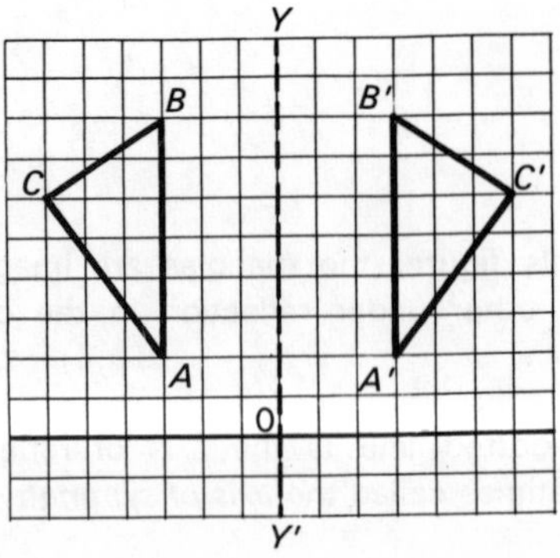

Exercise

2 Copy and complete the following diagrams so that each of the triangles PQR is reflected in YY'.

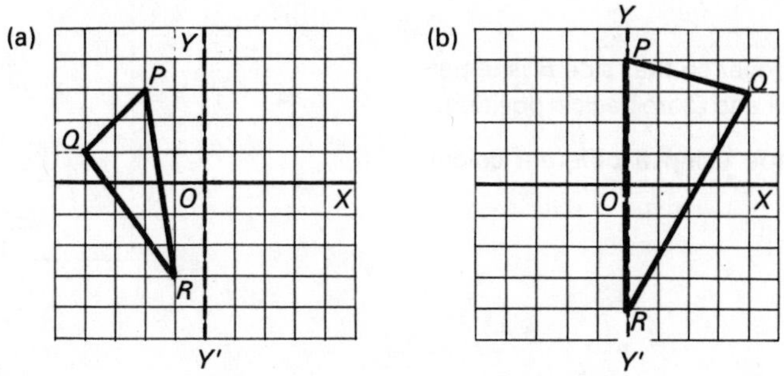

3 Copy and complete the following diagrams so that each of the triangles PQR is reflected in the x-axis (that is, XX').

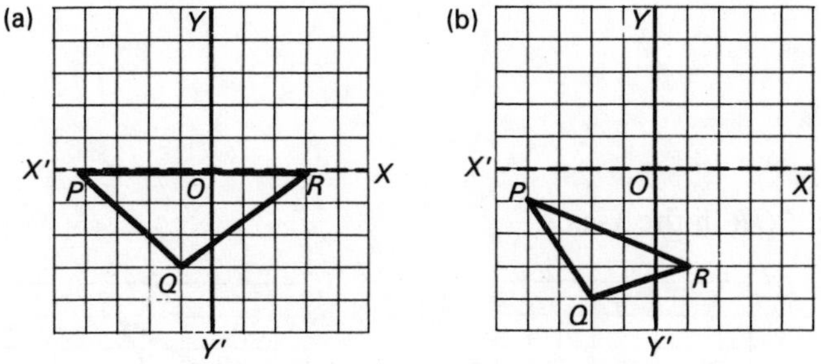

Continue with Section F

F Overlapping images

Draw a dotted line ZZ', 10 cm long, and place your stencil on top of your line as shown.

Trace out the shape nearest Q.

Mark the points P and Q.

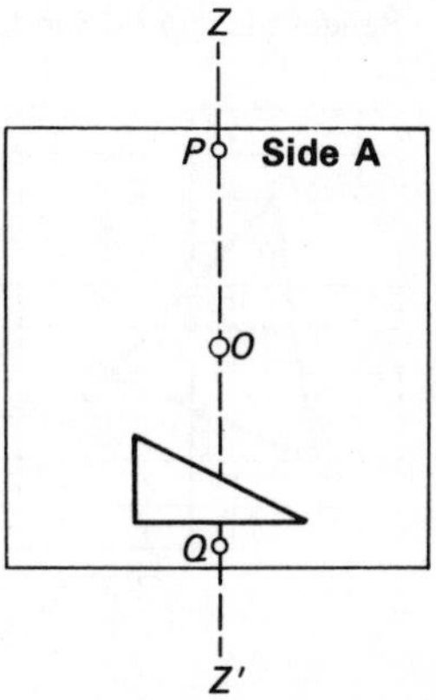

Turn the stencil over so that side *B* is uppermost and points *P* and *Q* are back in position.

Redraw the shape using a different colour.

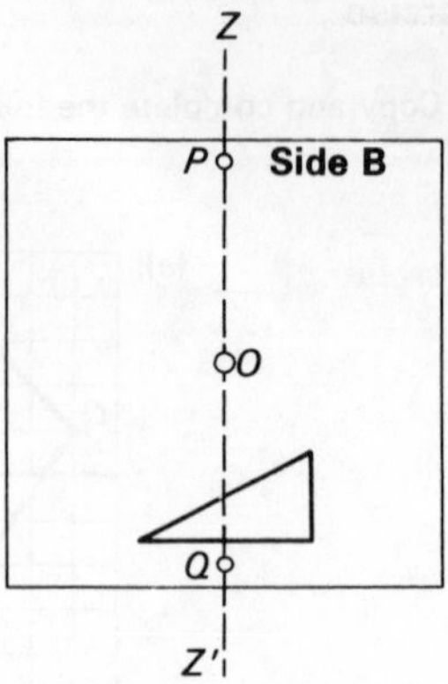

The final diagram should show the triangle and its image overlapping.

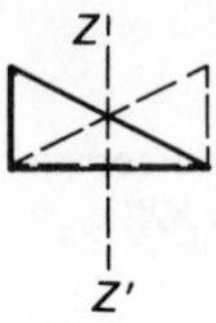

Example

Reflect triangle *PQR* in the *x*-axis.

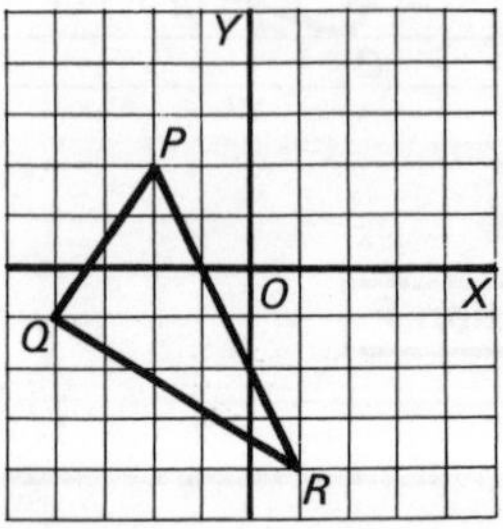

Mark the image points *P'*, *Q'* and *R'* and join them up, thus

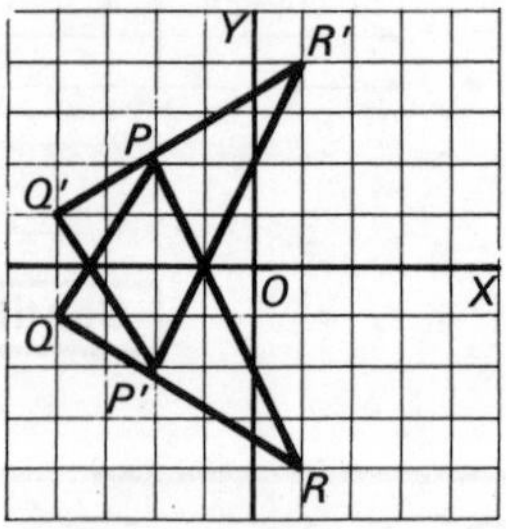

Exercise

1 Reflect triangle *PQR* in the *x*-axis.

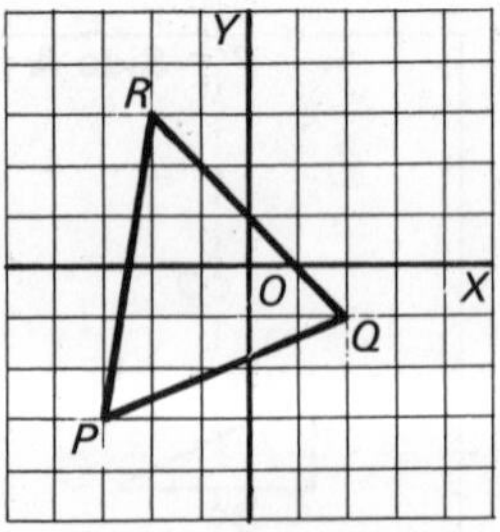

2 Reflect triangle *PQR* in the *y*-axis.

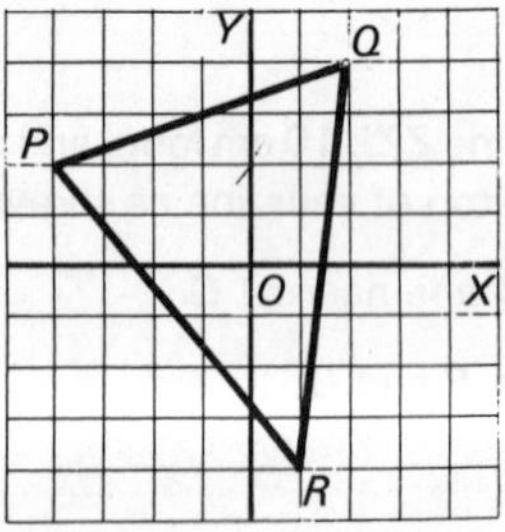

Continue with Section G

G Image in an axis

Exercise

In this diagram all the triangles are congruent.

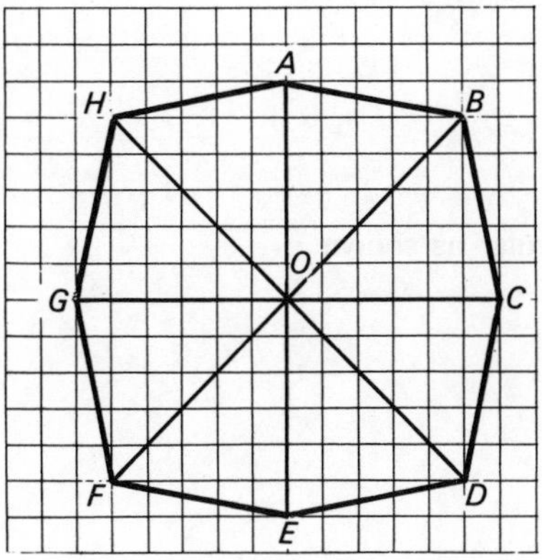

1 (a) Given a triangle and an axis of symmetry, you can state the image triangle. Copy the following table and complete it. The first line has been done for you.

Triangle	Axis of reflection	Image triangle
BOC	*AE*	*HOG*
BOD	*AE*	
AOB	*GC*	
BOC	*HD*	
HOG	*BF*	

1 (b) Given a triangle and its image under reflection in an axis, you can state the name of the axis of reflection. Copy the following table and complete it. The first line has been done for you.

Triangle	Image triangle	Axis of reflection
AOB	*AOH*	*AE*
COD	*AOH*	
AOH	*GOH*	
COD	*GOF*	

Continue with Section H

H Reflections using instruments

We can use a ruler and a set square to find the image of a point in a line.

Here are the steps we use to reflect point *B* in line *PQ*.

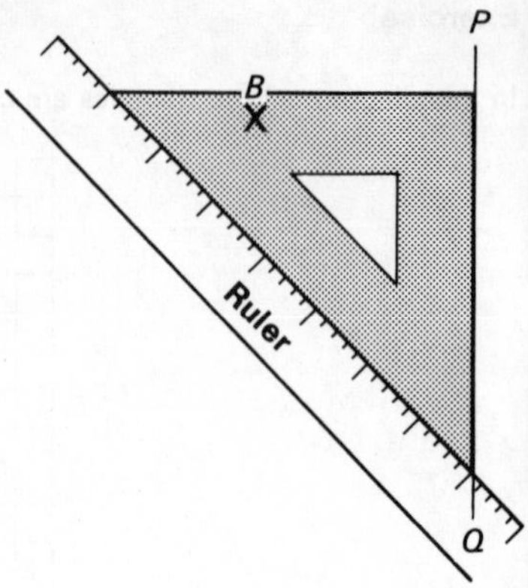

Step 1

Place your set square and ruler as shown.

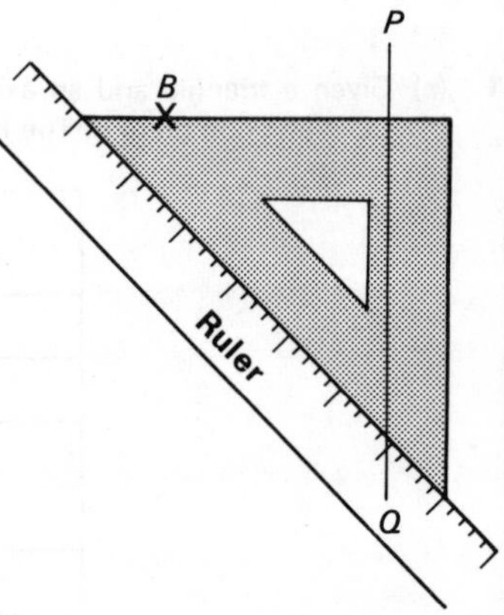

Step 2

Holding the ruler steady slide the set square down until the edge is lined up with the point *B*.

Draw a line along the top edge of the set square.

The line should be at right angles to *PQ*.

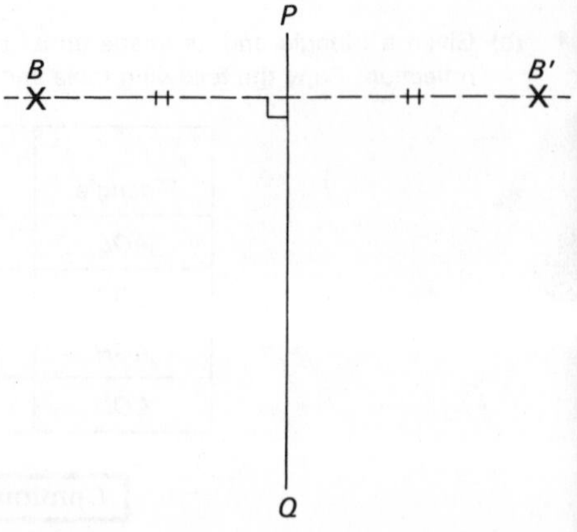

Step 3

Measure the distance from *B* to the line *PQ*.

B′ should be the same distance on the other side.

Mark the image point *B′*.

Reflection of two points

To reflect the line *AB* in *PQ* we reflect the point *A* obtaining *A′* and then the point *B* obtaining *B′*.

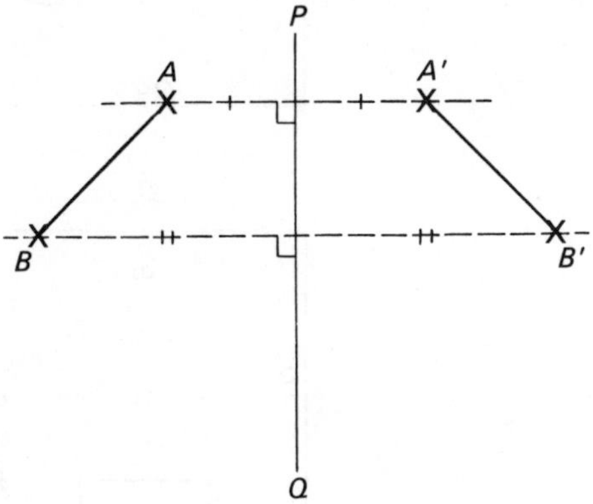

A′B′ is the image of *AB* under reflection in *PQ*.

Reflection of three points

The triangle *ABC* can be reflected in the line *XY* by reflecting each of the points *A*, *B*, and *C*, obtaining *A′*, *B′*, and *C′*.

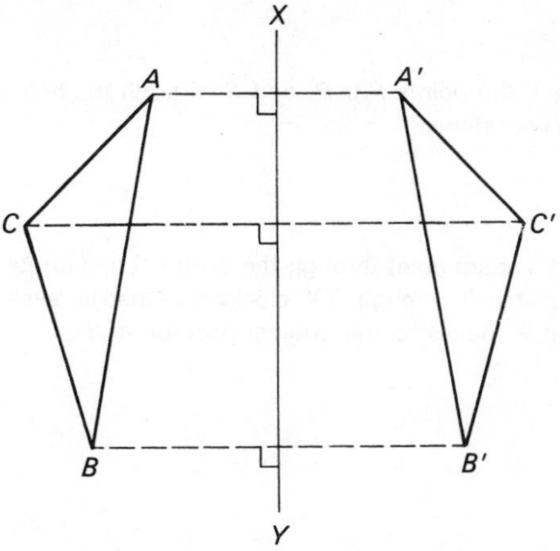

A′, *B′*, and *C′*, when joined up, give the image triangle.

Continue with Sheet M9/2 (reverse)

I Rotations

This diagram shows a pattern produced by the **rotation** of a basic shape.

The point *O* is called the **centre of rotation.**

This photograph shows a **rotation.**

Exercise

In your jotter trace the shape nearest *S* on your stencil.

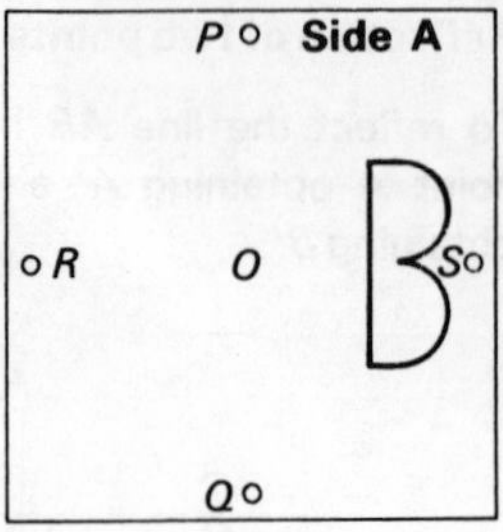

Mark the points *P*,*Q*,*R*, and *S* through the holes on your stencil.

Put a sharp point through the centre *O* and rotate the stencil through 90° clockwise (that is, such that *P* moves to the original position of *S*).

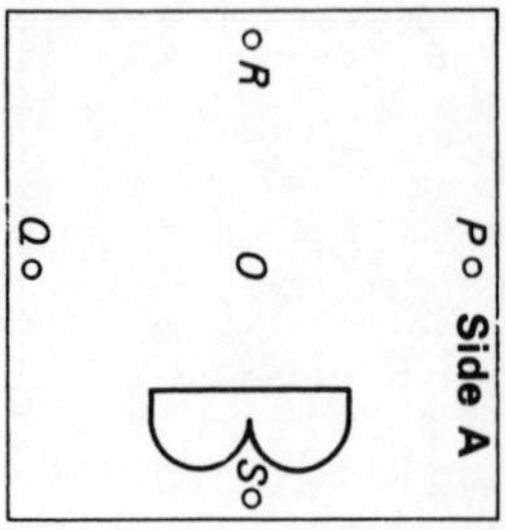

Redraw the shape.

Give your stencil a further clockwise rotation of 90° about O. Redraw the shape.

Give your stencil a fourth clockwise rotation of 90° and redraw the shape.

The final diagram should look like this

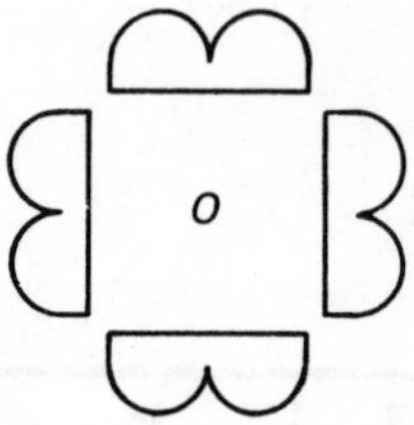

Note that in describing a rotation we must give
(a) **a centre of rotation** (the point *O*);
(b) **the angle of turn** (90° in the above example);
(c) **the direction** (clockwise or anticlockwise).

Continue with Sheet M9/3

J Image under a rotation

Example

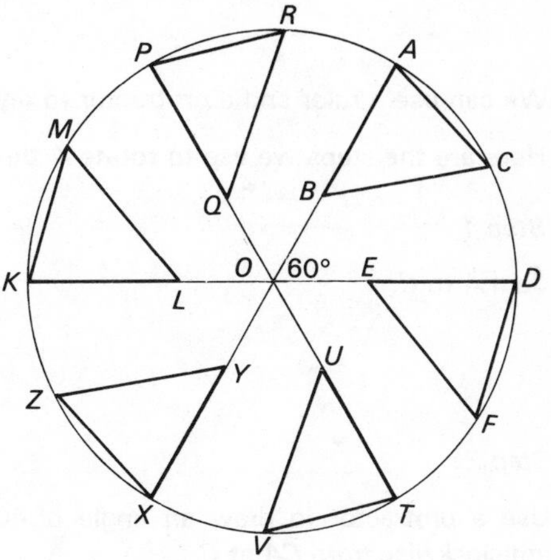

n this diagram the angles between the ines at O are equal to 60°. Each triangle is he image of one of the others under a otation about O.

Vhat is the image of triangle ABC under n anticlockwise rotation of 60°? The nswer is that triangle ABC has as image riangle PQR.

Ve can show this as

riangle $ABC \longrightarrow$ triangle PQR

Ve say that triangle ABC maps onto triangle PQR.

Note that $A \longrightarrow P$ (A maps onto P)

$B \longrightarrow Q$

$C \longrightarrow R$

So that $ABC \longrightarrow PQR$ (that is, the order of naming the triangle is important).

Exercise

Using the diagram above, copy and complete the table on the right. The first line has been done for you.

Triangle	Rotation	Image triangle
ABC	60° clockwise	*DEF*
ABC	120° anticlockwise	
UVT	180° clockwise	
ZYX	300° clockwise	

2 In this diagram the angles at O are each 45°, and the lengths OA, OB and so on are equal. Copy the following table and complete it. The first line has been done for you.

Triangle	Image triangle	Rotation
AOB	*BOC*	45°
DOE	*BOC*	
FOG	*COD*	
FOG	*BOC*	

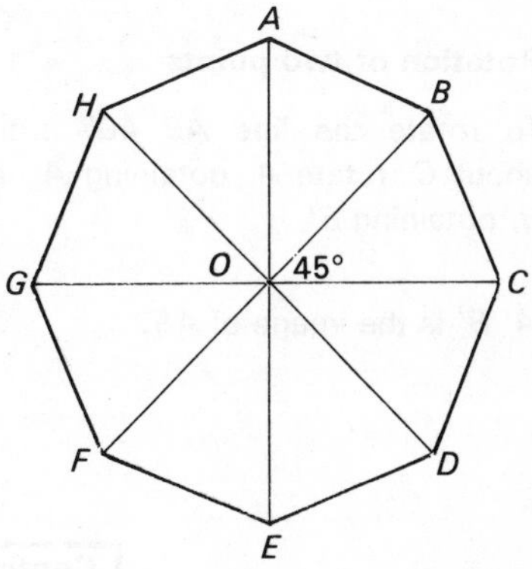

Continue with Section K

K Rotations using instruments

We can use a ruler and a protractor to find an image under a rotation about a point.

Here are the steps we use to rotate *A* through 40°, anticlockwise about *C*.

Step 1

Join *A* to *C*.

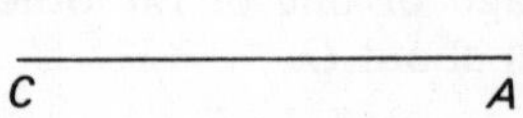

Step 2

Use a protractor to draw an angle of 40° anticlockwise from *CA* at *C*.

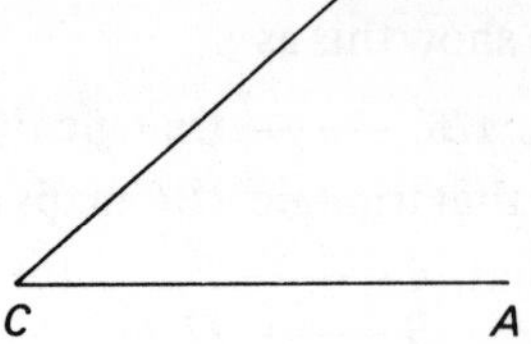

Step 3

Measure *CA* and mark *A′* the same distance from *C*.

A′ is the image of *A*, rotated through 40° anticlockwise.

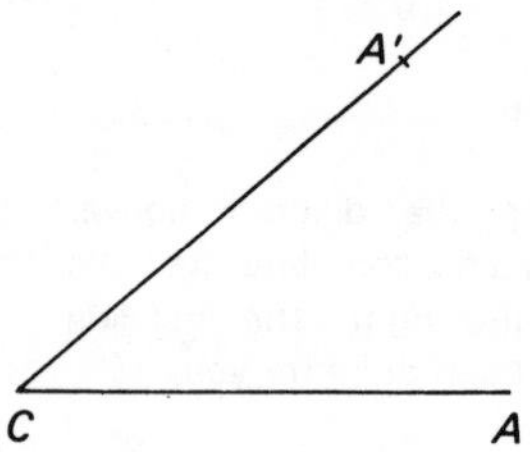

Rotation of two points

To rotate the line *AB* 40° anticlockwise about *C*, rotate *A*, obtaining *A′*, and rotate *B*, obtaining *B′*.

A′ B′ is the image of *AB*.

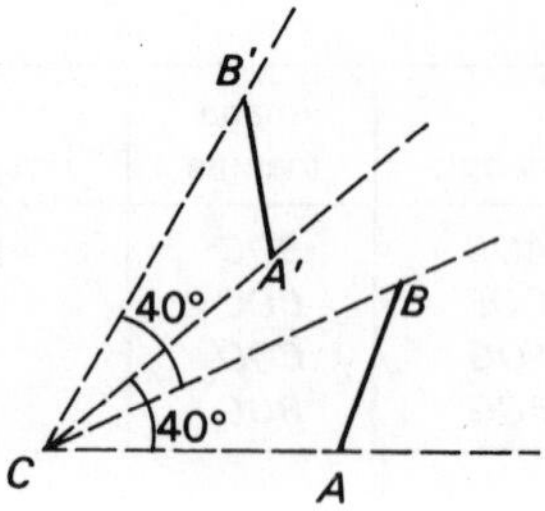

Continue with Sheet M9/3 (reverse)

L Enlargement

The photograph shows a light source projecting a shape onto a screen. The shape on the screen is called the **image**. Notice that the original shape is enlarged.

This can be shown in a diagram like this:

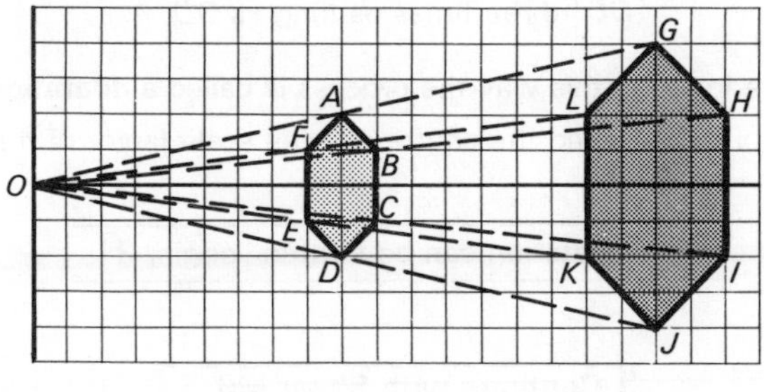

Measure the sides of hexagon *ABCDEF* and measure the sides of the image *GHIJKL*. You should find that the sides of the image are twice as long as the sides of the hexagon.

By measuring *OA* and *OG*, *OB* and *OH*, etc., you will find that each image point is twice as far from *O* as its object point.

Continue with Sheet M9/4

M Dilatation

In question 3 on Worksheet M9/4, your result should have looked like this:

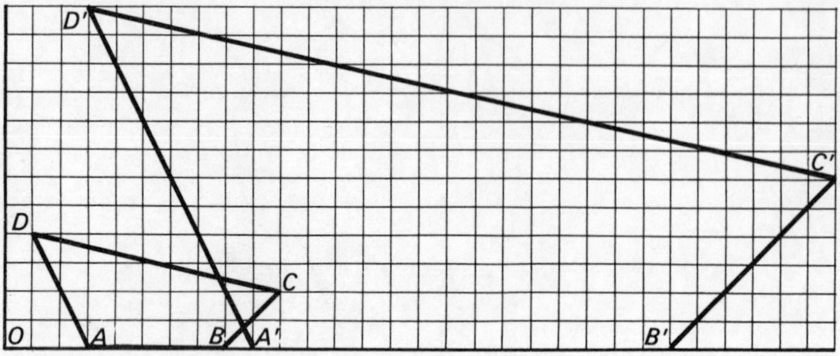

In order to make the image three times as large as the object, you made

OA' three times as long as *OA*,
OB' three times as long as *OB*,
OC' three times as long as *OC*,
OD' three times as long as *OD*.

When image points are found in this way the process is called a **dilatation.**

For this dilatation the origin is called the centre and the scale factor of the dilatation is 3.

This dilatation can be written [origin, 3].

Continue with Sheet M9/5

N Scale factors less than 1

Under the dilatation $\left[\text{origin}, \frac{1}{2}\right]$ the image of any point is half as far from the origin as the point itself is.

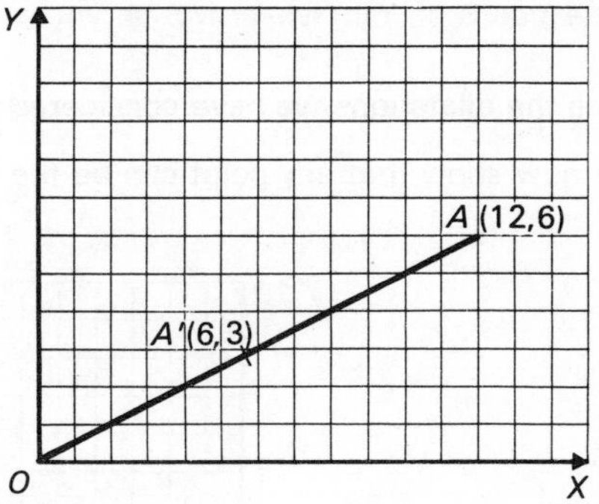

A' is the image of A under the dilatation $\left[\text{origin}, \frac{1}{2}\right]$ since $OA' = \frac{1}{2}\,OA$.

We can find the image of a triangle under the same dilatation by finding the image of each vertex in turn.

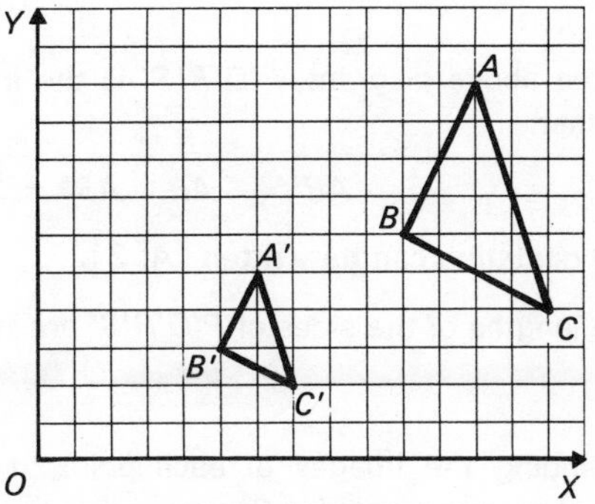

Triangle $A'B'C'$ is the image of triangle ABC under the dilatation $\left[\text{origin}, \frac{1}{2}\right]$ since

$$OA' = \tfrac{1}{2}\,OA$$
$$OB' = \tfrac{1}{2}\,OB$$
$$OC' = \tfrac{1}{2}\,OC$$

Notice that each side of the image triangle is half as big as the corresponding side of the original.

Continue with Sheet M9/6

O Dilatations with centres other than the origin

In all the dilatations we have considered so far, the centre has been the origin.

We now show that any point can be the centre of a dilatation.

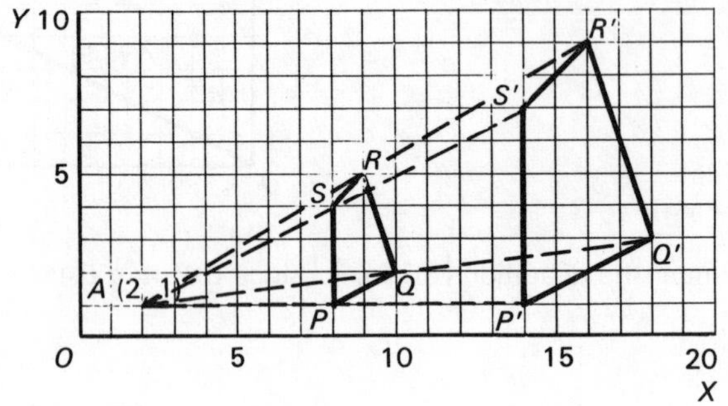

In the above diagram, $P'Q'R'S'$ is the image of $PQRS$ under a dilatation whose centre is A. Further

$$AR' = 2AR, \quad AS' = 2AS, \quad AQ' = 2AQ, \quad AP' = 2AP$$

The dilatation can be written $[A, 2]$.

The lengths of the sides of $P'Q'R'S'$ are twice the lengths of the sides of $PQRS$.

In finding the images of each point, it is useful to notice that for S, say:

From A to S we go 6 along and 3 up. The scale factor is 2. So from A to S', we go 12 along and 6 up.

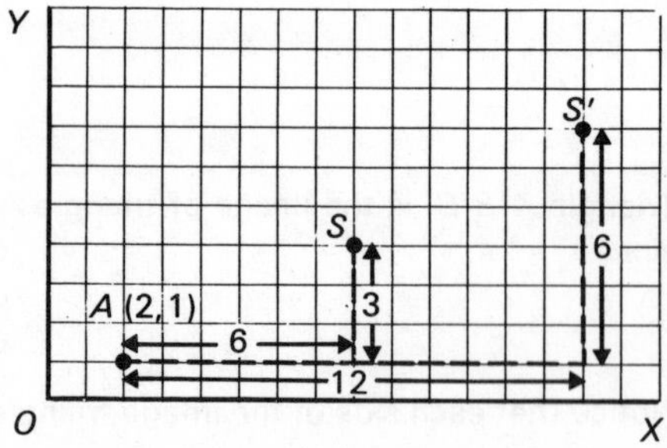

Continue with Sheet M9/7

P Dilatations using instruments

Dilatations can be drawn without squared paper.

Example

Given a point A and a point B like this:

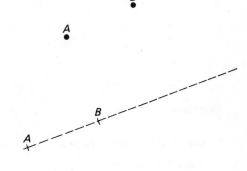

We can find the image of the point B under the dilatation $[A, 3]$ by joining A to B with a ruler and producing the line thus:

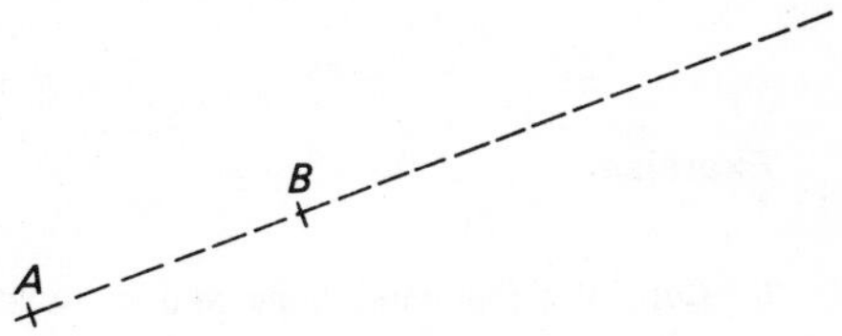

Measure AB and multiply by the scale factor, which is 3. Make AB' three times as long as AB.

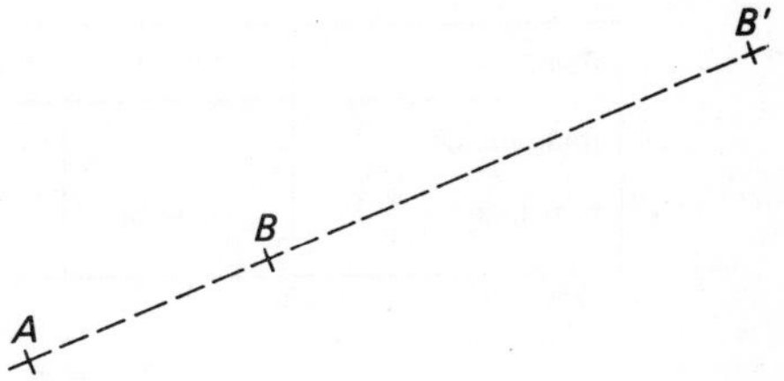

B' is the image of B under the dilatation $[A, 3]$.

Example

Given a point A, we can find the image of a line ST under the dilatation $[A, 3]$ like this:

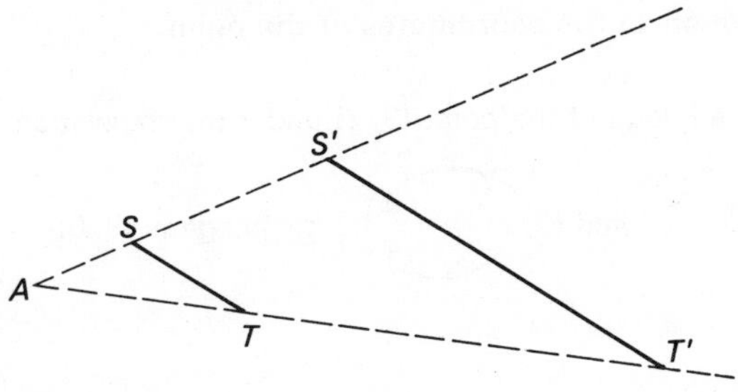

$AS' = 3AS$ and $AT' = 3AT$

The image of ST under the dilatation $[A, 3]$ is the line $S'T'$.

Continue with Sheet M9/8

Q Translations: images using components

Translations can be described by using components.

For example, in this diagram the point *A* has been moved to position *A'* by the translation $\begin{pmatrix}2\\5\end{pmatrix}$.

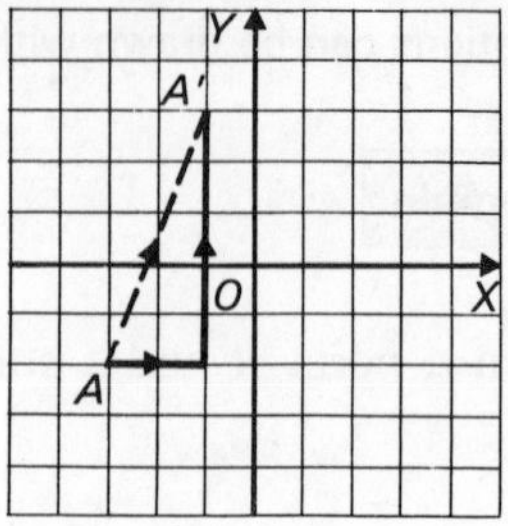

Exercise

1 Copy the following table and complete it by applying the translation $\begin{pmatrix}3\\1\end{pmatrix}$ to each point. Draw a diagram in each case.

Point	*A* (1, 4)	*B* (0, 3)	*C* (−1, 1)	*D* (2, −3)	*E* (−1, −4)	*F* (0, 0)
Image under translation $\begin{pmatrix}3\\1\end{pmatrix}$	*A'* (4, 5)					

This is the diagram for the first one. The point (1, 4) moves 3 along and 1 up.

Hence its image is the point (4, 5).

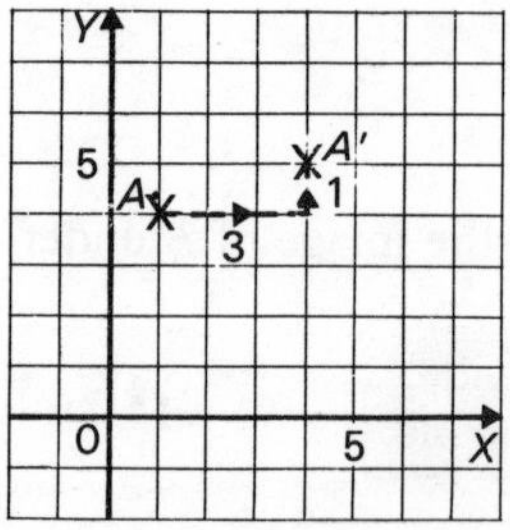

You will see that the image of a point under translation can be obtained by **adding the components of the translation to the coordinates of the point.**

For example, to find the image of the point (3, 2) under the translation $\begin{pmatrix}6\\4\end{pmatrix}$:

add $(3, 2) + \begin{pmatrix}6\\4\end{pmatrix}$: image is (9, 6)

Example

What is the image of the point (2, 7) under a translation $\begin{pmatrix}3\\5\end{pmatrix}$?

$2 + 3 = 5, \quad 7 + 5 = 12$: image is (5, 12)

Exercise

2 Write down the image points for the following.

Point	Translation	Point	Translation
(a) (3, 1)	$\begin{pmatrix}2\\4\end{pmatrix}$	(b) (6, 0)	$\begin{pmatrix}3\\1\end{pmatrix}$
(c) (97, 99)	$\begin{pmatrix}3\\1\end{pmatrix}$	(d) (23, −2)	$\begin{pmatrix}0\\6\end{pmatrix}$
(e) (−5, −4)	$\begin{pmatrix}2\\7\end{pmatrix}$	(f) (3, 8)	$\begin{pmatrix}-3\\4\end{pmatrix}$
(g) (7, −3)	$\begin{pmatrix}-2\\4\end{pmatrix}$	(h) (2, 3)	$\begin{pmatrix}-3\\-5\end{pmatrix}$

3 Copy and complete the following tables.

(a)

Point	(2, 2)	(3, 3)	(4, 4)	(5, 5)
Image under translation $\begin{pmatrix}3\\0\end{pmatrix}$				

(b)

Point	(2, 5)	(3, 7)	(4, 9)	(5, 11)
Image under translation $\begin{pmatrix}3\\-1\end{pmatrix}$				

Continue with Section R

R Translations: the straight line

The general equation of a straight line may be written as

$$y = mx + c$$

where

m is the **gradient**

c is the **intercept** on the *y*-axis

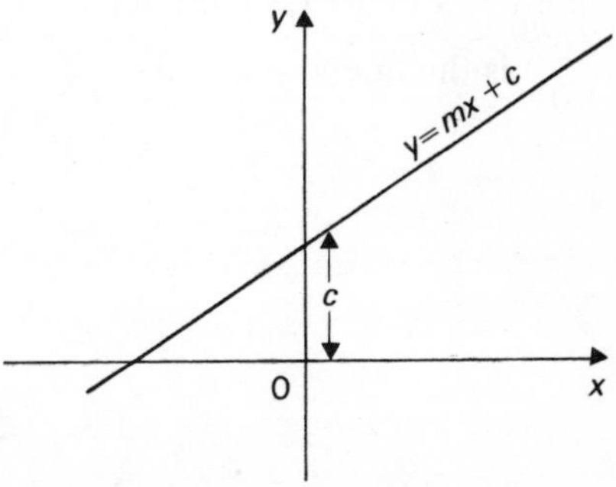

Example

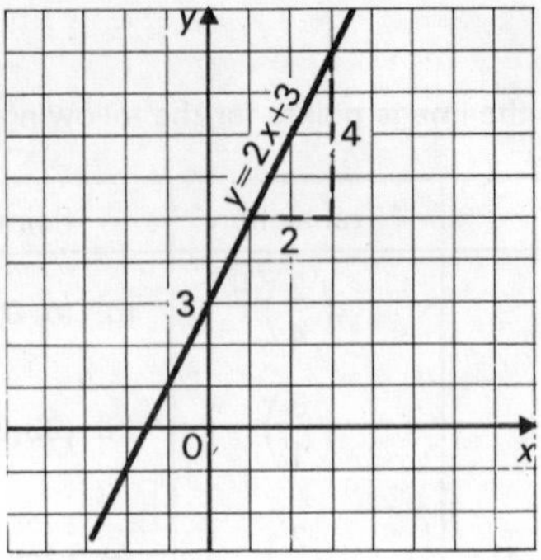

From the diagram

$$m = \frac{4}{2} = 2$$

$$c = 3$$

Equation is $y = \mathbf{2}x + \mathbf{3}$

Example

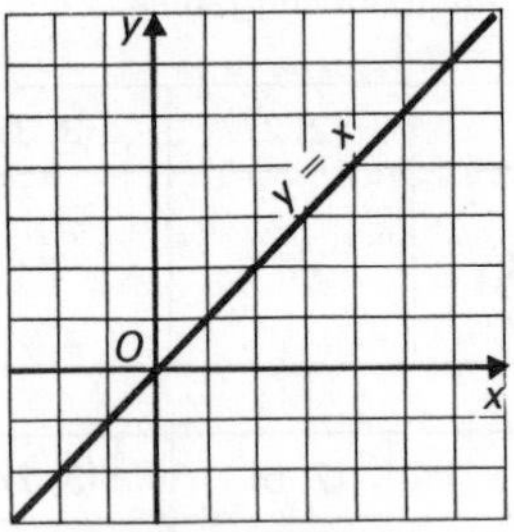

The diagram on the right shows the line $y = x$.

To find its image under the translation $\begin{pmatrix}3\\0\end{pmatrix}$, we could write down some of the points on the line and find the image of each point in turn under translation $\begin{pmatrix}3\\0\end{pmatrix}$.

Point on line $y = x$	(2, 2)	(3, 3)	(4, 4)	(5, 5)
Image under translation $\begin{pmatrix}3\\0\end{pmatrix}$	(5, 2)	(6, 3)	(7, 4)	(8, 5)

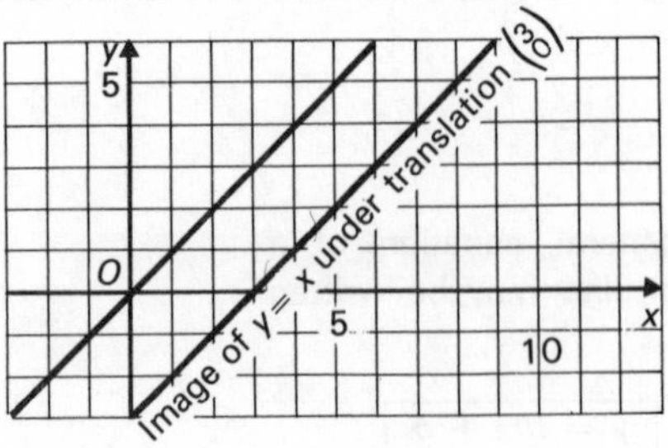

By plotting the image points we see that the image of the line $y = x$ under translation $\begin{pmatrix}3\\0\end{pmatrix}$ is the line $y = x - 3$.

Exercise

1 The diagram on the right shows the line whose equation is $y = 2x$. Write down the coordinates of the four given points in a table like the one on the previous page, and find the images of these points under translation $\begin{pmatrix}2\\0\end{pmatrix}$.

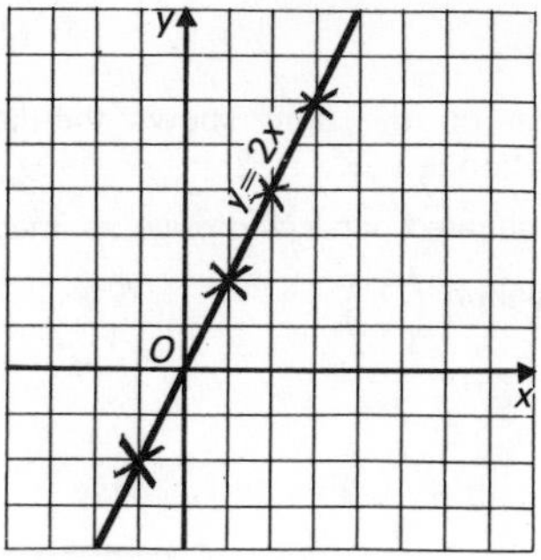

On squared paper, draw the line $y = 2x$ and its image under translation $\begin{pmatrix}2\\0\end{pmatrix}$.

Example

The diagram on the right shows the line whose equation is $y = -x$.

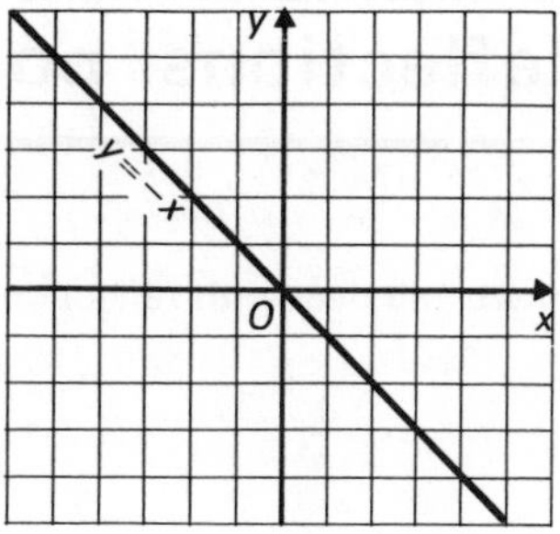

To find its image under translation $\begin{pmatrix}2\\1\end{pmatrix}$ we could write down the coordinates of some of the points on the line and find their images.

Points on line $y = -x$	$(-5, 5)$	$(-3, 3)$	$(-1, 1)$	$(2, -2)$	$(3, -3)$
Image under translation $\begin{pmatrix}2\\1\end{pmatrix}$	$(-3, 6)$	$(-1, 4)$	$(1, 2)$	$(4, -1)$	$(5, -2)$

The diagram on the right shows line $y = -x$ and its image under translation $\begin{pmatrix}2\\1\end{pmatrix}$.

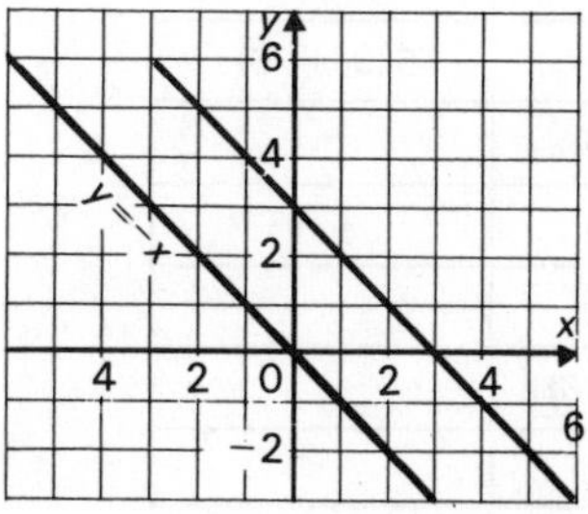

For the image, $m = -1$

$c = 3$

The equation of the image is

$$y = -x + 3$$

Under any translation, a line is moved to a new position parallel to the original.

Notice that two points would be sufficient to draw this image. You may even be able to do it with just one.

Exercise

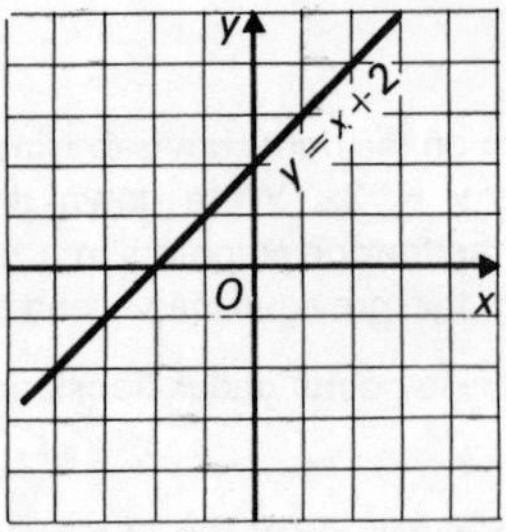

2 The diagram on the right shows the line whose equation is $y = x + 2$.
Draw it on squared paper and draw its image under translation $\begin{pmatrix}3\\1\end{pmatrix}$

Continue with Section S

S Reflections: points reflected in the axes

In this section we will deal with reflections.

Exercise

1 In this diagram each point is the image of one of the others under a reflection in either the x-axis or the y-axis.

(a) Copy and complete this table:

Point	Image under reflection in OX
$A(3, 6)$	$G(3, -6)$
$B(-2, 5)$	
$C(-3, 6)$	
$D(2, -1)$	
$E(-3, -6)$	
$F(4, -2)$	

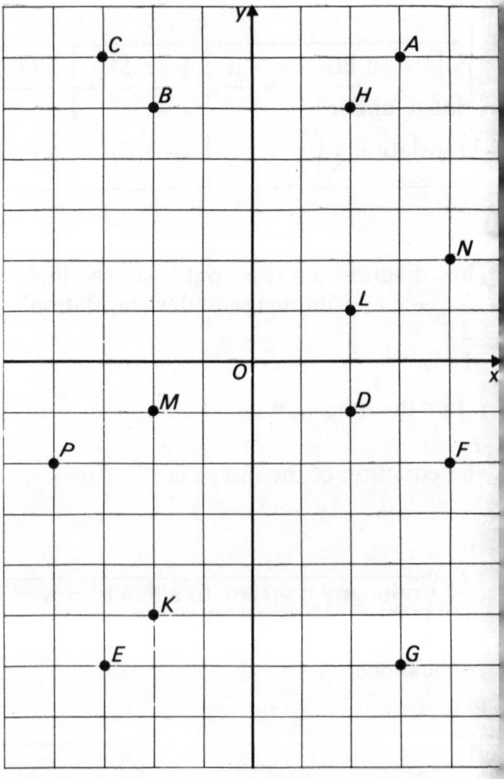

(b) Copy and complete this table:

Point	Image under reflection in *OY*
A (3, 6)	*C* (−3, 6)
B (−2, 5)	
C (−3, 6)	
D (2, −1)	
E (−3, −6)	
F (4, −2)	

(c) Study the pattern in part (a) above and then copy and complete this table for reflection in the *x*-axis.

Point	Image under reflection in *OX*
(3, 8)	(3, −8)
(6, 2)	
(−3, 2)	
(49, −7)	
(*a*, *b*)	

(d) Study the pattern in part (b) above and then copy and complete this table for reflection in the *y*-axis.

Point	Image under reflection in *OY*
(6, 2)	(−6, 2)
(21, 4)	
(−15, 81)	
(7, 7)	
(*a*, *b*)	

2 In a coordinate diagram plot the points *A* (2, 1), *B* (5, 0), and *C* (3, 3). Reflect each of these points in the *x*-axis to positions *A′*, *B′*, and *C′* and draw the triangle *A′B′C′*.

Triangle *A′B′C* is the image of triangle *ABC* under reflection in the *x*-axis.

3 In a coordinate diagram plot the points *P*(2, 5), *Q*(3, 7), *R*(4, 9), and *S*(5, 11). They should lie in a straight line. Reflect each of the points in the *y*-axis to positions *P′*, *Q′*, *R′*, and *S′*. The images should also lie in a straight line.

Write down the equation of the line through *P*, *Q*, *R*, and *S* and the equation of the line through *P′*, *Q′*, *R′* and *S′*.

Continue with Section T

T Lines reflected in the axes

In this diagram the line AB is reflected in the y-axis giving the image line $A'B'$.

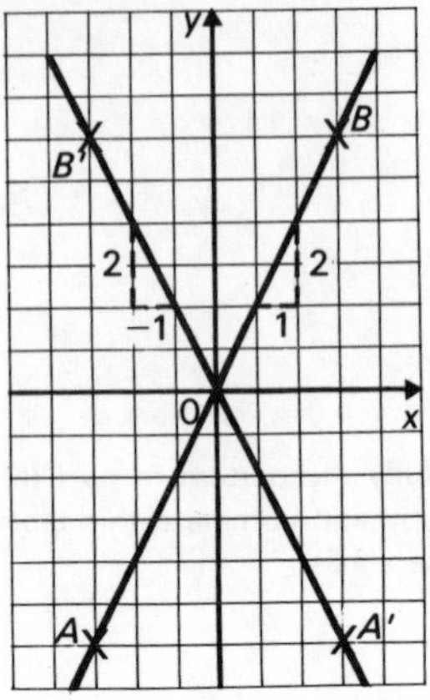

Equation of AB

$m = \frac{2}{1} = 2; \quad c = 0$

Equation is $y = 2x$

Equation of A'B'

$m = \frac{2}{-1} = -2; \quad c = 0$

Equation is $y = -2x$

So under reflection in the y-axis $\quad \mathbf{y = 2x \rightarrow y = -2x}$

Exercise

1 On squared paper draw the line $y = x + 1$ and its reflection in the y-axis.
2 On squared paper draw the line $y = 2x + 3$ and its reflection in the x-axis.

Continue with Section U

U Points reflected in other lines

In the diagram the axis of reflection shown has the equation $x = 5$. The points P, Q, and R have been reflected in the line $x = 5$.

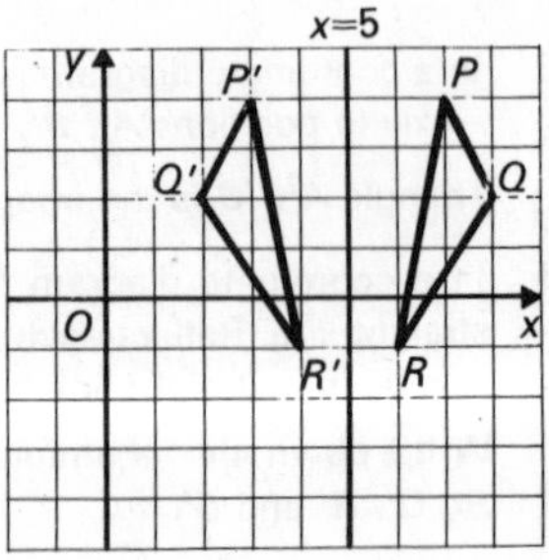

Check that the following table shows the coordinates of P, Q, R, and their images.

Point	$P(7, 4)$	$Q(8, 2)$	$R(6, -1)$
Image under reflection in line $x = 5$	$P'(3, 4)$	$Q'(2, 2)$	$R'(4, -1)$

Exercise

Copy and complete the following tables for reflection in the lines whose equations are given. Draw a coordinate diagram for each question.

1

Point	*A*(1, 3)	*B*(6, 4)	*C*(−1, 2)	*D*(−3, −2)	*E*(6, 93)
Image under reflection in line $x = 2$					

2

Point	*P*(3, 5)	*Q*(2, −1)	*R*(0, −5)	*S*(0, 0)	*T*(87, 2)
Image under reflection in line $y = -1$					

3

Point	(1, 1)	(2, 3)	(3, 5)	(4, 7)	(−3, 55)
Image under reflection in line $x = -1$					

Continue with Section V

V Rotations: coordinates

In this section we will deal with rotations. Remember that to describe a rotation we must know:

1. the **centre** of the rotation.
2. the **angle** of rotation.
3. whether the rotation is **clockwise or anticlockwise**.

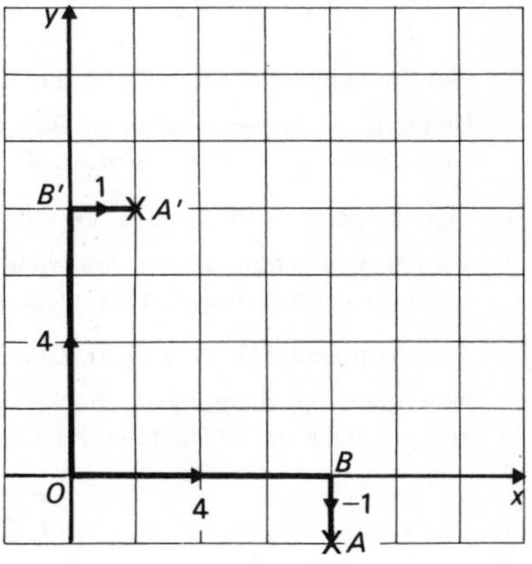

In this diagram the point *A* is to be given an anticlockwise rotation of 90° about *O*.

The path *OBA* ( ) shows the point *A* in terms of its coordinates, *A*(4, −1).

Rotate *OBA* through 90° anticlockwise about *O* obtaining *OB'A'* ( ).
A is the point (1, 4).

A(4, −1) → *A'*(1, 4)

Exercise

1 Copy and complete the following table.

To find the image of each point, imagine (or draw) each point in coordinate terms (forming paths like ●→↓, ↑←●, ●→↑).

Then rotate these lines through 90° anticlockwise about *O*.

Point	*A*(4, −1)	*B*(2, 1)	*C*(−4, 1)	*D*(0, −2)	*E*(−3, −1)
Image under anticlockwise rotation of 90° about *O*	*A*′(1, 4)				

2 Copy and complete this table.

Point	(0, 0)	(1, 2)	(2, 4)	(3, 6)	(4, 8)
Image under anticlockwise rotation of 90° about *O*					

You should find that all the points in the top row of the table lie on a straight line, and all the points in the bottom row lie on a straight line.

3 Look at the pattern of the coordinates in the table opposite, and in the tables for questions 1 and 2.

Copy and complete this table, *without drawing a diagram.*

Point		Image under anticlockwise 90° rotation about *O*
(4, −1)	⟶	(1, 4)
(−2, 1)	⟶	(−1, −2)
(1, 7)	⟶	(■, ■)
(−2, −6)	⟶	
(25, 3)	⟶	
(*a*, *b*)	⟶	

4 Plot the points *A* (0, 2), *B* (0, 6), and *C* (4, 4). Join them up to form a triangle *ABC*.

Under a clockwise rotation of 90° about *O* the image triangle is *A′B′C′*. Draw this triangle and write down the coordinates of *A′*, *B′*, and *C′*.

5 Plot the points *P*(4, 2), *Q*(6, 2), *R*(6, 6), and *S*(4, 6). Join them up to form rectangle *PQRS*.

Give this rectangle an anticlockwise rotation of 90° about *O* forming the image figure *P′Q′R′S′*. State the coordinates of these image points.

6 Plot the points *A* (1, 2), *B* (5, 2), *C* (5, 4), and *D* (1, 4). Join them up. What shape have you formed?

Now give your diagram an anticlockwise rotation of 90° about *O*. Plot the points *A′*, *B′*, *C′*, and *D′*, and join them up. Write down their coordinates.

Continue with Section W

W Half turns: coordinates

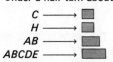

In the diagram the point A is given a rotation of 180° anticlockwise about O, giving the image point A' as shown.

This rotation through 180° is also called a **half-turn rotation.**

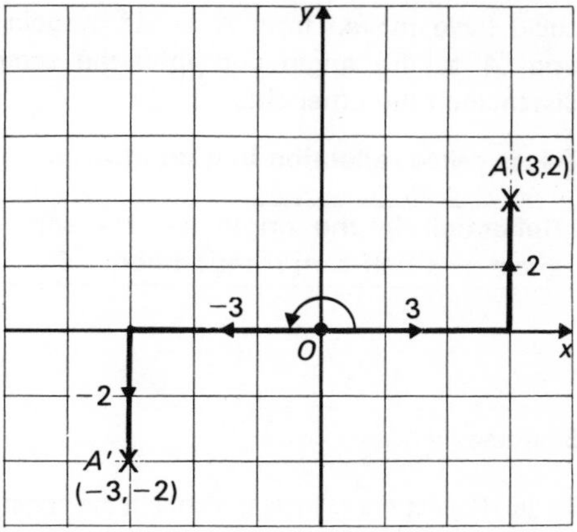

Exercise

1 Copy and complete the following table by drawing a diagram.

Point	$A(2, 1)$	$B(4, 1)$	$C(4, 4)$	$D(3, 5)$	$E(2, 4)$
Image under a half-turn about O	$A'(-2, -1)$				

2 Look at the pattern of the coordinates in question 1. Copy and complete this table *without drawing a diagram.*

Point		Image under half-turn about O
(7, 6)	⟶	(−7, −6)
(4, −2)	⟶	(−4, 2)
(3, 9)	⟶	▒
(−6, 2)	⟶	▒
(a, b)	⟶	▒

3 Plot the points $X(3, 3)$, $Y(5, 3)$, and $Z(4, 6)$. Join them up to form triangle XYZ.

Give this triangle a half-turn about O forming the image triangle $X'Y'Z'$. State the coordinates of these image points.

4 The diagram shows two regular pentagons $ABCDE$ and $EFGHA$. O is the mid-point of AE.

Copy and complete the following:

Under a half-turn about O,

C ⟶ ▒
H ⟶ ▒
AB ⟶ ▒
$ABCDE$ ⟶ ▒

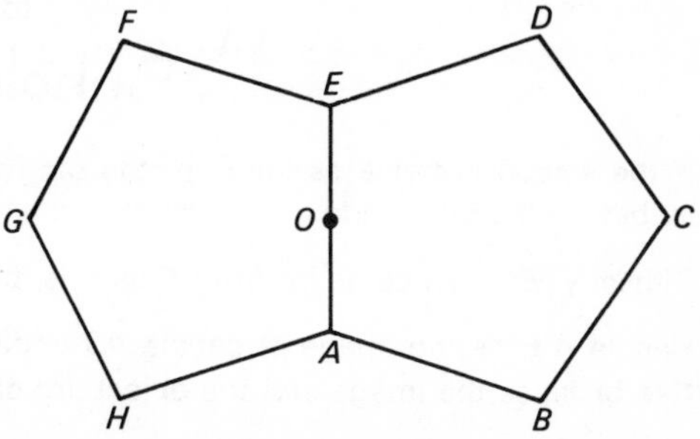

In the diagram at the top of page 289 we could have moved from $A \to A'$ by going from A to the origin and then the same distance on the other side.

This is called **reflection in a point.**

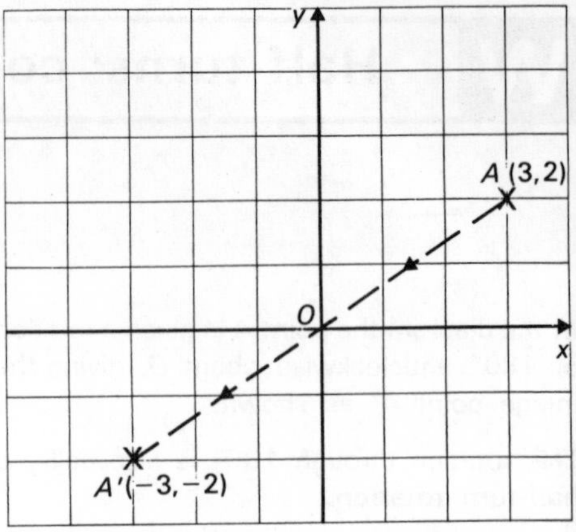

Reflection in the origin has the same effect as a **half-turn rotation about *O*.**

Exercise

5 (a) Reflect the following points in the origin: $P(1, 1)$, $Q(4, 1)$, $R(5, 3)$, $S(2, 3)$.

(b) Form the figures $PQRS$ and $P'Q'R'S'$.

(c) Write down the coordinates of P', Q', R', and S'.

Continue with Section X

X Dilatation: negative scale factor

Your teacher will show you a pin-hole camera.

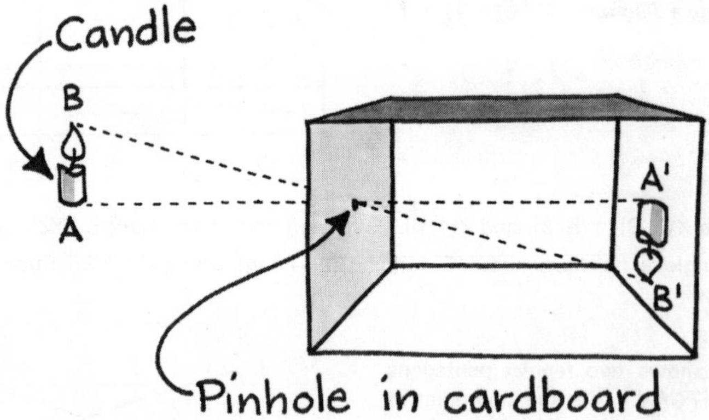

If the screen is twice as far from the pin-hole as the candle is, A' is twice as far from P as A is, but on the other side.

Similarly, B' is twice as far from P as B is, but *on the other side.*

Candle $A'B'$ is the image of candle AB under the dilatation $[P, -2]$. The scale factor is **negative** because the image and the object are on opposite sides of the centre P.

Example

To find the image of point A under the dilatation [origin, -2].

A is 3 units to the right of the origin and 2 units up.

Hence A' is 6 units to the **left** of A and 4 units **down**.

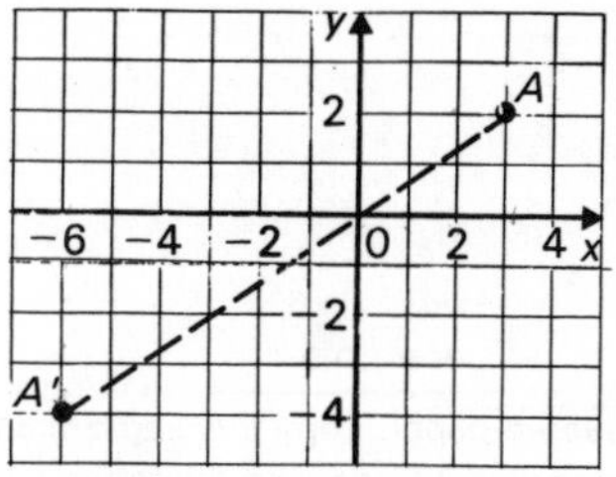

Example

To find the image of line AB under the dilatation [P, -3].

From P, A is 1 to the right and 2 up.

Since the scale factor is negative three, A' is 3 to the **left** of P and 6 units **down**.

B is 3 units to the right of P and 1 up.

So B' is 9 units to the **left** and 3 **down**.

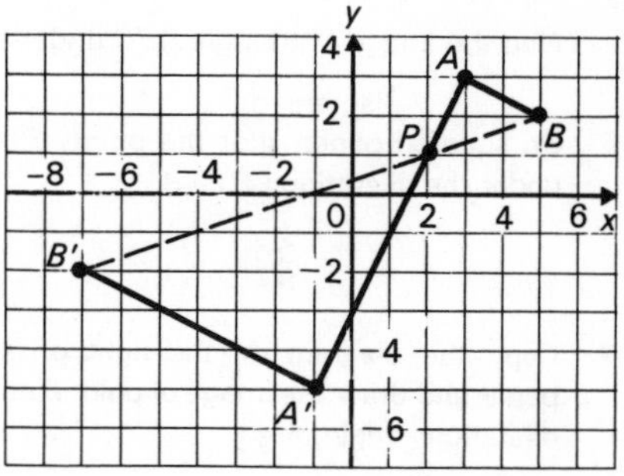

A' B' is the image of AB under the dilatation [P, -3].

Exercise

1 On squared paper, copy the diagram on the right and draw the image of line AB under the dilatation [origin, -2].

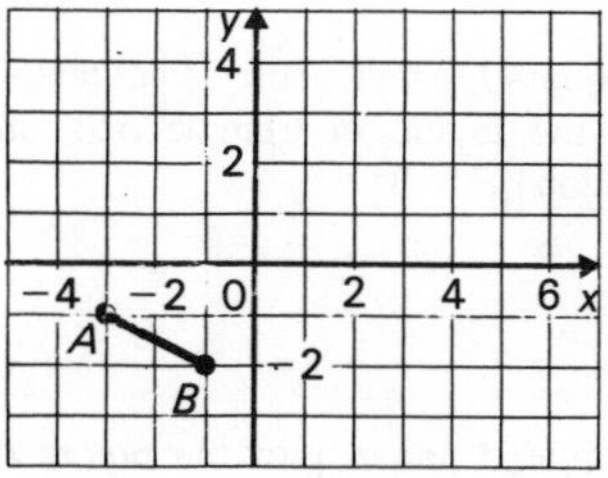

2 Copy the diagram on squared paper and draw the image of line PQ under the dilatation [R, -2].

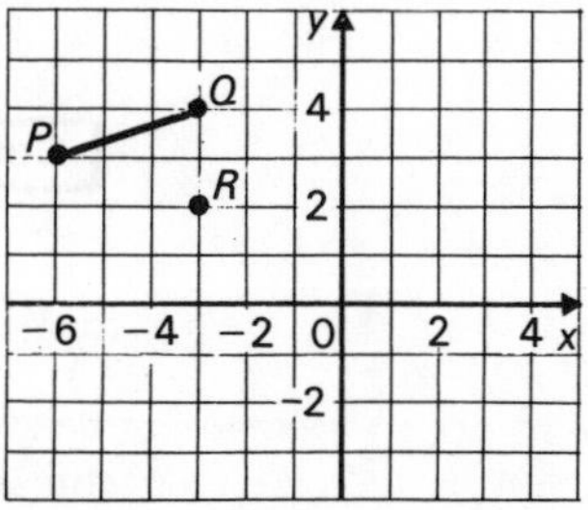

3 Copy this diagram on squared paper and draw the image of triangle *ABC* under the dilatation $[S, -1]$.

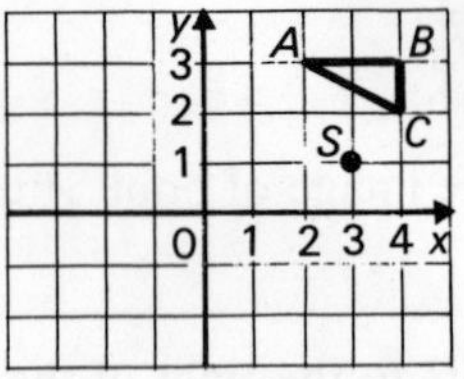

4 On squared paper, copy the diagram and draw the image of *A* under the dilatation $[P, -4]$.

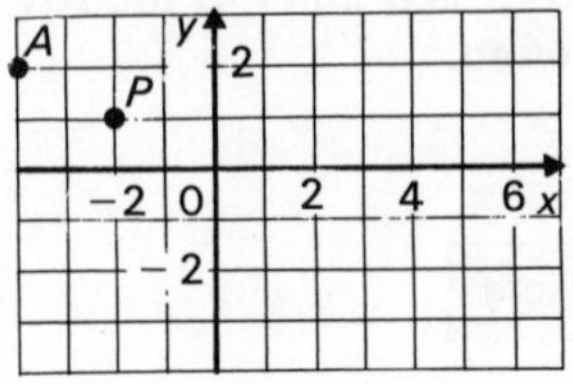

5 On squared paper, plot the points $A(1, 1)$, $B(4, 1)$, and $C(3, 2)$. Draw the triangle *ABC*. Find the image of triangle *ABC* under the dilatation $[\text{origin}, -2]$.

6 On squared paper, plot the points $P(-1, 1)$, $Q(-3, 2)$, and $R(2, 2)$. Draw the image of the line *PQ* under the dilatation $[R, -3]$.

7 Copy the diagram on the right on squared paper and draw the image of point *P* under the dilatation $[\text{origin}, -\frac{1}{2}]$.

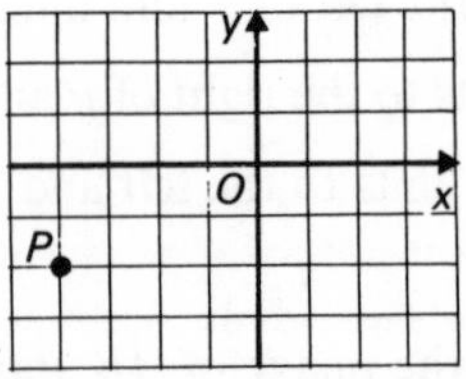

8 On squared paper, copy this diagram and draw the image of triangle *RST* under the dilatation $[F, -3]$.

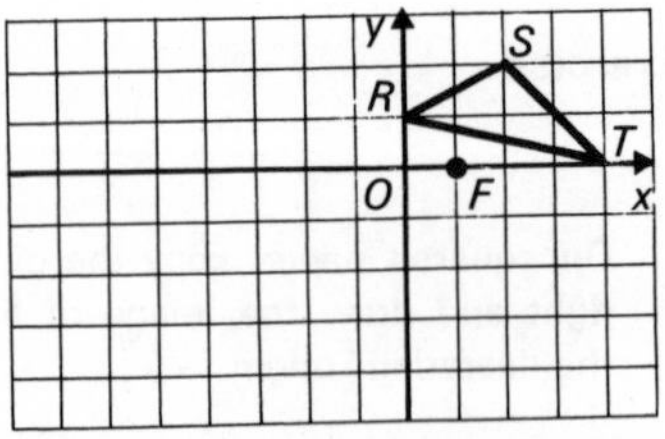

9 On squared paper, plot the points $A(1, -1)$, $B(5, -3)$, and $M(-1, 1)$, and draw the image of line *AB* under the dilatation $[M, -1\frac{1}{2}]$.

Continue with Section Y

Y Dilatations: negative scale factor using instruments

Dilatations with negative scale factors can be drawn without squared paper in much the same way as in Section P.

Example

To find the image of point R under the dilatation $[N, -2]$, we join N to R and produce a line on the **other side** of N.

Measure NR, and then measure off NR' so that $NR' = 2NR$, but R' is on the **other side** of N from R (**negative** scale factor).

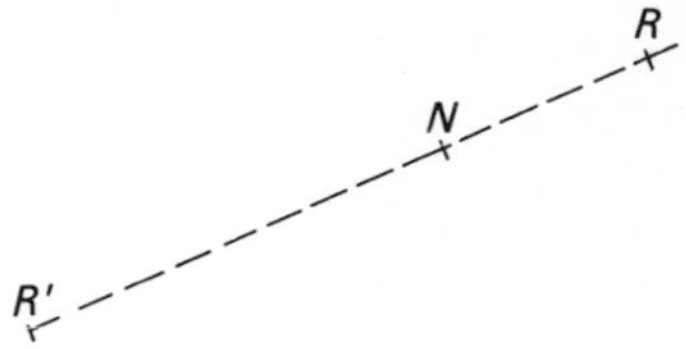

Example

To find the image of line AB *under the dilatation* $[R, -2]$, we require a line on the other side of R from AB and twice as far away.

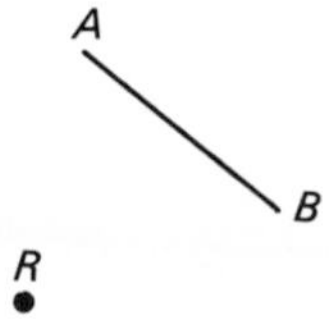

We should join A to R and B to R.

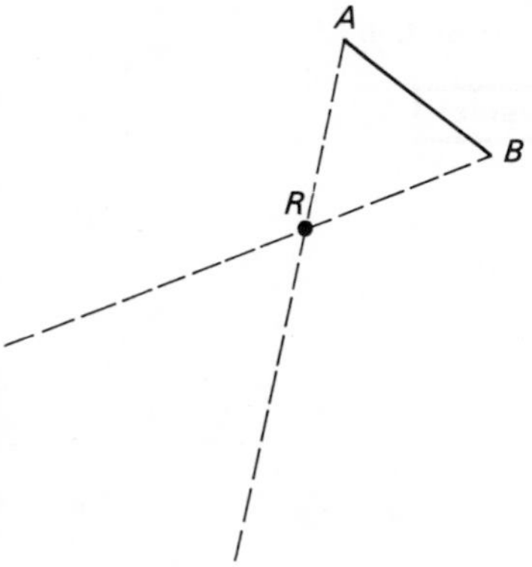

By using a ruler, find A' and B' such that $RA' = 2RA$ and $RB' = 2RB$.

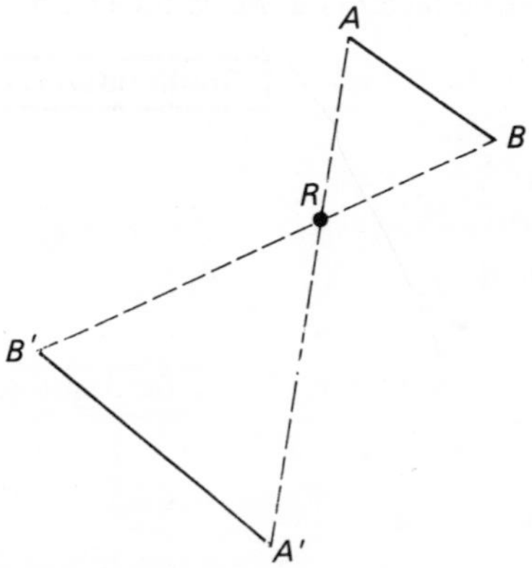

$A'B'$ is the image of AB under the dilatation $[R, -2]$.

Continue with Sheet M9/10

Z The centre of a dilatation

When the object and the image of a dilatation are known it is possible to find the centre of the dilatation by joining corresponding points.

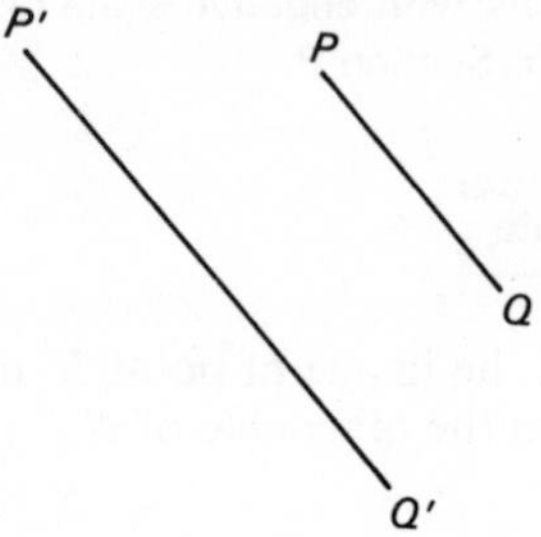

For example, to find the centre of the dilatation which transforms line *PQ* into line *P'Q'*, we join *P'P* and produce it. Then join *Q'Q* and produce it.

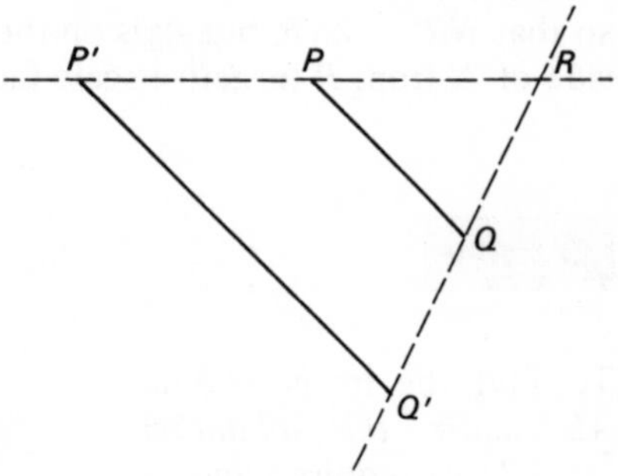

P'P and *Q'Q* produced meet at *R*. Hence *R* is the centre of the dilatation.

We can find the scale factor also since the scale factor is given by

$$\frac{P'R}{PR} \text{ or } \frac{Q'R}{QR} \text{ or } \frac{P'Q'}{PQ}.$$

Here the scale factor is 2. *PQ* is transformed into *P'Q'* by the dilatation $[R, 2]$.

Continue with sheet M9/10 (reverse)

& Progress check

Exercise

1 On squared paper plot the points $A(0, 1)$, $B(2, 2)$, and $C(4, 3)$.

Draw the line through A, B, and C and write down its equation.

Plot the images of A, B, and C under a translation $\begin{pmatrix} -2 \\ -3 \end{pmatrix}$ and write down the equation of the image line.

2 Plot the points $P(4, 1)$, $Q(0, 4)$, and $R(-4, 1)$.

Under reflection in the line $y = 1$, what are the coordinates of Q'?

What shape is formed by PQR and its image?

3 Plot the points $D(2, 2)$, $E(3, 2)$, $F(3, 4)$, and $G(2, 4)$, and join them up. What shape have you formed?

Give $DEFG$ a clockwise rotation of 90° about O and plot the image points D', E', F', and G'.

Write down their coordinates.

4 Plot the points $P(3, 4)$, $Q(5, 2)$, and $R(2, 1)$. Find the image of triangle PQR under the dilatation $[\text{origin}, -2]$.

5 Plot the points $M(-1, 2)$, $N(2, 4)$, and $S(1, -1)$. Draw the image of line MN under the dilatation $[S, -1]$.

6 Plot the points $F(-4, 5)$, $G(-2, -3)$, $F'(5, -1)$, and $G'(4, 3)$.

Given that $F'G'$ is the image of FG under a dilatation, find the centre of the dilatation and its scale factor.

Tell your teacher you have finished this Unit

APPENDIX Drawing parallel lines

How to draw a line through the point *Z* parallel to the line *XY*.

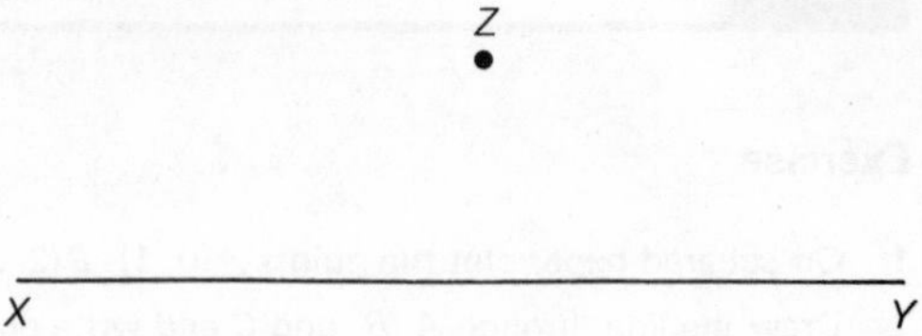

Step 1

Place one edge of your set square along the line *XY*.

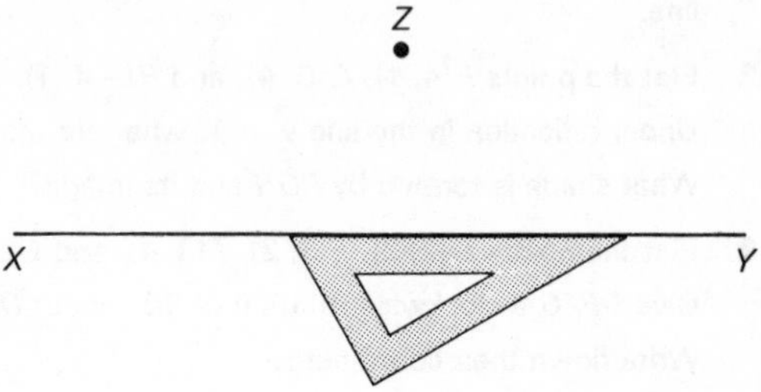

Step 2

Lay a ruler along another edge of the set square.

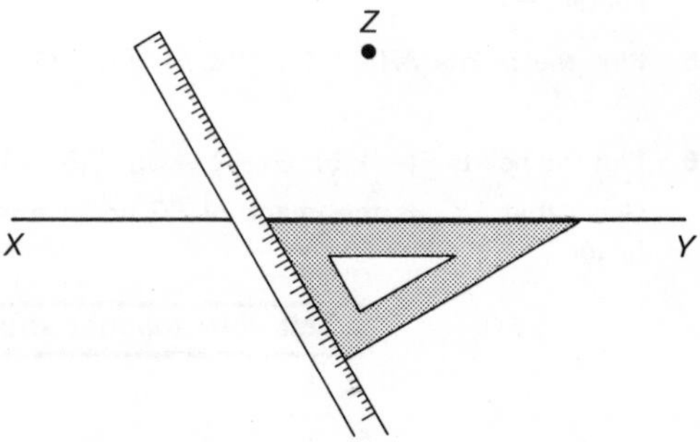

Step 3

Pressing firmly on the ruler, so that it cannot move, slide the set square up until the top edge is just below the point *Z*.

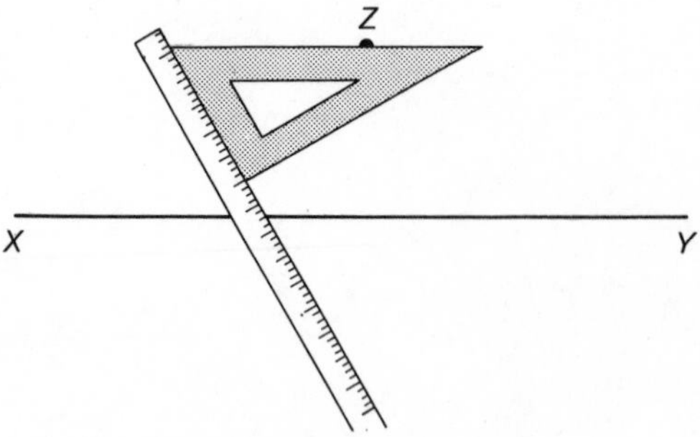

Step 4

Draw a line along the edge of the set square passing through the point.

This second line is parallel to the first one.

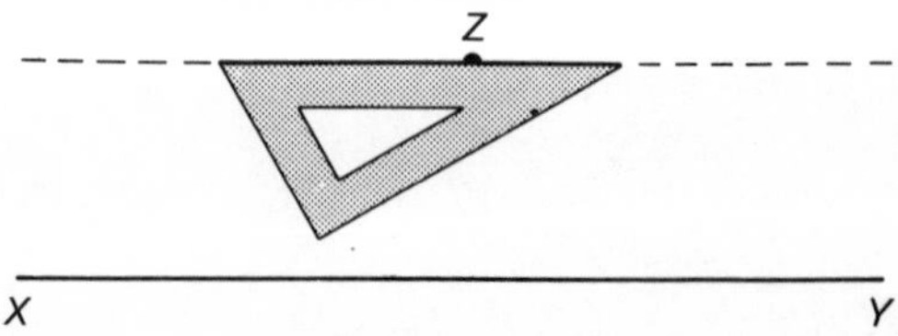

UNIT M10

Simultaneous Equations and Inequations

A Straight lines

The equation $2x + y = 6$ can be written as $y = -2x + 6$.

Earlier you learned that the graph of an equation like this was a straight line with gradient -2, cutting the y-axis at $(0, 6)$.

In a similar way, it can be shown that the graphs of equations like $3x + 4y = 12$ and $3x - 2y = 7$ are straight lines.

Once we know by looking at an equation that it represents a straight line, we need only find and plot **two points** on the line, and then we can draw the line.

Example

Graph the straight line $3x + 5y = 15$.

Two suitable points on the line are usually:
(a) the one with x coordinate equal to zero;
(b) the one with y coordinate equal to zero.

So, for $3x + 5y = 15$
when $x = 0$
$5y = 15$
$y = 3$
$(0, 3)$ lies on line.

when $y = 0$
$3x = 15$
$x = 5$
$(5, 0)$ lies on line.

The graph looks like this.

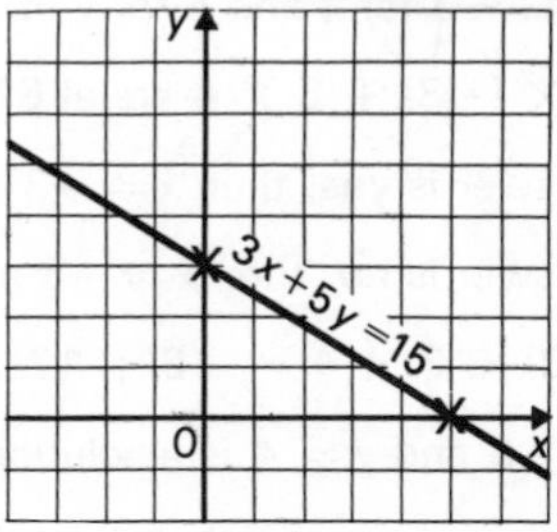

Exercise

In each of the following questions find two points on the line. Plot these points on a diagram and draw the the straight line.

1 Draw the straight line $3x + 7y = 21$ and copy and complete the following:

when $x = 0$ | when $y = 0$
$7y = 21$ | $\square = 21$
$y = 3$ | $x = \square$
$(0, 3)$ lies on the line. $(7, 0)$ lies on the line.

Now plot the points and draw the line.

2 Draw the straight line $2x - 5y = 10$ and copy and complete the following:

when $x = 0$ | when $y = 0$
$-5y = 10$ | $\square = \square$
$y = -2$ | $\square = \square$
$(\square, \square)$ lies on the line. $(\square, \square)$ lies on the line.

Now plot the points and draw the line.

3 Draw the straight line $3x + 2y = -6$ and copy and complete the following:

when $x = 0$
□ $= -6$
□ $=$ □
(□, □) lies on the line.

when $y = 0$
□ $=$ □
□ $=$ □
(□, □) lies on the line.

Now plot these points and draw the line.

4 Draw the straight line $x + 3y = 9$ and copy and complete the following:

when $x = 0$
□ $=$ □
□ $=$ □
(□, □) lies on the line.

when $y = 0$
$x = 9$
(□, □) lies on the line.

Now plot these points and draw the line.

5 Draw the straight line $4x + 5y = 20$ using the same method as above.

6 Draw the straight line $2x - 3y = 12$.

7 Draw the straight line $5x - 6y = 30$.

Continue with Section B

B Testing for solutions

The graph of an equation shows the **solution set** of the equation.

Here is the graph of $2x + 3y = 6$.

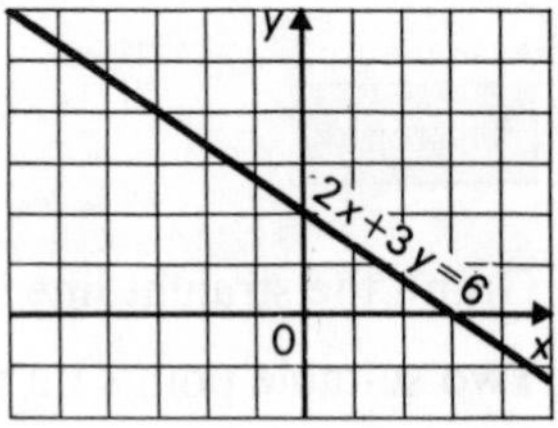

We can tell whether $x = -3$ and $y = 4$ is a solution of $2x + 3y = 6$ by the following method.

Substitute -3 for x and 4 for y in $2x + 3y = 6$

Does $2 \times (-3) + 3 \times 4$ equal 6?

If the answer is **yes**, then $x = -3$ and $y = 4$ **is** a solution.

If the answer is **no**, then $x = -3$ and $y = 4$ **is not** a solution.

$2 \times (-3) + 3 \times 4 = -6 + 12 = 6$

So $x = -3$ and $y = 4$ is a solution of $2x + 3y = 6$.

Check from your graph that the point $(-3, 4)$ is a point on the line.

Example

Is $x = 4$ and $y = 5$ a solution of $2x + 3y = 6$?

When $x = 4$ and $y = 5$,
$2x + 3y = 2 \times 4 + 3 \times 5 = 8 + 15 = 23$ (not equal to 6)
So $x = 4$ and $y = 5$ is not a solution of $2x + 3y = 6$.

Check from your graph that the point $(4, 5)$ is not a point on the line.

Exercise

1 Use the method of the example to check whether the following are solutions of the equation $2x + 3y = 7$.

(a) $x = 2$ and $y = 1$;

(b) $x = -3$ and $y = 4$;

(c) $x = 6$ and $y = -2$.

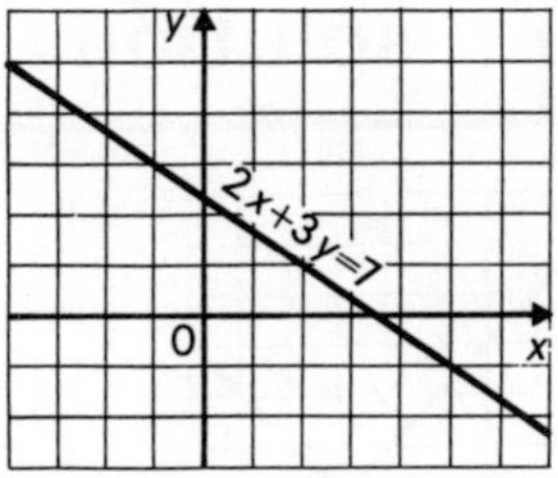

2 Check whether the following are solutions of the equation $x - 2y = 4$.

(a) $x = -1$ and $y = 2$;

(b) $x = 5$ and $y = 0.5$;

(c) $x = 2$ and $y = 1$.

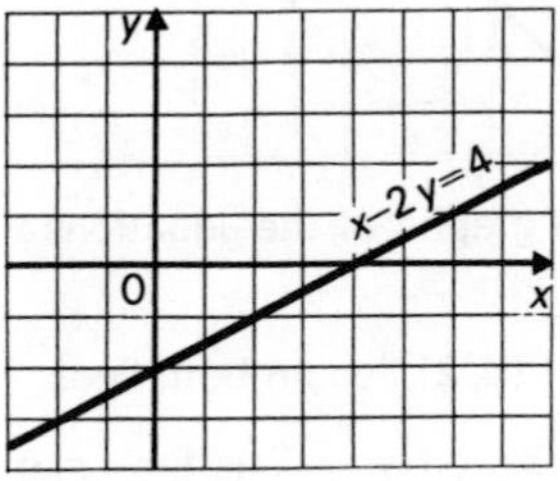

3 Check whether the following are solutions of the equation $-3x + 5y = 15$.

(a) $x = 2$ and $y = 4$;

(b) $x = -10$ and $y = -3$;

(c) $x = -3$ and $y = 1$.

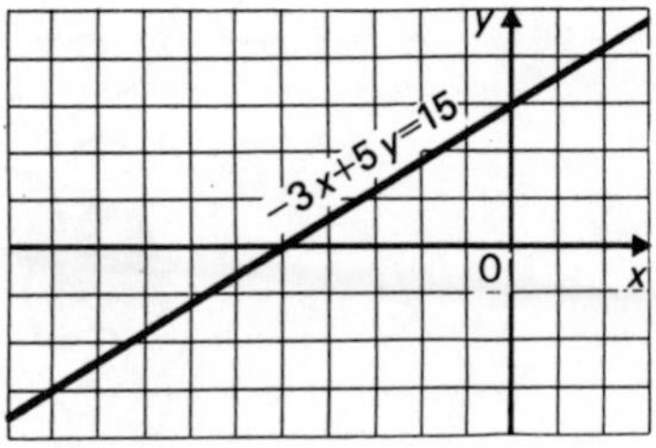

4 Here are graphs of the equations $x - 2y = 2$ and $2x - y = 7$.

Say whether each of the following points is a solution of

(i) the equation $x - 2y = 2$;

(ii) the equation $2x - y = 7$;

(iii) neither equation;

(iv) both equations.

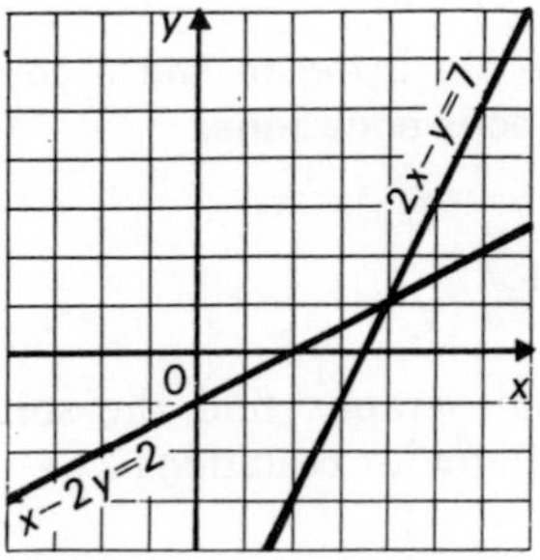

(a) (6, 2)	(b) (3, 1)	(c) (2, −3)
(d) (4, 1)	(e) (−2, 2)	(f) (3, −1)

Continue with Section C

C Simultaneous equations—graphical solution

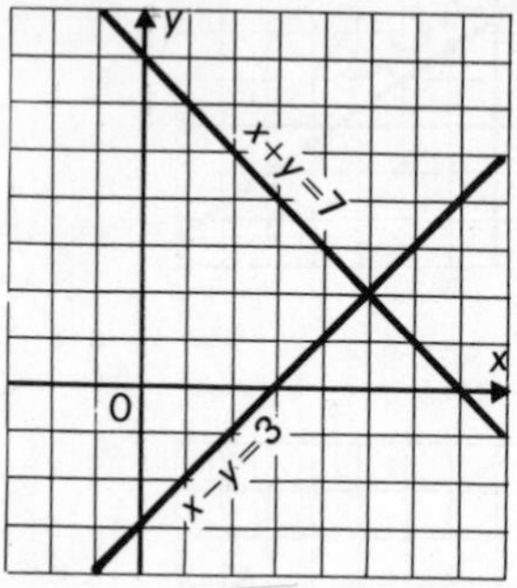

Here are graphs of the equations $x + y = 7$ and $x - y = 3$.

The point (5, 2) lies on both lines.

So $x = 5$ and $y = 2$ is the solution of the two equations.

When we are trying to find a common solution to two equations, the equations are called **simultaneous equations.**

Example

From their graphs find the solution of the simultaneous equations $2x - 5y = 10$ and $x - y = -1$.

Check the solution by substitution.

The point $(-5, -4)$ lies on both lines so $x = -5$ and $y = -4$ is the solution.

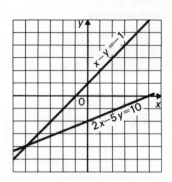

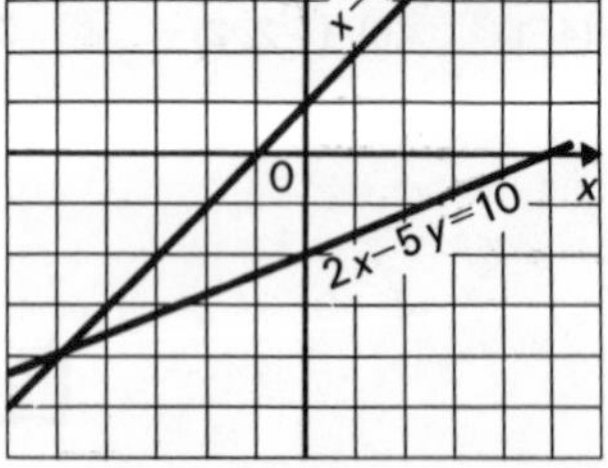

Check

$2x - 5y = 10$	$x - y = -1$
$2x - 5y = 2 \times (-5) - 5 \times (-4)$ $= -10 + 20$ $= 10$	$x - y = -5 - (-4)$ $= -5 + 4$ $= -1$

Exercise

In each question find the solution of the simultaneous equations from their graphs, and then check the result by substitution, as shown in the example above.

1 $2x - y = -1$
$3x + 2y = 16$

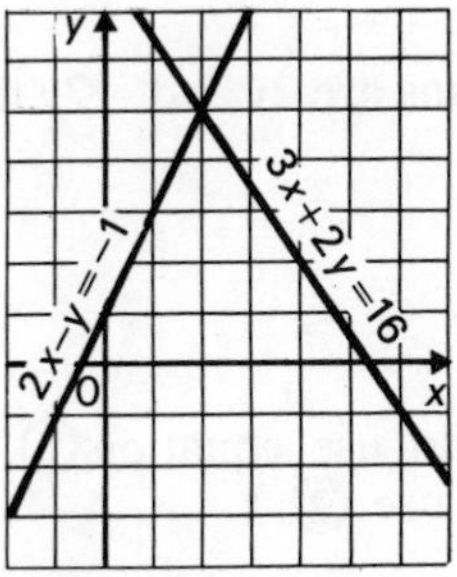

2 $2x + y = 5$
$-3x + 2y = -4$

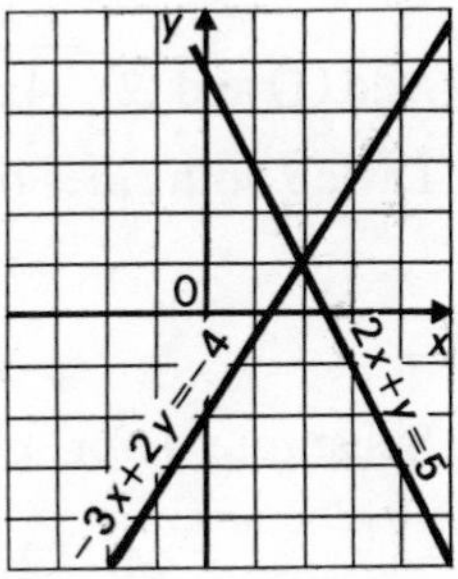

3 $3x - 4y = 10$
$2x + 3y = 1$

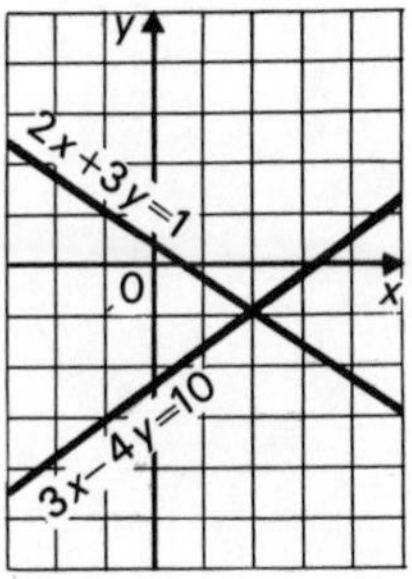

4 $3x + 2y = 6$
$x - 2y = 10$

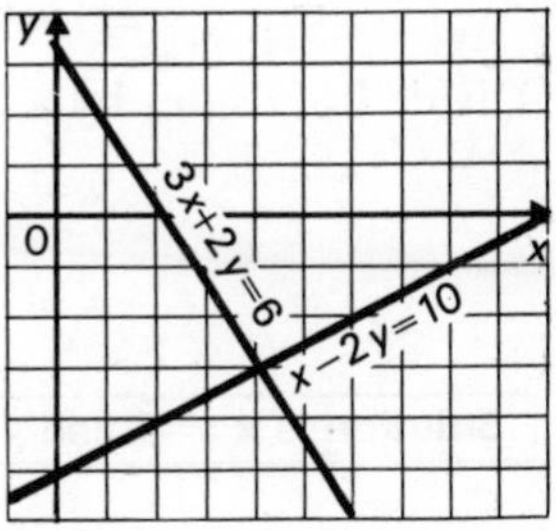

For questions 5 to 8 draw your own graphs.

5 $x + y = 5$
$3x - y = 3$

6 $x + 2y = 2$
$-x + 3y = -12$

7 $2x + y = 16$
$x - y = 5$

8 $2x + y = -4$
$x - 2y = -12$

Continue with Section D

D Solving simultaneous equations

It is possible to find the solution of simultaneous equations without drawing graphs.

Example

Solve the equations $3x + 2y = 6$
$x - 2y = 10$ (and then check the answer)

Start by labelling the equations ① and ②

$$3x + 2y = 6 \quad ①$$
$$x - 2y = 10 \quad ②$$

Add ① and ② $4x = 16$ (Since the y terms are $2y$ and $-2y$ they disappear)

Divide both sides by 4

$$x = \frac{16}{4}$$
$$x = 4$$

Substitute 4 for x in equation ②. (We could use equation ① but in this case it is easier to use ②.)

$$4 - 2y = 10$$

Subtract 4 from both sides

$$-2y = 10 - 4$$
$$-2y = 6$$

Divide both sides by -2

$$y = \frac{6}{-2}$$
$$y = -3$$

Solution is $x = 4$ and $y = -3$

Check

$3x + 2y = 6$	$x - 2y = 10$
$3x + 2y$ $= 3 \times 4 + 2 \times (-3)$ $= 12 + (-6)$ $= 6$	$x - 2y$ $= 4 - 2 \times (-3)$ $= 4 + 6$ $= 10$

You solved these equations graphically in Section C. Note that your answers are the same.

Exercise

Solve each pair of simultaneous equations, and check each answer.

1 $2x - 3y = 2$, $x + 3y = 19$

2 $-x + 2y = 8$, $x + 3y = 17$

3 $x + 4y = 21$, $3x - 4y = -1$

4 $-2x + 5y = 19$, $2x + y = -1$

Continue with Section E

E The disappearing terms

Example

Solve the equations $2x - 5y = -21$
$3x + 10y = 56$

(and then check the answer).

(If we add the two equations together we obtain $5x + 5y = 35$.
This is no use since neither the x term nor the y term has disappeared.)

Here is the method.
Label the equations $2x - 5y = -21$ ①
$3x + 10y = 56$ ②

Multiply both sides of equation ① by 2:

$$\begin{aligned} 4x - 10y &= -42 \\ 3x + 10y &= 56 \quad \text{(we leave ② as it was)} \end{aligned}$$

Add: $7x = 14$

Divide both sides by 7:

$$x = \frac{14}{7}$$

$$x = 2$$

Substitute 2 for x in equation ①:

$$4 - 5y = -21$$

Subtract 4 from both sides:

$$-5y = -21 - 4$$
$$-5y = -25$$

Divide both sides by -5:

$$y = \frac{-25}{-5}$$

$$y = 5$$

Solution is $x = 2$ and $y = 5$

Check

$2x - 5y = -21$	$3x + 10y = 56$
$2x - 5y$ $= 2 \times 2 - 5 \times 5$ $= 4 - 25$ $= -21$	$3x + 10y$ $= 3 \times 2 + 10 \times 5$ $= 6 + 50$ $= 56$

Exercise

Solve these simultaneous equations and check each answer.

1 $3x - 5y = -9$
$4x + 10y = 38$

2 $7x - 2y = 9$
$9x + 6y = 3$

3 $x - 4y = 1$
$3x + 8y = 23$

4 $5x + y = 13$
$6x - 4y = 26$

Continue with Section F

F Eliminating the *x*s or the *y*s

Consider the problem:

solve the equations
$$-3x + 4y = 17$$
$$6x + 7y = -4$$

(and then check the answer).

In such problems we try to arrange our equations so that either the *x* term or the *y* term disappears when we add the equations.

In mathematical language we talk about eliminating the *x*s or eliminating the *y*s.

Our aim is to build up the *x*s or the *y*s so that the terms have the **same magnitude** (or size), but with the **opposite sign**.

For example, $-5x$ and $+5x$, or $+6y$ and $-6y$.

Look back at the problem above.

We could build the *x*s up to $-6x$ and $+6x$ by doubling the terms in equation ①.

In this way we would **eliminate** the *x*s.

Example

$$-3x + 4y = 17 \qquad ①$$
$$6x + 7y = -4 \qquad ②$$

Multiply both sides of equation ① by 2:

$$-6x + 8y = 34$$
$$6x + 7y = -4 \text{ (we leave ② as it was)}$$

Add:
$$15y = 30$$

Divide both sides by 15:

$$y = \frac{30}{15}$$

$$y = 2$$

Substitute 2 for y in equation ②:

> You can substitute in ① or ②. The x term in ② is positive so it is easier to use ②.

$$6x + 14 = -4$$

Subtract 14 from both sides:

$$6x = -4 - 14$$
$$6x = -18$$

Divide both sides by 6:

$$x = \frac{-18}{6}$$

$$x = -3$$

Solution is $x = -3$, and $y = 2$

Check

$-3x + 4y = 17$	$6x + 7y = -4$
$-3x + 4y$ $= -3 \times (-3) + 4 \times 2$ $= 9 + 8$ $= 17$	$-6x + 7y$ $= 6 \times (-3) + 7 \times 2$ $= -18 + 14$ $= -4$

Example

Equations	**Method of solution**
$5x - 6y = 3$ ① $2x + 3y = 12$ ②	Eliminate the ys by building the y terms up to $-6y$ and $+6y$. Multiply equation ② by 2.

Exercise

1 Copy and complete the 'Method of solution' for each of the following.

Equations	Method of solution
$-x + 3y = 7$ ① $3x + 4y = 5$ ②	Eliminate the *x*s by building the □ terms up to □ and □. Multiply equation □ by □.
$x + 5y = -11$ ① $-5x + 2y = -26$ ②	Eliminate the □ by building the □ terms up to □ and □. Multiply equation □ by □.
$11x - 8y = 1$ ① $7x + 2y = 29$ ②	Eliminate the □ by building the □ terms up to □ and □. Multiply equation □ by □.

2 Solve these simultaneous equations and check each answer.

(a) $5x - 2y = 16$, $3x + 4y = 20$ (b) $-3x + 4y = 17$, $x - 5y = -13$

(c) $7x - 3y = -1$, $3x + y = -5$ (d) $x + 2y = 9$, $-4x + 3y = -3$

(e) $3x + 4y = 10$, $-6x + 5y = -7$ (f) $5x - 7y = 22$, $-10x - 8y = -22$

Continue with Section G

G Different coefficients—opposite signs

Example

Solve these simultaneous equations and check the answer.

$4x - 5y = -7$ ①

$3x + 2y = 12$ ②

Different numbers with opposite signs

10 is the lowest number which is a multiple of 2 and 5.

We can build up the *y* terms to $-10y$ and $+10y$.

Multiply equation ① by 2: $8x - 10y = -14$

Multiply equation ② by 5: $15x + 10y = 60$

Same numbers with opposite signs.

Add: $23x = 46$

Divide both sides by 23 $x = \frac{46}{23}$

$$\boxed{x = 2}$$

Substitute 2 for x in equation ①:

$$8 - 5y = -7$$

Subtract 8 from both sides:

$$-5y = -7 - 8$$
$$-5y = -15$$

Divide both sides by -5:

$$y = \frac{-15}{-5}$$

$$y = 3$$

Solution is $x = 2$ and $y = 3$

Check

$4x - 5y = -7$	$3x + 2y = 12$
$4x - 5y$ $= 4 \times 2 - 5 \times 3$ $= 8 - 15$ $= -7$	$3x + 2y$ $= 3 \times 2 + 2 \times 3$ $= 6 + 6$ $= 12$

Exercise

Solve these simultaneous equations and check each answer.

1 $2x - 3y = -4$
$5x + 2y = 9$

2 $7x - 3y = 24$
$4x + 5y = 7$

3 $5x + 2y = 14$
$4x - 5y = -2$

4 $5x + 3y = 19$
$7x - 4y = 43$

5 $6x - 5y = 17$
$5x + 2y = 8$

6 $8x + 3y = -14$
$3x - 2y = 1$

Continue with Section H

H Different coefficients—same signs

Example

Solve these simultaneous equations and check the answer.

$3x + 2y = 7$ ①
$4x + 3y = 9$ ②

Different numbers with same signs

6 is the lowest number which is a multiple of both 2 and 3. We can build up the y terms to $-6y$ and $+6y$.

Multiply equation ① by -3: $-9x \ -6\ y = -21$
Multiply equation ② by 2: $8x \ +6\ y = 18$

Same numbers with opposite signs

Add: $-x = -3$

Divide both sides by -1:

$$x = \frac{-3}{-1}$$

$$x = 3$$

Substitute 3 for x in equation ①:

$$9 + 2y = 7$$

Subtract 9 from both sides:

$$2y = 7 - 9$$
$$2y = -2$$

Divide both sides by 2:

$$y = \frac{-2}{2}$$

$$y = -1$$

Solution is $x = 3$ and $y = -1$

Check

$3x + 2y = 7$	$4x + 3y = 9$
$3x + 2y$ $= 3 \times 3 + 2 \times (-1)$ $= 9 - 2$ $= 7$	$4x + 3y$ $= 4 \times 3 + 3 \times (-1)$ $= 12 - 3$ $= 9$

Exercise

Solve these simultaneous equations and check each answer.

1 $7x + 4y = 9$
$6x + 5y = 3$

2 $5x + 4y = 17$
$6x + 3y = 15$

3 $8x - 3y = 19$
$5x - 2y = 12$

4 $2x - 3y = -1$
$7x - 4y = 16$

5 $7x + 6y = 20$
$5x + 2y = 12$

6 $2x + 3y = 13$
$3x + y = 16$

Continue with Section I

I Progress check

Exercise

1 On $\frac{1}{2}$ cm squared paper draw axes like these and then draw the graph of
$3x - 2y = 6$.

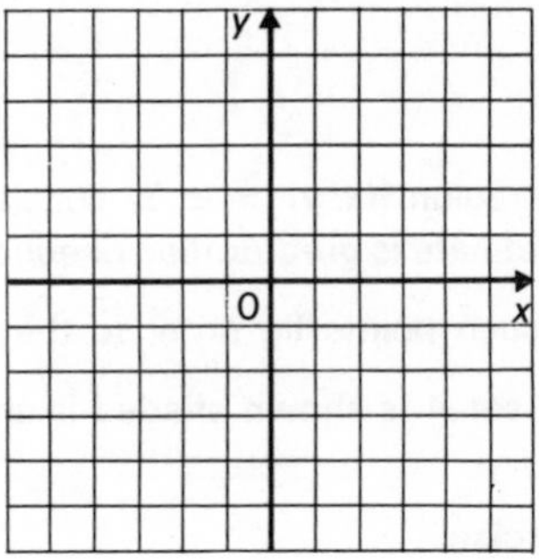

2 On $\frac{1}{2}$ cm squared paper draw the graph of the equations

$$x + 2y = -4$$
$$3x - 2y = 12$$

Use your graph to find the solution of these simultaneous equations.

3 Solve each pair of simultaneous equations, and check each answer.

(a) $3x - y = 4$, $4x + y = 10$

(b) $4x - y = 13$, $7x + 2y = 19$

(c) $5x + y = 13$, $4x - 3y = 18$

(d) $7x - 2y = 14$, $5x + 3y = 10$

(e) $2x + y = 0$, $5x + 2y = 1$

(f) $7x - 3y = 17$, $5x - 4y = 14$

Ask your teacher what to do next

J Regions of the plane

From now on *x* and *y* can take any values including fractions.

Consider the set $A = \{(x, y) : x \geq 3\}$.

This is read as

***'A* is the set of points (*x*, *y*) such that *x* is greater than or equal to 3'**

The **boundary line** is $x = 3$ and is shown here

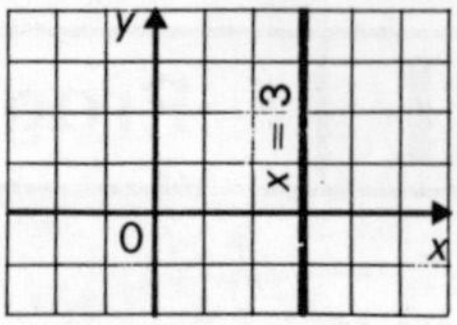

The region $\{(x, y) : x \geq 3\}$ consists of all points whose x coordinate is greater than or equal to 3.

All such points lie on or to the right of the line $x = 3$.

The set A is shown shaded in the diagram.

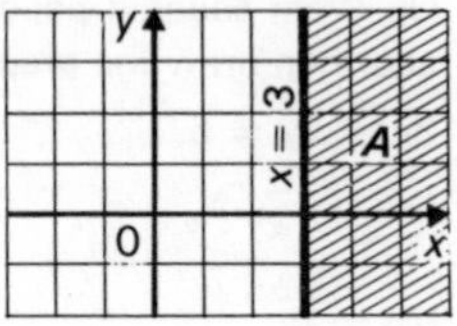

Exercise

On $\frac{1}{2}$ cm squared paper, use shading to show the following sets.

1 $J = \{(x, y) : x \geq 1\}$

2 $K = \{(x, y) : x \geq -1\}$

3 $L = \{(x, y) : x \geq 4\}$

4 $M = \{(x, y) : x \geq -3\}$

Consider the set $B = \{(x, y) : y \leqq 2\}$

We read this as

'B is the set of points (x, y) such that y is less than or equal to 2'

The boundary line is $y = 2$ and is shown here

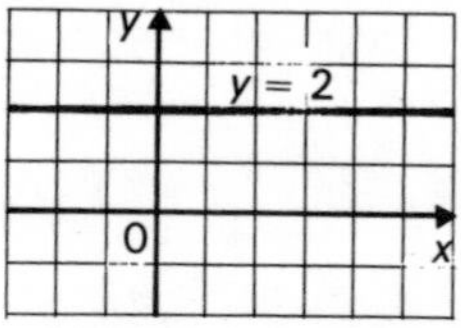

The region $\{(x, y) : y \leq 2\}$ consists of all points whose y coordinate is less than or equal to 2.

All such points lie on or below the line $y = 2$.

The set B is shown shaded in the diagram.

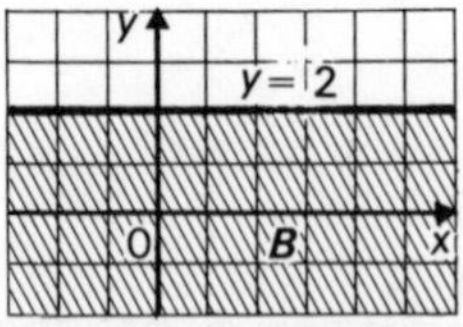

Exercise

On $\frac{1}{2}$ cm squared paper, use shading to show the following sets.

5 $Q = \{(x, y) : y \leq 3\}$

6 $R = \{(x, y) : y \leq -1\}$

7 $S = \{(x, y) : y \leq 2\}$

8 $T = \{(x, y) : y \leq -5\}$

Continue with Section K

K Intersections

The set $A = \{(x, y) : x \leq 4\}$ is shown here. To show that the boundary line is **included** we draw a **solid** line.

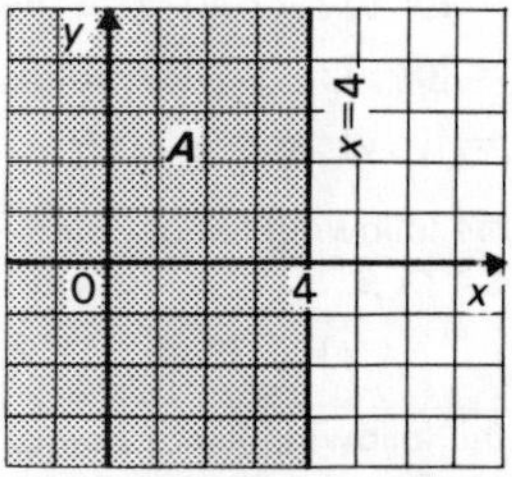

The set $B = \{(x, y) : x > 1\}$ is shown here. To show that the boundary line is **not included** we draw a **dotted** line.

Note: $x > 1$ may also be written as $1 < x$.

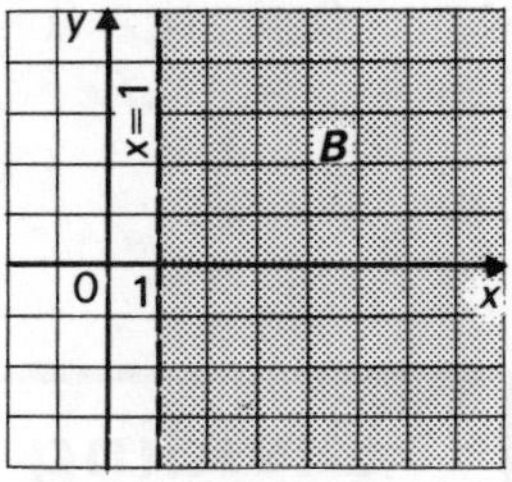

This diagram shows the set $A \cap B$.

We read this as *'A* **intersection** *B'* which means the *overlap* of set A and B.

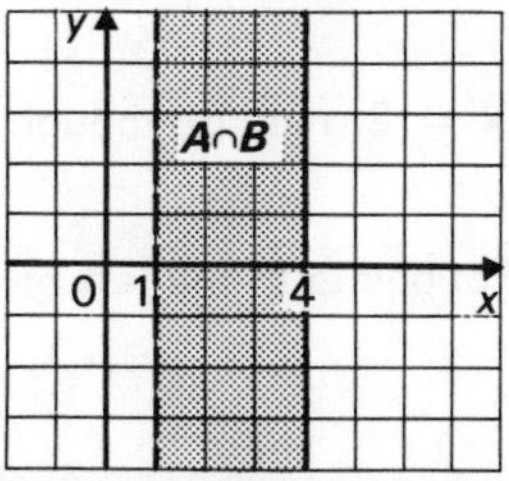

In set-builder notation

$$A \cap B = \{(x, y) : \underbrace{1 < x \leq 4}\}$$

We read this as
'x is greater than 1 but less than or equal to 4'

Another way of showing an intersection set is to use two different shadings.

The region with both shadings is the intersection set.

Example

$C = \{(x, y) : x < 4\}$
(note dotted boundary line)

$D = \{(x, y) : y \leq 3\}$
(note solid boundary line)

$C \cap D = \{(x, y) : \underbrace{x < 4 \text{ and } y \leq 3}\}$

In the intersection set both conditions must apply.

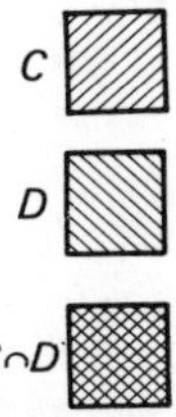

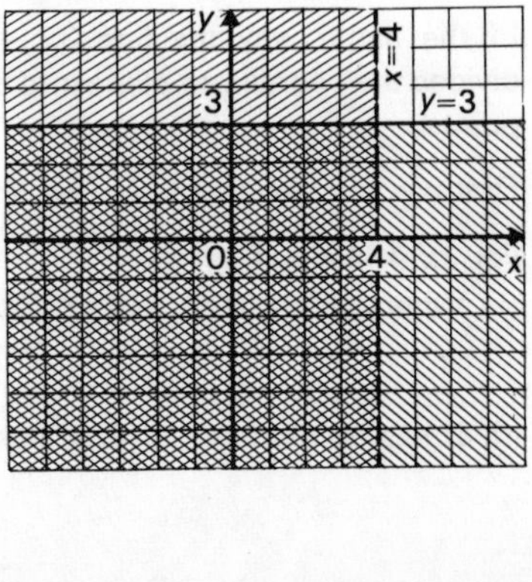

Exercise

1 On $\frac{1}{2}$ cm squared paper, use shading to show the following sets:

(a) $A = \{(x, y) : x \leq 2\}$; $B = \{(x, y) : y \leq 5\}$. Show A, B, and $A \cap B$.

(b) $C = \{(x, y) : x < 5\}$; $D = \{(x, y) : x \geq 1\}$. Show C, D, and $C \cap D$.

(c) $E = \{(x, y) : y \leq 4\}$; $F = \{(x, y : y > 2\}$. Show $E \cap F$ only.

(d) $G = \{(x, y) : x < -2\}$; $H = \{(x, y) : y > -3\}$. Show G, H, and $G \cap H$.

2 Copy the following list of points. Look at question 1(a). Underline those points which are members of the set $A \cap B$.

(1, 6) (3, 4) (1, 4) (−2, −2) (2, 5) (5, 2) (1.5, 4.5) (2.1, 1.2)

3 Copy the following list of points. Look at question 1(b). Underline those points which are members of set $C \cap D$.

(0, 3) (2, 6) (1, −1) (5, −5) (4.9, 0.7) (1.0001, 4) (3, 100) (4, −1000)

Continue with Section L

L Dividing the plane

The line $x = 3$ may be thought of as dividing the coordinate plane into three sets of points.

The set J of points to the **left** of the line:

$$J = \{(x, y) : x < 3\}$$

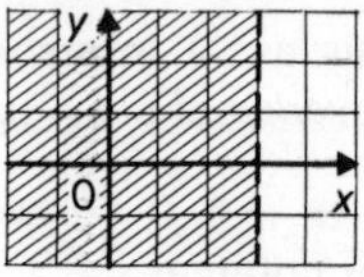

The set K of points **on** the line:

$$K = \{(x, y) : x = 3\}$$

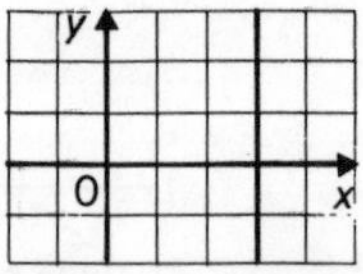

The set L of points to the **right** of the line:

$$L = \{(x, y) : x > 3\}$$

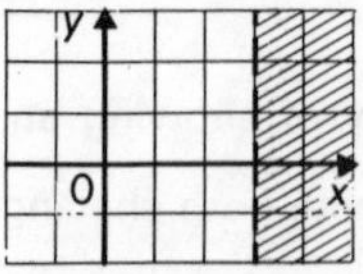

In the same way the line $3x + 4y = 12$ divides the coordinate plane into three sets of points.

First we find two points on the line.

For $3x + 4y = 12$

When $x = 0$	when $y = 0$,
$4y = 12$	$3x = 12$
$y = 3$	$x = 4$
(0, 3) lies on the line	(4, 0) lies on the line

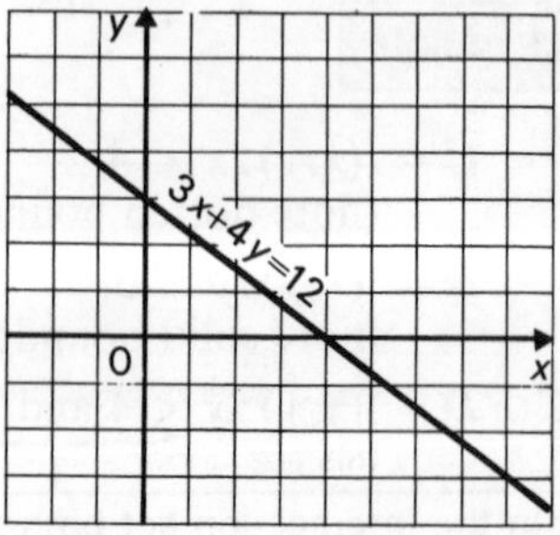

The line $3x + 4y = 12$ divides the coordinate plane into

the set A of points **above** the line,
the set B of points **on** the line, and
the set C of points **below** the line.

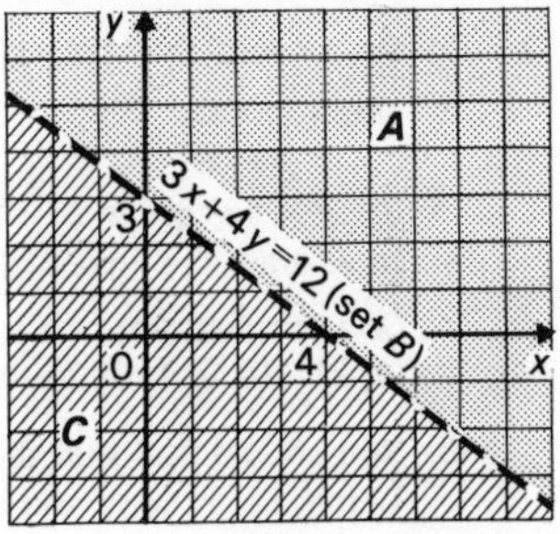

Exercise

1 Set A is shown in the diagram, with five points marked in it.

(a) Copy the table and use these points to complete it. One entry has been done for you.

Coordinates of point	Value of $3x + 4y$
$(-2, 6)$	$3 \times (-2) + 4 \times 6 = -6 + 24 = 18$

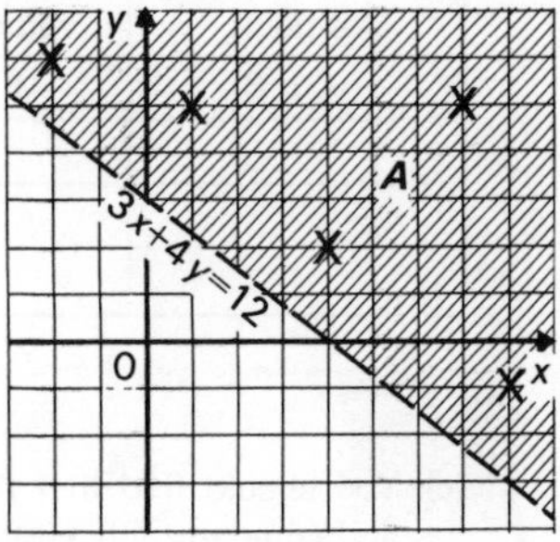

You should find that each value above is greater than 12.
Copy this line under your completed table.

In Set A, $3x + 4y > 12$

(b) Now consider points in Set B (points on the line $3x + 4y = 12$). Copy the table below and use the points marked on the line to complete it. One entry has been done for you.

Coordinates of point	Value of $3x + 4y$
$(4, 0)$	$3 \times 4 + 4 \times 0 = 12 + 0 = 12$

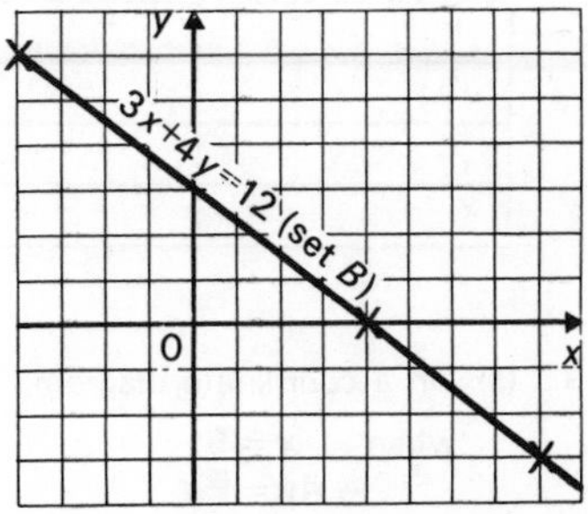

You should find that each value above is equal to 12.
Copy this line under your completed table.

In Set B, $3x + 4y = 12$

(c) Now consider points in Set C (points **below** the line $3x + 4y = 12$). Use the marked points to copy and complete the table below.

Coordinates of point	Value of $3x + 4y$

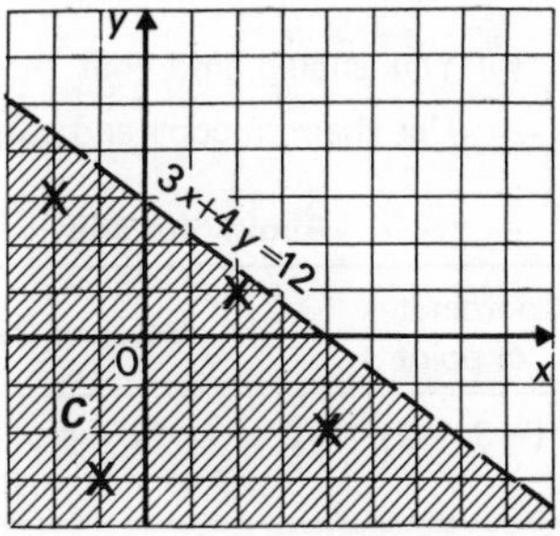

You should find that each value above is less than 12.
Copy this line under your completed table.

In Set C, $3x + 4y < 12$

2 (a) On a coordinate diagram draw the straight line $x + y = 4$. Copy and complete:

when $x = 0$,
$y =$ ▢
(▢, ▢) lies on line.
Now draw the line.

when $y = 0$,
$x =$ ▢
(▢, ▢) lies on line.

On your diagram plot the following points:
(1, 2) (4, 2) (5, 5) (−1, 6) (−3, 1) (−1, −4) (3, −2) (7, −2)

(b) You should find that there are four points marked on the grid **above** the line. Use them to copy and complete this table. One entry has been done for you.

Above the line

Coordinates of point	Value of $x + y$
(−1, 6)	$-1 + 6 = 5$

You should find that for points **above** the line
$x + y$ ▢ 4

Copy this under your completed table using the correct symbol (< or = or >)

(c) You should find that there are four points marked on the grid **below** the line. Use them to copy and complete this table.

Below the line

Coordinates of point	Value of $x + y$

You should find that for points **below** the line
$x + y$ ▢ 4

Copy this under your completed table using the correct symbol (< or = or >)

3 (a) On a coordinate diagram, draw the straight line $3x - 4y = 12$. Copy and complete:

when $x = 0$
$-4y =$ ▢
$y =$ ▢
(▢, ▢) lies on the line.

when $y = 0$
▢ = ▢
▢ = ▢
(▢, ▢) lies on the line.

Mark the following points on the grid:
(3, 4) (7, 1) (−2, 2) (−3, −2) (−1, −6) (1, −3) (2, −1) (6, −5)

(b) You should find that there are four points marked on the grid **above** the line. Use them to copy and complete this table. One entry has been done for you.

Above the line

Coordinates of point	Value of $3x - 4y$
(−3, −2)	$3 \times (-3) - 4 \times (-2) =$ $= -9 + 8 = -1$

You should find that for points **above** the line
$3x - 4y$ ▢ 12

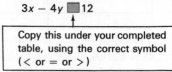

Copy this under your completed table, using the correct symbol (< or = or >)

(c) You should find that there are four points marked on the grid **below** the line. Use them to copy and complete this table.

Below the line

Coordinates of point	Value of $3x - 4y$

You should find that for points **below** the line
$3x - 4y$ ▢ 12

Copy this under your completed table using the correct symbol ($<$ or $=$ or $>$)

Continue with Section M

M Shading a region

Example

Use shading to show the region $2x + 3y < 12$.

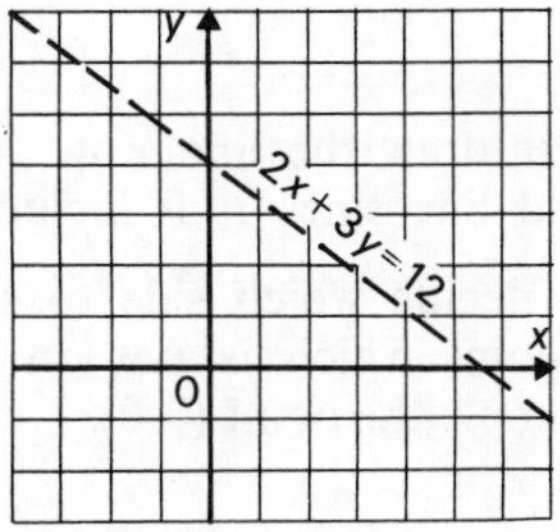

First draw the boundary line $2x + 3y = 12$. (Use a dotted line since points on the line are not in the required region.)

To decide which side to shade we choose any point which is not on the line.

Here, the point (0, 0) is not on the line.

Substitute $x = 0$ and $y = 0$ in $2x + 3y$. Is $2 \times 0 + 3 \times 0$ less than 12?

If the answer is **yes** shade the side that (0, 0) is on. If the answer is **no** shade the other side.

$2 \times 0 + 3 \times 0 = 0 + 0 = 0$, which is less than 12. So the region $2x + 3y < 12$ looks like this →

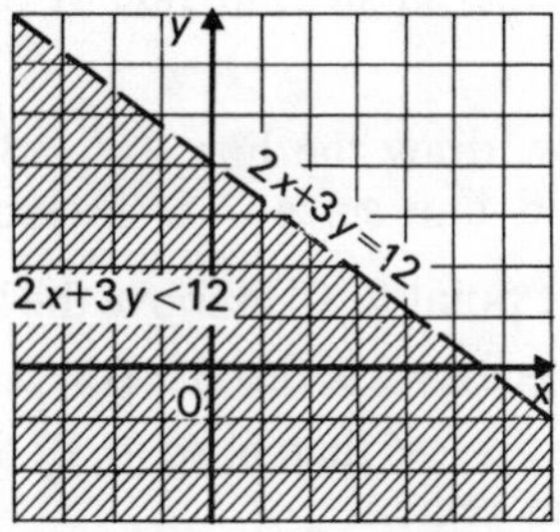

Exercise

On $\frac{1}{2}$ cm squared paper, use shading to show the following regions.

1 $x + 2y \le 4$
2 $x - 4y < 4$
3 $2x + y \ge 6$
4 $3x + y < 9$
5 $-3x - 2y < 6$
6 $2x - y \ge 6$
7 $4x + 3y > 12$
8 $4x + 10y \ge 20$
9 $2x + 10y > 15$

Continue with Section N

N Intersecting sets

Example

Show the intersection of the sets
$A = \{(x, y): x + 2y \le 6\}$ and $B = \{(x, y): 2x - 3y \ge 6\}$

First draw the line $x + 2y = 6$ (use a solid line since it is included in set A).

To decide which side to shade, choose a point which is not on the line, for example the point (0,0).

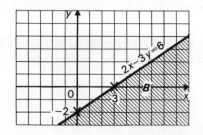

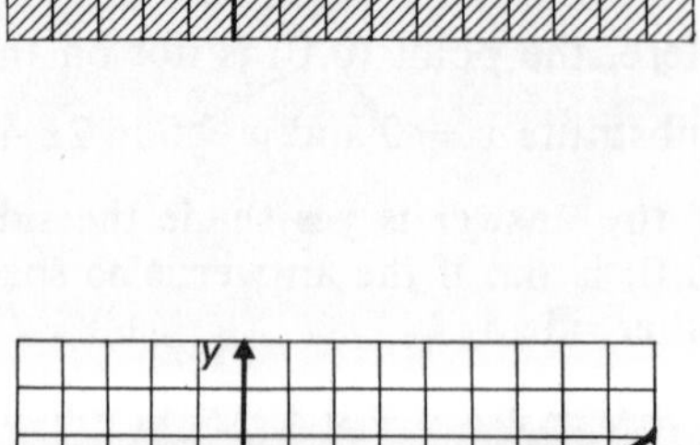

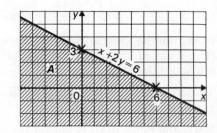

Is $0 + 2 \times 0 \le 6$?
Yes, so shade that side of the line as set A.

Now draw the line $2x - 3y = 6$ (use a solid line since it is included in set B).

The point (0,0) is above the line.
$2x - 3y = 2 \times 0 - 3 \times 0 = 0$.
This is less than 6, so (0, 0) lies in the 'less than' region.

Shade the other side of the line as set B.

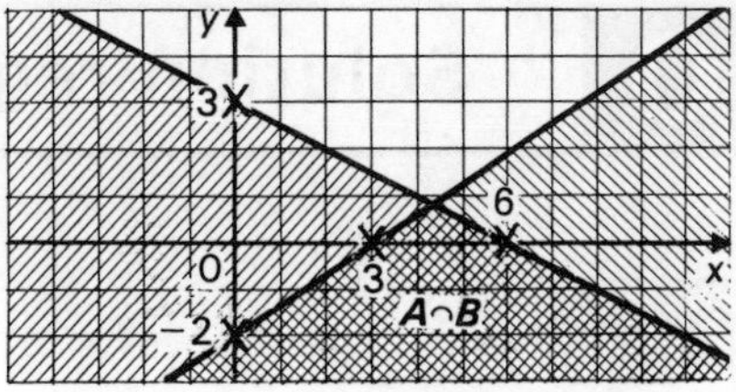

Since set A has been shaded 

and set B has been shaded 

then the region $A \cap B$ (A intersection B) will be shown like this 

The points (x, y) in the region $A \cap B$ are solutions of the inequations

$$x + 2y \leq 6$$
$$2x - 3y \geq 6$$

We shall call this region the **solution region** of the inequations

$$x + 2y \leq 6$$
$$2x - 3y \geq 6$$

Exercise

1 On $\frac{1}{2}$ cm squared paper, use shading to show the sets A, B, and $A \cap B$.

(a) $A = \{(x, y) : x - y \leq -1\}$, $B = \{(x, y) : x + y \leq 1\}$
(b) $A = \{(x, y) : 2x + y \leq 4\}$, $B = \{(x, y) : x + y \leq 6\}$
(c) $A = \{(x, y) : 3x - y > 9\}$, $B = \{(x, y) : x - 2y < 4\}$
(d) $A = \{(x, y) : 3x + 4y \leq 12\}$, $B = \{(x, y) : x + 3y \leq 6\}$
(e) $A = \{(x, y) : x - y \leq -2\}$, $B = \{(x, y) : x + y < 1\}$
(f) $A = \{(x, y) : x + 2y \leq 4\}$, $B = \{(x, y) : 2x + y \leq 6\}$
(g) $A = \{(x, y) : x - y \geq 0\}$, $B = \{(x, y) : 2x - y \geq 0\}$

Continue with Section O

0 Solution regions

Example

Show the solution region of the system of inequations
$3x + 4y \leq 24, \quad x + 3y \leq 12, \quad x \geq 0, \quad y \geq 0$

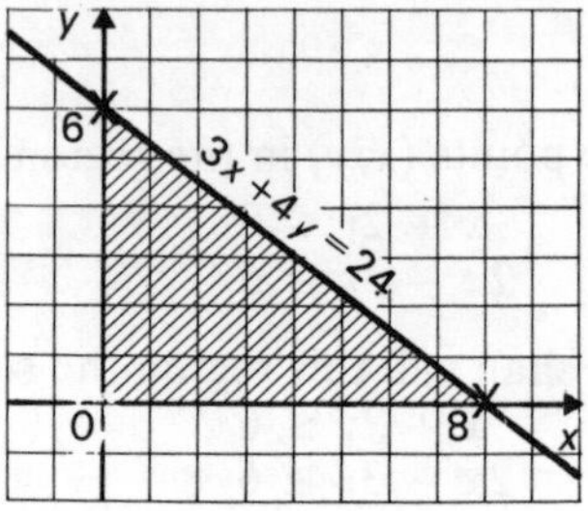

To draw $3x + 4y \leq 24$.
Boundary line is $3x + 4y = 24$.
Two points on the line are (0, 6) and (8, 0).
For (0, 0), $3x + 4y < 24$.
Required region is **below** or **on** $3x + 4y = 24$
and is shaded 

Note that since $x \geq 0$ and $y \geq 0$ we use only the first quadrant.

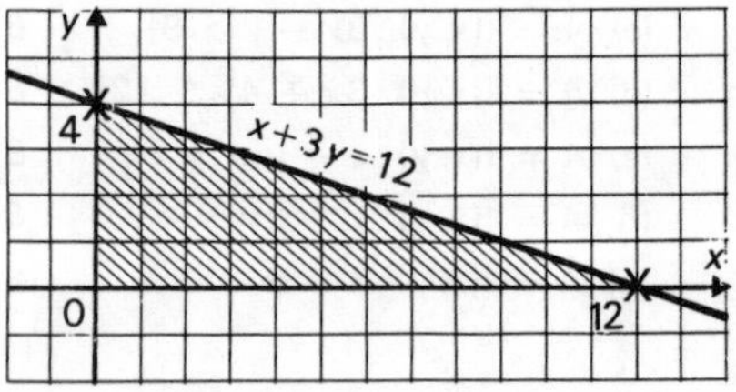

To draw $x + 3y \leq 12$.
Boundary line is $x + 3y = 12$.
Two points on the line are (0, 4) and (12, 0).
For (0, 0), $x + 3y < 12$.
Required region is **below** or **on** $x + 3y = 12$
and is shaded 

To show the solution region we combine these graphs in the same diagram.

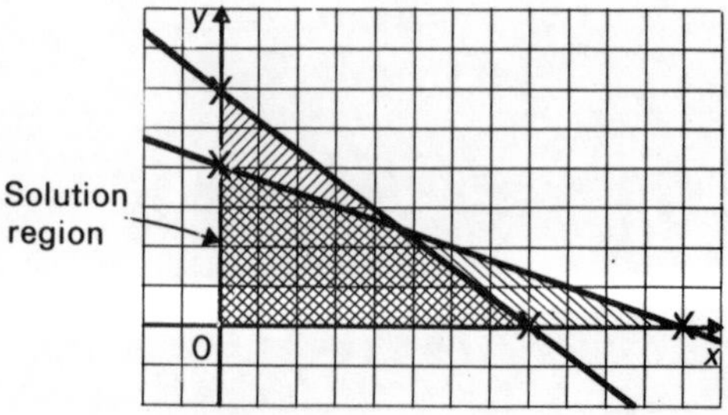

Having found our solution we can show it more clearly by re-drawing it showing the four boundary lines.

From the diagram we can read off some members of the solution region.

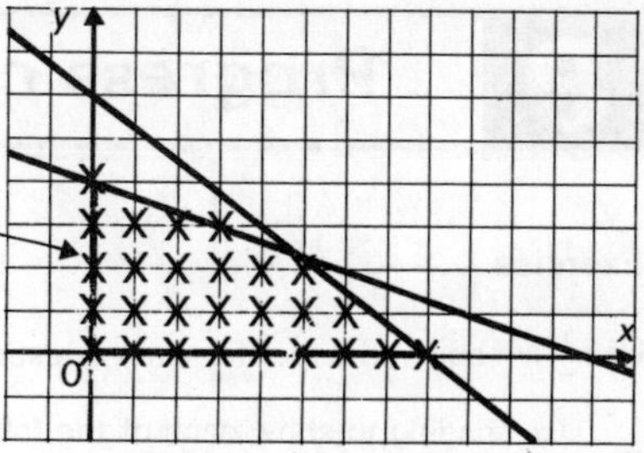

The members with whole number coordinates are:

(0, 4)
(0, 3) (1, 3) (2, 3) (3, 3)
(0, 2) (1, 2) (2, 2) (3, 2) (4, 2) (5, 2)
(0, 1) (1, 1) (2, 1) (3, 1) (4, 1) (5, 1) (6, 1)
(0, 0) (1, 0) (2, 0) (3, 0) (4, 0) (5, 0) (6, 0) (7, 0) (8, 0)

Exercise

On $\frac{1}{2}$ cm squared paper show the solution region of each of the following systems of inequations.

In each case write down the members with whole number coordinates.

1 $x + y \leq 3$, $x \geq 0$, $y \geq 0$

2 $0 \leq x \leq 3$, $0 \leq y \leq 2$, $x + y \leq 4$

3 $0 \leq x \leq 6$, $0 \leq y \leq 4$, $x + 2y \geq 10$

4 $x + y \leq 4$, $x - y \geq 2$, $y \geq 0$

5 $x + y \geq 4$, $x + 3y \leq 6$, $y \geq 0$

6 $2x - y \geq 0$, $x - 2y \leq 0$, $x + y \leq 4$

Continue with Section P

P Progress check

Exercise

Use $\frac{1}{2}$ cm squared paper for each question.

1 Use shading to show each of the following regions:

(a) $x \geq -3$ (b) $y < 4$ (c) $4x + 3y < 12$ (d) $6x - 5y \geq 30$

2 Show the sets A, B, and $A \cap B$.

$A = \{(x, y) : 3x + y \geq -6\}$, $B = \{(x, y) : 2x - y \leq 4\}$.

3 Show the solution region of the following system of inequations, and write down the members with whole number coordinates.

$x + y \leq 6$, $x - y \geq 1$, $x \geq 0$, $y \geq 0$

Tell your teacher you have finished this Unit

UNIT M11
Circles

A Isosceles triangles in circles

Circles and circular shapes occur in hundreds of everyday objects.
Clearly it is an important shape – a shape that requires detailed study.

O is the centre of the circle.
In the shaded triangle the sides *OA* and *OB* are equal because they are **radii** of the circle.

So the shaded triangle is **isosceles** and angle *A* = angle *B* (in shorthand, $\hat{A} = \hat{B}$).

(The side *AB* is a **chord** of the circle.)

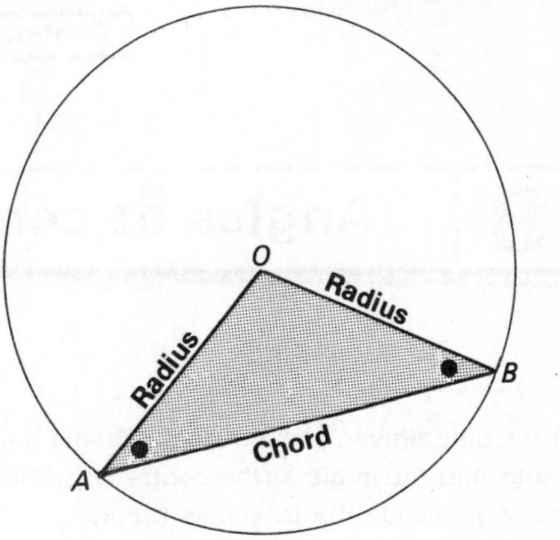

Example

In the triangle *OAB*, the angle at *A* is 30°. Find the sizes of the other angles in the diagram.

(a) $\widehat{B} = 30°$ (since $\triangle AOB$ is isosceles)
(b) $A\widehat{O}B = 120°$ (since the sum of the angles of a triangle is 180°)
(c) $C\widehat{O}B = 60°$ (since *AOC* is a straight line)

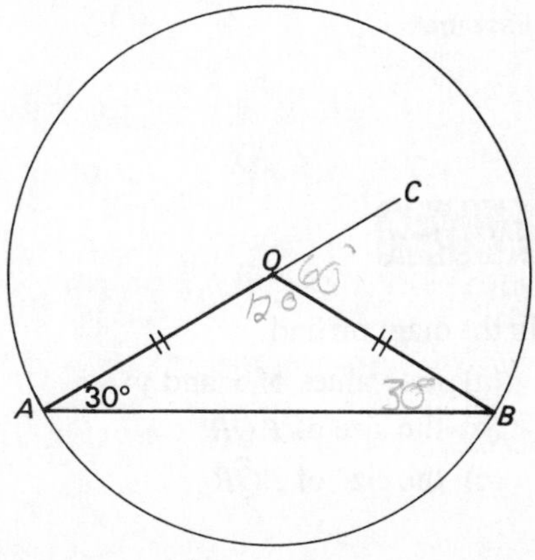

Exercise

1 The angle at *P* is 74°.

Find (a) the angle at *Q*;
(b) the angle $P\hat{O}Q$;
(c) the value of *r*.

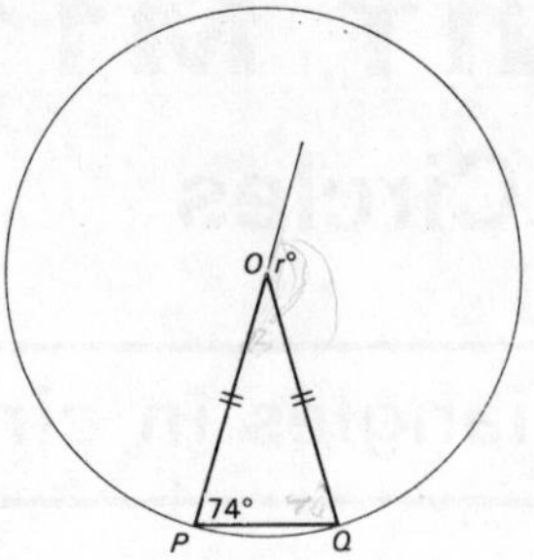

2 In each of the following make a rough copy of the diagram and mark on your diagram the sizes of the other angles (*O* is the centre of the circle).

(a)

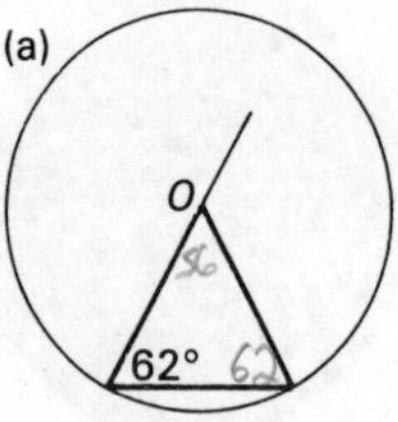

(b)

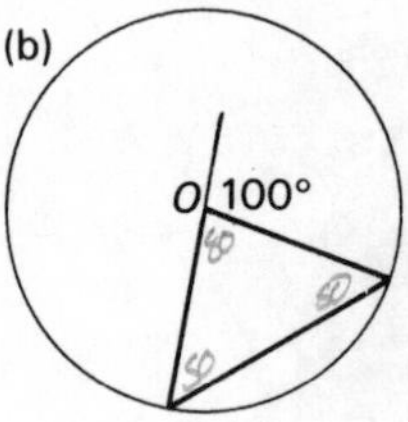

(c)

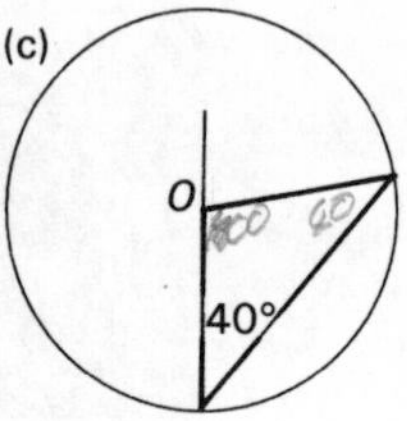

(d)

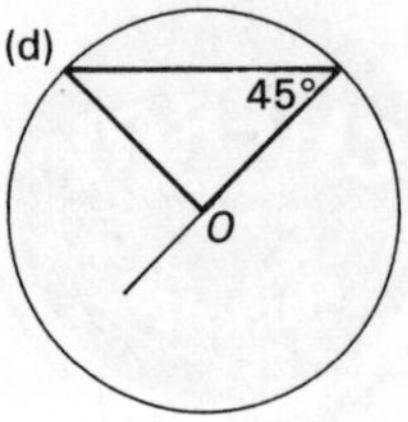

Continue with Section B

B Angles at centre and circumference

In the diagrams in section A you should have found that the angle at the centre was **twice** the angle inside the isosceles triangle.

Check that this was the case in each of your diagrams.

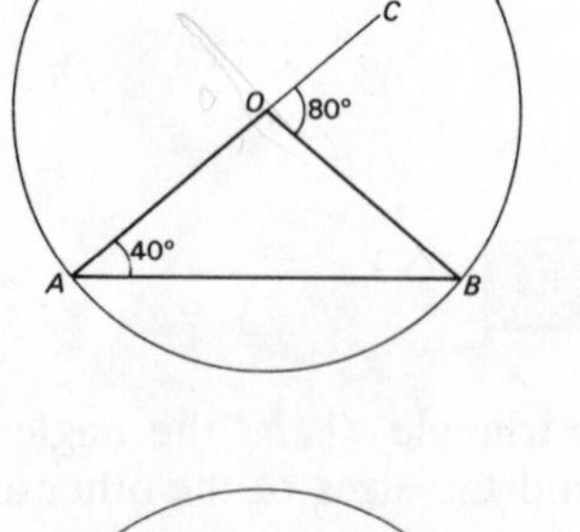

Example

In the diagram find
(a) the values of *x* and *y*;
(b) the size of $P\hat{O}R$;
(c) the size of $P\hat{Q}R$

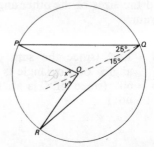

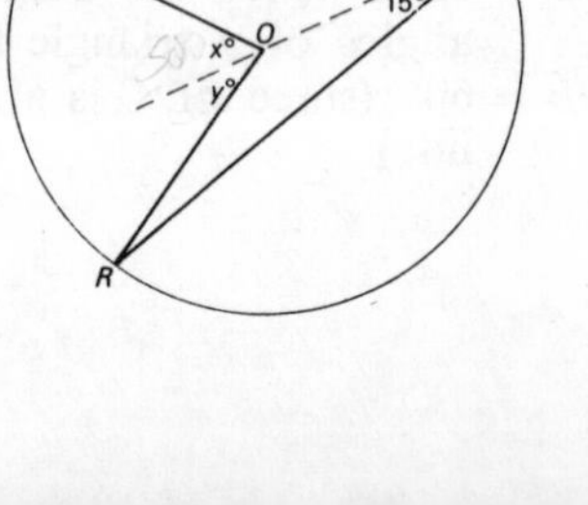

(a) From triangle POQ, $x = 2 \times 25 = 50$
From triangle ROQ, $y = 2 \times 15 = 30$

(b) $P\widehat{O}R = 80°$.

(c) $P\widehat{Q}R = 40°$.

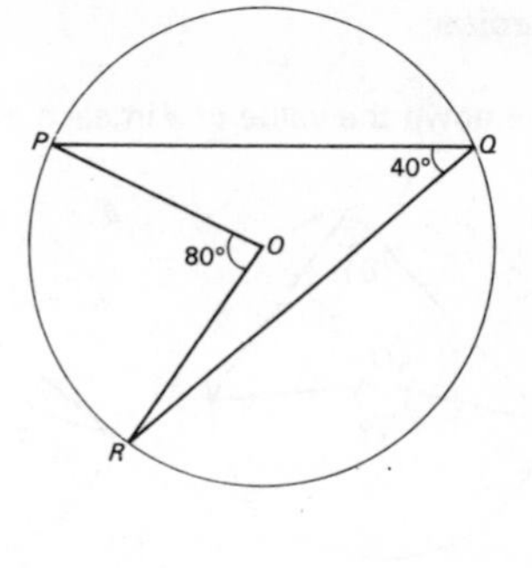

Exercise

In each of the following draw sketches of *both* diagrams. In part (a) find the values of x and y. In part (b) fill in the size of the shaded angle.

1

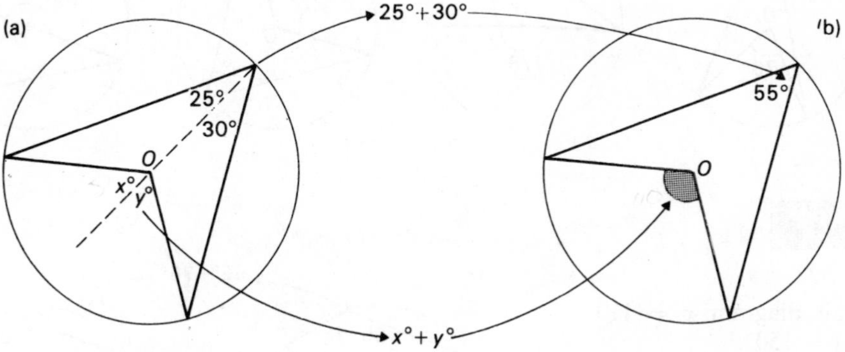

2

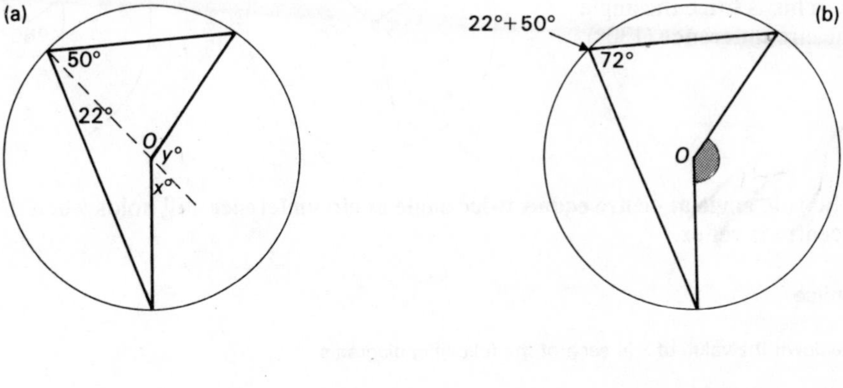

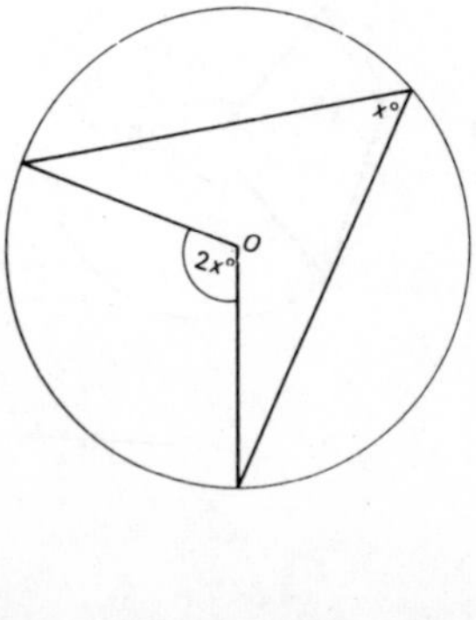

In each diagram, the angle at the centre of the circle is **twice** the angle at the circumference

Exercise

Write down the value of x in each of the following diagrams, (do **not** copy the diagrams).

3

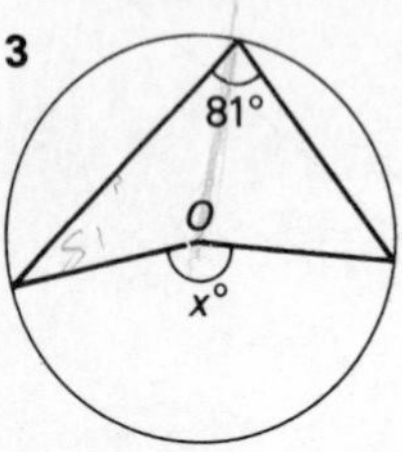

4

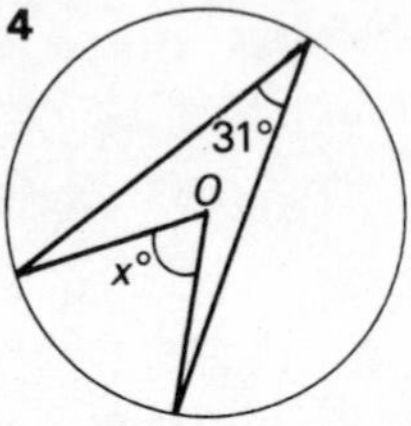

5

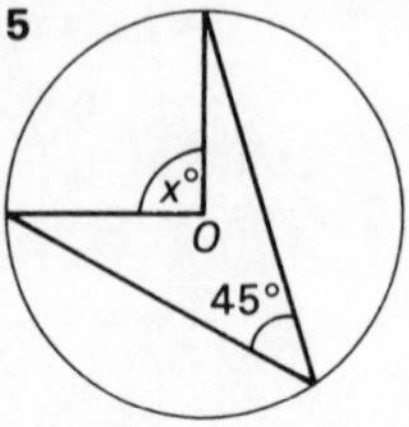

6

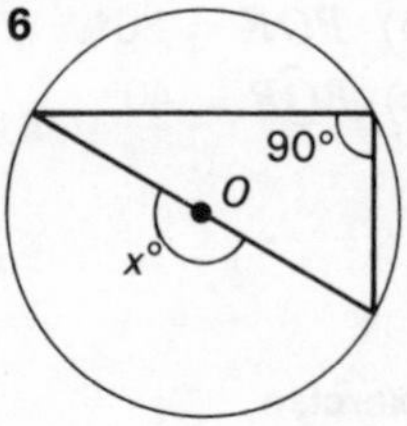

7

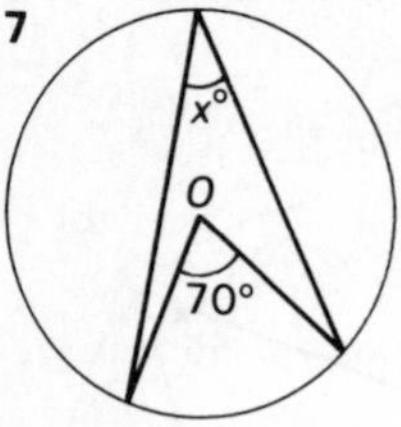

8

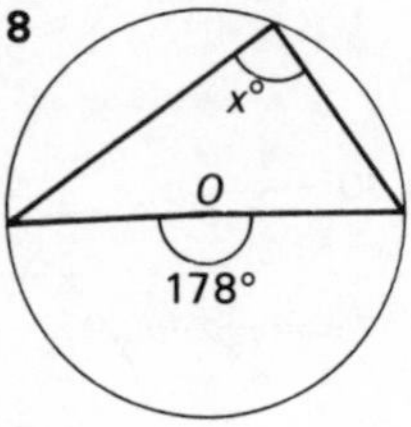

9

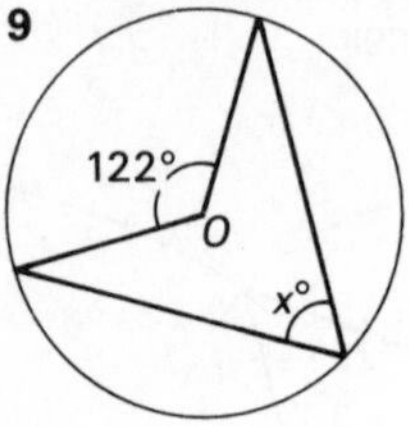

10

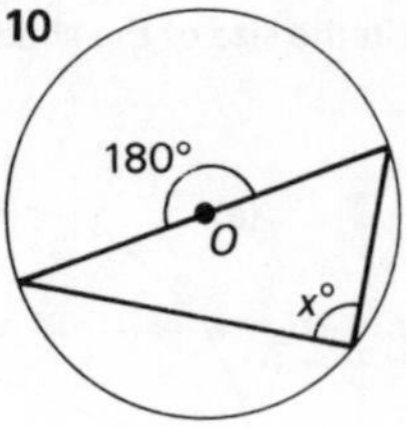

Example

In this diagram $x = 110°$ and $y = 150°$.

So the angle at the centre is 260°. This is **twice** the angle at the circumference (130°).

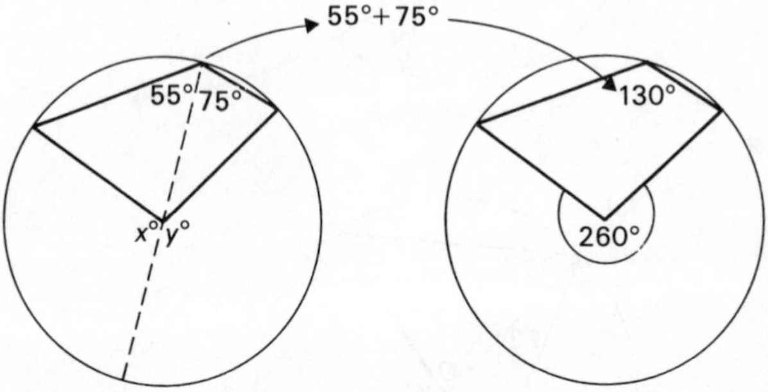

So the rule **angle at centre equals twice angle at circumference** still holds when the angle at the centre is reflex.

Exercise

Write down the value of x in each of the following diagrams.

11

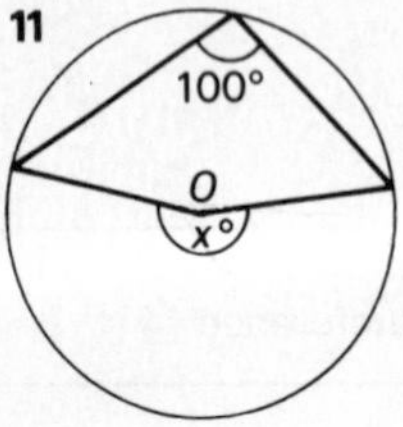

12

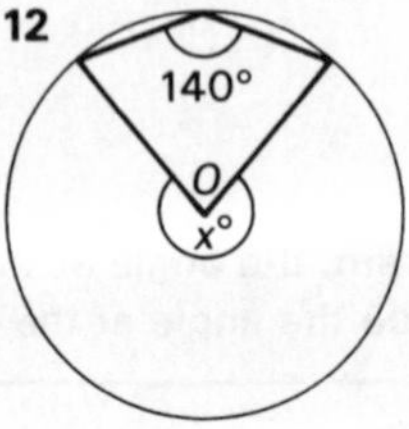

13

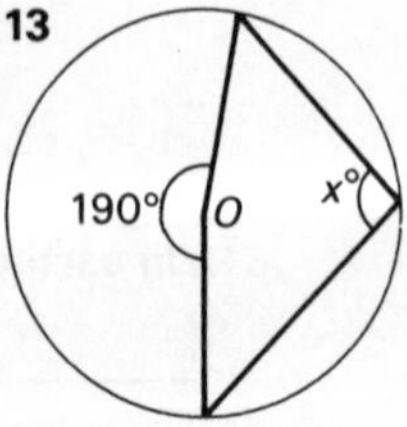

14

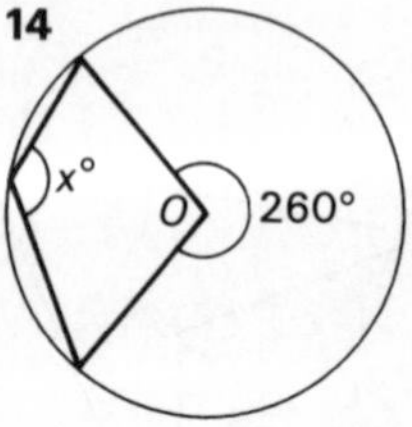

Continue with Section C

C Angles at the circumference

Exercise

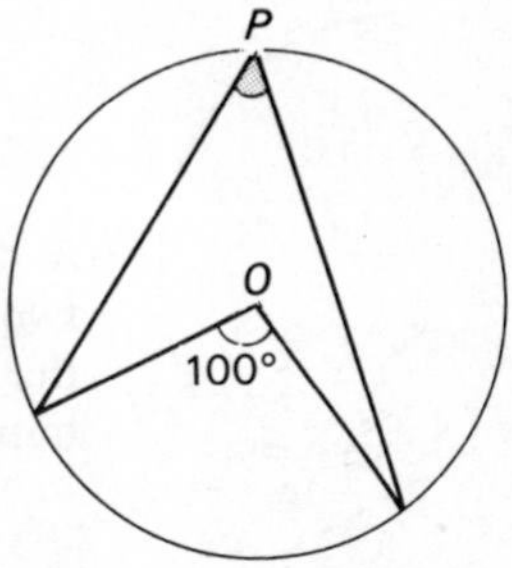

1 In this diagram the angle at the centre of the circle is 100°, so the shaded angle at P is 50°, that is, half the angle at the centre O.

As P moves round the circle, it can take up different positions, as shown below.

Copy the diagrams (but larger) with an angle at the centre of 100°.

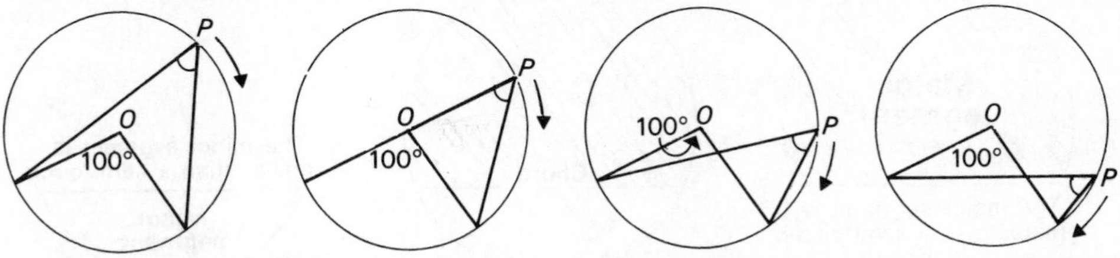

In each case **measure** the angle P with a protractor. Write down your four answers.

> **Note:** You should have found that angle P was 50° in each case.
> **The angle at the circumference is ALWAYS half the angle at the centre.**

Write down the value of x in each of the following diagrams.

2

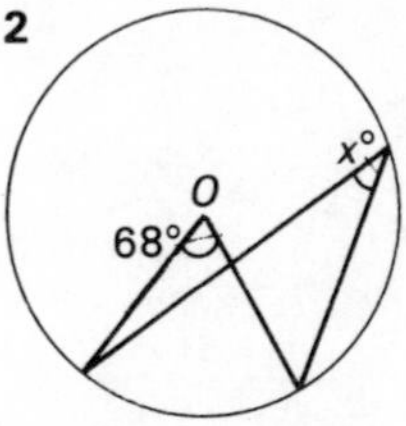

3

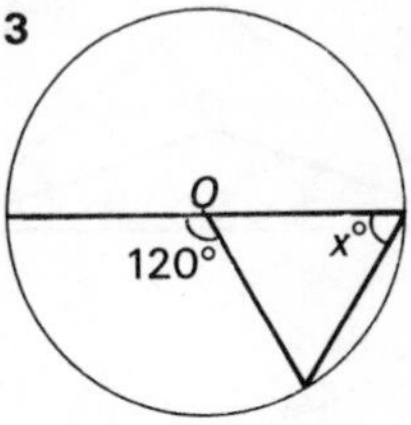

4

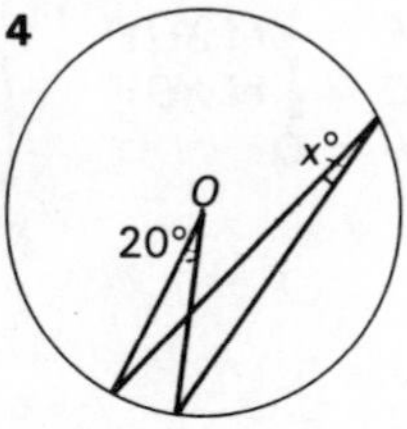

5

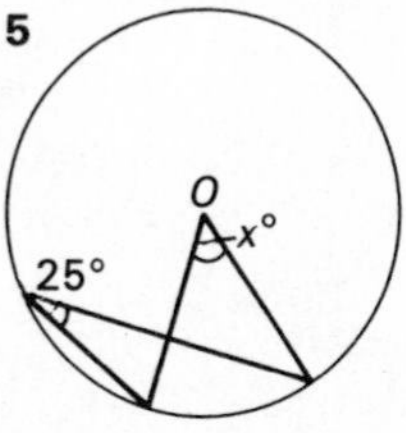

6

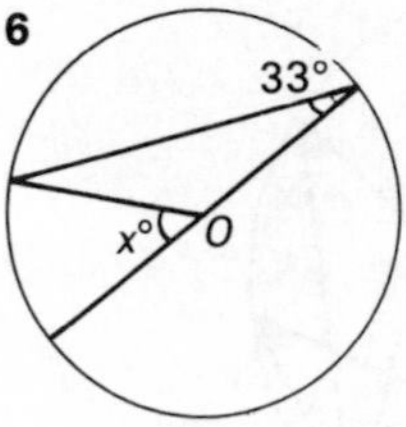

7

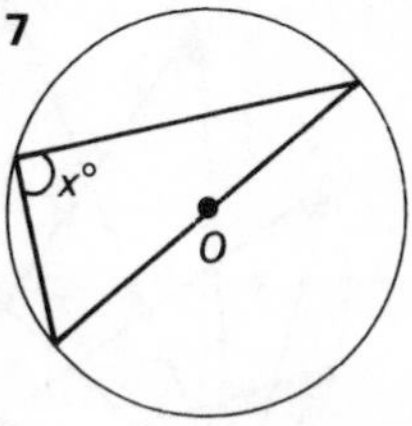

8

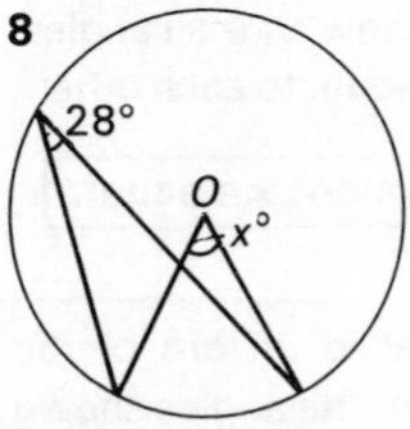

9

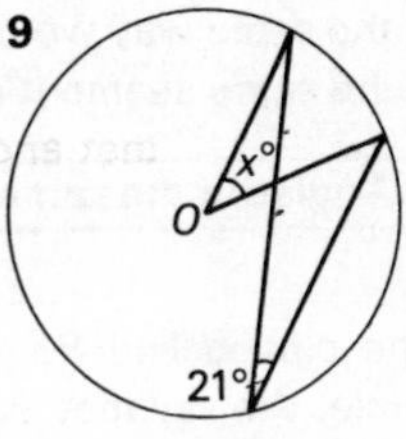

Continue with Section D

D Angles in the same segment

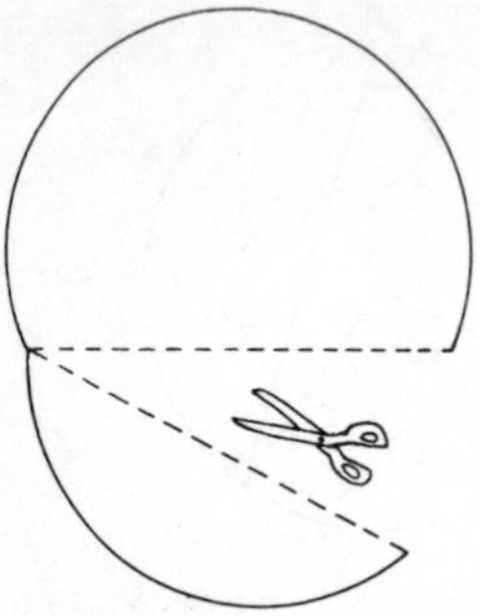

A chord divides a circle into two parts or **segments** called the **major segment** and the **minor segment**.

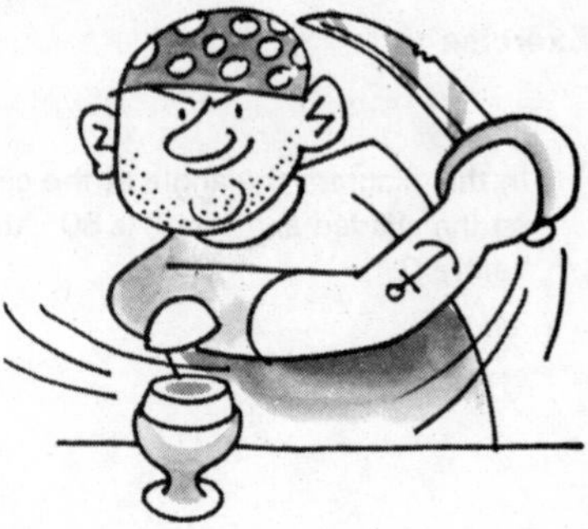

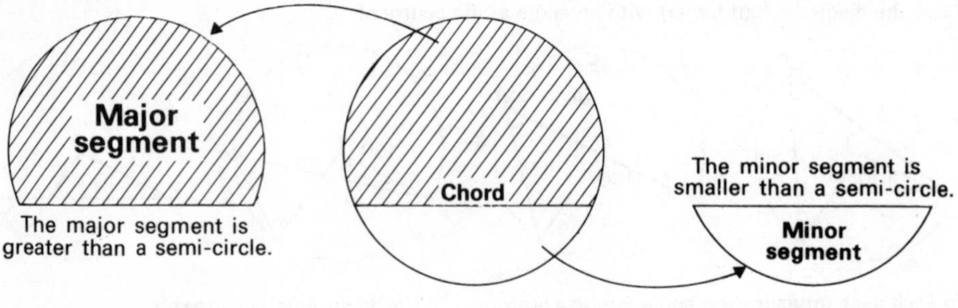

We can show that angles in the same segment are always equal.

$P = \frac{1}{2}$ of $X\hat{O}Y$
and $Q = \frac{1}{2}$ of $X\hat{O}Y$
So $\hat{P} = \hat{Q}$

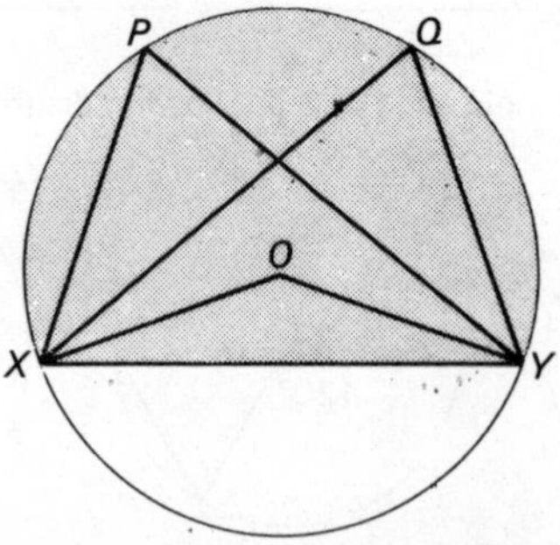

In the same way we can show that all angles in the same segment are equal to each other.

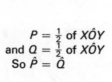

Angles in the same segment are equal.

The curved line *RS* is called an **arc** of the circle. We say that 'each of the angles shown **stands on** the arc *RS*'.

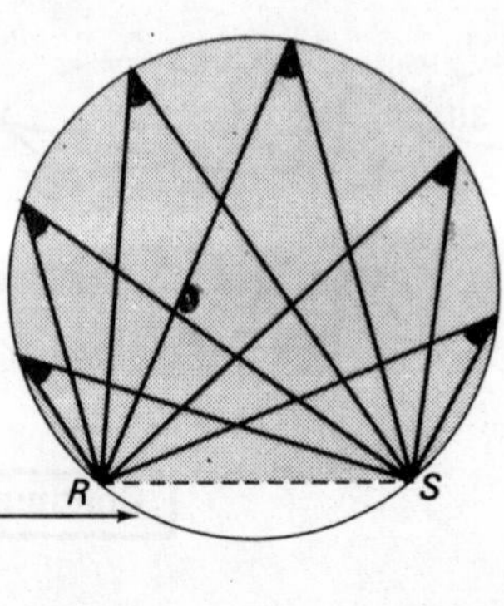

Example

In the diagram find the values of x, y, z, t, and v.

$x = 50$ since $P\hat{Q}S$ and $P\hat{R}S$ stand on same arc PS.

$y = 30$ since $P\hat{S}Q$ and $P\hat{R}Q$ stand on same arc PQ.

$z = 70$ since $Q\hat{P}R$ and $Q\hat{S}R$ stand on same arc RQ.

The sum of the angles of the triangle PSQ is 180°.

So

$$\begin{aligned} x + z + t + y &= 180 \\ 50 + 70 + t + 30 &= 180 \\ t + 150 &= 180 \\ t &= 30 \end{aligned}$$

$v = 30$, since $S\hat{P}R$ and $S\hat{Q}R$ stand on same arc SR.

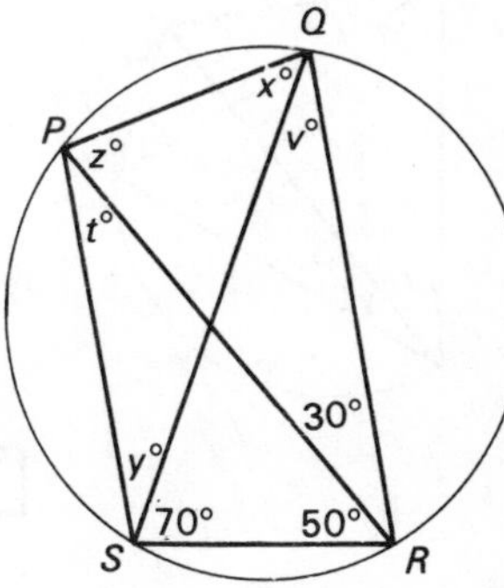

Exercise

Make a rough copy of each diagram and write the sizes of the other angles on your diagram as you calculate them.

1 Find the values of *x* and *y*.

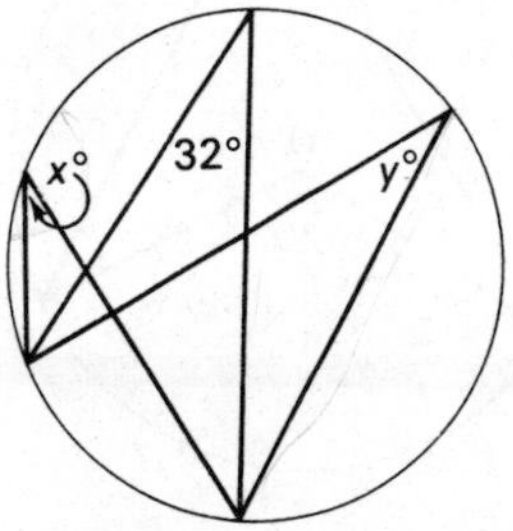

2 Find the values of *p* and *q*.

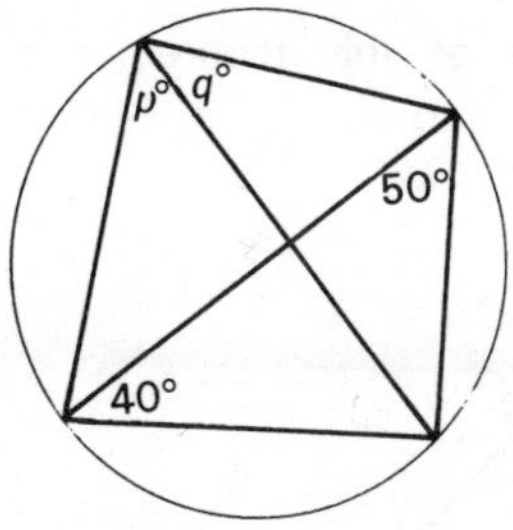

3 (a) Find the values of *x*, *y*, and *z*.

(b) What is the size of the angles standing on arc *AB*?

(c) What is the size of the angles standing on arc *BC*?

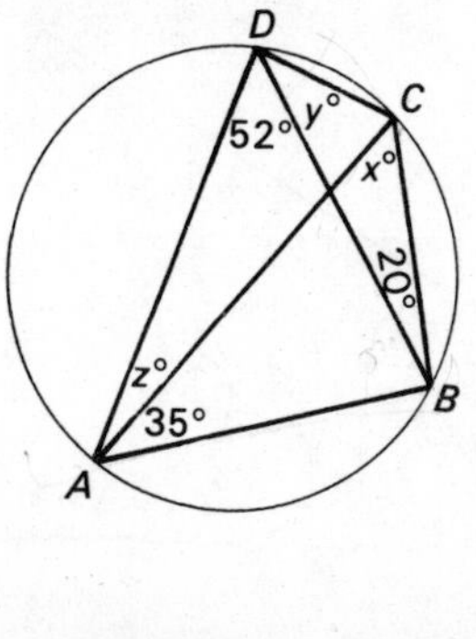

4 (a) Find the values of *a*, *b*, *c*, and *d*.

(b) What is the size of the angles standing on arc *AC*?

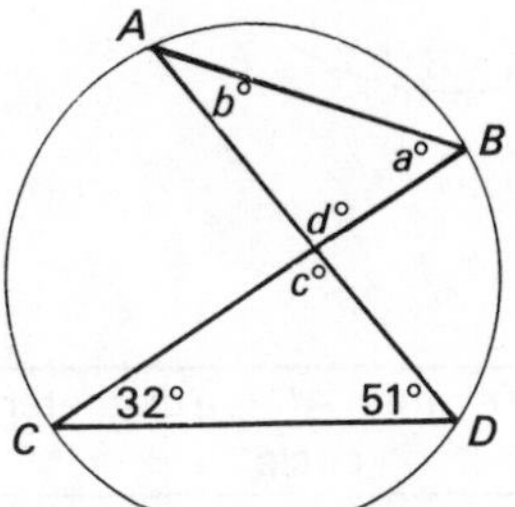

5 Find the values of x, y, and z.

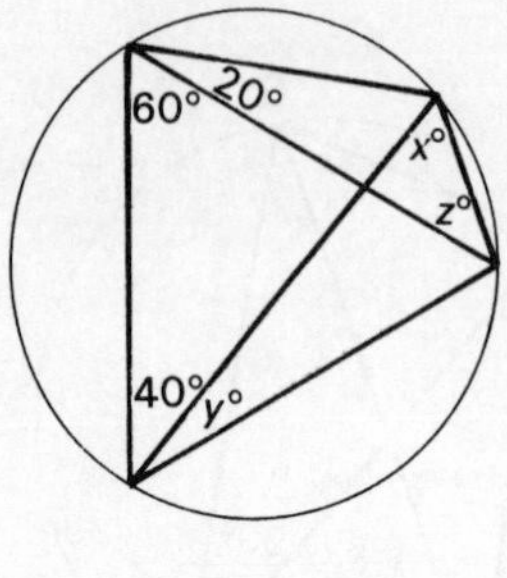

6 Find the values of x, y, and z.

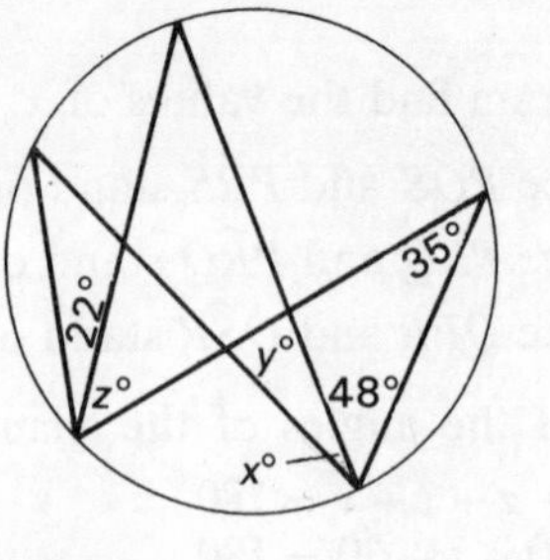

Continue with Section E

E Angles in a semi-circle

We have seen that the angle at the centre of a circle is **twice** the angle at the circumference.

A special case of this theorem requires further study.

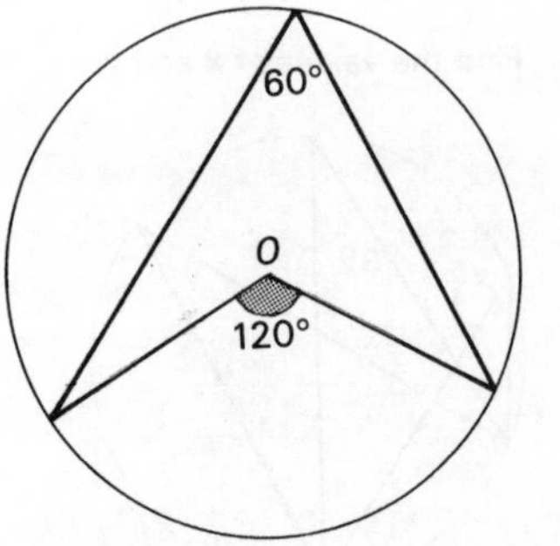

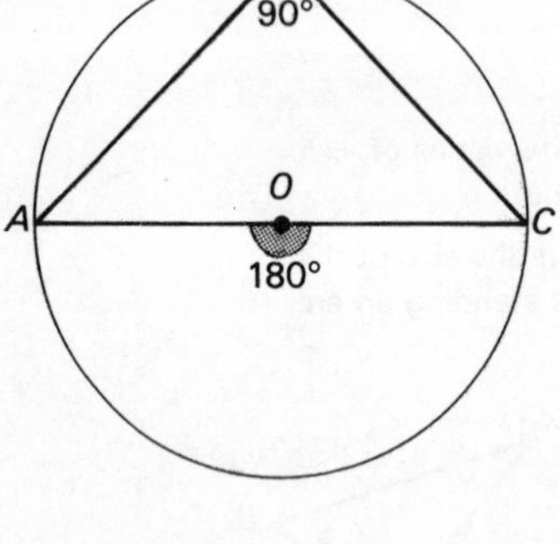

If the angle at the circumference is 90°, then the angle at the centre will be 180° (a straight angle).

In such a case AC is a diameter of the circle.

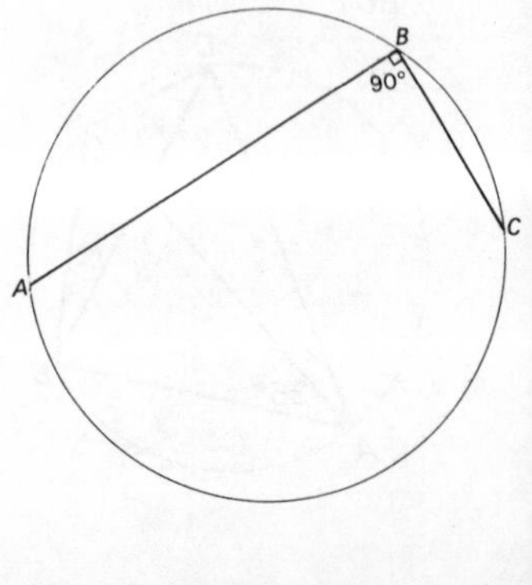

If $A\hat{B}C = 90°$, then AC is a diameter of the circle.

If *PQ* is a diameter of the circle then any angle in the semi-circle is a right-angle.

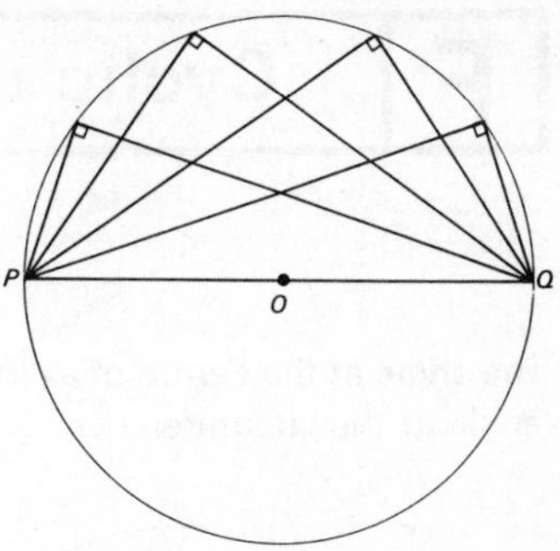

Example

Which of the lines *AD* or *BE* could be a diameter of this circle?

AD subtends an angle of
$25° + 30° + 35° = 90°$
at the circumference, so *AD* is a diameter.

BE subtends an angle of
$30° + 35° + 40° = 105°$
at the circumference, so *BE* is **not** a diameter.

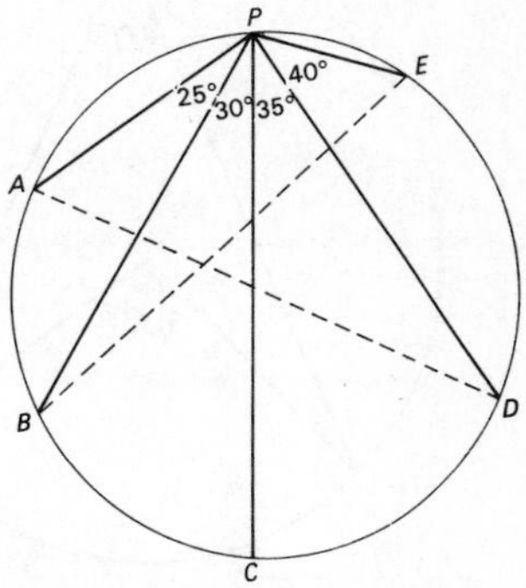

Exercise

1 Which of the lines *BE* or *DA* could be a diameter of the circle?

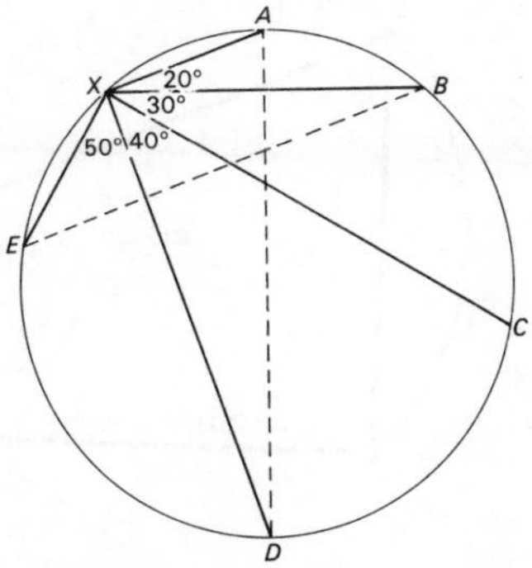

2 *PR* is a diameter.

(a) What is the size of $\widehat{Q}$?

(b) What is the size of $\hat{P}$?

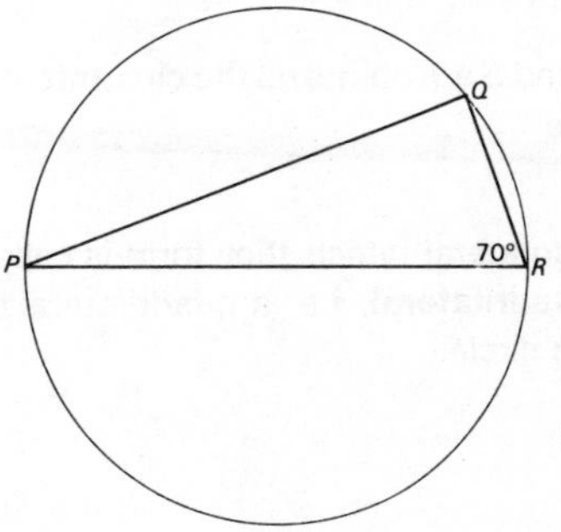

3

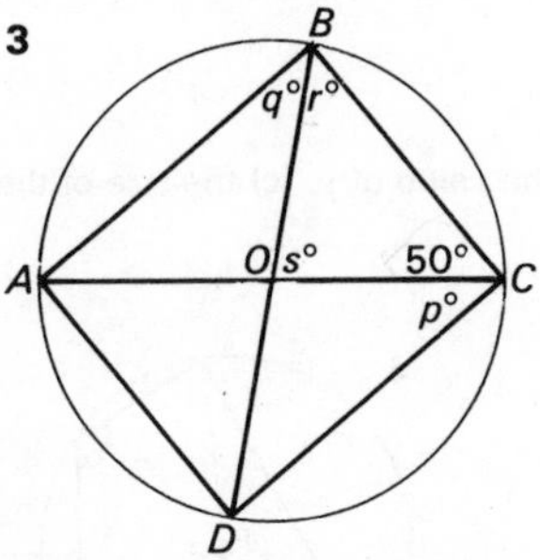

(a) What shape is *ABCD*?

(b) Write down the values of *p*, *q*, *r*, and *s*.

4

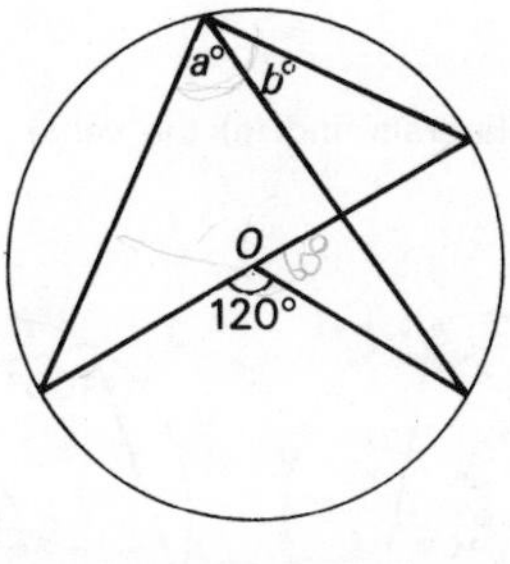

Write down the values of *a* and *b*.

5

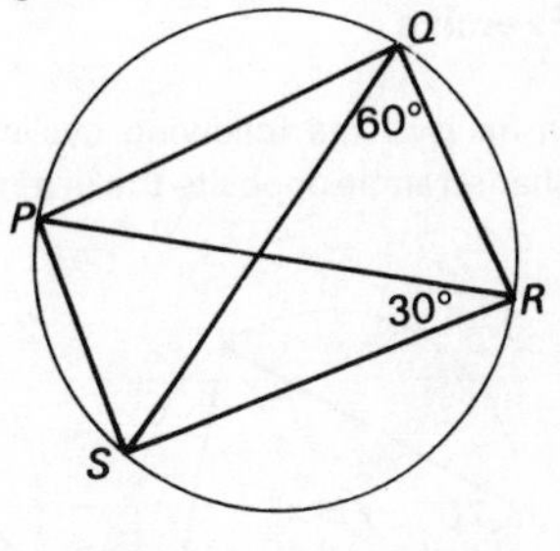

Show that *PR* is a diameter of the circle.

Continue with Section F

F Cyclic quadrilaterals

The angle at the centre of a circle is twice the angle at the circumference.

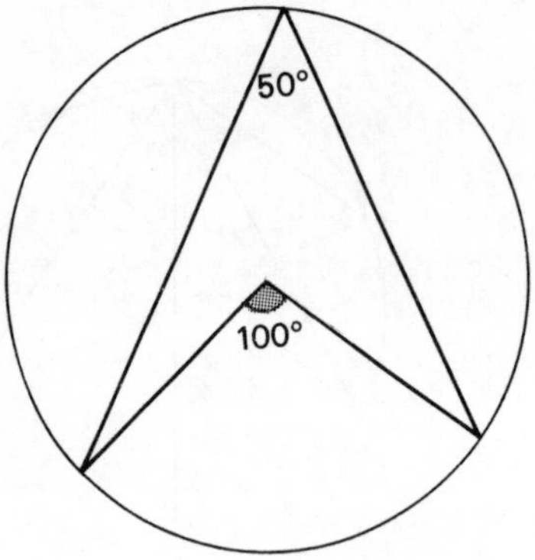

This property still holds even when the angle at the centre is reflex.

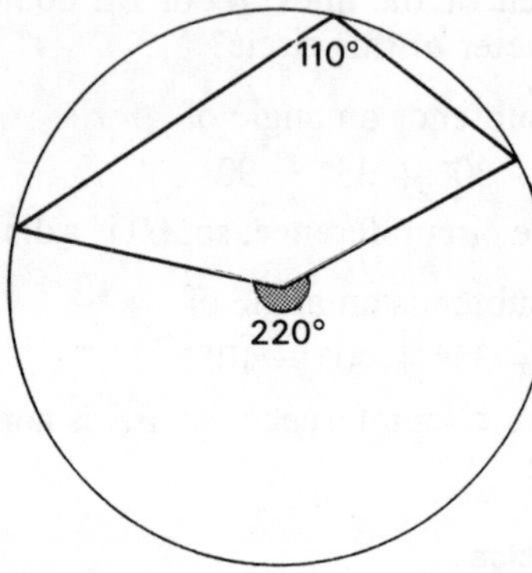

P, *Q*, *R*, and *S* are points on the circumference of a circle.

The quadrilateral which they form is called a **cyclic quadrilateral**, i.e. a quadrilateral that fits into a circle.

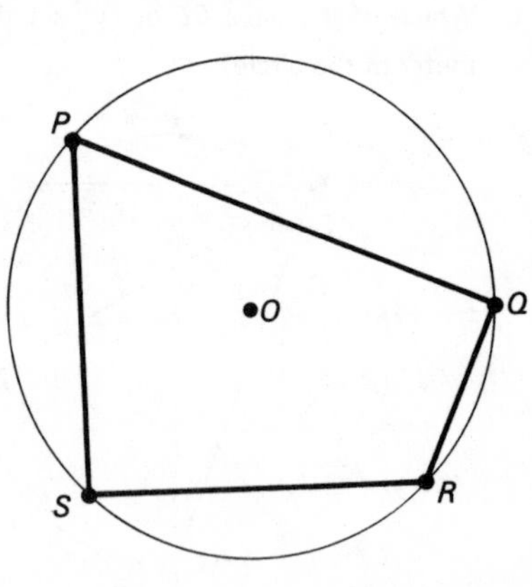

Exercise

In each of the following cyclic quadrilaterals find (a) the value of *x*, (b) the value of *y*, (c) the size of the shaded angle opposite the given angle.

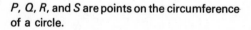

1

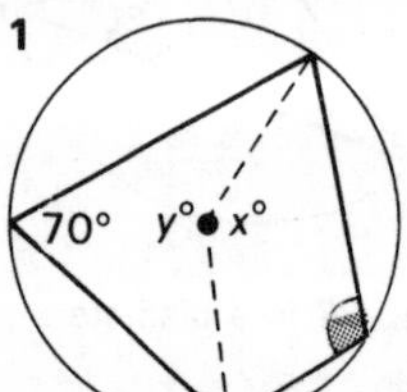

2

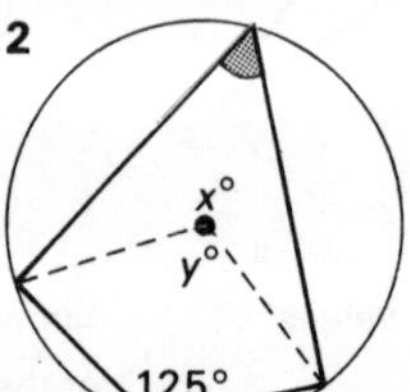

3

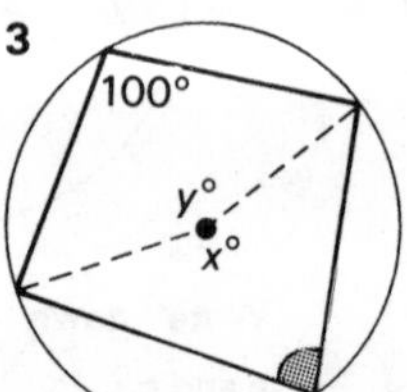

4

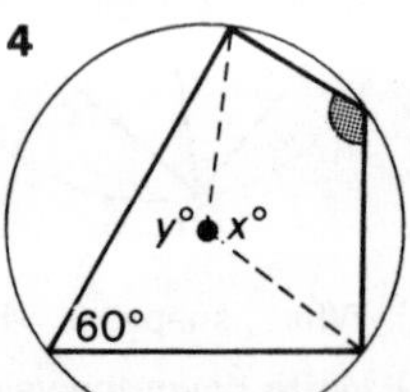

Example

Find x, y, and the shaded angle.

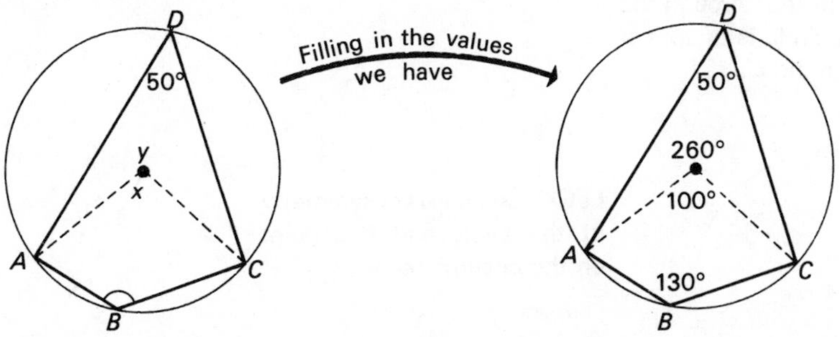

In the above diagram $\hat{B}$ and $\hat{D}$ are said to be opposite angles of the cyclic quadrilateral.

Notice that they add up to 180°.

Now check back to questions 1 to 4. Add together the two opposite angles in each case. Each pair should add up to 180°.

The sum of the opposite angles of a cyclic quadrilateral is 180°

Example

In the cyclic quadrilateral $PQRS$ find the values of x and y.

$\hat{P} + \hat{R} = 180°$, so $x = 180 - 85 = 95$
Also $\hat{Q} + \hat{S} = 180°$, so $y = 180 - 115 = 65$

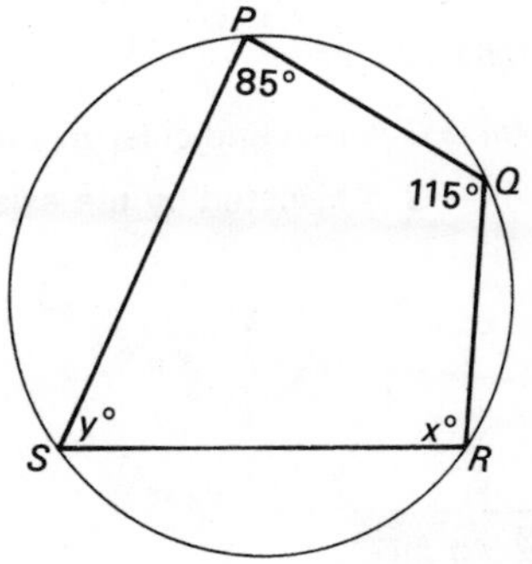

Exercise

In each of the following cyclic quadrilaterals, find the values of p and q.

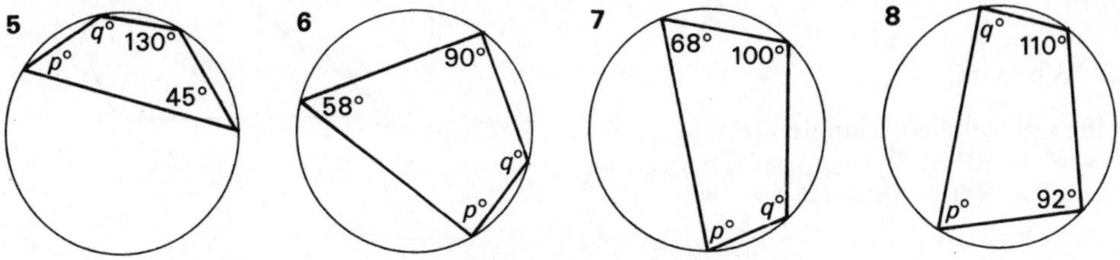

Continue with Section G

G Symmetry in a circle

Any straight line through the centre of a circle is an axis of symmetry of the circle.

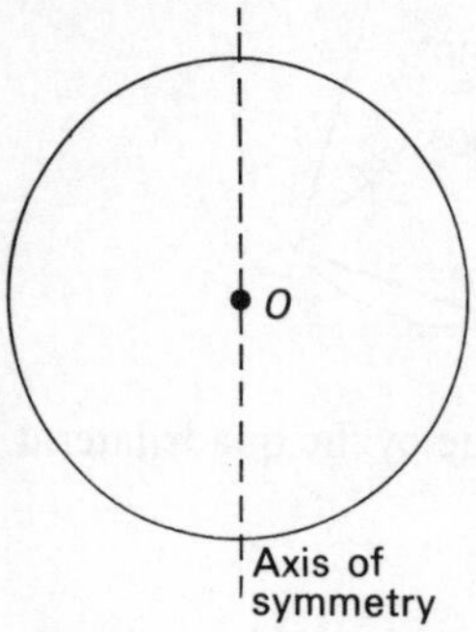

Let XY be an axis of symmetry of the circle and P a point on the circumference.

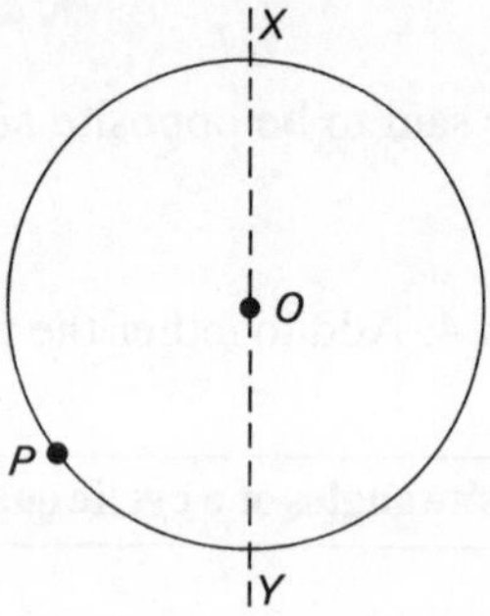

If P is reflected in the line XY we obtain an image point Q. Join P to Q. Let PQ cut the axis of symmetry at N.

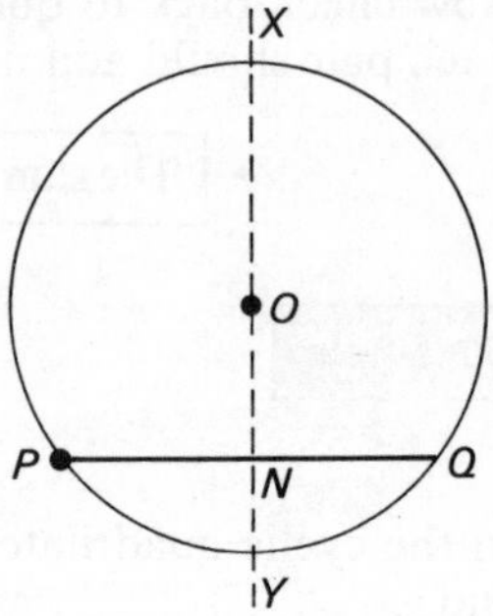

It follows that

(a) PQ is perpendicular to the axis of symmetry XY;
(b) PQ is bisected by the axis of symmetry.

Example

In a circle of radius 10 cm, the perpendicular distance of a chord from the centre of the circle is 6 cm. Find the length of the chord.

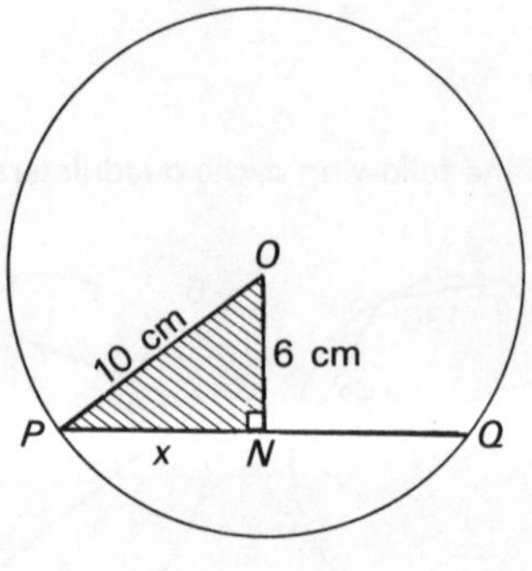

Let PN be x cm.

In the right-angled triangle OPN,

$x^2 + 6^2 = 10^2$ by Pythagoras' Theorem

$x^2 = 100 - 36 = 64$

$x = 8$

So $PN = 8$ cm, but since ON is the perpendicular from the centre of the circle to the chord, N is the mid point of PQ.

So $PQ = 2 \times PN = 2 \times 8 = 16$ cm

Example

N is the mid-point of a chord of length 12 cm of a circle centre O. $ON = 5$ cm. Find the radius of the circle.

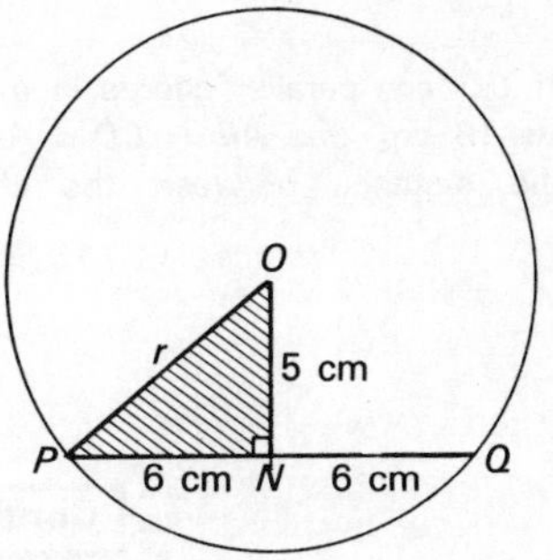

Let the radius be r cm.

Since $PQ = 12$ cm, $PN = 6$ cm.
In right-angled triangle PON,

$$\begin{aligned} r^2 &= 5^2 + 6^2 \\ &= 25 + 36 \\ &= 61 \\ r &= 7.81 \end{aligned}$$

The radius is 7.81 cm.

Exercise

1 The radius of a circle is 6 cm.
PQ is a chord 8 cm long.
Find its distance, *d*, from the centre of the circle.

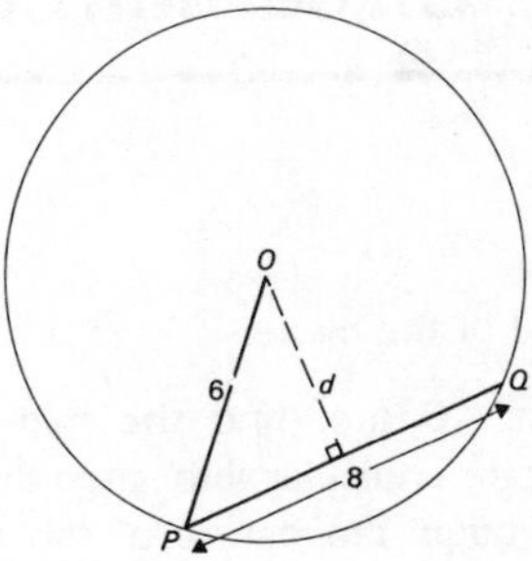

2

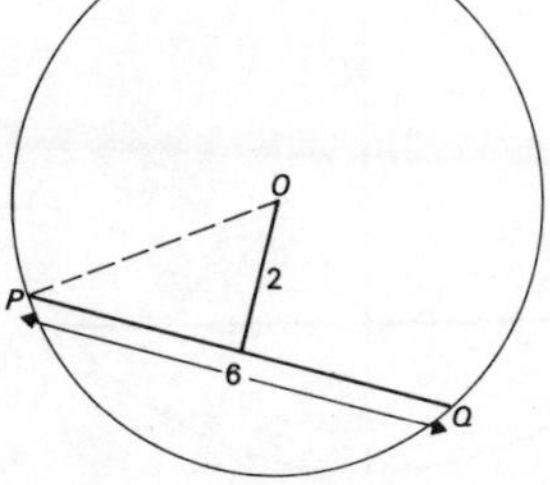

A chord of a circle is 6 cm long and is 2 cm from the centre of the circle.

Find the radius of the circle.

3 Calculate the length of a chord which is 8 cm from the centre of a circle whose radius is 10 cm.

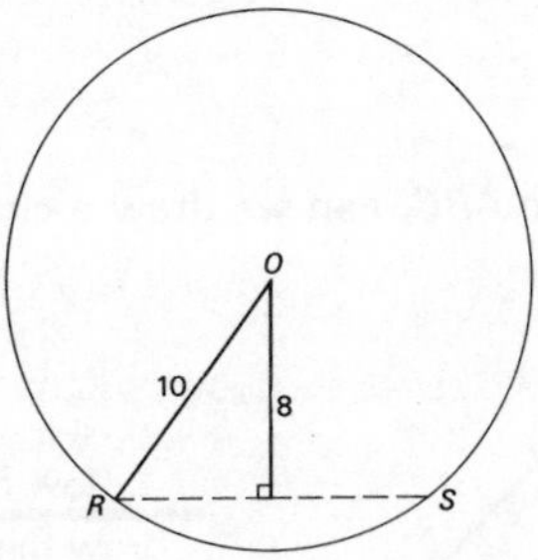

4

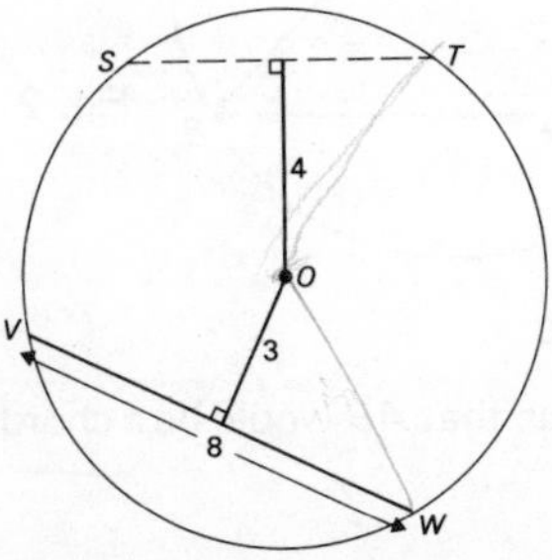

A chord of length 8 cm is distant 3 cm from the centre of a circle.

Find the length of a chord of the same circle which is 4 cm from the centre.

(*Hint*: First find the radius of the circle.)

5 *AB* and *CD* are parallel chords in a circle of radius 13 cm, and $AB = CD = 10$ cm. Find the distance between the chords.

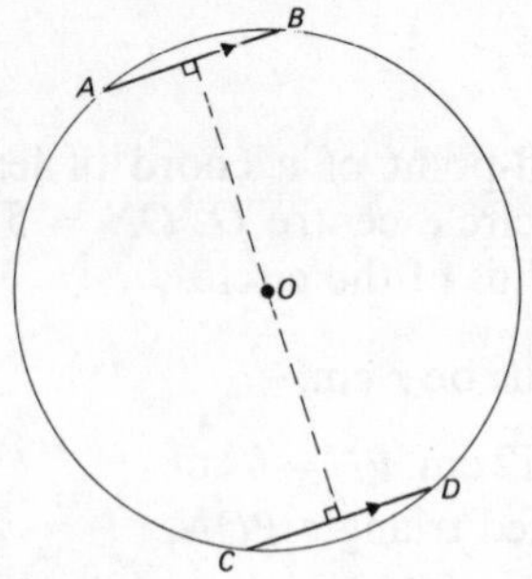

Continue with Section H

H Circumcircles

AB is a chord of the circle.

If we **bisect** *AB* (i.e. find the mid-point) and draw a perpendicular line, then this line will pass through the centre of the circle.

This line is called the **perpendicular bisector** of *AB*.

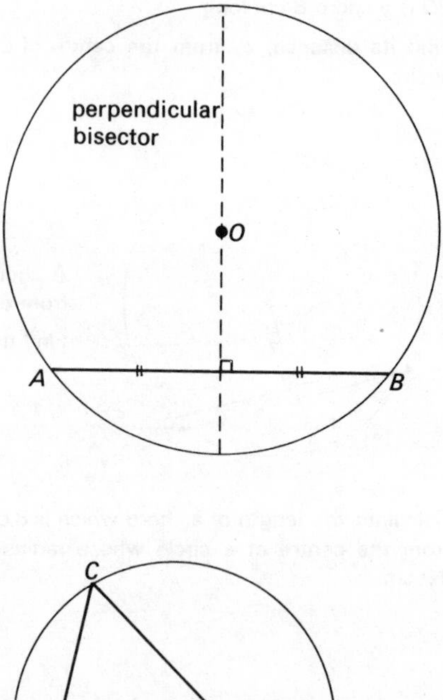

Given triangle *ABC*, can we draw a circle round it?

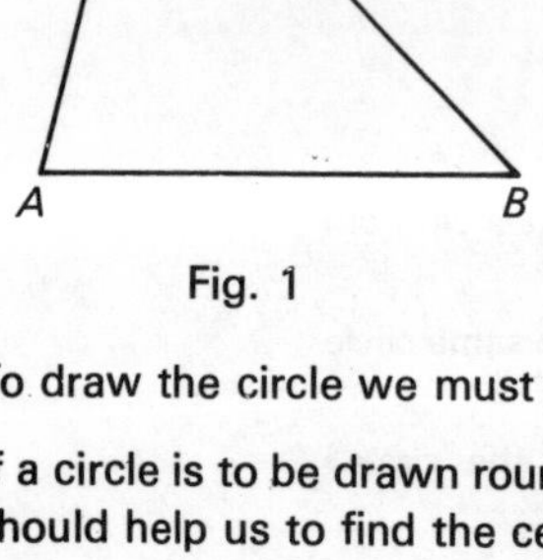

Fig. 1

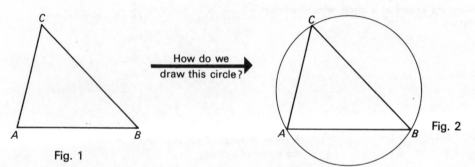

How do we draw this circle?

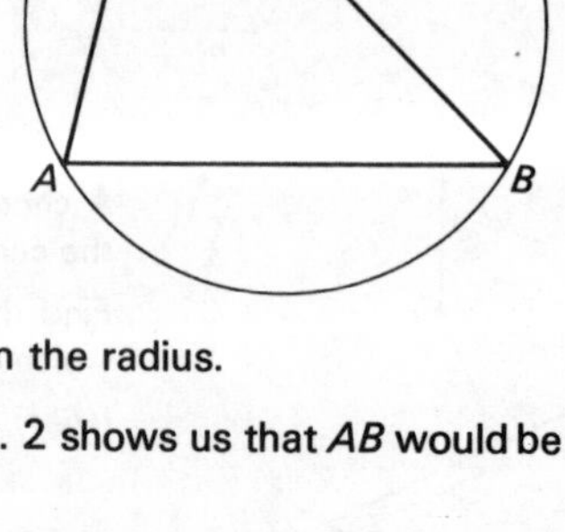

Fig. 2

To draw the circle we must find the centre and then the radius.

If a circle is to be drawn round triangle *ABC* then fig. 2 shows us that *AB* would be a chord – this should help us to find the centre.

Draw a triangle like the one shown.

Now find the mid-point of *AB* and draw the perpendicular bisector (use a set square to make the right-angle). The centre will lie somewhere on this line.

Draw the perpendicular bisector of *BC*.

Draw the perpendicular bisector of *AC*.

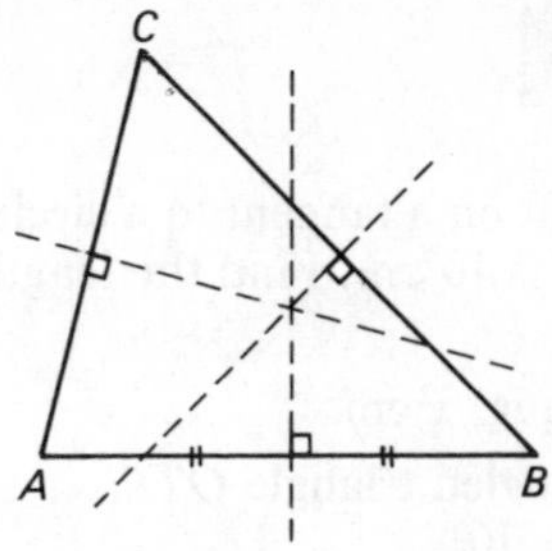

The 3 perpendicular bisectors should intersect at **one** point.

This point is the centre of your circle. Call it *O*.

Now with compasses centred on *O* and with radius *OB* (or *OA* or *OC*) draw a circle.

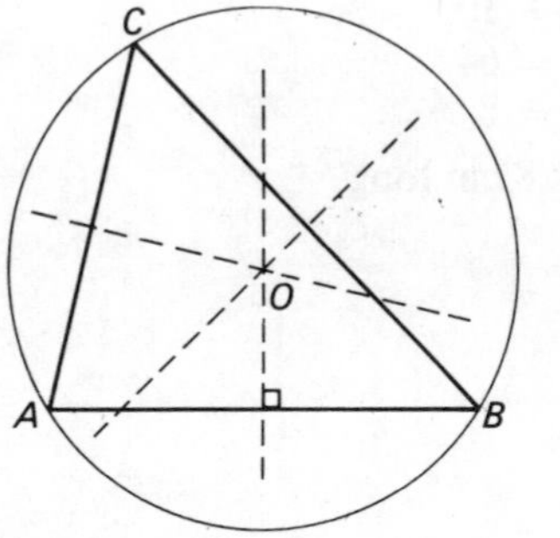

A circle that fits round a triangle like this is called a **circumcircle**.

Exercise

1 Draw any two triangles and show them to your teacher. Now draw the circumcircles for these two triangles.

Continue with Section I

I Tangents

In this diagram *ST* is a **tangent**. *C* is called the **point of contact**.

Since *CD* is an axis of symmetry, angle $O\hat{C}T$ is a right angle.

The angle between a tangent and the radius through its point of contact is a right-angle.

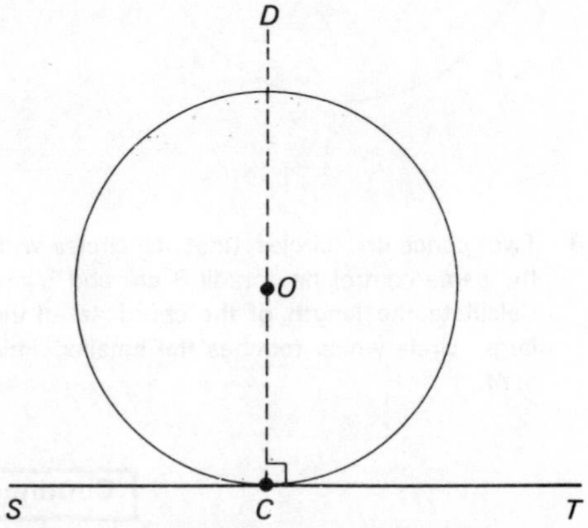

Example

P is a point on a tangent to a circle of radius 6 cm. The distance of *P* from the centre *O* of the circle is 10 cm. Find the length of the tangent from *P* to the circle.

Let *TP* equal *x* cm.
In right-angled triangle *OTP*,

$x^2 + 6^2 = 10^2$
$x^2 + 36 = 100$
$x^2 = 100 - 36$
$= 64$
$x = 8$

So *PT* is 8 cm long.

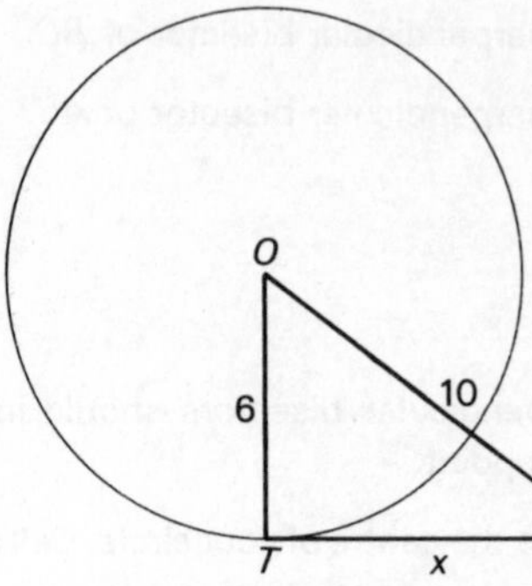

Exercise

1 Find the length of a tangent drawn to a circle of radius 8 cm from a point 12 cm from its centre.

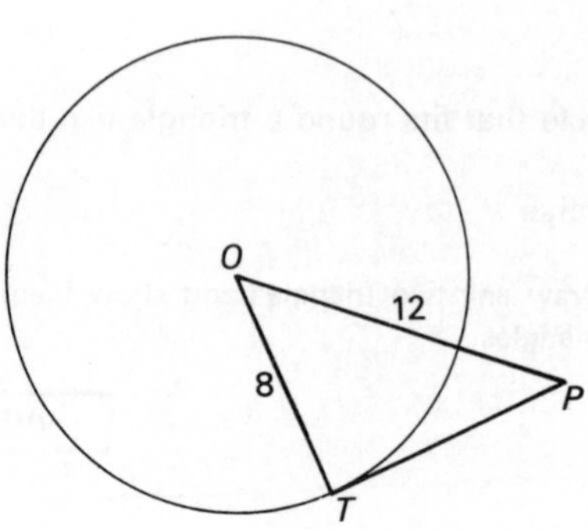

2

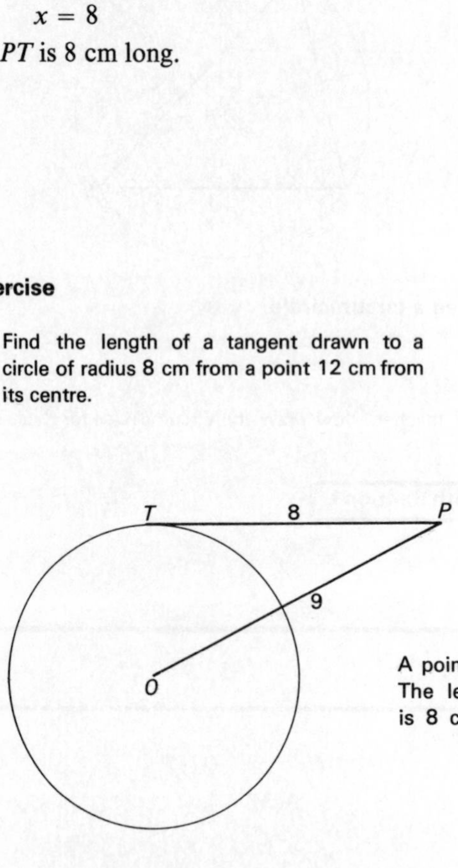

A point *P* is 9 cm from the centre of a circle. The length *PT* of the tangent to the circle is 8 cm. Calculate the radius of the circle.

3 Two concentric circles (that is, circles with the same centre) have radii 3 cm and 5 cm. Calculate the length of the chord *AB* of the larger circle which touches the smaller circle at *M*.

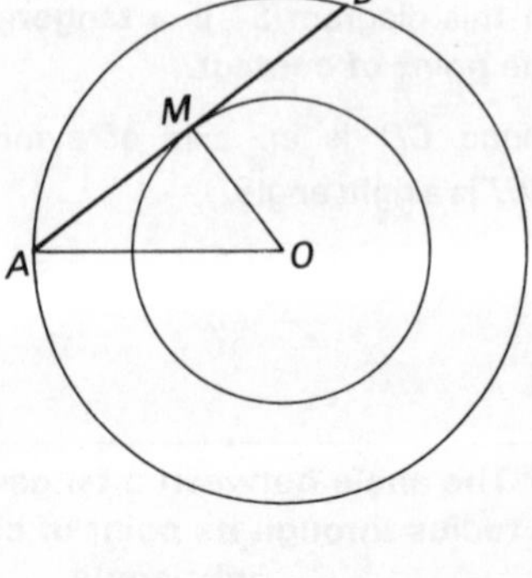

Continue with Section J

J Progress check

Exercise

In each question the point O is the centre of the circle.

1 Find the size of the shaded angles in each of the following diagrams.

(a)

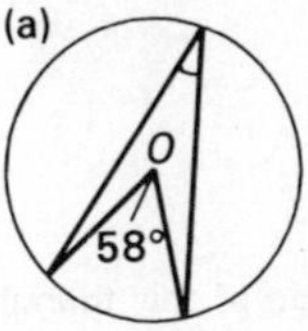

(b)

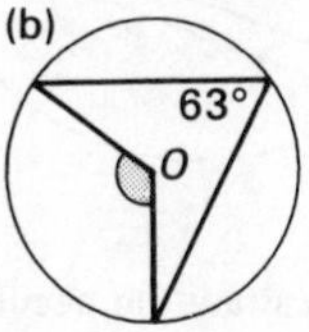

(c)

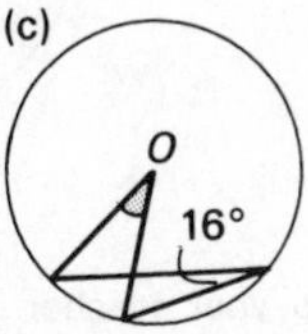

(d)

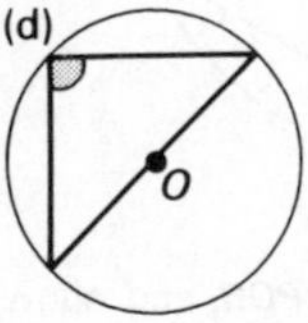

(e)

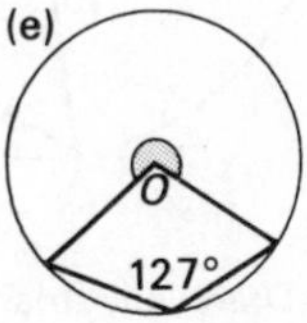

2 Find the values of x and y in each of the following diagrams.

(a)

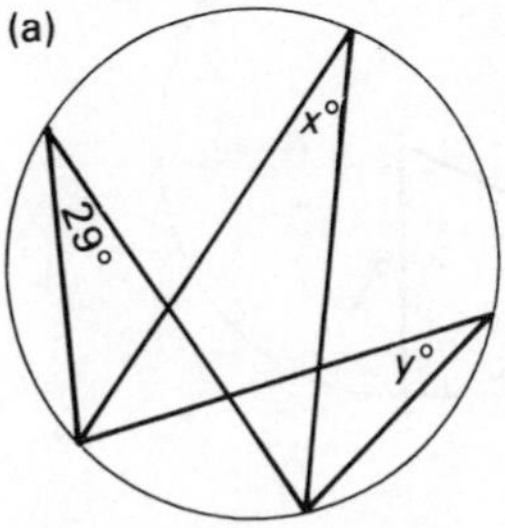

(b)

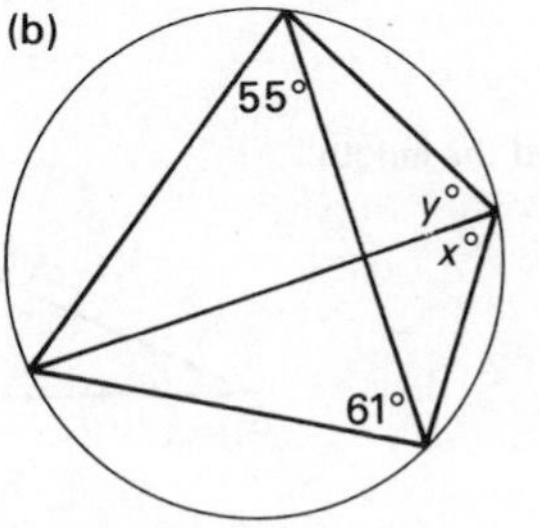

(c)

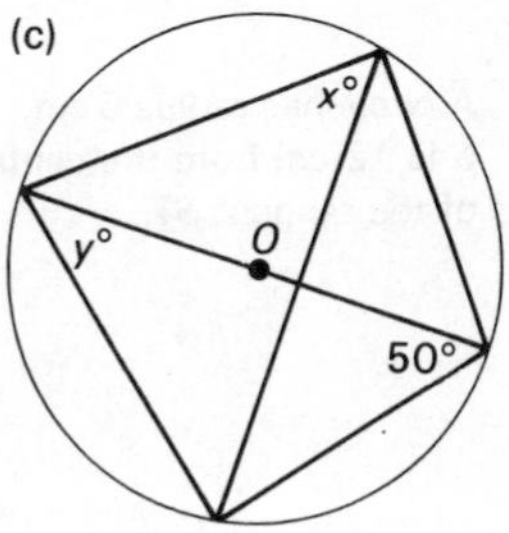

3 Which of the lines BD and AC is a diameter of this circle? Give a reason for your answer.

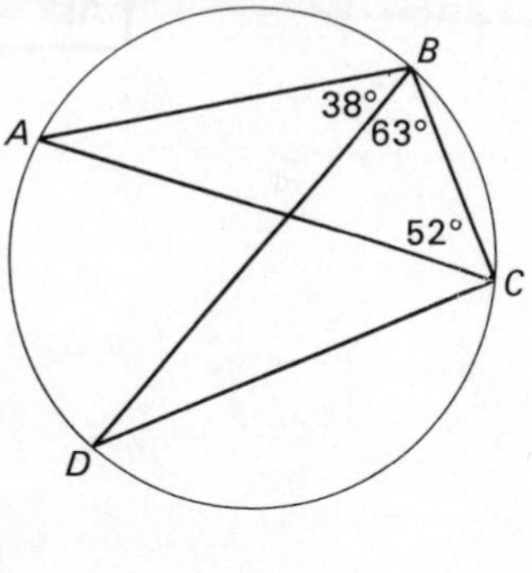

4 Find the values of p and q in each of the following diagrams.

(a)

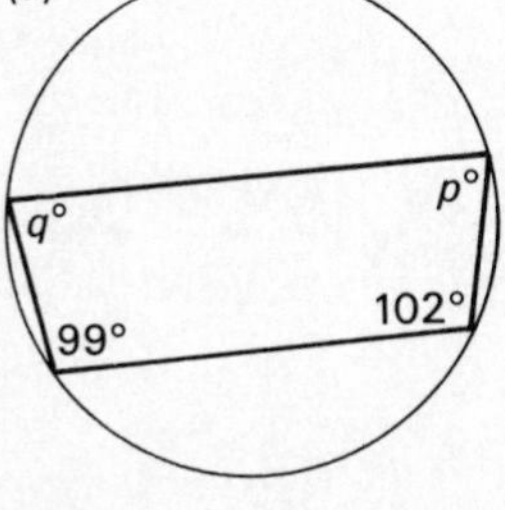

(b)

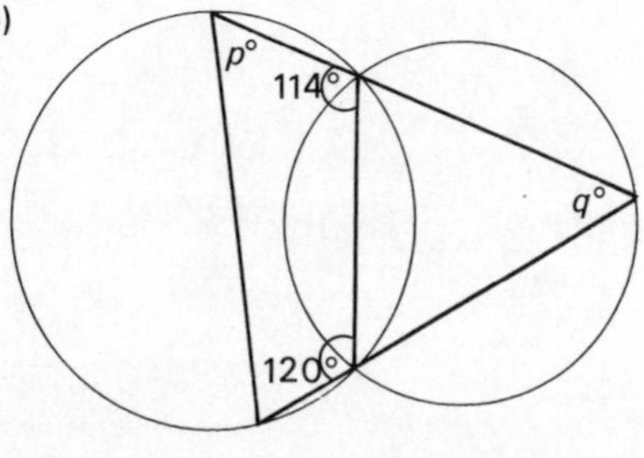

5 Find d.

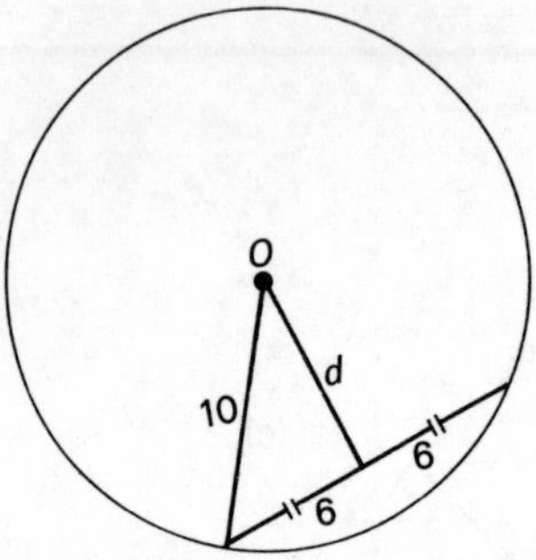

6 Find the radius of the circle.

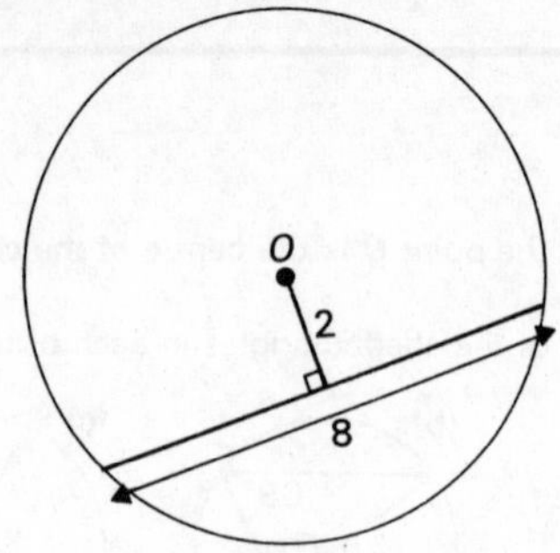

7 Draw any triangle PQR and show it to your teacher. Now draw the circumcircle of this triangle.

8 A circle has radius 5 cm.
S is 12 cm from the centre O. Find the length of the tangent ST.

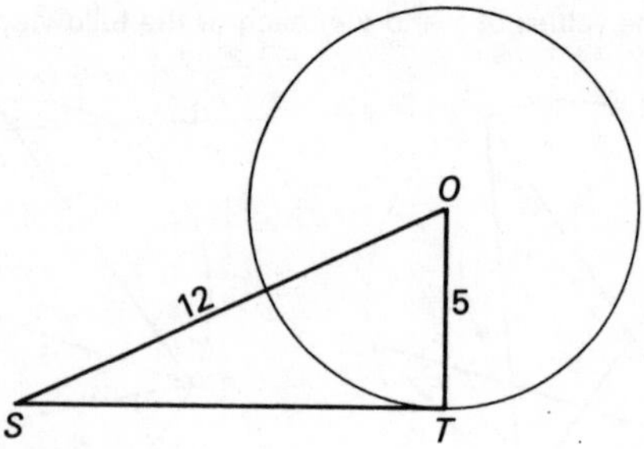

Ask your teacher what to do next

K Common tangents

If two circles touch as shown in the diagram, they are said to **touch externally** at the point of contact *R*.

AB is called a **common tangent** to the circles.

XY is an axis of symmetry of the diagram. The points *P, Q,* and *R* all lie on this line which is perpendicular to *AB*.

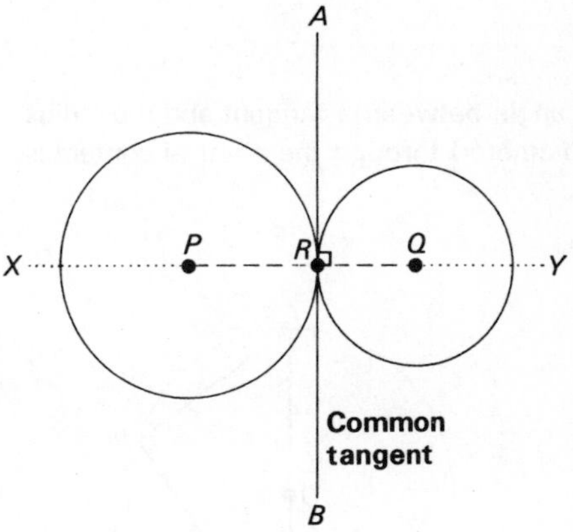

Two circles can also touch as shown in this diagram. In this case they are said to **touch internally**.

Again a common tangent *AB* can be drawn which is perpendicular to the line through the centres.

The points *P, Q,* and *R* should be in a straight line.

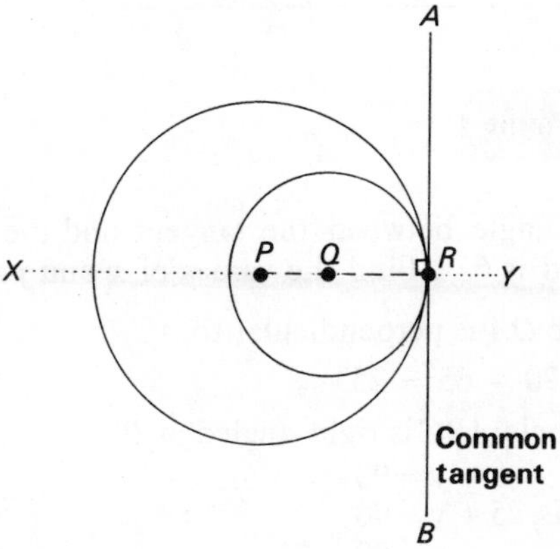

Exercise

1 Draw a diagram like the one at the top of the page showing two circles with radii of 4 cm and 3 cm, the circles **touching externally**. Draw the common tangent *AB*.
(*Hint*: Draw a line *XY* about 16 cm long as an axis of symmetry. The two centres and the point of contact all lie on this line.)

2 Draw a diagram like the one above showing two circles with radii of 4 cm and 3 cm, with the circles **touching internally**. Draw the common tangent.
(*Hint*: Start with the line *XY*.)

Continue with Section L

L Tangent and chord

We are going to remind ourselves of two of the results we have already found.

The angle between a tangent and the radius (or diameter) through the point of contact is 90°.

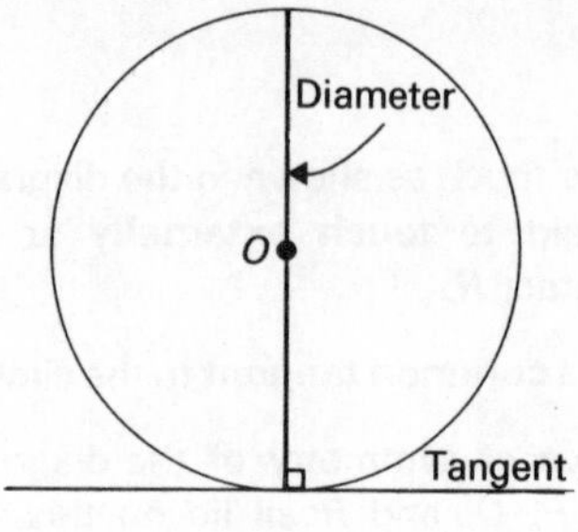

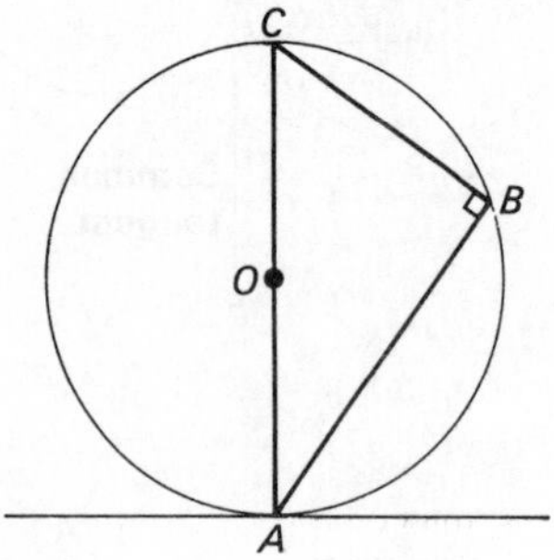

An angle in a semi-circle is 90°.

Example

The angle between the tangent and the chord is 65°. Find the values of x and y.

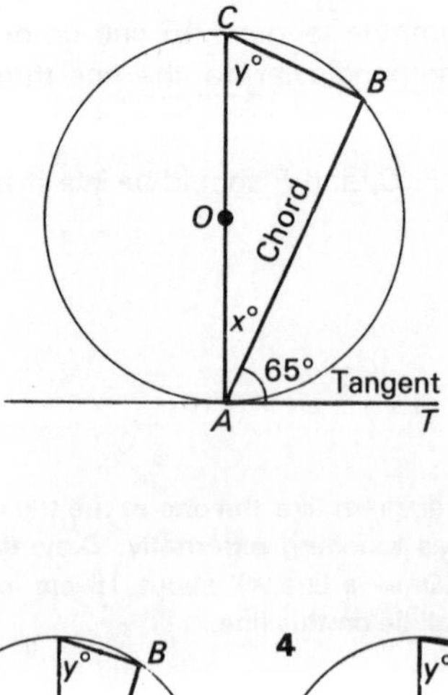

Since OA is perpendicular to AT,

$x = 90 - 65 = 25$

Triangle ABC is right-angled at B,

so $x + y = 90$

that is, $25 + y = 90$

$y = 90 - 25$

$= 65$

Exercise

Find the values of x and y in each diagram.

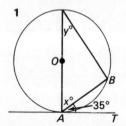

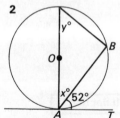

1

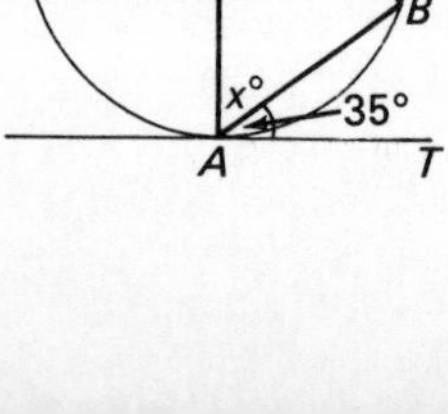

2

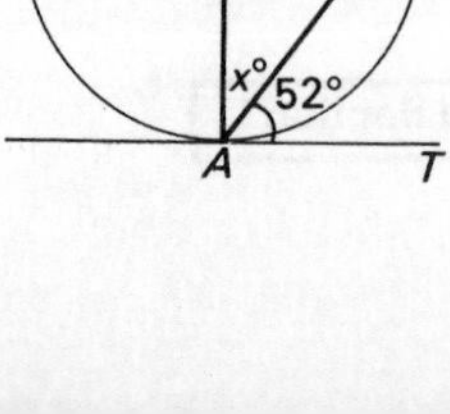

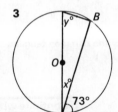

3

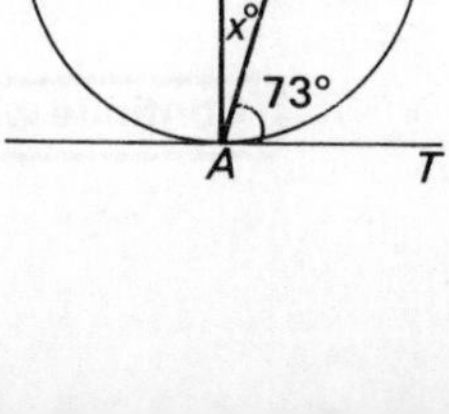

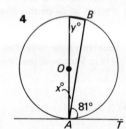

4

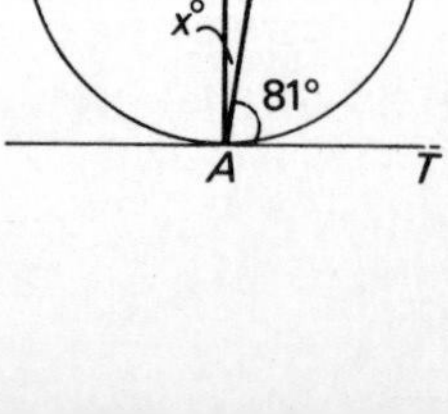

Find the values of x, y, and z in each diagram.

5

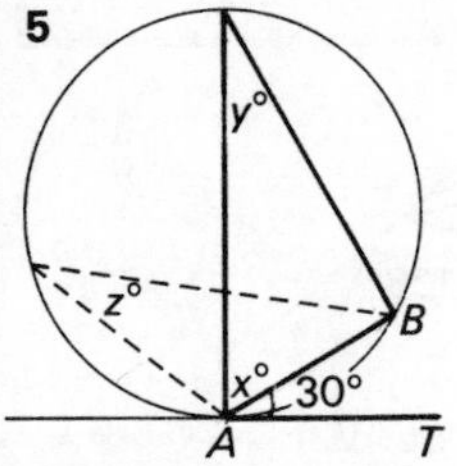

6

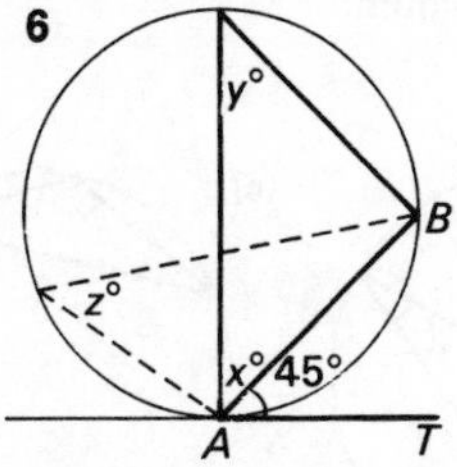

7

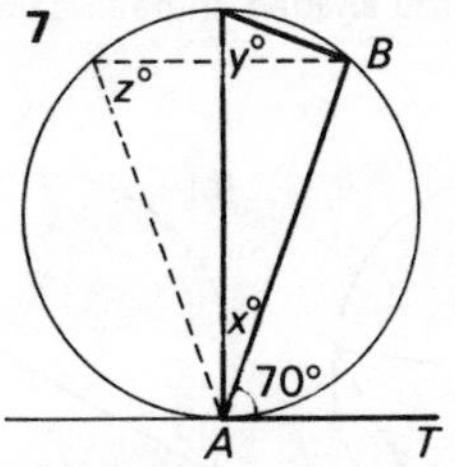

8

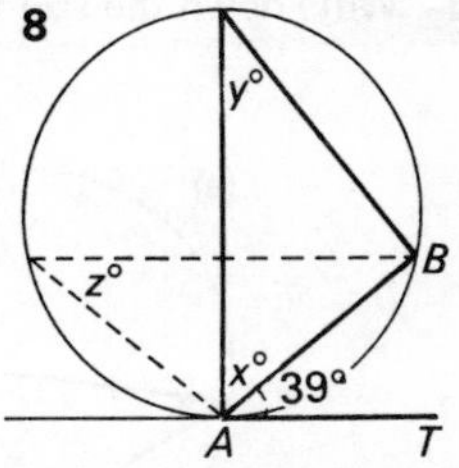

In each of questions 5 to 8 compare the value of $B\hat{A}T$ and angle z. What do you notice?

> $B\hat{A}T$ = angle z in each case.

Angle BAT is called the **angle between tangent and chord**.
Angle z is called the **angle in the alternate segment**.

> The angle between a tangent and chord equals the angle in the alternate segment.

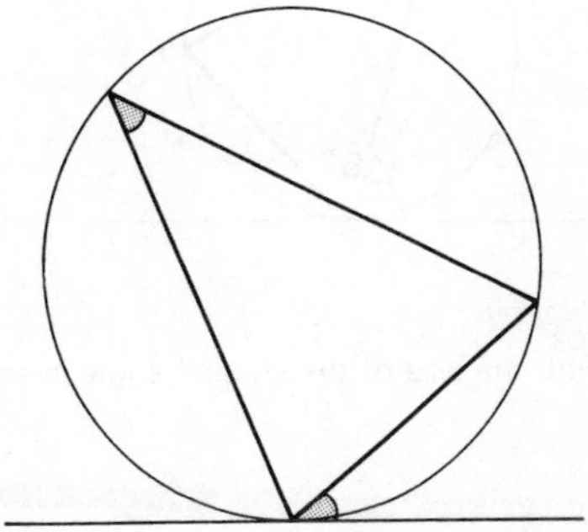

Example

Write down the values of

(a) $B\hat{D}E$ (b) $D\hat{E}B$ (c) $D\hat{B}E$

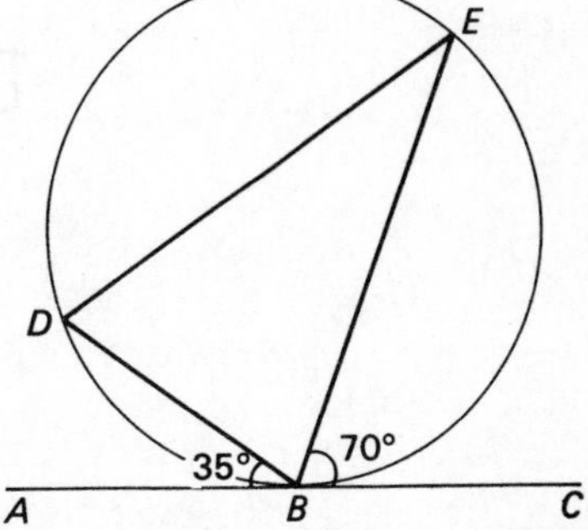

(a) With BE as chord,

$E\hat{B}C = B\hat{D}E$

So $B\hat{D}E = 70°$

(b) With BD as chord,

$A\hat{B}D = D\hat{E}B$

So $D\hat{E}B = 35°$

(c) In triangle DEB the sum of the angles is 180°.

So $D\hat{B}E = 180° - (70° + 35°)$
$= 75°$

Exercise

9 Write down the size of the shaded angle in each figure:

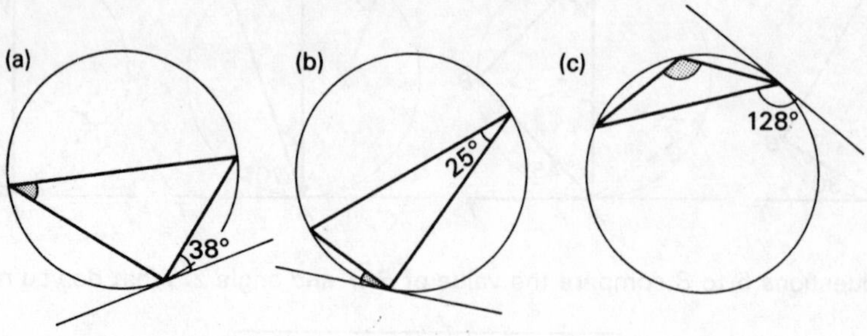

10 Find (a) $B\hat{C}T$, (b) $C\hat{A}B$.

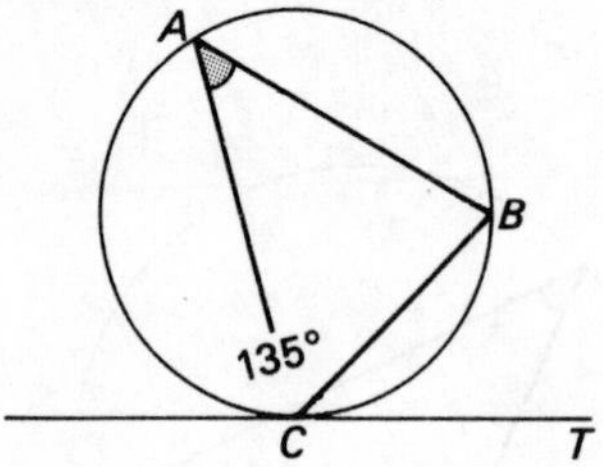

11 Find the size of the shaded angle in each of the following figures.

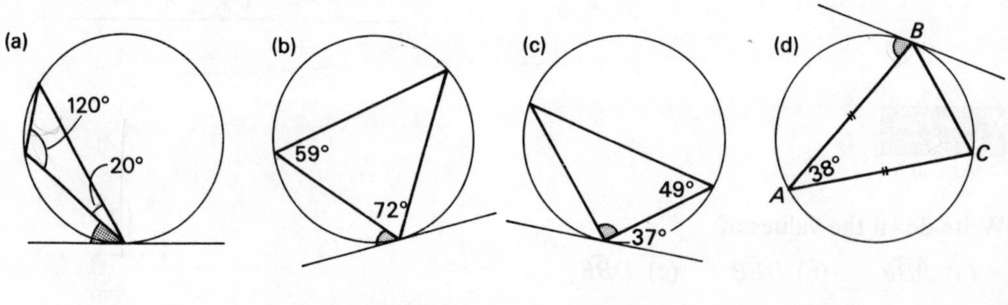

Continue with Section M

M Tangent kite

If two tangents, *PX* and *PY*, are drawn from a point *P* to a circle, and if the radii *OX* and *OY* are drawn, then the shape formed is a **kite**.

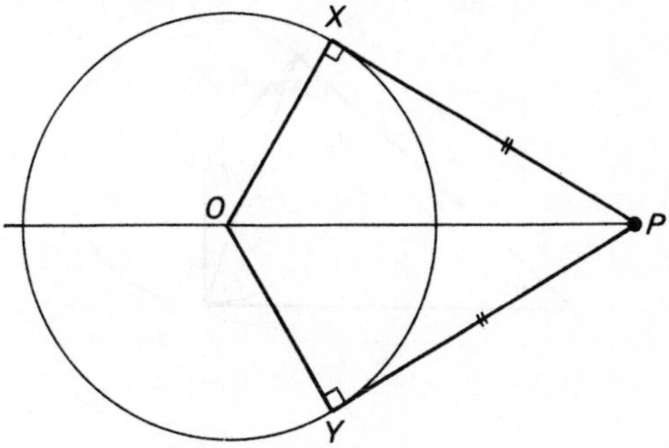

Such a diagram is called a **tangent kite**.

OP is an axis of symmetry for the diagram. The two tangents are equal in length ($PX = PY$).

Example

P is a point 8 cm from *O*, the centre of a circle of radius 6 cm.
Find the lengths of the tangents from *P* to the circle.

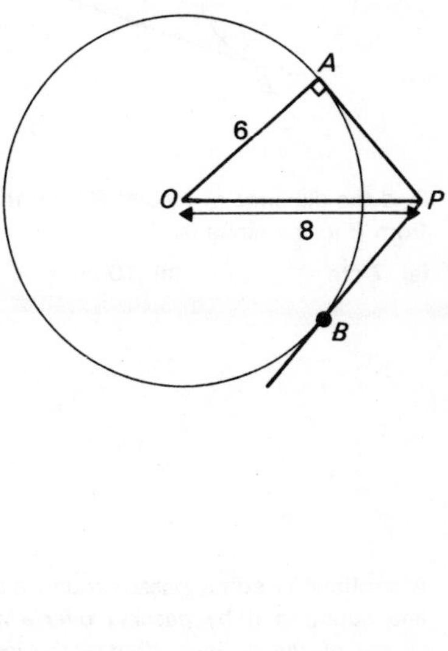

$OA = 6$ cm, $OP = 8$ cm and $O\widehat{A}P = 90°$, since the angle between a tangent and a radius at the point of contact is a right angle.

So in triangle *OAP*

$$\begin{aligned} 6^2 + AP^2 &= 8^2 \\ 36 + AP^2 &= 64 \\ AP^2 &= 28 \\ AP &= \sqrt{28} \\ &= 5.29 \end{aligned}$$

The lengths of the tangents *AP* and *BP* are 5.29 cm.

Exercise

1 For each of the following diagrams find values for *a*, *b*, *c*, and *d*.

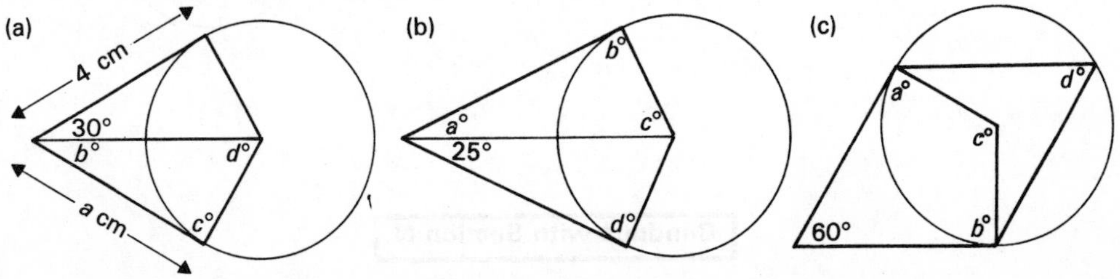

(d)

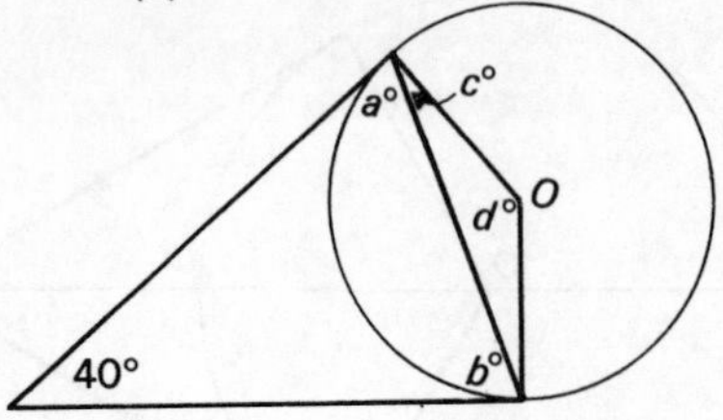

(e)

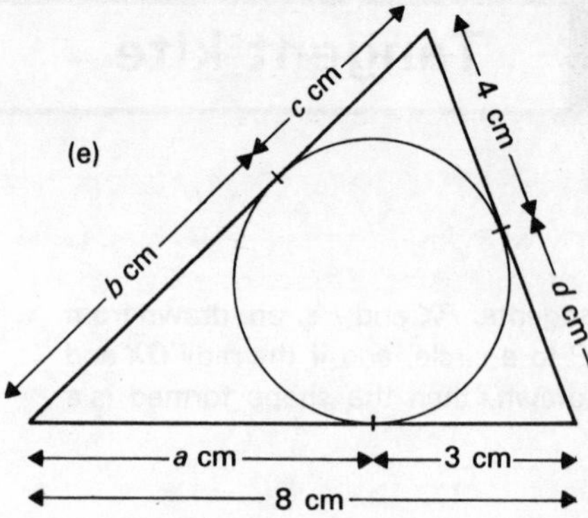

2 Find the lengths of *AP* and *BP* in each case.

(a)

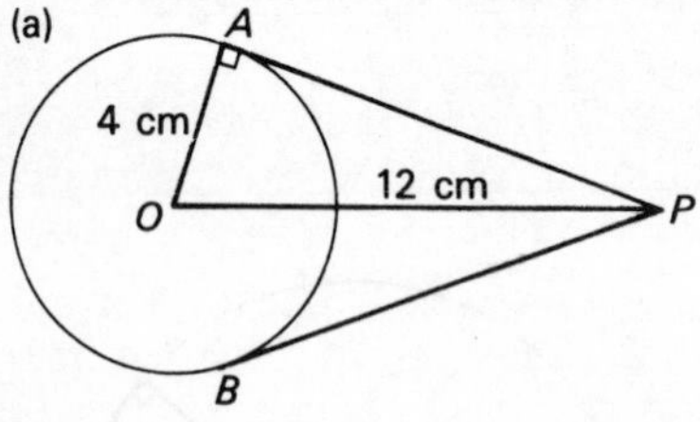

(b)

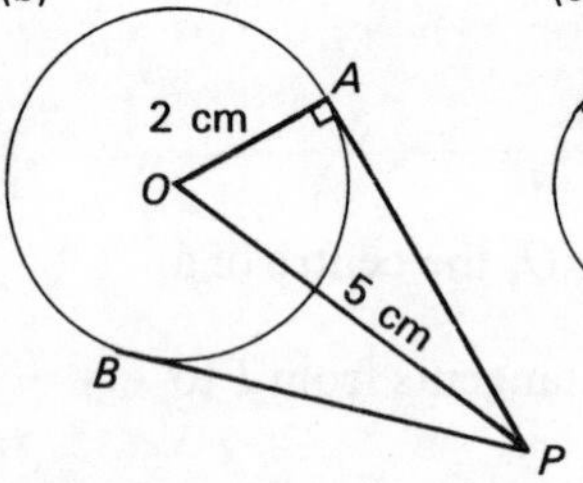

(c)

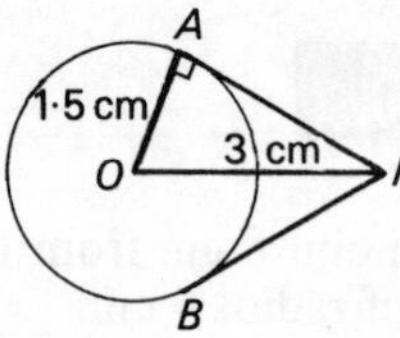

3 Find the distance of a point *P* from the centre of a circle of radius 10 cm, when the length of a tangent from *P* to the circle is

(a) 7 cm (b) 10 cm (c) 4 cm

4 A continuous string passes round a pulley of radius 4 cm, and supports it by passing over a nail 12 cm above the centre of the pulley. What is the length of each straight portion of the string?

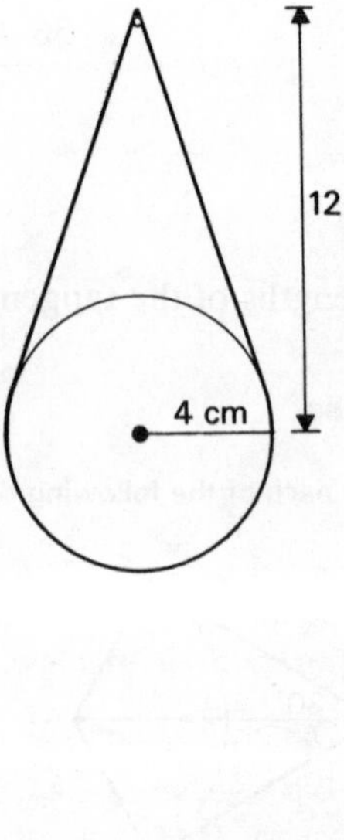

Continue with Section N

N In-circles

Previously we considered the problem of drawing a circle round a triangle.
Such a circle is called a **circumcircle.**

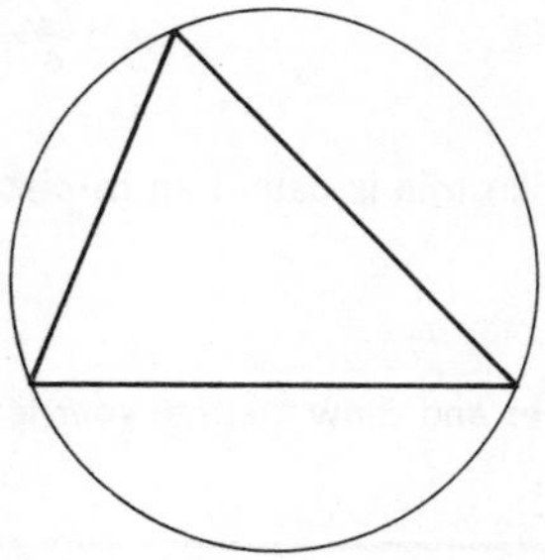

Now we consider this problem.

Given triangle *ABC*, can we draw a circle **inside** it?

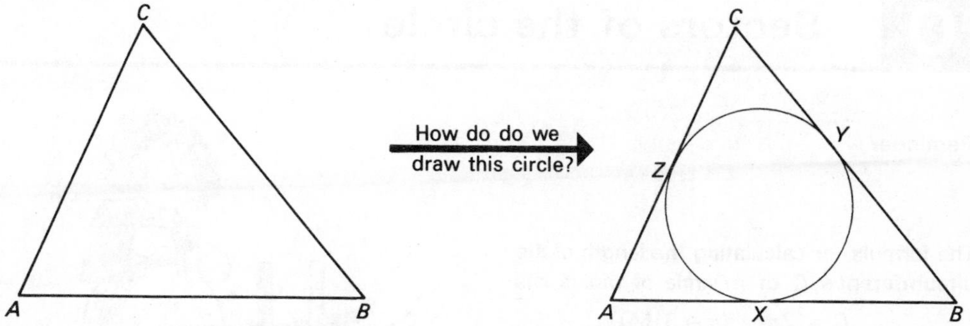

To draw a circle that fits exactly inside triangle *ABC* we must first find its centre, and then the radius.

We see from the diagram that *BX* and *BY* would be tangents to the circle. The symmetry of such tangents tells us that the centre will lie on a line half-way between *BX* and *BY*.

Draw a triangle *ABC* — make it fairly large.

Measure $A\hat{B}C$ with a protractor and draw the bisector of $A\hat{B}C$ as shown. The centre will be somewhere on this line.

Draw the bisector of $B\hat{C}A$.

Draw the bisector of $C\hat{A}B$.

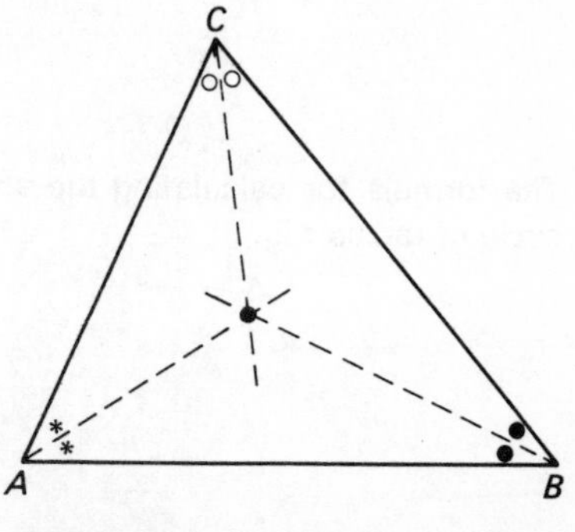

The three bisectors should intersect at **one** point. This point is the centre of your circle. Call it *O*.

With a compass centred on *O* take a radius to just touch the sides of triangle *ABC* and draw a circle.

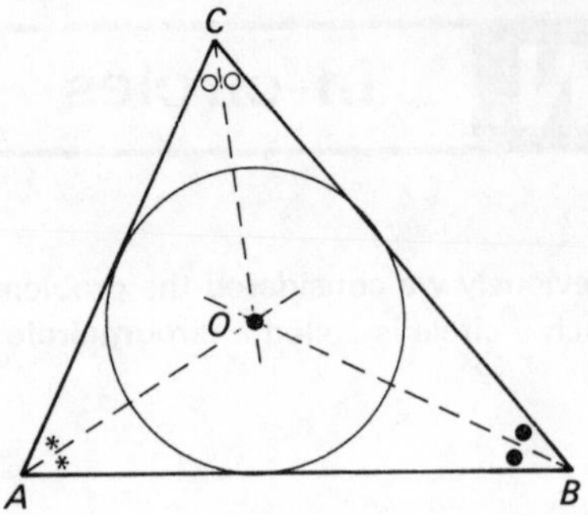

A circle that fits inside a triangle like this is called an **in-circle.**

Exercise

1 Draw two reasonably large triangles and show them to your teacher. Now draw the in-circles for these triangles.

Continue with Section O

O Sectors of the circle

Reminder

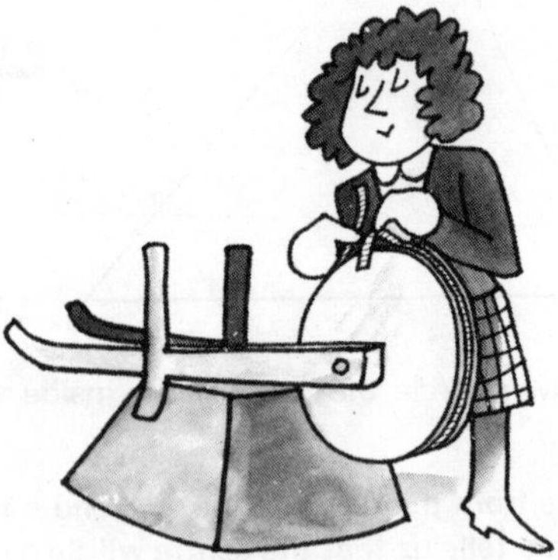

The formula for calculating the length of **the circumference** *C* of a circle of radius *r* is

$$C = 2\pi r \quad (\pi \approx 3.14)$$

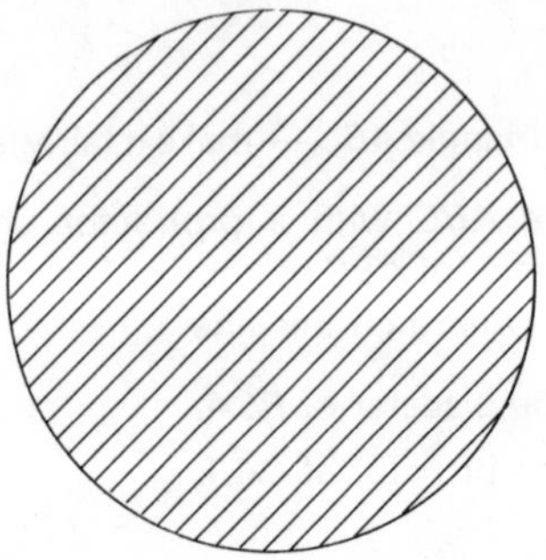

The formula for calculating the **area** *A* of a circle of radius *r* is

$$A = \pi r^2$$

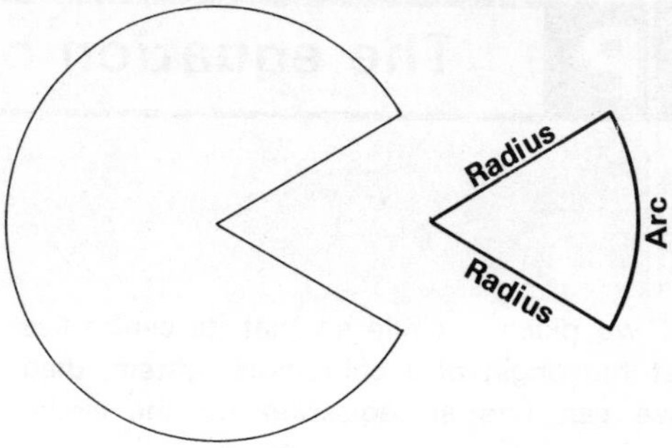

This circle has had a 'slice' cut from it.

The 'slice' is called a **sector**. A sector is bounded by two radii and an arc.

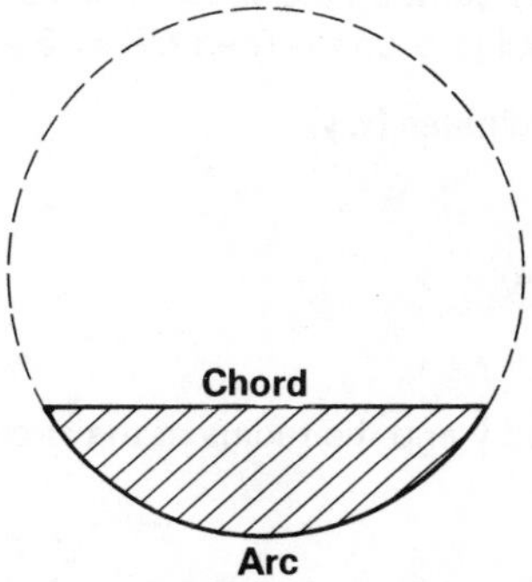

Do not confuse a **sector** with a **segment**. A segment is bounded by a chord and an arc. Remember a sector is like a slice of cake.

Example

Find (a) the arc length (l) and (b) the area of the sector of a circle of radius 3 cm, when the angle in the sector is 60°.

$$\begin{aligned}(a)\ C &= 2\pi r\\ &= 2 \times 3.14 \times 3\\ &= 18.84\end{aligned}$$

The given sector takes up $\frac{1}{6}$th of the circle

$$\begin{aligned}\text{So } l &= \tfrac{1}{6}\text{th of } 18.84\\ &= 3.14\\ \text{Arc length} &= 3.14 \text{ cm}\end{aligned}$$

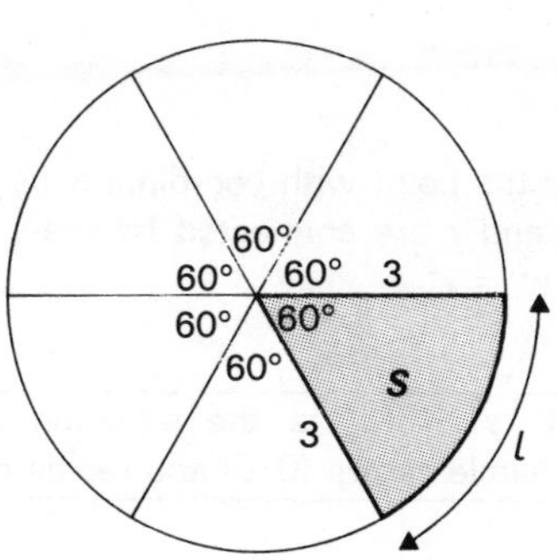

$$\begin{aligned}(b)\ A &= \pi r^2\\ &= 3.14 \times 9\\ &= 28.26\\ \text{So } S &= \tfrac{1}{6}\text{th of } 28.26\\ &= 4.71\\ \text{Area of sector} &= 4.71 \text{ cm}^2\end{aligned}$$

Exercise

1 The radius of a circle is 18 cm. Find the arc length of a sector subtending each of the following angles at the centre of the circle:
(a) 60° (b) 90° (c) 120° (d) 150° (e) 270°

2 The radius of a circle is 10 cm. Find the area of a sector whose angle at the centre of the circle is
(a) 90° (b) 72° (c) 216° (d) 324°

Continue with Section P

P The equation of a circle

If we place a circle so that its centre lies at the origin of a coordinate system, then we can find an **equation** for the circle.

Suppose P is any point on the circumference of a circle of radius 5 units. Then $OP = 5$.

Let P have coordinates (x, y).

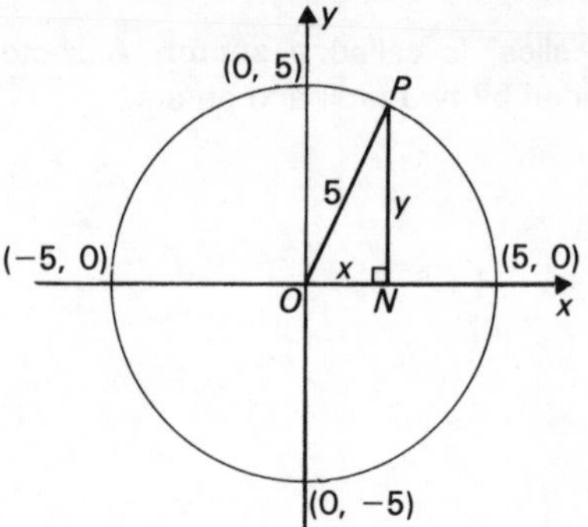

We can link x and y and the radius of the circle by using Pythagoras' Theorem in the right-angled triangle OPN.

$$x^2 + y^2 = 5^2$$

that is
$$x^2 + y^2 = 25$$

We call $x^2 + y^2 = 25$ the equation of the circle with centre (0, 0) and radius 5 units.

We can find the equation of a circle centre (0, 0) and radius r units in just the same way.

If P is the point with coordinates (x, y), then x, y, and r are connected by the equation $x^2 + y^2 = r^2$.

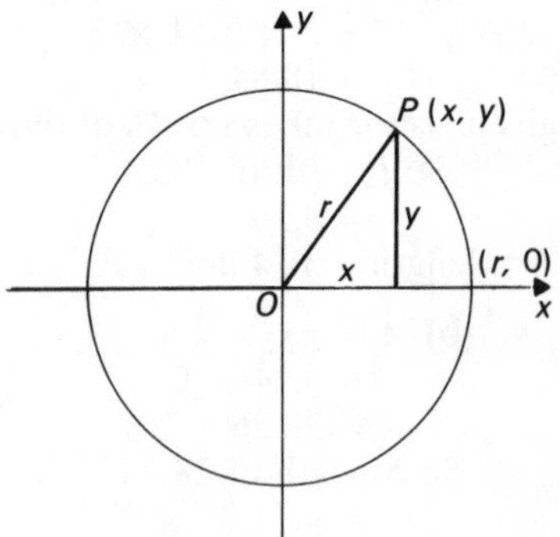

$x^2 + y^2 = r^2$ is the equation of the circle centre (0, 0) and radius r.

Example

Write down the equation of the circle centre (0,0) and radius (a) 7, (b) 1.

The equations are:

(a) $x^2 + y^2 = 7^2$, that is $x^2 + y^2 = 49$

(b) $x^2 + y^2 = 1^2$, that is $x^2 + y^2 = 1$

Exercise

1 Find the equation of the circle whose centre is (0, 0) and whose radius is

(a) 3 (b) 7 (c) $\sqrt{13}$

Example

Find the radius of the circle centre (0,0) with equation $x^2 + y^2 = 81$.

We need to write the equation in the form $x^2 + y^2 = r^2$ to find the value of r.

$x^2 + y^2 = 81$ may be written as $x^2 + y^2 = 9^2$, so $r = 9$. The radius is 9 units.

Exercise

2 Find the radius of the circle, centre (0, 0) whose equation is

(a) $x^2 + y^2 = 9$ (b) $x^2 + y^2 = 100$ (c) $x^2 + y^2 = 64$

Example

Find whether the point $Q(9,4)$ lies inside, outside, or on the circle $x^2 + y^2 = 64$.

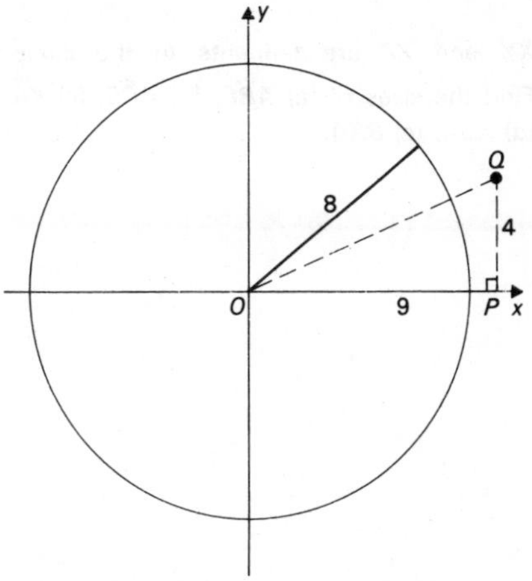

The radius of the given circle is 8 units.

If $OQ > 8$, then Q lies *outside* the circle.
If $OQ < 8$, then Q lies *inside* the circle.
If $OQ = 8$, then Q lies *on* the circle.

We need to find the length of OQ. Using Pythagoras in triangle OPQ,

$OQ^2 = 9^2 + 4^2 = 81 + 16 = 97$

$OQ = \sqrt{97} \approx 9.85$

$OQ > 8$ so Q lies **outside** the circle.

Exercise

3 A circle has equation $x^2 + y^2 = 25$. Which of the following points lie **on** the circumference of the circle?

(a) $(0, -5)$ (b) $(3, 4)$ (c) $(3, -4)$ (d) $(3, 2)$
(e) $(24, 1)$ (f) $(\sqrt{8}, -\sqrt{17})$ (g) $(2\sqrt{3}, \sqrt{13})$

4 Find which of the following points lie (i) inside, (ii) outside or (iii) on, the circle $x^2 + y^2 = 100$.

(a) $(-6, 8)$ (b) $(7, 9)$ (c) $(7, 7)$ (d) $(-1, 10)$

5 Find the radius and then write down the equation of the circle whose centre is (0, 0) and which passes through the point

(a) $(3, 5)$ (b) $(-2, -4)$ (c) $(-5, 7)$

Continue with Section Q

Q Progress check

Exercise

1 Tangents at each end of a chord *AB* meet at *P*. *AB* cuts *OP* at *N* so that *ON* = 9 cm and *NP* = 16 cm.

If the radius of the circle is 15 cm, calculate

(a) the lengths of the tangents from *P* to the circle;

(b) the length of the chord *AB*.

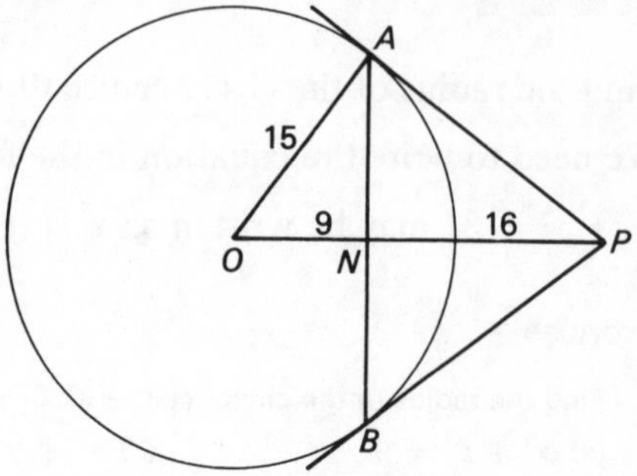

2 *XY* and *XZ* are tangents to the circle. Find the sizes of (a) $A\widehat{B}C$, (b) $A\widehat{C}B$, (c) $X\widehat{A}B$, (d) $X\widehat{B}A$, (e) $B\widehat{X}A$.

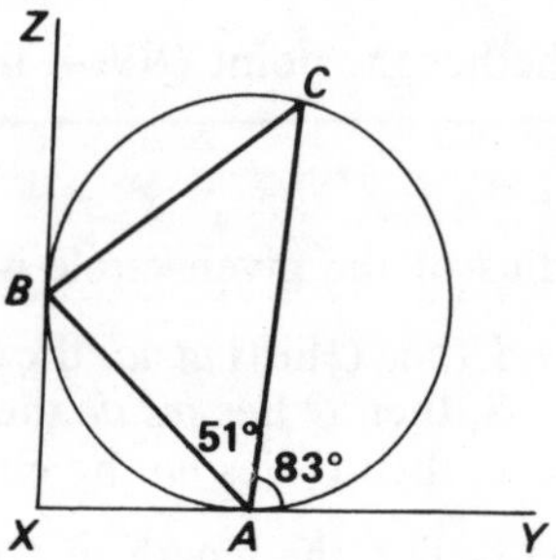

3 Triangle *ABC* is isosceles with *AC* = *BC* = 9 cm. The in-circle with centre *O* is drawn and touches the triangle at *X*, *Y*, and *Z*.

If *AX* = 3 cm write down the lengths of (a) *CX*, (b) *CY*, (c) *YB*, (d) *BZ*, (e) *AZ*.

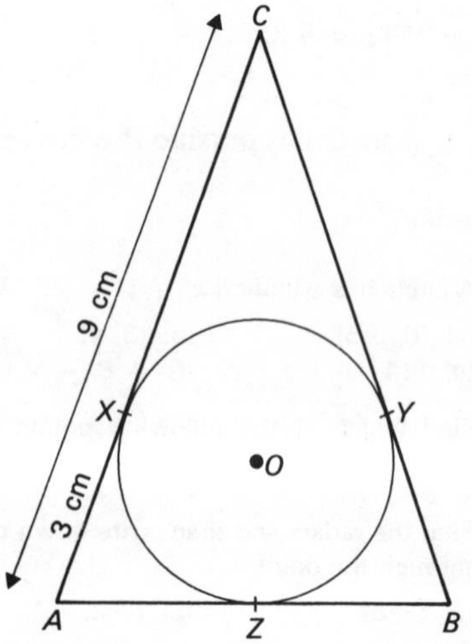

4 *AB* is a chord of a circle.

The tangents to the circle at *A* and *B* meet at *T*. *AC* is a chord of the circle parallel to *TB*.

If $\widehat{T} = 64°$, calculate the size of $C\widehat{B}T$.

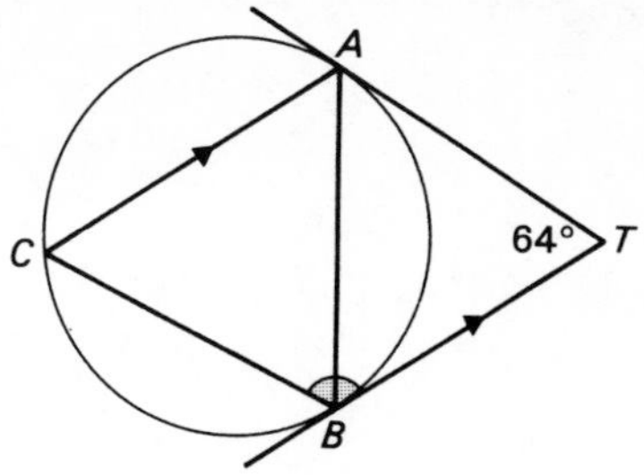

5 The radius of the in-circle of the triangle *PQR* is 4 cm.

If *O* is the in-centre and $OP = \sqrt{32}$ cm, $OQ = \sqrt{80}$ cm, and $OR = 5$ cm, calculate the length of each side of the triangle *PQR*.

(*Hint*: To calculate *PQ* find *PX* and *XQ* and add them.)

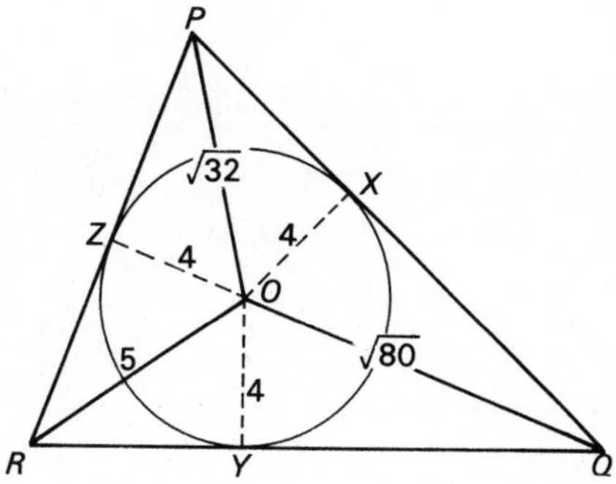

6 *OAB* is a sector of a circle of radius 12 cm.

(a) If $x = 45°$, calculate the arc length *AB* and the area of the sector *OAB*.

(b) If $x = 70°$ calculate the arc length *AB* and the area of the sector *OAB*.

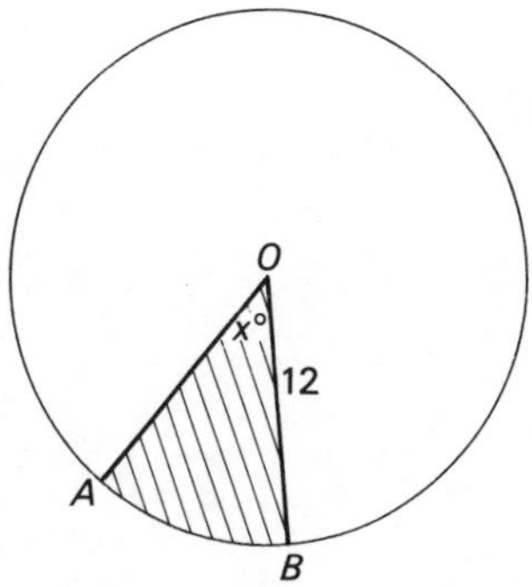

7 Write down the equations of the two circles in the diagram, whose centres are at *O*.

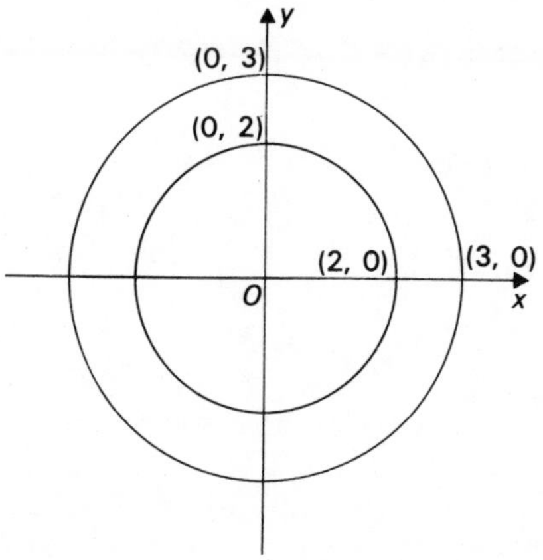

8 What is the radius of each of the following circles?

(a) $x^2 + y^2 = 25$ (b) $x^2 + y^2 = 80$

Tell your teacher you have finished this Unit

UNIT M12

The Cosine and Tangent Functions

A Sine function

In the diagram the circle has a radius of 1 unit, i.e. $OP = 1$ unit.

NP is perpendicular to ON.

In the right-angled triangle ONP,

$$\sin x° = \frac{NP}{OP}$$
$$= \frac{NP}{1}$$

$$\sin x° = NP$$

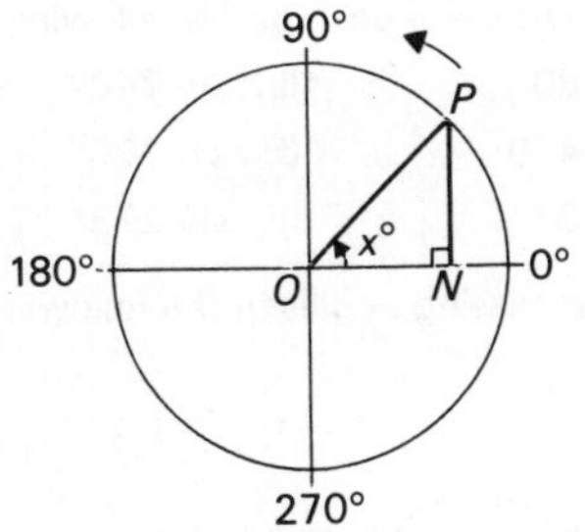

This means that the length of NP represents the sine of angle x. When we plot the length of NP against x, the angle of rotation of OP, we get the graph of the sine curve shown below.

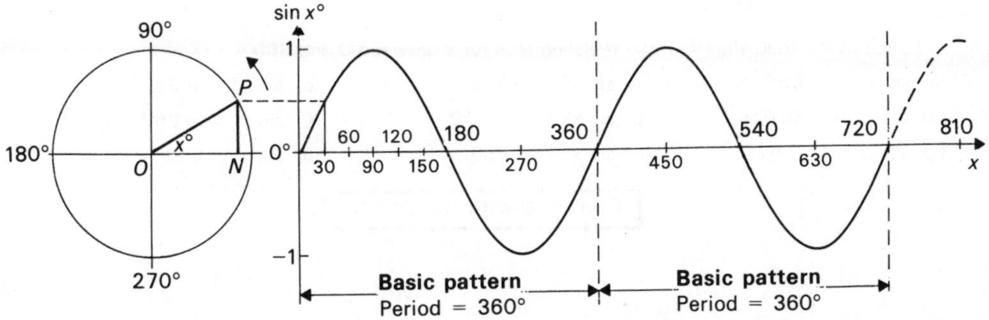

The basic pattern is repeated every 360°. We say that the **period** of the sine function is 360°.

From the graph we note the following:

(a) The value of $\sin x°$ is never greater than $+1$ or less than -1.

(b) The value of $\sin x°$ is positive between 0° and 180° and negative between 180° and 360°.

We can show this on the quadrants of a rotating-arm diagram.

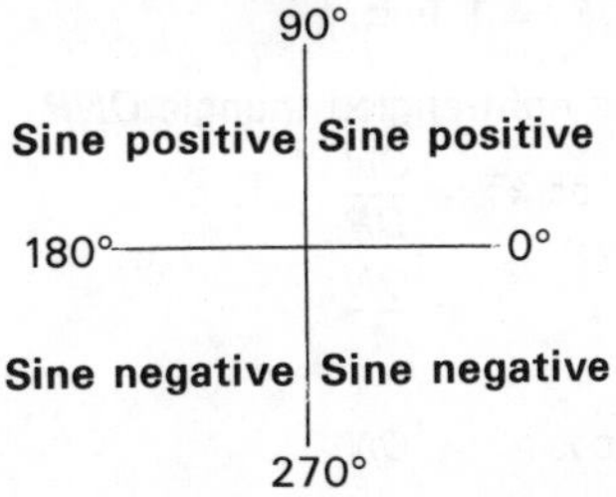

Exercise

(You will need tables of sines.)

1 In each of the following find $x°$.

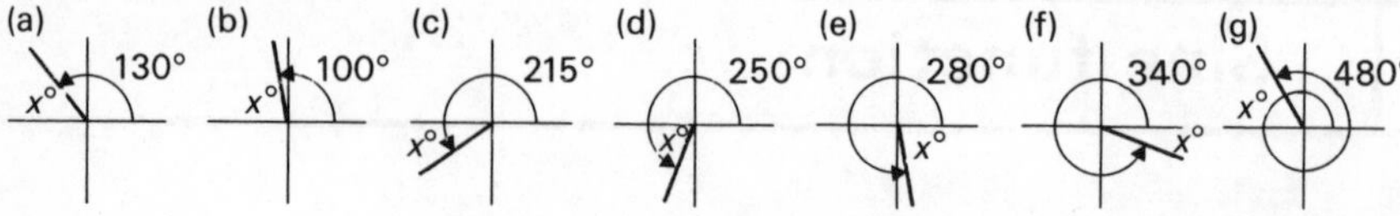

2 Find the value of each of the following:

(a) sin 80° (b) sin 240° (c) sin 170° (d) sin 318°
(e) sin 430° (f) sin 180° (g) sin 92° (h) sin 270°
(i) sin 0° (j) sin 273° (k) sin 90° (l) sin 700°

3 Find the missing angles in the following sine curves.

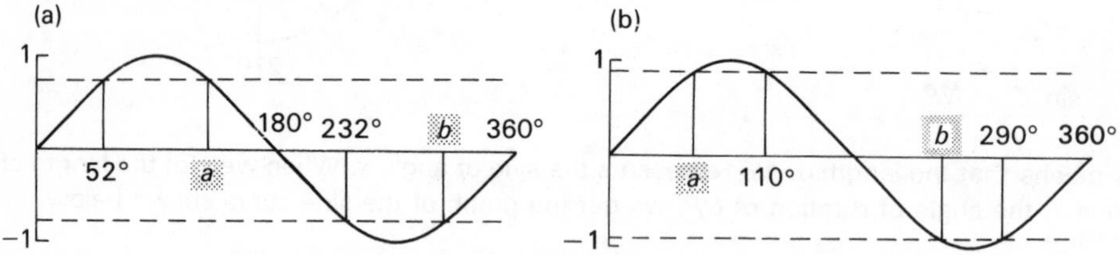

4 For each of the following find two replacements for x between 0 and 360.

(a) $\sin x° = 0.866$ (b) $\sin x° = 0.906$ (c) $\sin x° = 0.342$
(d) $\sin x° = -0.707$ (e) $\sin x° = -0.719$ (f) $\sin x° = 0.956$
(g) $\sin x° = -0.574$ (h) $\sin x° = 0.259$ (i) $\sin x° = -0.777$

Continue with Section B

B Cosine function

The circle has a radius of 1 unit
i.e. $OP = 1$ unit.

In the right-angled triangle ONP

$$\cos x° = \frac{ON}{OP}$$

$$= \frac{ON}{1}$$

So $\cos x° = ON$

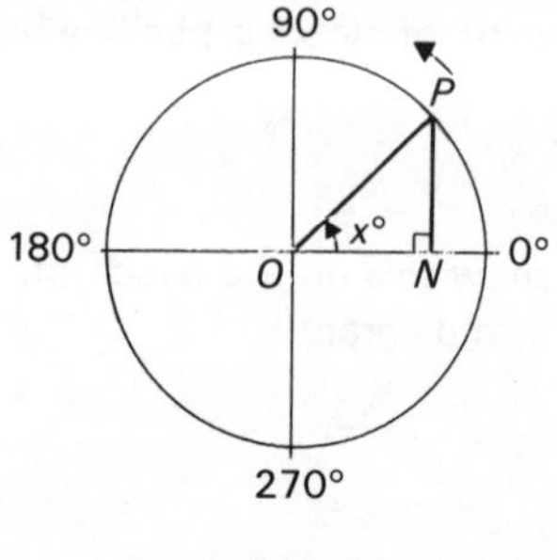

The length of ON represents the cosine of angle x.

If ON lies to the **right of centre** its length is taken to be **positive**.

If ON lies to the **left of centre** its length is taken to be **negative**.

The radius OP of the circle is always positive. Let P rotate in the direction of the arrow.

At the start, $x = 0°$, P and N coincide, so $ON = OP$.

$$\cos 0° = \frac{ON}{OP} = \frac{1}{1} = 1$$

$$\cos 0° = 1$$

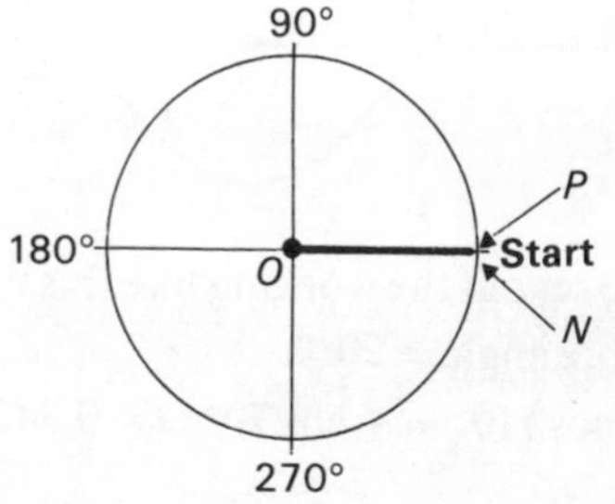

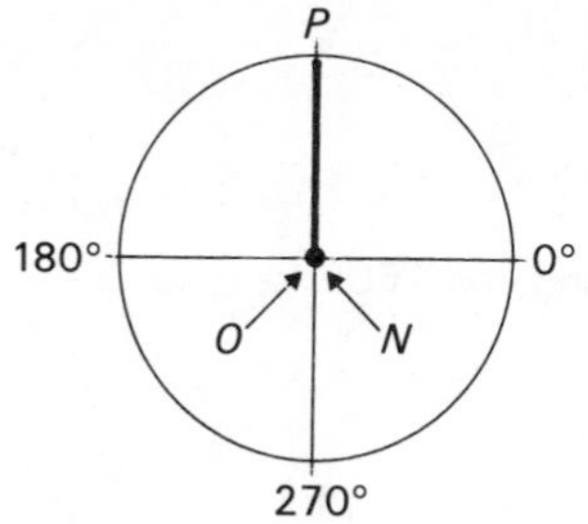

When $x = 90°$, O and N coincide so $ON = O$.

$$\cos 90° = \frac{ON}{OP} = \frac{0}{1} = 0$$

$$\cos 90° = 0$$

When $x = 180°$, P and N coincide, so $-ON = OP$ (ON lies to the **left** of O, in the **negative** direction).

$$\cos 180° = \frac{-ON}{OP} = \frac{-1}{1} = -1.$$

$$\cos 180° = -1$$

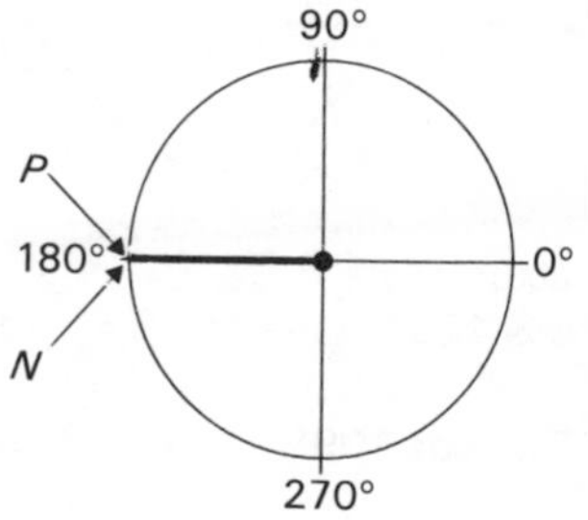

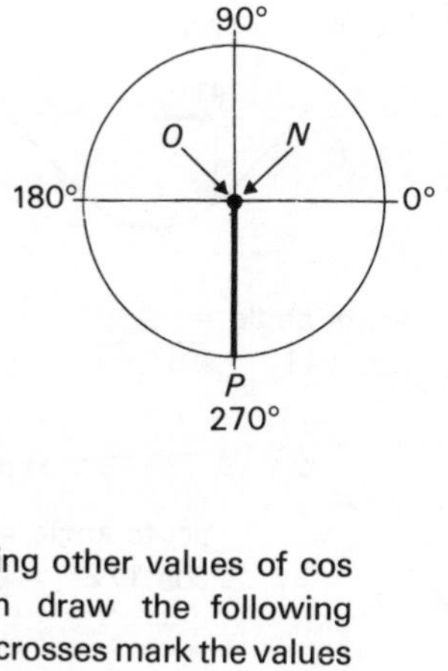

When $x = 270°$, O and N coincide so $ON = 0$

$$\cos 270° = \frac{ON}{OP} = \frac{0}{1} = 0$$

$$\cos 270° = 0$$

By calculating other values of $\cos x°$ we can draw the following graph. The crosses mark the values calculated above.

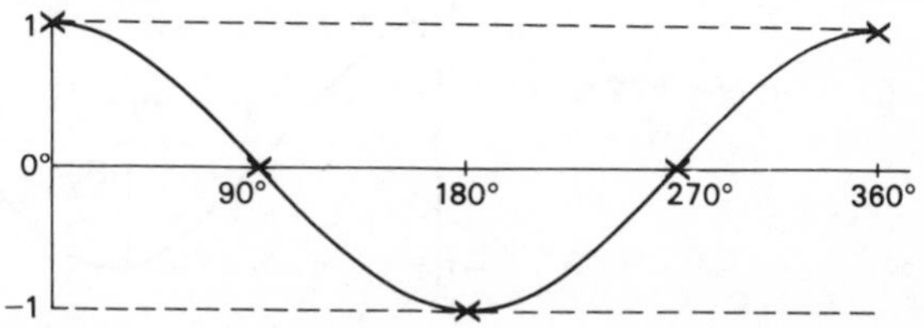

Example

To find cos 110° (you need tables of cosines).

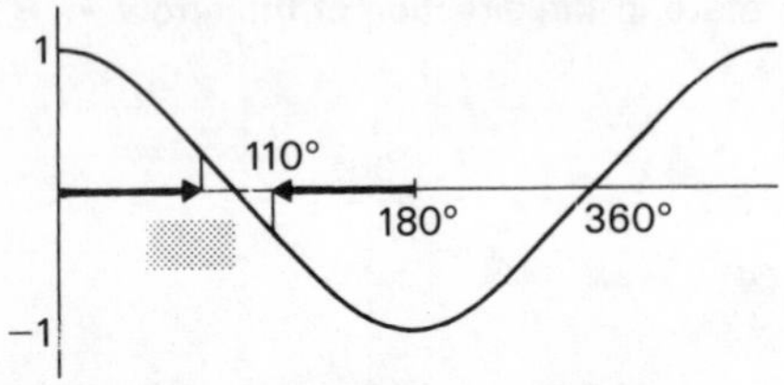

Look at this sketch of the cosine curve. 110° is 70° less than 180°, so cos 110° has the same numerical value as cos 70°, but is **negative.**

We set out the working like this:
acute angle = 70°
so cos 110° = −cos 70° = −0.342 ← Use your tables to check that cos 70° = 0.342

Exercise

In each question copy and complete the working.

1 Find cos 125°.

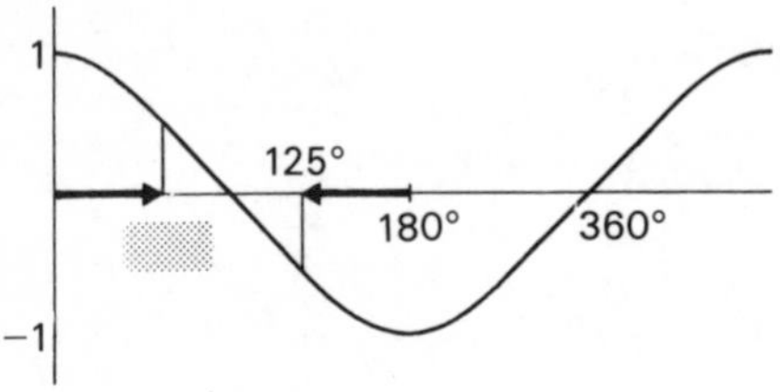

acute angle = □
cos 125° = −cos □ = − □

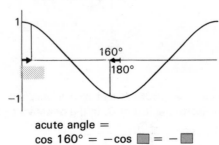

2 Find cos 160°.

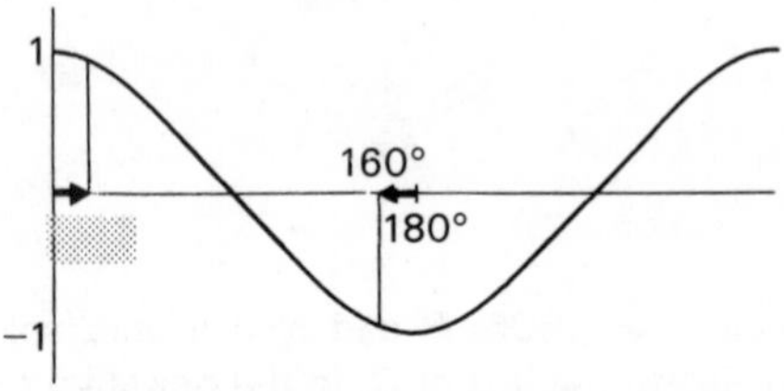

acute angle =
cos 160° = −cos □ = − □

3 Find cos 109°.

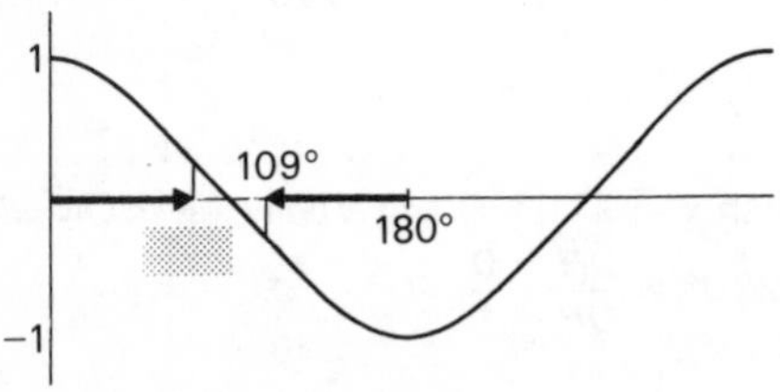

acute angle = □
cos 109° = □

4 Find cos 141°.

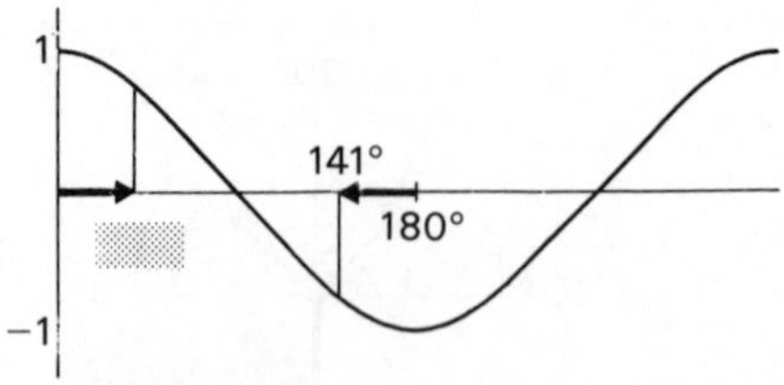

acute angle = □
cos 141° = □

5 Find cos 172°.

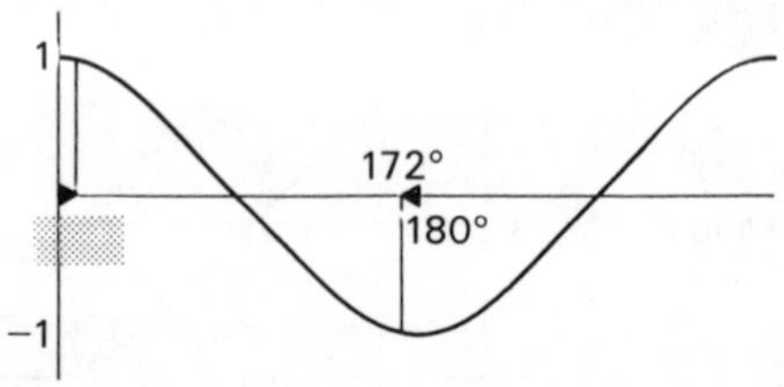

acute angle = □
cos 172° = □

Example

To find cos 205°.

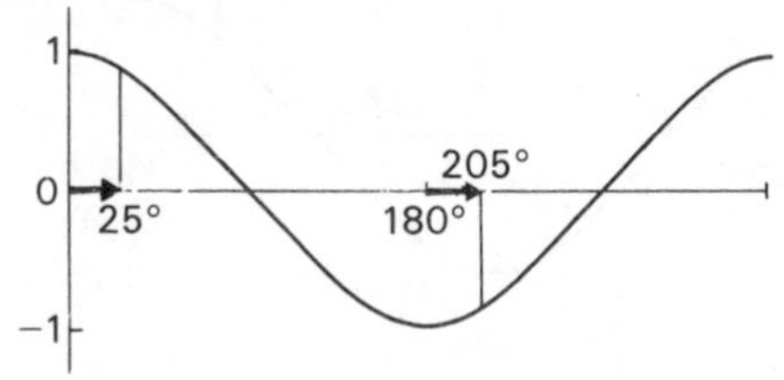

Look at the diagram. 205° is 25° more than 180°, so cos 205° has the same numerical value as cos 25° but is **negative.**

So cos 205° = −cos 25° = −0.906.

Exercise

In each question copy and complete the working.

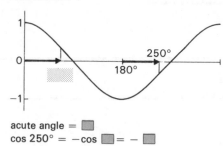

6 Find cos 250°.

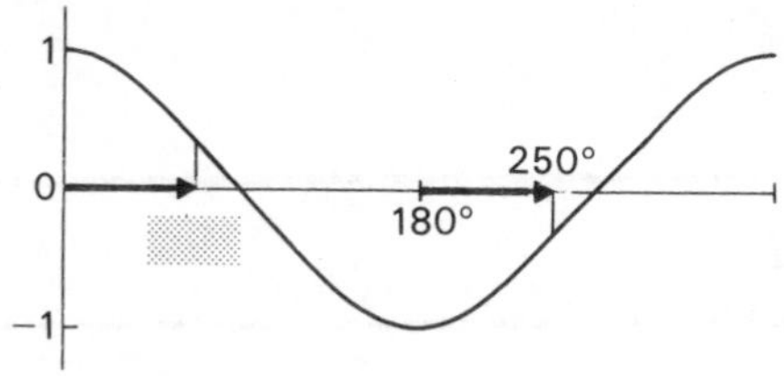

acute angle = ▢
cos 250° = −cos ▢ = − ▢

7 Find cos 242°.

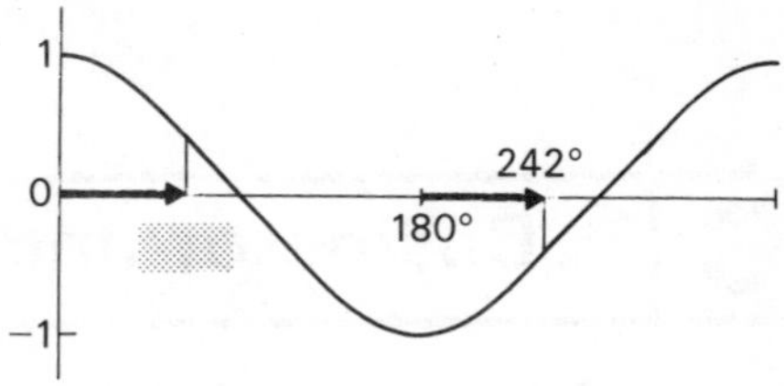

acute angle = ▢
cos 242° = −cos ▢ = ▢

8 Find cos 198°.

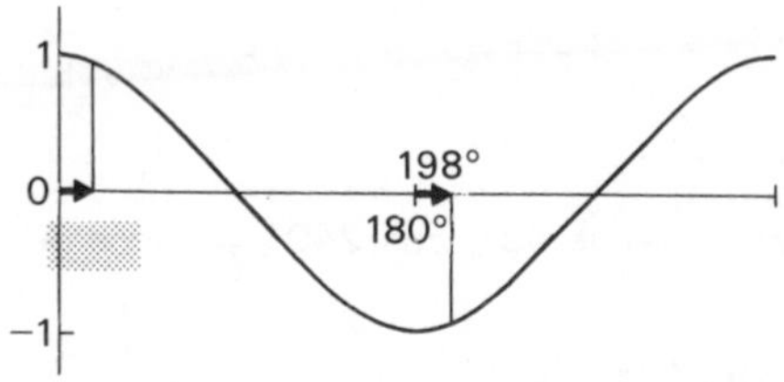

acute angle = ▢
cos 198° = ▢

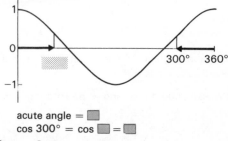

9 Find cos 300°.

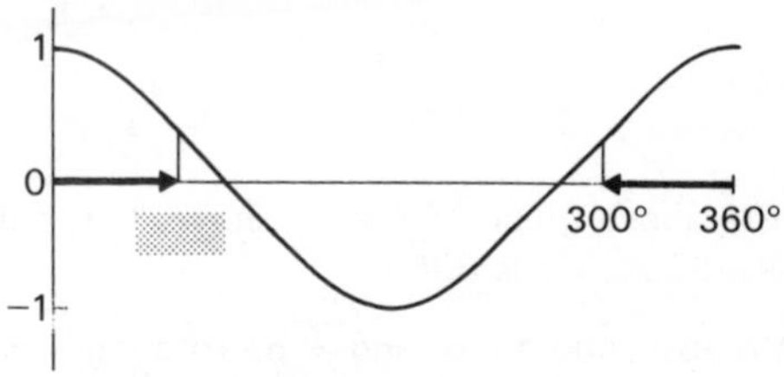

acute angle = ▢
cos 300° = cos ▢ = ▢

Note: Cosines of angles greater than 270° and less than 360° have **positive** values.

10 Find cos 312°.

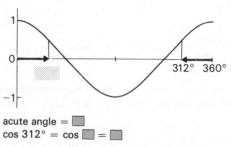

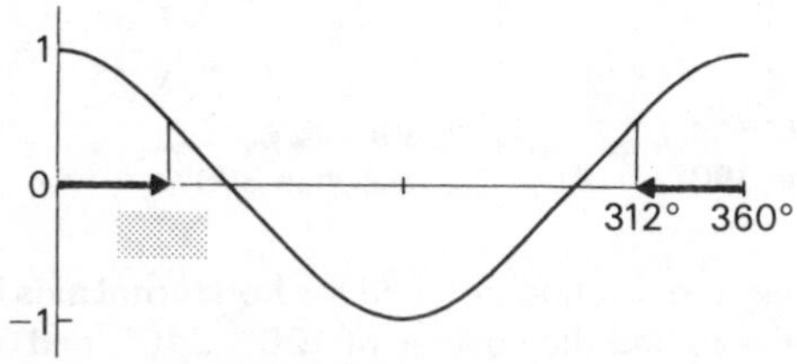

acute angle = ▢
cos 312° = cos ▢ = ▢

11 Find cos 348°.

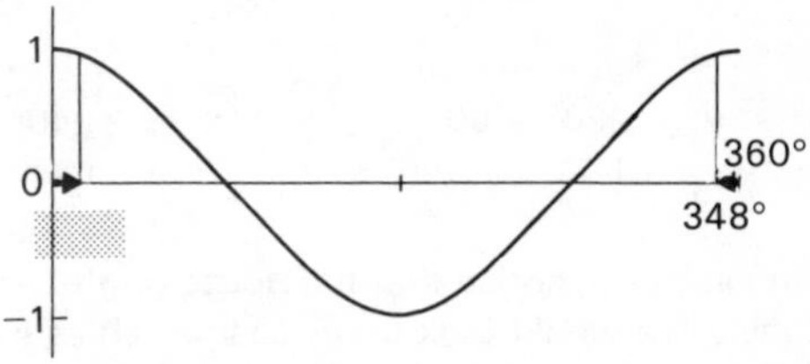

acute angle = ▢
cos 348° = ▢

Example

To find cos 234°.

Draw a sketch of the cosine curve, mark the angle 234°.

The corresponding *acute* angle is 54°.

So cos 234° = −cos 54° = −0.588.

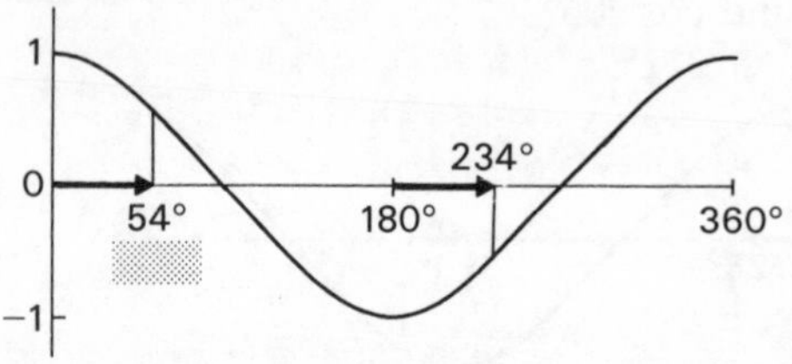

Exercise

For each of the following, draw a sketch and then find the value as shown above.

12 cos 131° **13** cos 197° **14** cos 294°

Continue with Section C

C Cosine of angles

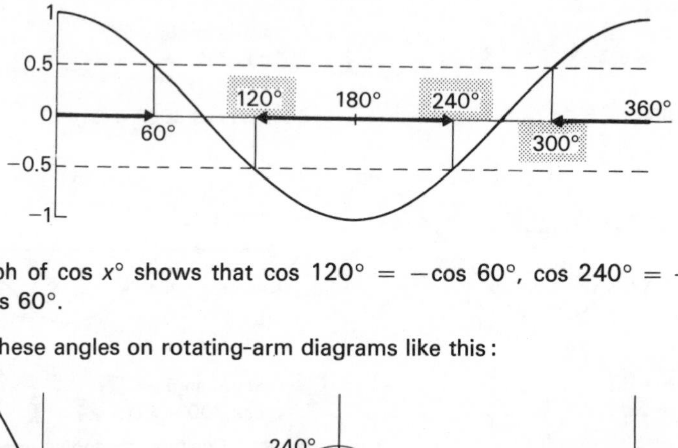

The above graph of cos x° shows that cos 120° = −cos 60°, cos 240° = −cos 60°, and cos 300° = cos 60°.

We can show these angles on rotating-arm diagrams like this:

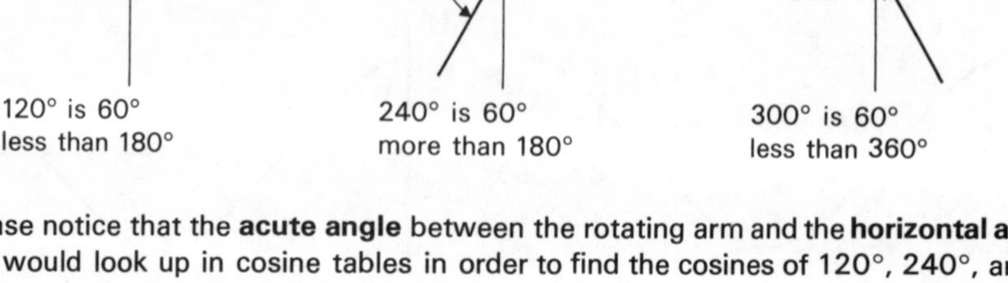

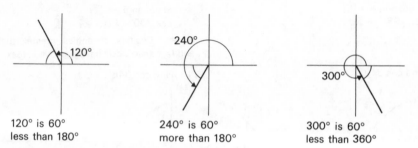

120° is 60° less than 180°

240° is 60° more than 180°

300° is 60° less than 360°

In each case notice that the **acute angle** between the rotating arm and the **horizontal axis** is the angle we would look up in cosine tables in order to find the cosines of 120°, 240°, and 300°.

Look at the graph of cos $x°$ again.

If x is between 0 and 90 then cos $x°$ is **positive**.

If x is between 90 and 270 then cos $x°$ is **negative**.

If x is between 270 and 360 then cos $x°$ is **positive**.

It is useful to show this on a diagram.

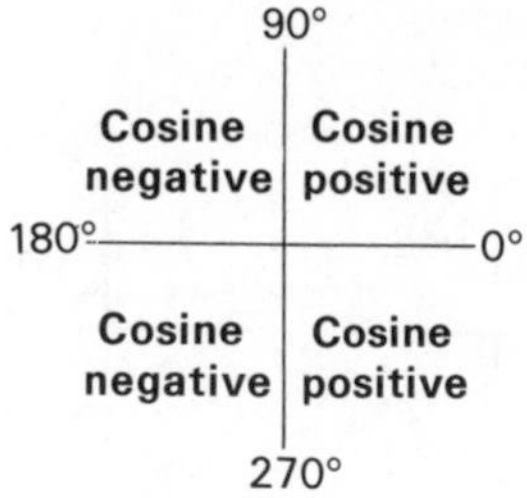

We are now ready to find the cosines of angles using this diagram.

Example

To find cos 160°.

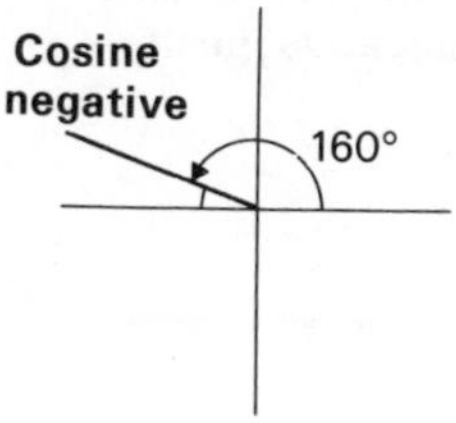

Draw a rotating-arm diagram for 160°.

Beside the rotating arm write whether cosine is **positive** or **negative** in this position.

Write down the acute angle between the arm and the horizontal:

acute angle = 20°
so cos 160° = −cos 20° = −0.940

Exercise

1 Find cos 235°. Copy the diagram. Copy and complete the working.

acute angle = □
so cos 235° = −cos □ = −□

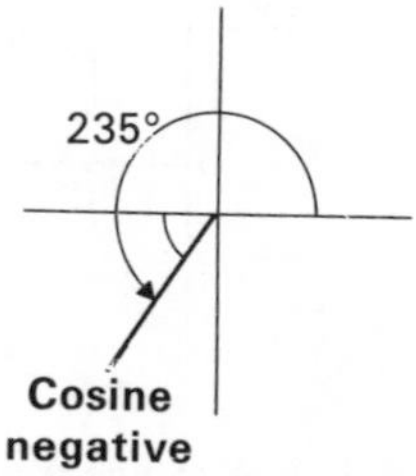

For each of the following draw a diagram and write the working as above, to find the value of the cosine of the angle.

2 170°	**3** 350°	**4** 230°	**5** 155°
6 305°	**7** 201°	**8** 117°	**9** 342°

From the graph of cos $x°$ we can read off some 'special' angles.

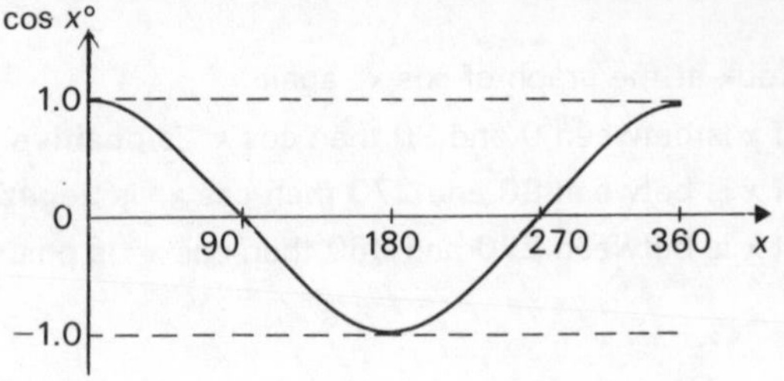

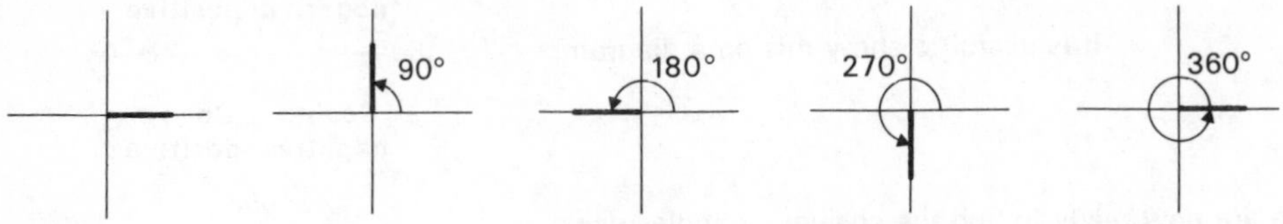

cos 0° = 1   cos 90° = 0   cos 180° = −1   cos 270° = 0   cos 360° = 1

Notice that the least value of cos $x°$ is -1 and the greatest value is $+1$.

We can summarize all this in a diagram:

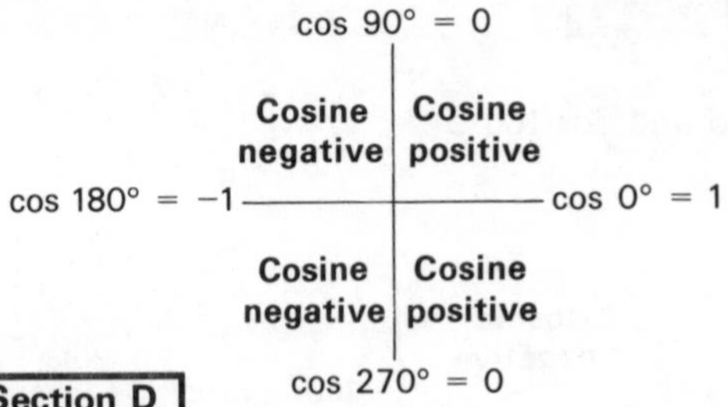

Continue with Section D

D Find the angle

If we have to find values of x for which cos $x° = 0.866$, we can use the graph of cos $x°$ to show that $x = 30$ or 330.

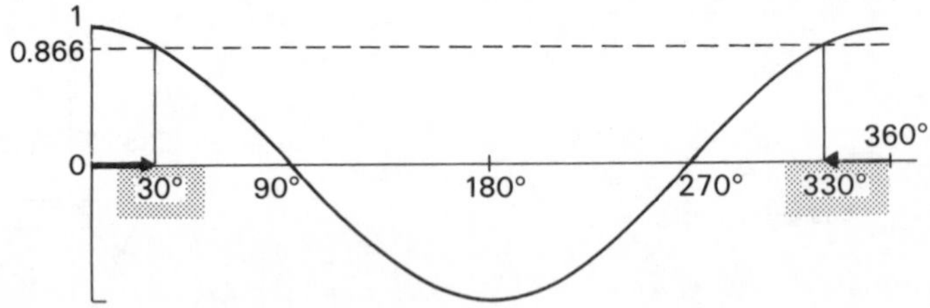

Another method is to use a rotating-arm diagram.

Example

Find values of x such that cos $x° = 0.866$.

The cosine is **positive** so the rotating arm must lie to the **right** of the vertical axis.

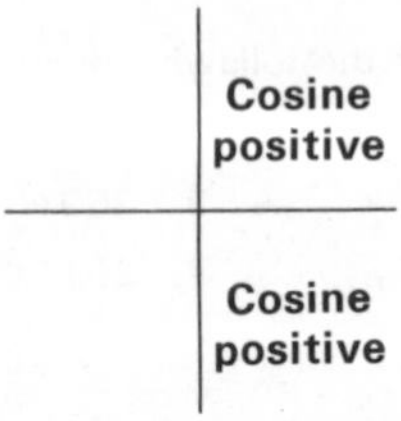

From tables, the acute angle whose cosine is 0.866 is 30°.

In the regions where the cosine is positive mark two positions of the arm which make 30° angles with the horizontal.

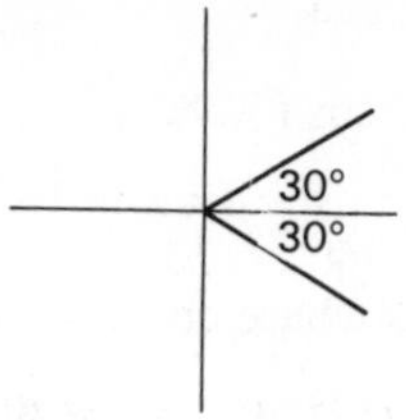

So the rotating arm has turned through 30° or (360° − 30°).

So x = 30 or 330.

Exercise

1 Find values of x such that $\cos x° = -0.423$. Copy the diagram.

Copy and complete the working.

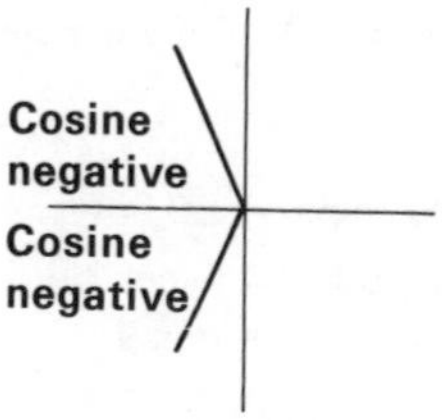

$\cos x° = -0.423$

Acute angle = 65° ← from tables

So x = (180 − ▢) or (180 + ▢)

= ▢ or ▢

For each of the following draw a diagram write out the working as above, and find the values of x.

2 $\cos x° = 0.940$	**3** $\cos x° = -0.866$	**4** $\cos x° = 0.777$
5 $\cos x° = 0.530$	**6** $\cos x° = -0.375$	**7** $\cos x° = 0.574$
8 $\cos x° = 0.966$	**9** $\cos x° = -0.829$	**10** $\cos x° = 0.636$

Continue with Section E

E Negative angles

The graph of $\cos x°$ can be extended to include negative angles and angles greater than 360°.

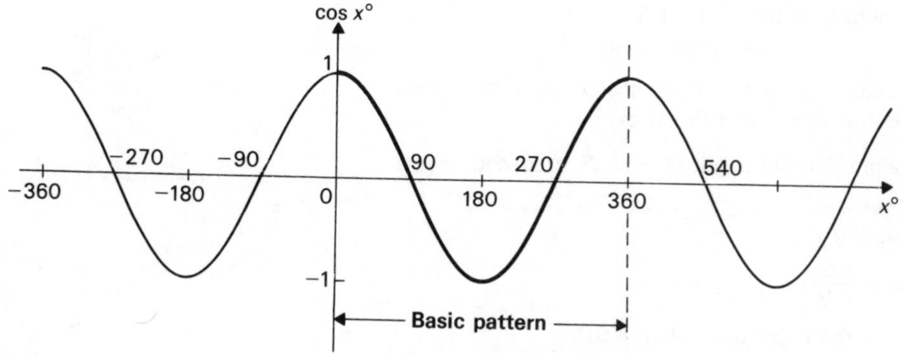

The **period** of $\cos x°$ is 360°, so its values are repeated every 360°.

Example

To find cos (−380°).

−380° is drawn *clockwise* from the start 380° = 360° + 20°, so arm is 20° from the horizontal and lies where cosine is positive.

So cos (−380°) = cos 20° = 0.940.

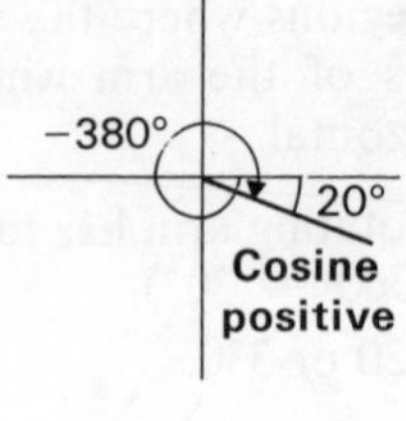

Exercise

1 Find cos 500°. Copy the diagram. Copy and complete the working.

Acute angle = ▢
So cos 500° = −cos ▢
= −▢

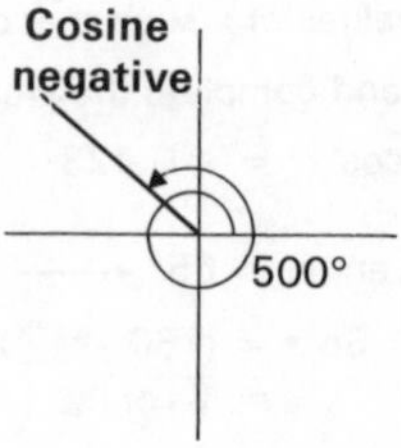

For each of the following draw a diagram and write the working as above, to find the value of the cosine of the angle.

2 −430° **3** 400° **4** −390° **5** −615°

Draw diagrams and find the values of the following without using tables.

6 cos 1080° **7** cos (−900°)

Continue with Section F

F Tangent function

In the diagram the radius of the circle is 1 unit, i.e. *ON* = 1.

AB is a tangent to the circle at *N*:

Angle *ONB* = 90°

P is a point on the circumference of the circle which rotates in the direction of the arrow.

The straight line through *O* and *P* produced meets *AB* at *Q*.

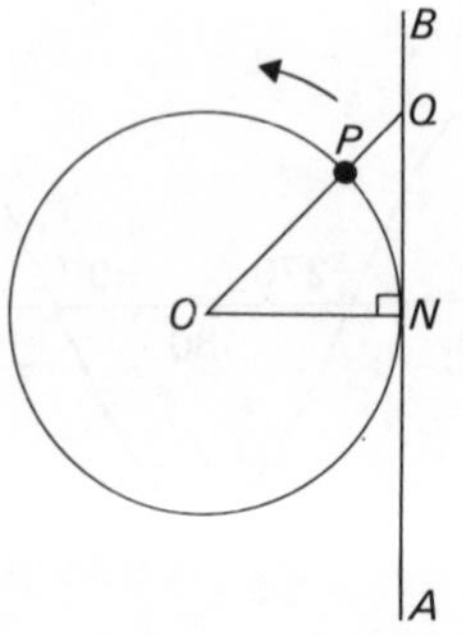

In triangle *ONQ*:

$$\tan N\hat{O}Q = \frac{NQ}{ON} = \frac{NQ}{1} = NQ$$

let $x°$ = the angle of rotation $N\hat{O}Q$.
$\tan x° = NQ$

The length of *NQ* is numerically equal to the tangent of angle *x*.

First we examine the tangent of certain angles of rotation.

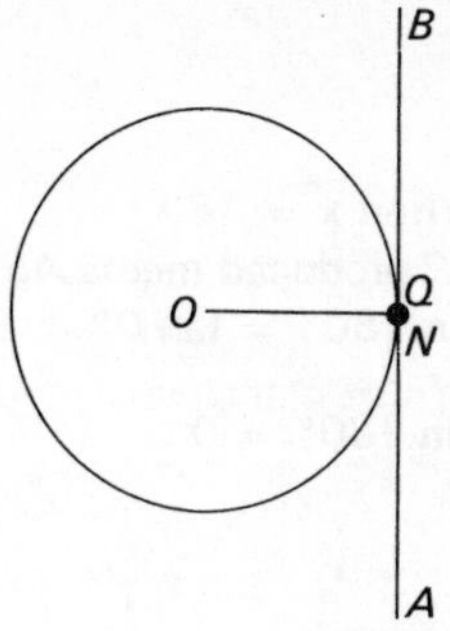

When $x = 0$, N and Q concide and $NQ = 0$.

$$\tan 0° = \frac{NQ}{ON} = \frac{0}{1} = 0$$

$\tan 0° = 0$

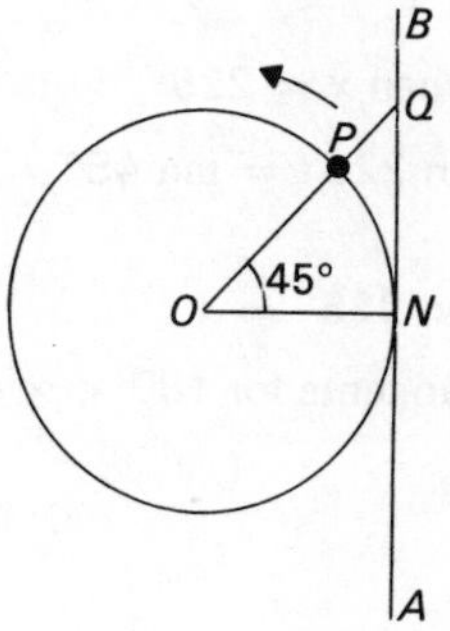

When $x = 45°$

$$\tan 45° = \frac{NQ}{ON} = \frac{NQ}{1} = NQ = 1.00$$

$\tan 45° = 1$

Values of NQ **above** the starting level are taken to be **positive**, so tangents of angles for $0 < x < 90$ are positive.

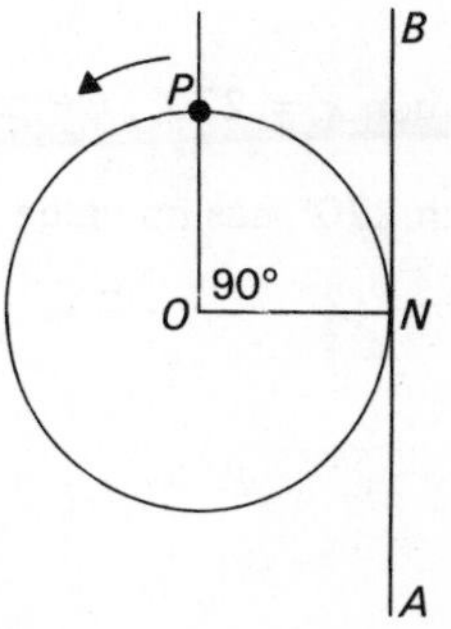

When $x = 90°$, OP is parallel to AB, so OP produced does not meet AB.

tan 90° does not have a value.

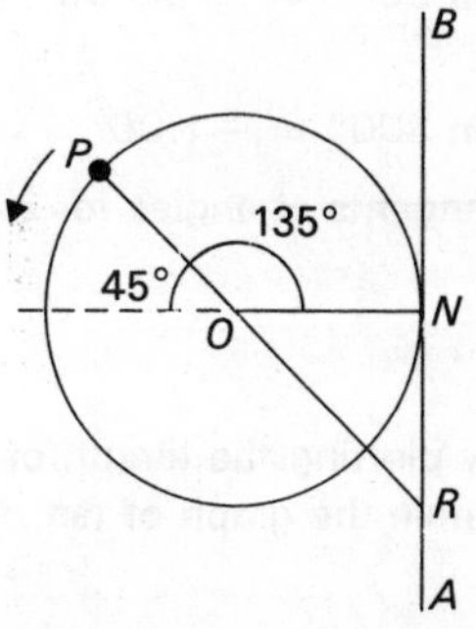

When $x = 135°$

$\tan 135° = -\tan 45°$

(As before we consider the **acute** angle made with the horizontal.)

$$\tan 135° = -\frac{NR}{ON} = -\frac{NR}{1} = -1.00$$

$\tan 135° = -1$

Values of NR **below** the starting level are taken to be **negative**, so tangents of angles for $90 < x < 180$ are negative.

When x = 180
OP produced meets *AB* at *N*.
tan 180° = tan 0° = 0.

tan 180° = 0

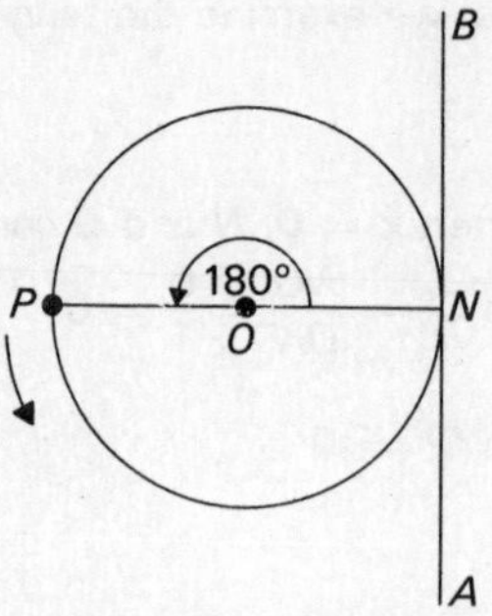

When $x = 225$

$$\tan 225° = \tan 45° = \frac{NQ}{ON} = \frac{NQ}{1} = NQ = 1.00$$

tan 225° = 1
Tangents for $180 < x < 270$ are **positive.**

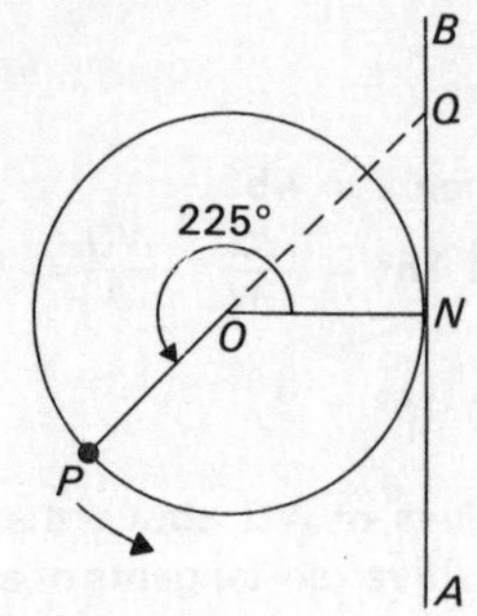

When $x = 270°$, *OP* produced is parallel to *AB*.

tan 270° has no value

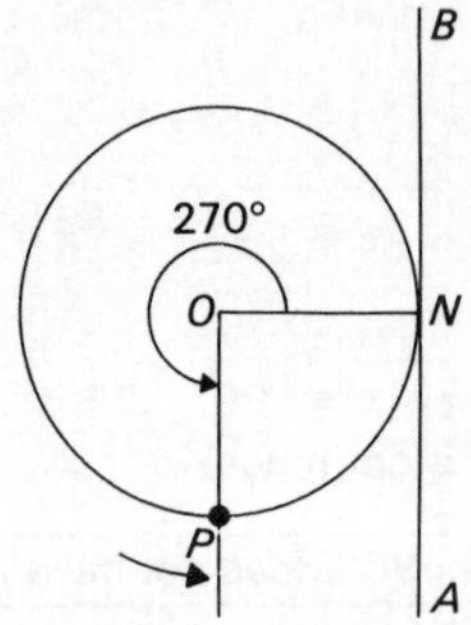

When $x = 315°$

$$\tan 300° = -\tan 45° = \frac{-NR}{ON} = \frac{-NR}{1} = -NR = -1.00$$

tan 300° = −1.00
Tangents of angles for $270 < x < 360$ are **negative.**

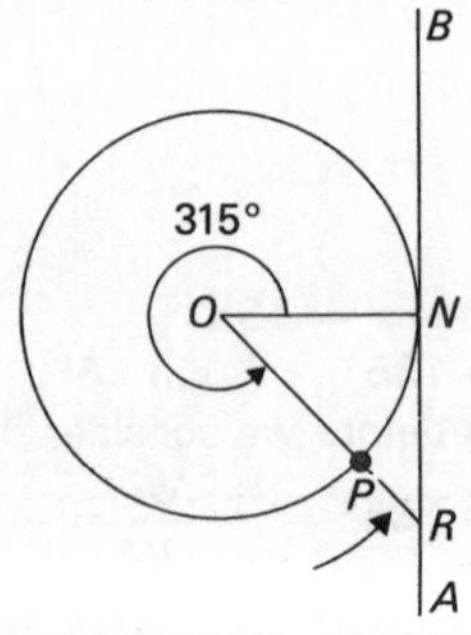

By plotting the length of *NQ* (or of *NR* for negative values) against the angle of rotation, $x°$, we obtain the graph of tan $x°$.

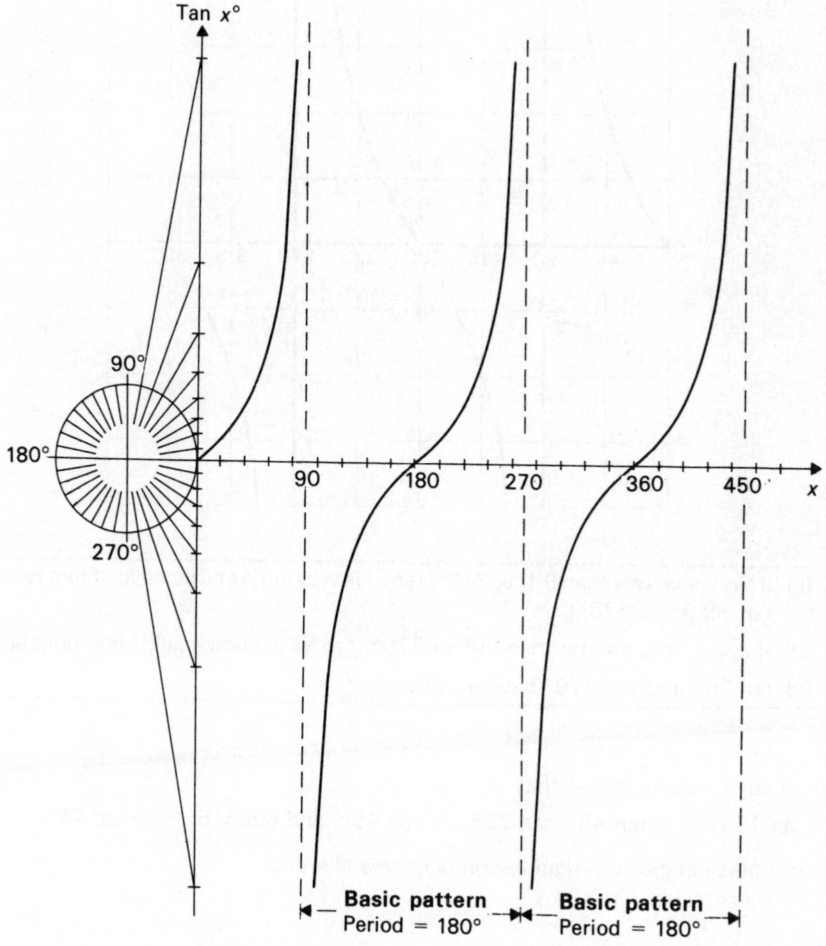

Note: (a) The graph repeats every 180°, its **period is 180°**.

(b) The tangent curve has breaks at 90° and 270°, at these angles we say that the graph is **discontinuous**. There are no values for tan 90° and tan 270°.

The following graph of tan $x°$ was drawn by using values from a table of tangents.

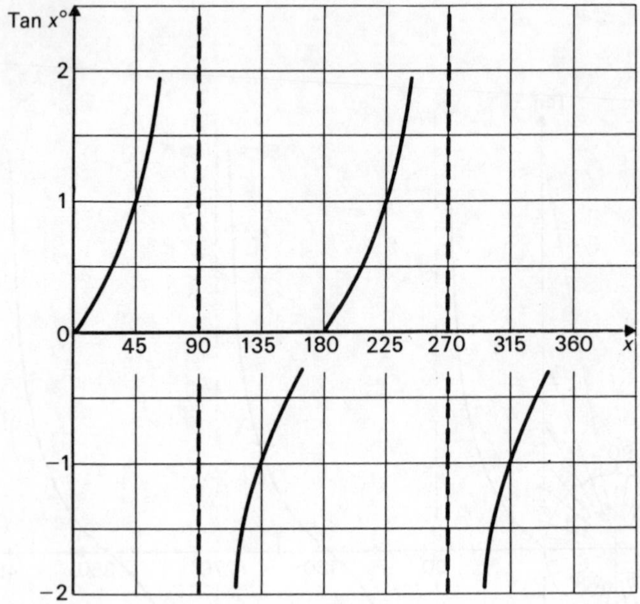

Note: (a) If x is a little less than 90° or 270°, tan $x°$ is very large and positive. (From tables, tan 89.9° = 573).

(b) If x is a little greater than 90° or 270°, tan $x°$ is numerically large but negative.

(c) tan 90° and tan 279° have no value.

The graph of tan $x°$ above shows that

$$\tan 135° = -\tan 45°, \ \tan 225° = \tan 45°, \text{ and } \tan 315° = -\tan 45°.$$

We can show these angles on rotating-arm diagrams like this:

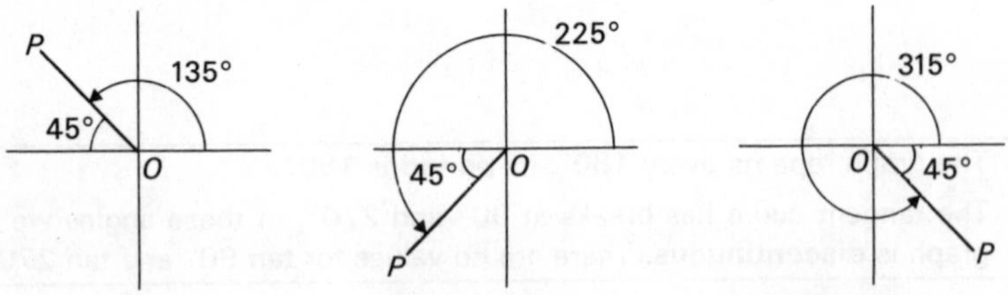

135° is 45° less than 180°

225° is 45° more than 180°

315° is 45° less than 360°

In each case, the **acute angle** between the rotating arm and the **horizontal axis** is the angle we would look up in tangent tables in order to find the tangents of 135°, 225°, and 315°.

Look at the graph of tan $x°$ again.

If x is between 0 and 90, then tan $x°$ is **positive.**
If x is between 90 and 180 then tan $x°$ is **negative.**
If x is between 180 and 270 then tan $x°$ is **positive.**
If x is between 270 and 360 then tan $x°$ is **negative.**

It is useful to show this on a diagram →

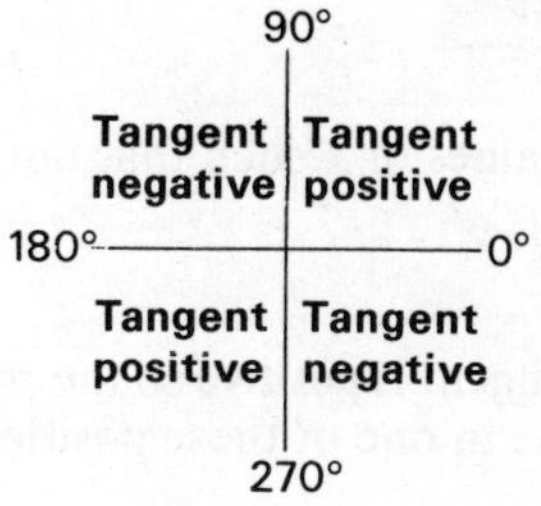

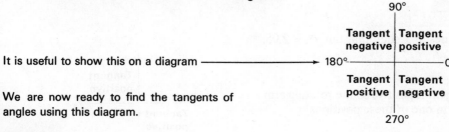

We are now ready to find the tangents of angles using this diagram.

Example

To find tan 160°.

Draw a rotating-arm diagram for 160°. Beside the rotating arm write whether tangent is **positive** or **negative** in this position.

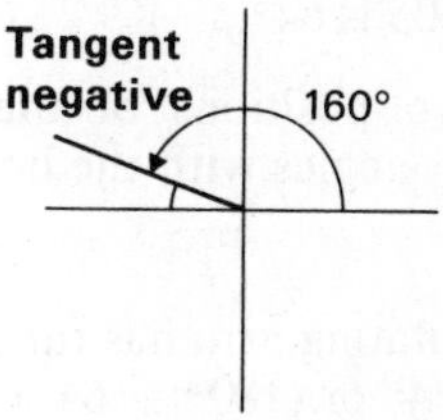

Write down the acute angle between the arm and the horizontal

acute angle $= 20°$
So tan 160° $= -\tan 20°$
$= -0.364$

Exercise

1 Find tan 300°. Copy the diagram. Copy and complete the working.

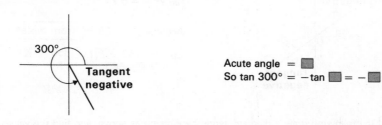

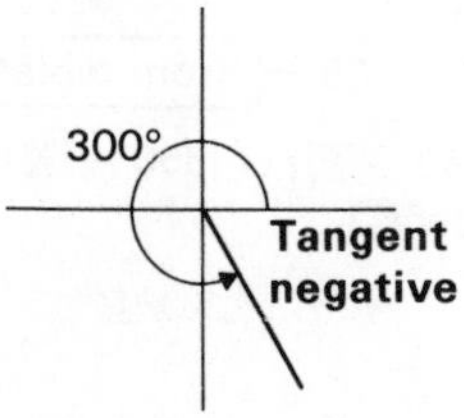

Acute angle = ■
So tan 300° = − tan ■ = − ■

For each of the following draw a diagram and write the working as above, to find the tangent of the angle.

2 290°	**3** 134°	**4** 201°	**5** 110°
6 350°	**7** 174°	**8** 183.5°	**9** 327.4°

Continue with Section G

G Tangents of angles

Example

Find values of x such that $\tan x° = 2.05$.

The tangent is **positive** so the rotating arm must lie in one of these positions

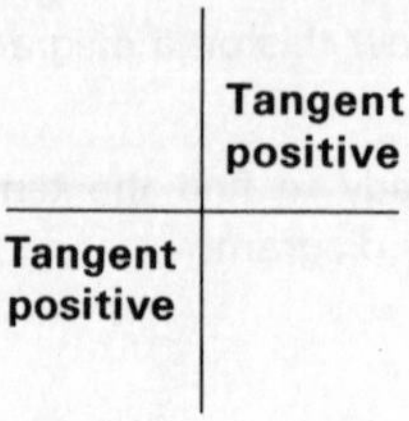

From tables the acute angle whose tangent is 2.05 is 64°.

Mark two positions of the arm which make 64° angles with the horizontal.

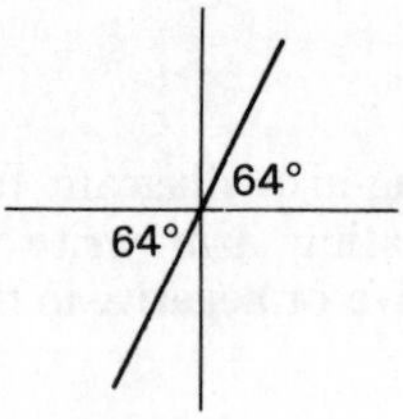

So the rotating arm has turned through
$64°$ or $(180° + 64°)$
So $x = 64$ or 244.

Exercise

1 Find the values of x such that $\tan x° = -0.7$. Copy the diagram. Copy and complete the working.

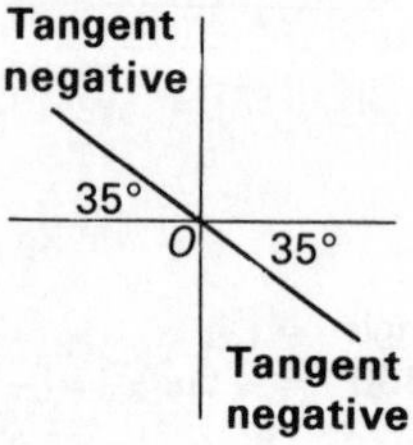

$\tan x° = -0.7$

Acute angle = 35° ← from tables

So $x = (180 - \square)$ or $(360 - \square)$
$= \square$ or $\square$

For each of the following draw a diagram, write the working as above, and find the values of x.

2 $\tan x° = -1.192$ **3** $\tan x° = 4.011$ **4** $\tan x° = 0.194$
5 $\tan x° = -0.296$ **6** $\tan x° = -1.45$ **7** $\tan x° = 5.005$

Continue with Section H

H Angles greater than 360°

The graph of tan $x°$ can be extended to include negative angles and angles greater than 360°.

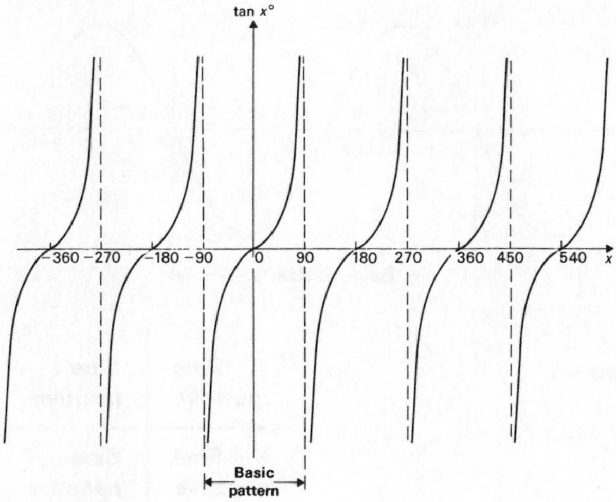

The **period** of tan $x°$ is 180°.

Example

To find tan (−430°).

−430° is drawn clockwise from the start. 430° = 360° + 70°, so arm is 70° from the horizontal and lies where tangent is negative.

So tan (−430°) = −tan 70° = −2.747.

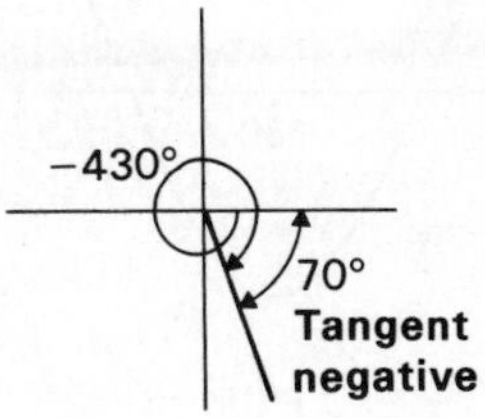

Exercise

1 Find tan (−130°). Copy the diagram. Copy and complete the working.

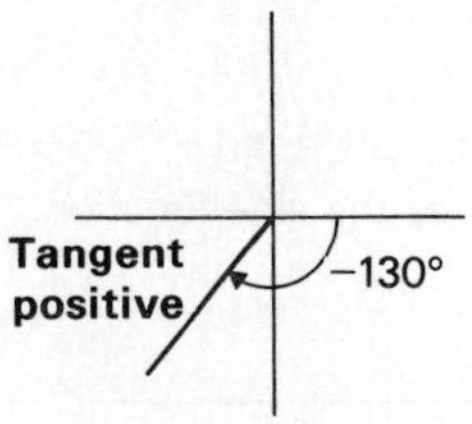

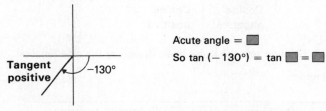

Acute angle = ▩
So tan (−130°) = tan ▩ = ▩

For each of the following draw a diagram and write the working as above, to find the value of the tangent of the angle.

2 500°	**3** 384°	**4** 672°	**5** −55°
6 −280°	**7** −300°	**8** −400°	**9** 700°

Continue with Section I

I Summary

Sine function

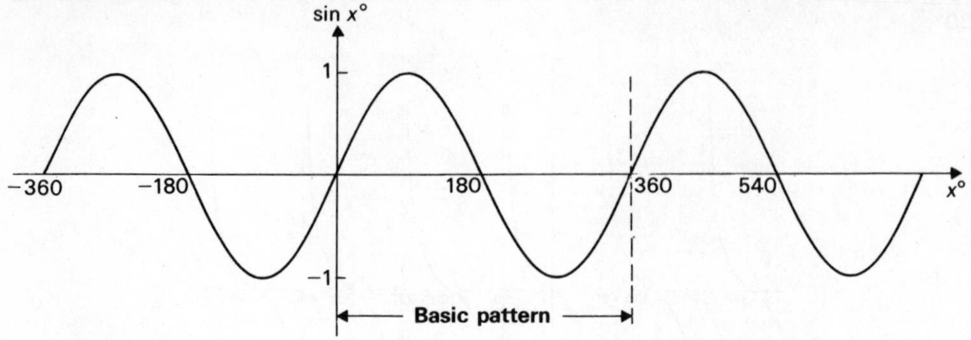

In a rotating-arm diagram

Sine positive	**Sine positive**
Sine negative	**Sine negative**

Cosine function

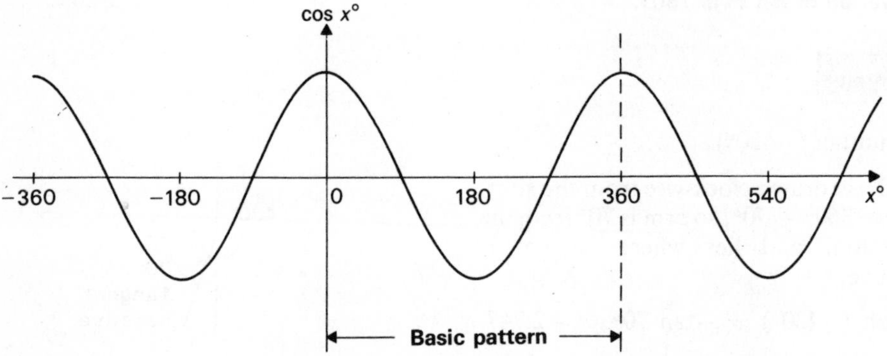

In a rotating-arm diagram

Cosine negative	**Cosine positive**
Cosine negative	**Cosine positive**

Notice that the cosine function has the same basic design as the sine function.

In a rotating-arm diagram,

0° to 90° is called the **first quadrant** **90° to 180°** is called the **second quadrant**	**Second quadrant**	**First quadrant**
180° to 270° is called the **third quadrant** **270° to 360°** is called the **fourth quadrant**	**Third quadrant**	**Fourth quadrant**

Tangent function

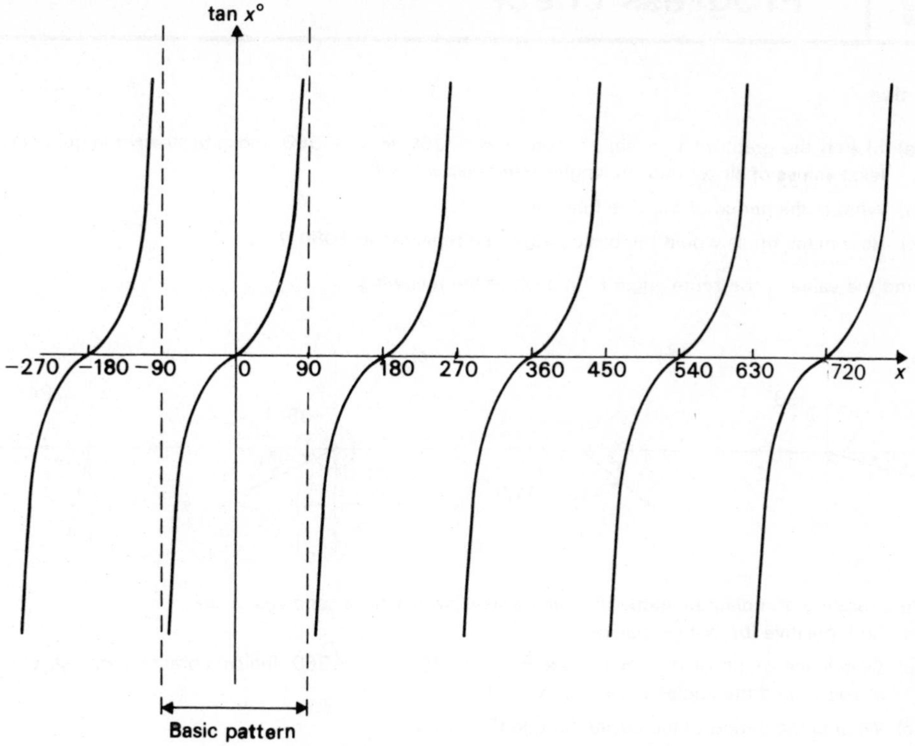

In a rotating-arm diagram

Tangent negative	**Tangent positive**
Tangent positive	**Tangent negative**

We can combine the diagrams for the three trigometric functions in one diagram like this:

in the 2nd quadrant only the **sine** is positive (the other two are negative)

in the 1st quadrant **all** three trigonometric functions are positive

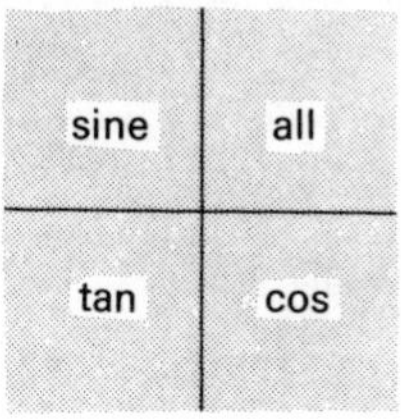

in the 3rd quadrant only the **tangent** is positive

in the 4th quadrant only the **cosine** is positive.

Exercise

1 Find the value of each of the following:

(a) sin 155° (b) cos 125° (c) tan 161° (d) tan 219°
(e) cos 303° (f) sin 450° (g) cos (−320°)

2 Find values of x between 0 and 360 such that

(a) $\sin x° = 0.259$ (b) $\cos x° = -0.940$ (c) $\tan x° = 0.510$

Continue with Section J

J Progress check

Exercise

1 (a) Sketch the graph of $y = \sin x°$ from $x = -360$ to $x = 360$. Indicate clearly the greatest and least values of $\sin x°$ and the angles where $\sin x° = 0$.

(b) What is the period of the sine function?

(c) How many times would the basic pattern be repeated in 1080°?

2 Find the value of the acute angle $x°$ in each of the following

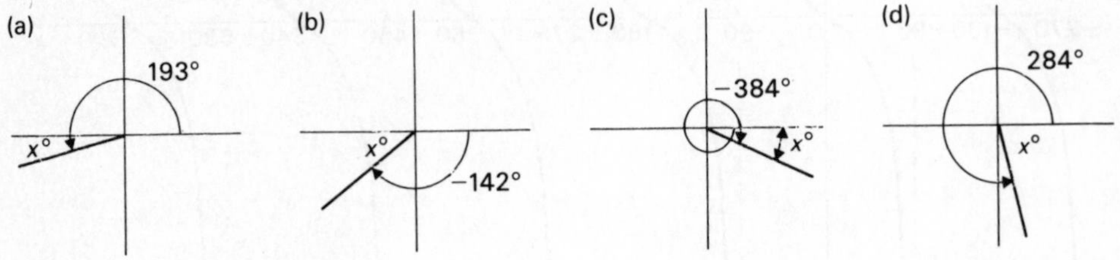

3 In a rotating-arm diagram name the quadrants in which $\sin x°$ and $\cos x°$ are
(a) both positive (b) both negative.

4 (a) Sketch the graph of $y = \cos x°$ from $x = -360$ to $x = 360$. Indicate greatest and least values of $\cos x°$ and the angles where $\cos x° = 0$.

(b) What is the period of the cosine function?

5 (a) Find cos 165°. (b) Find cos 220°. (c) Find cos 304°.

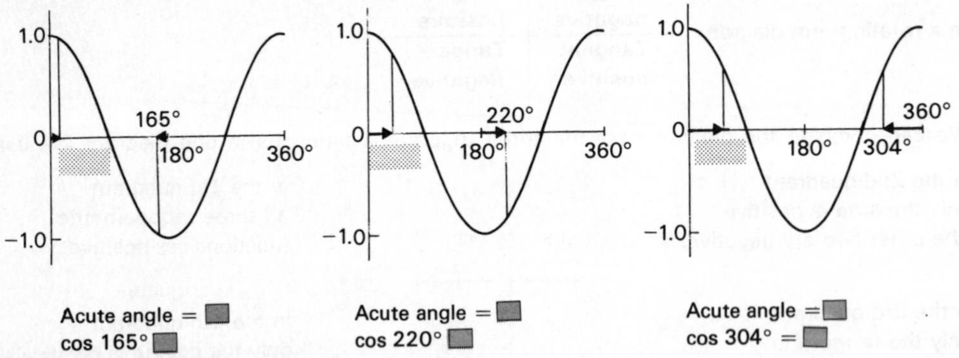

6 Obtain values for the following:

(a) cos 280° (b) sin −200° (c) cos −130°
(d) cos 43° (e) sin 180° (f) sin 655°.

7 Sketch the graph of $\tan x°$ from $x = -90$ to $x = 90$.

(b) What is the period of the tangent function?

8 Obtain values for the following:

(a) tan 74° (b) tan 153° (c) tan 189°
(d) tan −112° (e) tan −384° (f) tan 800°

9 For each of the following, find two values of x between 0 and 360 which satisfy each equation:

(a) $\sin x^\circ = 0.853$ (b) $\sin x^\circ = -0.549$

(c) $\tan x^\circ = 0.807$ (d) $\tan x^\circ = -2.539$

(e) $\cos x^\circ = 0.418$ (f) $\cos x^\circ = -0.292$.

Ask your teacher what to do next

K Combining graphs

For many applications of mathematics it is necessary to draw the graph obtained by combining the graphs of two or more functions.

The following example illustrates one method.

Example

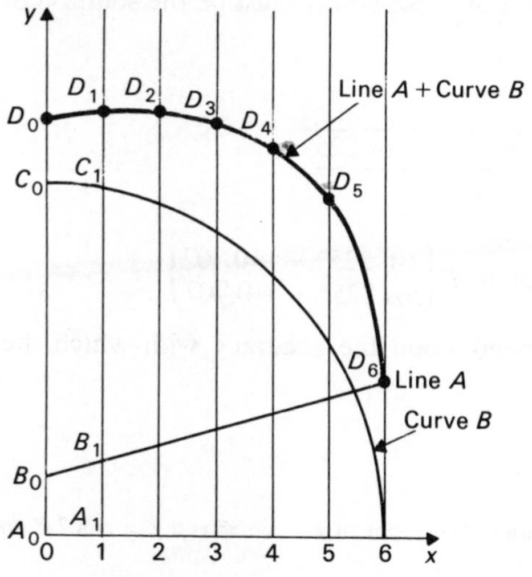

To draw the graph which represents Line A + Curve B.

(a) Draw the graphs of the functions using the same axes (see diagram).

(b) By means of a pair of compasses or dividers add the corresponding y values (or ordinates) of each function.

At $x = 0$

Set compasses to the length A_0B_0 (A_0B_0 is the ordinate of line A at $x = 0$). Transfer this setting to C_0 and mark point D_0.

At $x = 1$

Set compasses to A_1B_1. Transfer this setting to C_1 and mark the point D_1.

Repeat the process for $x = 2, 3, 4, 5$, and 6. (*Note*: At $x = 6$ the ordinate of curve B is zero.) Draw a smooth curve through the points $D_0, D_1, D_2 \ldots, D_6$.

This curve is the graph of Line A + Curve B.

Continue with Sheet M12/1

L Graphical solutions of trigonometrical equations

Example

Find the values of x between 0 and 360 for which $\sin x° = \cos x°$.

Draw the graphs of $y = \sin x$ and $y = \cos x$ on the same axis.

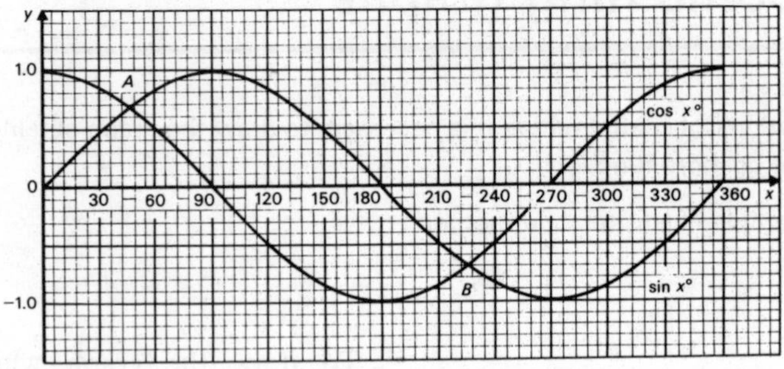

The curves intersect at A and B. The value of x at these points must be the solution of equation $\sin x° = \cos x°$.

At point A, $x = 45$ and at point B, $x = 225$.

So $\sin x° = \cos x°$ when $x = 45$ or 225.

Tables of sines and cosines give the following

For point $A\begin{cases} \sin 45° = 0.707 \\ \cos 45° = 0.707 \end{cases}$ and hence, for point $B\begin{cases} \sin 225° = -0.707 \\ \cos 225° = -0.707 \end{cases}$.

Note that solutions obtained graphically depend upon the accuracy with which the graphs are drawn.

Exercise

(Use 2 mm squared paper)

1 Copy and complete the following table and then draw the graphs of $y = \sin x°$ and $y = \cos 2x°$ on the same axes for $0 \le x \le 90$.
(**Scales**: Vertical: 4 cm = 1 unit: horizontal: 1 cm = 10°).

x	0	10	20	30	40	50	60	70	80	90
$2x$	0	20	40				120			180
$\sin x°$	0	0.17	0.34				0.87			1.0
$\cos 2x°$	1	0.94	0.77				−0.5			−1.0
$\sin x° + \cos 2x°$	1	1.11	1.11				0.37			0.0

(a) From the graph find a value for x such that $\sin x° = \cos 2x°$.

(b) Draw the graph of $\sin x° + \cos 2x°$ on the same axes.
(i) What is the maximum value of $\sin x° + \cos 2x°$?
(ii) Find a value of x for which $\sin x° + \cos 2x° = 0.6$.

Example

Find graphically an approximate solution of the equation $\sin x° + \cos 2x° = \frac{x}{10}$ which lies between $x = 0$ and $x = 90$.

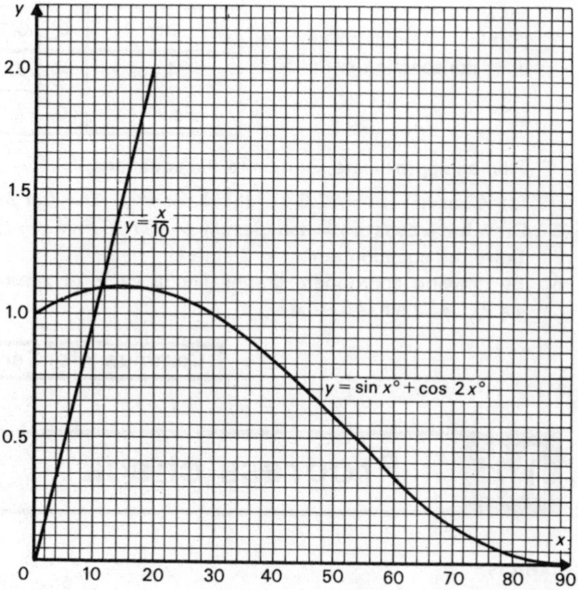

Step 1

Draw the graph of $y = \sin x° + \cos 2x°$.

Step 2

Using the same scales and axes draw the graph of $y = \frac{x}{10}$.

(When $x = 0, y = 0$; when $x = 20$, $y = 2$. The graph is the straight line joining the points $(0,0)$ and $(20, 2)$.) This is shown in the figure.

The solution of the equation $\sin x° + \cos 2x° = \frac{x}{10}$ is the value of x where the straight line and the curve intersect.

From the graph $x \simeq 11$.

Check this answer by substitution in the equation $\sin x° + \cos 2x° = \frac{x}{10}$.

Exercise

From the graphs of $y = \frac{x}{30}$ and $y = 3 \sin x° - 5 \cos x°$ find approximate solutions to the following:

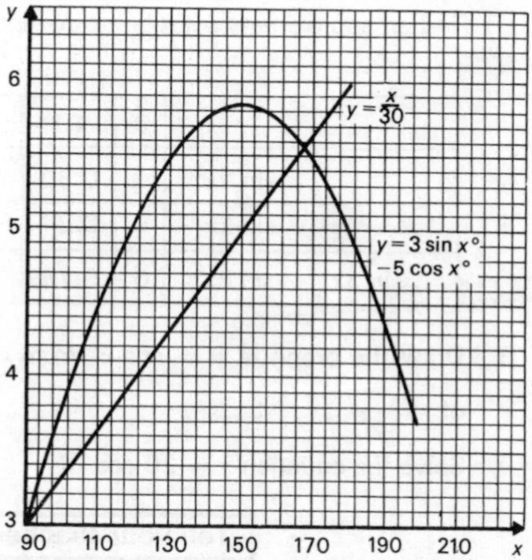

2 (a) $3 \sin x° - 5 \cos x° = 3.9$.

(b) $3 \sin x° = 3.9 + 5 \cos x°$

(c) $3 \sin x° = 5 \cos x° + 5.1$.

(d) $3 \sin x° - 5 \cos x° = \frac{x}{30}$.

3 Draw the graph of $y = \tan x°$ from $x = 0$ to $x = 60$; with the same axes and units draw the graph of $y = \frac{x}{40}$.

Solve the equation $x = 40 \tan x°$.

4 Copy and complete the tables below and draw the graphs of $y = \tan 2x°$ and $y = 4 \cos x° - 1$.
(**Scales**: Vertical: 2 cm = 1 unit; horizontal: 1 cm = 5°.)

x	0	5	10	15	20	25	30	35
$2x$	0	10	20					70
$\tan 2x°$	0	0.18	0.36					2.75
$4 \cos x°$	4	3.98	3.94					3.28
$4 \cos x° - 1$	3	2.98	2.94					2.28

Find an approximate solution to the equations
(a) $4 \cos x° - 1 = 2.6$ (b) $4 \cos x° - 1 = \tan 2x°$ (c) $\tan 2x° = 1.2$.

5 Draw the graphs of $y = \tan x°$ and $y = 2 \sin x°$ from $x = 0$ to $x = 70$.
Solve the equation $\tan x° = 2 \sin x°$.

6 By drawing appropriate graphs find a value of x between 0 and 30 which satisfies the equation $\sin 2x° = 2 \sin (45 - x)°$.

Continue with Section M

M Progress check

Exercise

1 Copy and complete the table below and draw the graphs of $y = \sin 2x°$ and $y = \sin 3x°$ on the same axes. Hence draw the graph of $y = \sin 2x° + \sin 3x°$.
(Use 2 mm squared paper. **Scales**: Vertical: 4 cm = 1 unit; horizontal: 1 cm = 10°.)
Estimate the maximum value of y and the corresponding angle.

x	0	10	20	30	40	45	50	60	70	80	90
$2x$	0	20	40			90			140		180
$\sin 2x°$	0	0.34	0.64						0.64		0
$3x$	0	30	60	90					210		270
$\sin 3x°$	0	0.5	0.87						−0.5		−1.0

2 Copy and complete the following table by abstracting the necessary information from the table above.
Hence draw the graph of $y = \sin 3x° - \sin 2x°$ (scales as before).
Find an approximate solution to the equation $\sin 3x = \sin 2x$.

x	0	10	20	30	40	45	50	60	70	80	90
$\sin 3x°$	0	0.50	0.87						−0.5		−1.0
$\sin 2x°$	0	0.34	0.64						0.64		0.0
$\sin 3x° - \sin 2x°$	0	0.16							−1.14		

3 Draw the graph of $y = \cos x°$ from $x = 0$ to $x = 90$. With the same axes and units draw the graph of $y = \dfrac{x}{20}$.
Solve the equation $x = 20 \cos x°$.

Tell your teacher that you have finished this Unit

ANSWERS

UNIT M1 Similarity

A **1** Fig. 3 **2** Fig. 4 **3** Fig. 3 **4** Fig. 1 **5** Fig. 2 **6** Fig. 2 **7** Fig. 2 **8** Fig. 1 **9** Fig. 4 **10** Fig. 3

B **1**

Length	Measured distance	
	in smaller photo	in larger photo
Length of photo	3.5 cm	10.5 cm
Breadth of photo	2.8 cm	8.4 cm
Length of guitar	1.8 cm	5.4 cm
Height of guitar player	2.6 cm	7.8 cm
Diameter of drum	0.7 cm	2.1 cm

2 Enlargement 17.4 cm × 12.9 cm **3** AB = 75 cm; CD = 120 cm
4 Lounge 4.5 m × 3.75 m, Dining room 3.75 m × 3.0 m, Kitchen 3.0 m × 3.0 m

C **2** Actual length = 3.5 mm **3** Width = 1.5 cm, height = 2.5 cm
4 (a) Length = 3.6 cm, breadth = 2.4 cm (b) Length = 1.6 cm, breadth = 0.9 cm

E **1** (a) Side EG (opposite $\widehat{F}$) (b) Side EF (opposite $\widehat{G}$)
PR = 3 cm, EG = 6 cm, $EG/PR = 6/3 = 2$; PQ = 2.5 cm, EF = 5 cm, $EF/PQ = 5.0/2.5 = 2$ **2** Side BC : side MN : $\widehat{L}$; side AC : side LN : $\widehat{M}$; side AB : side LM : $\widehat{N}$.
BC = 8 cm, MN = 12 cm, $MN/BC = 12/8 = 1.5$; AC = 4 cm, LN = 6 cm, $LN/AC = 6/4 = 1.5$; AB = 6 cm, LM = 9 cm, $LM/AB = 9/6 = 1.5$. Scale factor = 1.5.
Triangles LMN and ABC are similar. **3** $k = 2$ **4** $k = \frac{1}{2}$ **5** Enlargement; $k > 1$; $k = 1.5$ **6** Reduction; $k < 1$; $k = 0.7$ **7** Enlargement; $k > 1$; $k = 1.4$

F **1** $US = 6$ **2** $AB = 9$; $CA = 12$ **3** $k = 0.7$; $DE = 4.55$; $FD = 5.6$
4 $k = 1.4$; $LM = 10.36$; $MN = 8.96$

G **1** Enlargement; $k = 3$ **2** Reduction; $k = 0.7$ **3** Enlargement; $k = 1.2$
4 Reduction; $k = 0.6$ **5** Enlargement; $k = 2.1$ **6** $ZX = 13.5$
7 $k = 0.7$; $ST = 3.5$; $TU = 5.6$ **8** $k = 1.2$; $BC = 9.0$; $CA = 10.2$
9 $k = 0.6$; $DE = 5.46$; $EF = 3.3$ **10** $k = 2.1$; $MN = 12.18$; $LM = 14.28$

H Progress check

I **1** $k = 3.5$; $QR = 8.4$; height = 8.4 m **2** Height 12.5 m **3** 1.2 m
4 $x = 4.5$ **5** $k = 0.8$; distance = 18.4 km **6** $x = 10$ **7** 80

J **1** (b) QR = 7.2 cm; RP = 6.0 cm (d) YZ = 5.4 cm; ZX = 4.5 cm (e) $\widehat{A} = 49°$, $\widehat{P} = 49°$, $\widehat{X} = 49°$, $\widehat{B} = 39°$, $\widehat{Q} = 39°$, $\widehat{Y} = 39°$, $\widehat{C} = 92°$, $\widehat{R} = 92°$, $\widehat{Z} = 92°$
2 Similar: $k = 0.7$ **3** and **4** Not similar **5** Similar: $k = 2$

K **2** $k = 1.5$; area = 18 cm^2 **3** $k = 5$; area = 75 cm^2 **4** $k = \frac{1}{2}$; area = 1.25 cm^2
5 (a) 5.3066 cm^2 (b) 5.3066 cm^2 **6** 16 cm^2 **7** 16 cm

L **1** $k = 3$; volume = 54 litres **2** $k = 2$; volume = 64 cm^3 **3** $k = \frac{1}{3}$; 0.5 litres
4 $k = \frac{1}{2}$; volume = 9 cm^3

M Progress check

UNIT M2 Vectors

C **2** $\begin{pmatrix}5\\2\end{pmatrix}$ **3** $\begin{pmatrix}2\\1\end{pmatrix}$ **4** $\begin{pmatrix}6\\2\end{pmatrix}$ **5** $\begin{pmatrix}2\\1\end{pmatrix}$ **6** $\begin{pmatrix}3\\0\end{pmatrix}$

F **2** $\begin{pmatrix}-3\\2\end{pmatrix}$ **3** $\begin{pmatrix}-2\\-3\end{pmatrix}$ **4** $\begin{pmatrix}2\\-2\end{pmatrix}$ **5** $\begin{pmatrix}1\\-3\end{pmatrix}$ **6** $\begin{pmatrix}-1\\-3\end{pmatrix}$

H **1**(a) $\begin{pmatrix}3\\2\end{pmatrix}$ (b) $\begin{pmatrix}4\\-1\end{pmatrix}$ (c) $\begin{pmatrix}-3\\-2\end{pmatrix}$ (d) $\begin{pmatrix}-2\\5\end{pmatrix}$ (e) $\begin{pmatrix}6\\-1\end{pmatrix}$ (f) $\begin{pmatrix}-6\\1\end{pmatrix}$ (g) $\begin{pmatrix}0\\2\end{pmatrix}$ (h) $\begin{pmatrix}4\\0\end{pmatrix}$

I **1** $\underline{v} = \begin{pmatrix}2\\3\end{pmatrix}$; $\underline{s} = \begin{pmatrix}4\\-3\end{pmatrix}$; $\underline{a} = \begin{pmatrix}-3\\-2\end{pmatrix}$

J **2** length of $\underline{u}$ = 5.4 units; $\underline{w}$ = 4.1 units; $\underline{v}$ = 3.6 units; $\underline{a}$ = 5 units; $\underline{b}$ = 6.4 units; $\underline{c}$ = 2 units

K **1** $\sqrt{25} = 5$ units **2** $\sqrt{40} = 6.32$ units **3** $\sqrt{50} = 7.07$ units
4 $\sqrt{13} = 3.61$ units **5** $\sqrt{25} = 5$ units **6** $\sqrt{10} = 3.16$ units
7 $\sqrt{20} = 4.47$ units **8** $\sqrt{10} = 3.16$ units **9** $\sqrt{26} = 5.10$ units
10 $\sqrt{29} = 5.39$ units **11** $\sqrt{16} = 4$ units **12** $\sqrt{32} = 5.66$ units

L **1** $\begin{pmatrix}4\\5\end{pmatrix}$ **2** $\begin{pmatrix}4\\3\end{pmatrix}$ **3** $\begin{pmatrix}4\\6\end{pmatrix}$ **4** $\begin{pmatrix}2\\6\end{pmatrix}$ **5** $\begin{pmatrix}8\\5\end{pmatrix}$ **6** $\begin{pmatrix}5\\7\end{pmatrix}$ **7** $\begin{pmatrix}7\\7\end{pmatrix}$ **8** $\begin{pmatrix}5\\7\end{pmatrix}$

M **2** $\underline{u} = \begin{pmatrix}3\\-1\end{pmatrix}$; $\underline{v} = \begin{pmatrix}1\\3\end{pmatrix}$; $\underline{u}+\underline{v} = \begin{pmatrix}4\\2\end{pmatrix}$

3 $\underline{u} = \begin{pmatrix}3\\1\end{pmatrix}$; $\underline{v} = \begin{pmatrix}1\\-2\end{pmatrix}$; $\underline{u}+\underline{v} = \begin{pmatrix}4\\-1\end{pmatrix}$

4 $\underline{u} = \begin{pmatrix}3\\1\end{pmatrix}$; $\underline{v} = \begin{pmatrix}2\\3\end{pmatrix}$; $\underline{u}+\underline{v} = \begin{pmatrix}5\\4\end{pmatrix}$

5 $\underline{u} = \begin{pmatrix}2\\0\end{pmatrix}$; $\underline{v} = \begin{pmatrix}0\\2\end{pmatrix}$; $\underline{u}+\underline{v} = \begin{pmatrix}2\\2\end{pmatrix}$

6 $\underline{u} = \begin{pmatrix}3\\-3\end{pmatrix}$; $\underline{v} = \begin{pmatrix}1\\2\end{pmatrix}$; $\underline{u}+\underline{v} = \begin{pmatrix}4\\-1\end{pmatrix}$

N **7** $\begin{pmatrix}7\\6\end{pmatrix}$ **8** $\begin{pmatrix}4\\5\end{pmatrix}$ **9** $\begin{pmatrix}5\\2\end{pmatrix}$ **10** $\begin{pmatrix}-2\\-5\end{pmatrix}$ **11** $\begin{pmatrix}-1\\-2\end{pmatrix}$ **12** $\begin{pmatrix}-4\\1\end{pmatrix}$ **13** $\begin{pmatrix}3\\-2\end{pmatrix}$

14 $\begin{pmatrix}1\\4\end{pmatrix}$ **15** $\begin{pmatrix}2\\0\end{pmatrix}$ **16** $-\underline{x} = \begin{pmatrix}-3\\-4\end{pmatrix}$ **17** $-\underline{z} = \begin{pmatrix}-7\\-3\end{pmatrix}$ **18** $-\underline{w} = \begin{pmatrix}2\\-8\end{pmatrix}$

19 $-\underline{t} = \begin{pmatrix}-4\\1\end{pmatrix}$

O **3** (a) $\begin{pmatrix}12\\9\end{pmatrix}$ (b) $\begin{pmatrix}-10\\5\end{pmatrix}$ (c) $\begin{pmatrix}-21\\-7\end{pmatrix}$ (d) $\begin{pmatrix}15\\3\end{pmatrix}$ (e) $\begin{pmatrix}0\\8\end{pmatrix}$ $\begin{pmatrix}12\\-8\end{pmatrix}$

P **1** (a) $\begin{pmatrix}-10\\-5\end{pmatrix}$ (b) $\begin{pmatrix}-12\\-4\end{pmatrix}$ (c) $\begin{pmatrix}6\\-3\end{pmatrix}$ (d) $\begin{pmatrix}-8\\0\end{pmatrix}$ (e) $\begin{pmatrix}-10\\5\end{pmatrix}$ (f) $\begin{pmatrix}9\\3\end{pmatrix}$

Q Progress check

S **1** $\underline{u} = \begin{pmatrix}2\\1\end{pmatrix}$; $\underline{v} = \begin{pmatrix}2\\-2\end{pmatrix}$; $\underline{w} = \begin{pmatrix}0\\4\end{pmatrix}$; $\underline{u}+\underline{v} = \begin{pmatrix}4\\-1\end{pmatrix}$; $\underline{u}+\underline{v}+\underline{w} = \begin{pmatrix}4\\3\end{pmatrix}$

2 $\underline{a} = \begin{pmatrix}2\\1\end{pmatrix}$; $\underline{b} = \begin{pmatrix}1\\-3\end{pmatrix}$; $\underline{c} = \begin{pmatrix}-2\\0\end{pmatrix}$; $\underline{a}+\underline{b} = \begin{pmatrix}3\\-2\end{pmatrix}$; $\underline{a}+\underline{b}+\underline{c} = \begin{pmatrix}1\\-2\end{pmatrix}$

3 $\underline{u} = \begin{pmatrix}3\\1\end{pmatrix}$; $\underline{v} = \begin{pmatrix}-1\\2\end{pmatrix}$; $\underline{w} = \begin{pmatrix}-2\\-3\end{pmatrix}$; $\underline{u}+\underline{v} = \begin{pmatrix}2\\3\end{pmatrix}$; $\underline{u}+\underline{v}+\underline{w} = \begin{pmatrix}0\\0\end{pmatrix}$

4 (a) $\begin{pmatrix}-2\\2\end{pmatrix}$ (b) $\begin{pmatrix}-2\\0\end{pmatrix}$ (c) $\begin{pmatrix}-3\\0\end{pmatrix}$

T **2** (a) $\begin{pmatrix}5\\-2\end{pmatrix}$ (b) $\begin{pmatrix}-4\\6\end{pmatrix}$ (c) $\begin{pmatrix}6\\3\end{pmatrix}$ (d) $\begin{pmatrix}20\\-5\end{pmatrix}$ **4** (a) $\begin{pmatrix}-1\\-2\end{pmatrix}$ (b) $\begin{pmatrix}-5\\3\end{pmatrix}$
(c) $\begin{pmatrix}-6\\-12\end{pmatrix}$ (d) $\begin{pmatrix}10\\15\end{pmatrix}$

U **1** $\underline{u} + \underline{v} = \begin{pmatrix}4\\6\end{pmatrix}$; $2(\underline{u} + \underline{v}) = \begin{pmatrix}8\\12\end{pmatrix}$; $2\underline{u} = \begin{pmatrix}6\\8\end{pmatrix}$; $2\underline{v} = \begin{pmatrix}2\\4\end{pmatrix}$;
$2\underline{u} + 2\underline{v} = \begin{pmatrix}8\\12\end{pmatrix}$; $2(\underline{u} + \underline{v}) = 2\underline{u} + 2\underline{v}$ **3** $\underline{u} + \underline{v} = \begin{pmatrix}10\\12\end{pmatrix}$;
$\frac{1}{2}(\underline{u} + \underline{v}) = \begin{pmatrix}5\\6\end{pmatrix}$ $\frac{1}{2}\underline{u} = \begin{pmatrix}3\\2\end{pmatrix}$; $\frac{1}{2}\underline{v} = \begin{pmatrix}2\\4\end{pmatrix}$; $\frac{1}{2}\underline{u} + \frac{1}{2}\underline{v} = \begin{pmatrix}5\\6\end{pmatrix}$;
$\frac{1}{2}(\underline{u} + \underline{v}) = \frac{1}{2}\underline{u} + \frac{1}{2}\underline{v}$

V **1** $\begin{pmatrix}2\\1\end{pmatrix}$ **2** $\begin{pmatrix}2\\5\end{pmatrix}$ **3** $\begin{pmatrix}2\\5\end{pmatrix}$ **4** $\begin{pmatrix}2\\2\end{pmatrix}$ **5** $\begin{pmatrix}-6\\-1\end{pmatrix}$ **6** $\begin{pmatrix}-3\\-3\end{pmatrix}$ **7** $\begin{pmatrix}-3\\-4\end{pmatrix}$

X **1** (a) $\overrightarrow{RP}$ (b) $\overrightarrow{PS}$ (c) $\overrightarrow{PQ}$ (d) $\overrightarrow{RP}$ (e) $\overrightarrow{RP}$ (f) $\overrightarrow{QS}$ (g) *O* (h) *O*
2 (a) *WX* is parallel to *ZY* (b) $WX = \frac{1}{2}ZY$ (c) $XY = \underline{a} + \underline{b}$
3 (a) $\underline{u}$ (b) $\underline{u} + \underline{v}$ (c) $\underline{v}$ (d) $\underline{u}$ (e) $\underline{u} + \underline{v}$. Lines *EA* and *DB* and parallel and equal in length.
4 (a) $\underline{a} + \underline{b}$ (b) $\underline{a} - \underline{b}$. *N* is the mid-point of *LM*.
5 (a) $\underline{y}$ (b) $\underline{x} + \underline{y}$ (c) $2(\underline{x} + \underline{y})$ (d) $2\underline{x}$ (e) $2\underline{y}$ (f) $2\underline{x} + 2\underline{y}$. So $\overrightarrow{AC} = 2\overrightarrow{AF}$, so *A*, *F*, and *C* lie in a straight line.

Y **1** $\overrightarrow{BC} = \overrightarrow{BA} + \overrightarrow{AC} = \underline{u} + \underline{v}$; $\overrightarrow{PQ} + \overrightarrow{PA} + \overrightarrow{AQ} = \frac{1}{4}\underline{u} + \frac{1}{4}\underline{v}$. So $4\,\overrightarrow{PQ} = \underline{u} + \underline{v}$. Because $\overrightarrow{BC} = 4\overrightarrow{PQ}$, *PQ* is parallel to *BC* and is a quarter the length of *BC*.
2 (a) $4\underline{a} - 4\underline{b}$ (b) $2\underline{a} + 2\underline{b}$ (c) $2\underline{a} + 2\underline{b}$ (d) $\underline{a} + \underline{b}$. But $\overrightarrow{ED} = \overrightarrow{EO} + \overrightarrow{OD} = -\underline{b} + \underline{a} + \underline{b} = \underline{a}$. So $\overrightarrow{ED} = \frac{1}{4}\overrightarrow{OA}$, so *ED* is parallel to *OA*. **3** (a) $2\underline{a} + \underline{b} + \underline{c}$ (b) $2\underline{a} = \underline{b} - \underline{c}$.

Z Progress check

UNIT M3 Simple equations and inequations

A **1** $x = 3$ **2** $x = 4$ **3** $x = 3$ **4** $x = 4$ **5** $x = 1$ **6** $x = 2$ **7** $x = 4$ **8** $x = 0$

C **1** 12 **2** 5 **3** 7 **4** 6 **5** 6 **6** 40 **7** 8 **8** 12 **9** 12 **10** 19
11 20 **12** 4 **13** −3 **14** −3 **15** 0 **16** −7 **17** −8 **18** −2
19 11 **20** −6 **21** −4 **22** $10 - a$ **23** $9 - b$ **24** $20 - p$ **25** $-15 - q$
26 $1 - t$ 27- $-2 - b$ **28** $10 + b$ **29** $4 + r$ **30** $9 + c$ **31** $7 + a$
32 $11 + c$ **33** $q + p$ **34** $t - r$ **35** $a + b$ **36** $s - q$ **37** $z + y$ **38** $d - a$
39 $r - d$ **40** $v + t$

D **1** 7 **2** 7 **3** 4 **4** 21 **5** 12 **6** 3 **7** 13 **8** 9 **9** −4 **10** 9 **11** −7
12 −4 **13** −7 **14** 5 **15** −8 **16** 6 **17** 4.5 **18** 2.5 **19** −3.2
20 −2.5 **21** −0.5 **22** 2.5 **23** −2.8 **24** 1.2
25 $\frac{5}{p}$ **26** $-\frac{8}{r}$ **27** $\frac{p}{5}$ **28** $-\frac{d}{7}$ **29** $\frac{b}{a}$ **30** $-\frac{k}{b}$ **31** $\frac{p}{a}$ **32** $\frac{10}{c}$

E **1** 28 **2** 35 **3** 24 **4** 21 **5** 16 **6** 6 **7** 90 **8** 22 **9** −48 **10** 63
11 10 **12** −44 **13** −15 **14** −56 **15** 40 **16** −15 **17** 4 **18** 30
19 −21 **20** 8 **21** −7 **22** 44 **23** −4 **24** −98 **25** $9b$ **26** $-10k$ **27** $8c$
28 ap **29** $-ab$ **30** $-cd$

F **1** 4 **2** 4 **3** 2 **4** 3 **5** 14.5 **6** 1 **7** 5.5 **8** 4.2 **9** 1 **10** 3.5 **11** 1.5
12 3.1 **13** 3 **14** −5 **15** −2 **16** −2 **17** 2 **18** −8 **19** 2 **20** −4

21 0.5 **22** 3 **23** −6 **24** −1 **25** −9 **26** 2.5 **27** −1.25 **28** 4
29 −12 **30** 1.6 **31** −5 **32** 3 **33** −4 **34** 9 **35** −4.5 **36** 5.4

G **1** 3 **2** 3 **3** 4 **4** 2 **5** 3 **6** $\frac{q+3}{p}$ **7** $\frac{b-1}{a}$ **8** $\frac{c+d}{b}$ **9** $\frac{p-d}{c}$ **10** 4
11 2 **12** 3 **13** 1 **14** −1 **15** 10 **16** −5 **17** 2 **18** 4 **19** 1
20 $\frac{q+5}{p}$ **21** $\frac{s-7}{r}$ **22** $\frac{c-b}{a}$ **23** $\frac{w+v}{t}$

H **1** $3x+6$ **2** $4y-12$ **3** $3p+21$ **4** $-2p-10$ **5** $-3a+9$ **6** $-x+3$
7 $4x-28$ **8** $2p+2q$ **9** $ay-3a$ **10** $ax+aq$ **11** $bc-bd$ **12** $-ap+aq$
13 5 **14** 1 **15** −8 **16** 5 **17** 1.5 **18** 2 **19** −3 **20** 4 **21** 1 **22** 2
23 −2 **24** 4 **25** 7 **26** −4 **27** 7 **28** $\frac{q-3p}{p}$ **29** $\frac{d+30}{3}$ **30** $\frac{c+ab}{a}$
31 $\frac{d-3+ab}{a}$ **32** $\frac{b-a+cd}{c}$

I Progress check

J **1** $x<5$ **2** $x>5$ **3** $y<-2$ **4** $a\le 6$ **5** $t\ge -5$ **6** $p<4$ **7** $y>-3$
8 $x<-6$ **9** $x\ge 12$ **10** $p<0$ **11** $p\ge 0$ **12** $x>1$

K **6** $x\le 0$ **7** $x>0$ **8** $x<1$ **9** $x\le 2$ **10** $x\ge 1$ **11** $x<0$ **12** $x\ge 0$

L **1** $6<9$ **2** $-5<-2$ **3** $3x>12$ **4** $5x<17$ **5** $2x>19$ **6** $3x\le 15$
7 $7x\ge 25$ **8** $8x\le 14$ **9** $x>6$ **10** $x>2$ **11** $x\le 3$ **12** $x\ge 7$ **13** $x<-5$
14 $x>2$ **15** $x\ge -2$ **16** $x>5$ **17** $x\le 7$ **18** $x\le -2$

M **1** $x<1$ **2** $x\ge 5$ **3** $x>-10$ **4** $x\le 1$ **5** $y>16$ **6** $p<3$ **7** $p\ge -2$
8 $a\le 0$ **9** $q>0$ **10** $q\le -5$ **11** (a) $-8<-3$ (b) $8>3$
12 (a) $-1>-6$ (b) $1<6$ **13** (a) $-5<7$ (b) $5>-7$ **14** (a) $-4>-8$
(b) $1<2$ **15** (a) $-3<6$ (b) $1>-2$ **16** (a) $-5<10$ (b) $1>-2$
17 $p<-4$ **18** $q\ge -1$ **19** $p>2$ **20** $x\le 2$ **21** $y<-6$ **22** $x<1$
23 $y\ge -8$ **24** $x>0$ **25** $p\le 0$

N **1** $x<-10$ **2** $x>-4$ **3** $x\le 9$ **4** $x\ge 2$ **5** $x<0$ **6** $x\ge 1$ **7** $x>1$
8 $x<4$ **9** $a>3$ **10** $t<-0.4$ **11** $x\ge 2$ **12** $x\le -1$ **13** $x\le 2$ **14** $x\le 1$
15 $x\ge 1$ **16** $x<2$ **17** $x>-4$ **18** $x<1$ **19** $x\ge 2.5$ **20** $x>-7$

O **1** $x\le 8$ **2** $x\ge 2$ **3** $x\ge 7$ **4** $x\ge 3$ **5** $x>-8.4$ **6** $x=5$ **7** $x=7$
8 $x=9$ **9** $x\ge 12$ **10** $x>-10$ **11** $x\ge 4$ **12** $x>3.5$ **13** $x>-4$
14 $x=-6.8$ **15** $x\le 6$ **16** $x<15$ **17** $x\ge 3$ **18** $x\le 24$ **19** $x>0.5$
20 $x=2$ **21** $x\ge 35$ **22** $x<12.5$ **23** $x=15$ **24** $x\ge 2$ **25** $x<-7$

P **1** $3x+11=35$; $4\frac{2}{3}$ **2** $2x-7=53$; 30 **3** $x+(x+25)=65$; 20, 45
4 $8x=5x+36$; 12 **5** $2(2x+3)+2x=72$; 11, 25 **6** 12, 24, 30
7 $2x+5<20$; $x\le 7$ **8** $3(x-5)<45$; $x<20$ **9** $4x-x>30$; $x>10$
10 $(x+3)+x<35$; $x<16$ **11** length < 10 cm

Q **1** $r=\frac{P-2w}{2}$ **2** $b=\frac{2S-na}{n}$ **3** $a=\frac{2S-hb}{h}$ **4** $t=\sqrt{\frac{2S}{a}}$ **5** $v=\sqrt{\frac{2E}{m}}$
6 $r=\sqrt{\frac{V}{\pi h}}$ **7** $d=\frac{r^2}{p^2}$ **8** $a=\frac{b^2-D^2}{4c}$ **9** $R=\frac{c^2+h^2}{2h}$ **10** $d=\sqrt{\frac{V}{\sqrt{H}}}$
11 $x=\frac{c}{a+b}$ **12** $r=\frac{c}{k+b}$ **13** $n=\frac{t}{t-d}$ **14** $n=\frac{Ir}{E-IR}$ **15** $h=\frac{3V}{\pi r^2}$
16 $l=\frac{A-\pi r^2}{\pi r}$ **17** (a) $S=\frac{v^2-u^2}{2f}$ (b) $u=\sqrt{v^2-2fS}$ **18** $n=\frac{T-a+d}{d}$

19 (a) $r = \frac{mv^2}{F}$ (b) $v = \sqrt{\frac{vF}{m}}$ **20** $t = \frac{M^2 - p^2}{p^2}$ **21** (a) $q = \frac{p - Rp}{R}$ (b) $p = \frac{Rq}{1 - R}$

R Progress check

UNIT M4 Solution of right-angled triangles

A **1** $k = \frac{15}{5} = 3$

B **1** $k = 5; h = 10; \frac{2}{3}$ **2** $k = 1.5; h = 6; \frac{4}{3}$ **3** $k = 2.5; h = 5; \frac{1}{2}$

C **1** $\frac{3}{4}$ **2** $\frac{2}{5}$ **3** $\frac{7}{5}$ **4** $\frac{2}{7}$ **5** $\frac{4}{3}$ **6** $\frac{12}{5}$ **7** $\frac{15}{8}$ **8** $\frac{6}{8}$

D

Angle	20°	30°	40°
Opposite side	36	58	84
Tangent	0.36	0.58	0.84

E **1** (a) 0.087 (b) 0.176 (c) 0.268 (d) 0.364 (e) 0.700 (f) 0.091 (g) 0.173 (h) 0.189 (i) 0.708 (j) 0.997 (k) 0.075 (l) 0.521
2 tan 30° = 0.577; tan 40° = 0.839; tan 50° = 1.192; tan 60° = 1.732
3 (a) 1.146 (b) 2.747 (c) 1.217 (d) 1.725 (e) 1.000 (f) 5.671 (g) 1.897 (h) 3.333 (i) 15.89

F **1** (a) $x = 20.5$ (b) $x = 39.6$ (c) $x = 57.4$ (d) $x = 70.4$ (e) $x = 56.4$ (f) $x = 60.0$ (g) $x = 72.3$ **2** (a) $x = 56.3$ (b) $x = 71.6$ (c) $x = 14.4$ or 14.5 (d) $x = 40.6$ (e) $x = 80.1$ (f) $x = 71.6$ (g) $x = 57.1$ **3** $x = 38.7$ **4** $x = 56.3$ **5** $x = 42.0$ **6** $x = 32.0$ **7** $x = 49.4$ **8** $x = 41.2$

G **1** (a) $x = 4.9$ (b) $x = 6.71$ (c) $x = 17.32$ (d) $x = 4.37$ (e) $x = 16.7$

H **1** $x = \frac{3}{5}$ **2** $x = \frac{5}{13}$ **3** $x = \frac{15}{17}$ **4** $x = \frac{6}{10}$

I

Angle	30°	45°	60°	75°	90°
Opposite side	50	71	87	97	100
Sine	0.50	0.71	0.87	0.97	1.00

2 (a) 0.574 (b) 0.809 (c) 0.480 (d) 0.103 (e) 0.996 (f) 0.735

J **1** (a) 60.0 (b) 49.0 (c) 19.0 (d) 46.6 (e) 81.0 or 81.1 or 81.2 or 81.3 (f) 64.5 or 64.6 (g) 14.3 or 14.4

K (a) 3.42 (b) 4.02 (c) 15.3 (d) 5.14 (e) 25.4 (f) 5.82

L **1** 15.0 or 15.1 **2** 30.0 **3** 36.9 **4** 53.1 **5** 14.5 **6** 36.9

M **1** 64.1 or 64.2 **2** 68.2 **3** 23.6 **4** 44.4 **5** 50.2 **6** 65.6

N **2** (a) 0.996 (b) 0.985 (c) 0.940 (d) 0.766 (e) 0.991 (f) 0.907 (g) 0.129 (h) 0.999 (i) 0.540

O **1** 3.39 **2** 2.12 **3** 1.87 **4** 3.94 **5** 6.63 **6** 1.51 **7** 1300

P **3** 45.6 **4** 66.4 **5** 54.3 or 54.4 **6** 68.0 **7** 48.2 **8** 36.9

Q **1** 19.4 or 19.5 **2** 6.58 **3** 51.3 **4** 67.4 **5** 5.45 **6** 4.88

R Progress check

S **1** 5.66 m **2** 13.9 m **3** 12.8 m **4** 22
5 (a) 4.67 m (b) 12.3 cm
6 (a) 17.1 m (b) 12.5 m (c) 13.2 m
7 (a) $PR = 8.97$ cm (b) $LN = 17.0$ cm (c) $RT = 9.06$ cm

T **1** 536 m **2** 37.3 m **3** 1.27 m **4** (a) 2.30 m (b) 1.93 m **5** (a) 1790 m (b) 3.3°

U **1** (a) 68.2° (b) 73.3° **2** 2.07 m **3** 1.74 m **4** $ST = SV = 38.6$ **5** $AB = 9.00$ m
altitude = 5.36 m; area = 24.1 m^2

V **1** 25.7 km **2** 32.2 km **3** 56.4 km **4** 35.6°

W Progress check

UNIT M5 Simple Functions and their Graphs

B **1** {(0, 0), (1, 3), (2, 6), (4, 12)} **2** {(0, 0), (2, 1), (6, 3), (10, 5)}
3 {(0, 1), (3, 7), (6, 13), (7, 15)} **4** {(0, 2), (3, 3), (6, 4), (12, 6)} **5** {10, 17, 21, 25}
6 {4, 18, 26, 64} **7** {6, 24, 30, 42} **8** {0, 2, 6, 9, 10} **9** {0, 16, 24, 26}

D **1** $f(0) = 2$; $f(1) = 3$; $f(2) = 4$; $f(3) = 5$ **2** $f(4) = 12$; $f(7) = 21$; $f(9) = 27$;
3 $f(3) = 10$; $f(9) = 34$; $f(12) = 46$ **4** $f(0) = 15$; $f(2) = 11$; $f(3) = 9$; $f(5) = 5$
5 $f(x) = 5x + 6$, $x \in \{3, 9, 12\}$

E **1** Domain $\{-2, -1, 0, 1, 2\}$; range $\{-8, -4, 0, 4, 8\}$ **2** Domain $\{-2, -1, 0, 1\}$
range $\{-2, 0, 2, 4\}$ **3** Domain {1, 2, 3, 4}; range {0, 1, 2, 3}

F Progress check

H **1** $f(1.8) = 3.6$; $f(2.4) = 4.8$; $f(3.2) = 6.4$; $f(3.8) = 7.6$

I **1** $b = 5$; $c = 8$; $d = 12$; $e = 17$; $g = 20$ **2** $h = 11$; $i = 15$; $j = 18$; $k = 26$
3 $m = 5$; $n = 7$; $p = 8$; $q = 10$ **4** $b = 13$; $c = 6$; $d = 16$
5 $q = 4$; $r = 4.5$; $s = 6$; $t = 6.5$

J **1** $a = 6$ **2** $a = 5$ **3** $a = 6$ **4** $a = 3$ **5** $a = 3$ **6** $a = 9$

K **1** $g(-3) = -7$; $g(0) = 2$; $g(3) = 11$ **2** $c(2) = 6.28$; $c(3) = 9.42$; $c(4) = 12.56$
3 (a) $h(-2) = -9$, $h(2) = 3$; (b) Range: $-9 \leq h(x) \leq 3$; (d) (i) -1; (ii) 1
4 (a) $g(-2) = 6$; $g(6) = -2$ (b) Range: $-2 \leq g(x) \leq 6$ (d) (i) 1.4 (ii) 5.4

L **1** $m = 3$; $g(6) = 21$; $g(0) = 3$ **2** $q = 2$; $f(6) = 14$; $f(-2) = -2$
3 $d = 2$; $h(0) = -3$; $h(3) = 3$; $h(-3) = -9$ **4** $r = 2$; $g(5) = 22$; $g(-4) = -14$

N Progress check

UNIT M6 Periodicity and the Sine Function

A **4** (a) about 3.5 cm **5** 4 cm; 4 cm; 2 cm **6** 2.5 cm **7** 3.7 cm

B **1** (a) 0400, 1600 (b) 1000, 2200 **2** (a) 24 min (b) 0.4 m **3** (a) 0100; 0700; 1300; 1900 (b) between 0224 and 0536; between 1424 and 1736 (c) 12 hours

C **3** (a) 150 (b) 310 (c) 425 (d) 210

D **1** (a) 0.41 cm (b) 0.91 cm (c) 1.0 cm (d) 0.98 cm (e) 0.74 cm (f) 0.0 cm
(g) −0.21 cm (h) −0.81 cm (i) −1.0 cm (j) −0.5 cm **2** (a) 0.87 cm (b) −0.87 cm
3 (a) 30° and 150° (b) 210° and 330° **4** (a) 162° (b) 108° (c) 54° **5** (a) 204°
(b) 312° (c) 234° **6** (a) 90° (b) 270° **7** 0°; 180°; 360°

E **1** (a) 0.21 cm (b) 1.0 cm (c) −0.74 cm. **2** 30°; 150°; 390°; 510°. **3** 210°; 330°; 570°; 690°

F

Angle x	60	90	120	150	180	210	240	270	300	330	360
Sin $x°$	0.87	1	0.87	0.5	0.0	−0.5	−0.87	−1	−0.87	−0.5	0

1 0.81 **2** 0.59 **3** −0.31 **4** −0.74 **5** −0.81 **6** −0.21

G **1** (a) 100° (b) 260° (c) 280° **2** (a) 160° (b) 200° (3) 340°
3 (a) 125° (b) 235° (c) 305° **4** (a) 135° (b) 225° (c) 315°

H **1** sin 20° = 0.342 **2** sin 35° = 0.574 **3** sin 48° = 0.743 **4** sin 71° = 0.946
5 − sin 60° = − 0.866 **6** − sin 25° = − 0.423 **7** − sin 72° = − 0.951
8 − sin 39° = − 0.629 **9** − sin 20° = − 0.342 **10** − sin 45° = − 0.707
11 − sin 78° = − 0.978 **12** − sin 52° = − 0.788 **13** 0.974 **14** − 0.875
15 − 0.545

I Progress check

J **1** − 0.819 **2** − 0.940 **3** 0.731 **4** − 0.883 **5** 0.974 **6** − 0.940 **7** 0.707
8 − 0.643 **9** − 0.174

K **1** 215° or 325° **2** 40° or 140° **3** 240° or 300° **4** 230° or 310° **5** 51° or 129°
6 195° or 345° **7** 77° or 103° **8** 210° or 330° **9** 189° or 351°
10 65.5° or 114.5°

L **1** sin 30° = 0.5 **2** (a) sin 60° = 0.866 (b) sin 60° = 0.866 (c) sin 10° = 0.174
(d) sin 180° = 0.000 **3** − sin 40° = − 0.643 **4** (a) − − sin 60° = − 0.866
(b) − sin 45° = − 0.707 (c) − sin 75° = − 0.966 (d) − sin 90° = − 1
5 sin 70° = 0.940 **6** (a) sin 35° = 0.574 (b) sin 72° = 0.951 (c) sin 18° = 0.309
(d) sin 90 = 1.000 **7** − sin 30° = − 0.5 **8** (a) − sin 27° = − 0.454
(b) − sin 63° = − 0.891 (c) − sin 34° = − 0.559 (d) − sin 58° = − 0.848

M **1**

$x°$	120	150	180	210	240	270	300	330	360
sin $x°$	0.87	0.5	0	−0.5	−0.87	−1.0	−0.87	−0.5	0
2 sin $x°$	1.74	1.0	0	−1.0	−1.74	−2.0	−1.74	−1.0	0

(b) (i) Twice the values for $y = \sin x$ (ii) 360°, 360° (c) (i) half the values for $y = \sin x$ (ii) 360°
2 2 sin x: greatest value +2, least value −2; $\frac{1}{2}\sin x$: greatest value $+\frac{1}{2}$, least value $-\frac{1}{2}$.
3 (a) 5 and −5 (b) 0.8 and −0.8 (c) b and $-b$ **4** (a) 4 (b) 0.75 (c) 1 **5** Greatest values: 1, least values: −1. **6** (a) 360° (b) 120° (c) 72° (d) 480° (e) 450° (f) 300°
7 (a) $y = 2 \sin x$ (b) $y = \frac{1}{2}\sin 2x$ (c) $y = \sin 1.5x$ (d) $y = 10 \sin \frac{2}{3}x$ (e) $y = 0.7 \sin 1.6x$
8 (a) $y = 3 \sin x$; $a = 90°$; $b = 180°$; $c = 270°$ (b) $y = 8 \sin 3x$; $a = 30°$; $b = 60°$; $c = 90°$ (c) $y = 1.5 \sin 1.8x$; $a = 50°$; $b = 100°$; $c = 150°$
9 $y = \sin(60 + x)°$; 360° **10** The curve is displaced by 30° to the right. Period 360°.

UNIT M7 Equations of Straight Lines

A **2** $\frac{3}{7}$ **3** $\frac{6}{4} = \frac{3}{2}$ **4** $\frac{2}{7}$ **5** $\frac{7}{2}$ **6** $\frac{7}{3}$ **7** $\frac{11}{4}$ **8** $\frac{6}{6} = 1$ **9** $\frac{5}{6}$

B **1** $\frac{2}{6} = \frac{1}{3}$ **2** $\frac{4}{6} = \frac{2}{3}$ **3** 1 **4** 3 **5** $\frac{5}{6}$ **6** $\frac{3}{7}$ **7** $\frac{1}{8}$

C **1** $-\frac{5}{3}$ **2** −6 **3** $-\frac{2}{7}$ **4** −1 **5** $-\frac{3}{5}$ **6** $-\frac{3}{4}$ **7** (a) $\frac{4}{3}$ (b) $-\frac{1}{3}$ (c) −5 (d) $\frac{1}{3}$ (e) $\frac{1}{5}$
(f) −2 (g) $-\frac{2}{5}$ (h) 8

D **1** (a) $\frac{7}{4}$ (b) $-\frac{7}{4}$ (c) -2 (d) $-\frac{1}{2}$ (e) $\frac{4}{7}$ (f) $-\frac{1}{2}$ (g) 2 (h) $\frac{7}{4}$ (i) $\frac{1}{2}$ (j) 2
2 (a) and (h); (d) and (f); (g) and (j)

G **1** (a) $m_{AB} = -\frac{2}{5}$ (b) $m_{DC} = -\frac{2}{5}$ (c) $m_{AD} = \frac{3}{2}$ (d) $m_{BC} = \frac{3}{2}$
2 (a) $m_{PQ} = -1$ (b) $m_{PS} = \frac{1}{4}$ (c) $m_{SR} = -1$ (d) $m_{QR} = \frac{3}{2}$
3 (a) $m_{AB} = 1$ (b) $m_{AD} = -4$ (c) $m_{DC} = 1$ (d) $m_{CB} = -\frac{2}{3}$

H **1** (4, 8), (5, 10), (6, 12). **2** (6, 3), (8, 4), (10, 5), $m = \frac{1}{2}$ **3** (−2, 6), (−3, 9), (2, −6); $m = -3$ **4** 4 **5** 5 **6** $\frac{1}{4}$ **7** $-\frac{1}{3}$ **8** −2 **9** −4 **10** −1 **11** 7.

I **1** (3, 7), (4, 9), (−2, −3); $m = 2$; (0, 1) **2** (3, 13), (1, 7), (−2, −2); $m = 3$; (0, 4)
3 (3, −11), (−1, 1), (−2, 4); $m = -3$; (0, −2) **4** 3; (0, −1) **5** 1; (0, 2)
6 5; (0, −2) **7** 3; (0, 0) **8** −2; (0, 5) **9** −4; (0, −3) **10** $-\frac{1}{3}$; (0, 1)
11 −5; (0, 0) **12** 3; (0, −5)

J **1** $y = \frac{1}{2}x + 1$ **2** $y = 4x$ **3** $y = \frac{2}{3}x$ **4** $y = \frac{1}{4}x + 3$ **5** $y = \frac{3}{5}x + 2$
6 $y = \frac{5}{4}x + 1$ **7** $y = -\frac{1}{3}x$ **8** $y = -2x - 4$ **9** $y = -\frac{1}{4}x + 2$ **10** $y = x - 2$
11 $y = -\frac{2}{5}x - 3$ **12** $y = -2x$

K **1** 2 cm per minute. **2** (a) $\frac{3}{2}$ cm per minute (b) 3 cm per minute (c) 1 cm per minute
3 5 cm per minute. **4** (a) The line through (1, 5) (b) tortoise (c) 10 cm; 4 cm; 6 cm.
(d) 9 cm; 15 cm; 18 cm **5** (a) car (b) cyclist (c) walker. **6** (a) 40 km per h
(b) 35 km per h (c) 25 km per h (d) 6 km per h.

L **1** (a) $\frac{1}{2}$h (b) 1 km (c) 4 h (d) 12 km (e) 3 km (f) 3 km per h (g) 1 h
(h) 12 km (i) 12 km per h (j) 14.00
2 (a) $\frac{1}{2}$h (b) 1 km (c) 1 h (d) 12 km (e) 12 km per h (f) $\frac{1}{2}$h (g) 10.30 (h) 3 h
(i) 12 km (j) 4 km per h (k) 13.30
3 (a) $\frac{1}{4}$h (b) 10 km (c) 09.30 (d) 1 h (e) 60 km per h (f) $\frac{1}{4}$ hour (g) 1 h (h) 60 km per h
(i) 1 h (j) 12.45 (k) 2 h (l) 60 km per h
4 (a) 10.00 (b) 12 km (e) 10 km per h (d) 15 minutes (e) 11.15 (f) yes (g) 11.45
(h) 45 km per h (i) $22\frac{1}{2}$ km (j) 12.15 (k) 24 km (l) 12.25

M Progress check

N **1** $m_{AB} = 2$ **2** $m_{CD} = 1$ **3** $m_{EF} = \frac{1}{3}$ **4** $m_{GH} = \frac{1}{2}$ **5** $m_{JK} = \frac{8}{3}$ **6** $m_{LM} = \frac{7}{4}$
7 $m_{MN} = \frac{1}{3}$ **8** $m_{RS} = \frac{1}{2}$ **9** $m_{VT} = 1$ **10** $m_{AB} = 8$ **11** $m_{CD} = -1$ **12** $m_{EF} = 2$
13 $m_{GH} = -\frac{2}{3}$ **14** $m_{JK} = \frac{1}{5}$ **15** $m_{LM} = -1$ **16** $m_{NM} = 2$ **17** $m_{PQ} = -\frac{3}{4}$
18 $m_{RS} = -\frac{4}{3}$

O **1** (a), (i). **2** (c), (f) **3** (b), (g), (j) **4** (d), (e), (h),
5 (a) $m_{AB} = 0$; *AB* parallel to x-axis. (b) m_{CD} not defined; *CD* parallel to *y*-axis.,
(c) $m_{EF} = 1$. (d) m_{GH} not defined; *GH* parallel to *y*-axis.
(e) $m_{JK} = 0$; *JK* parallel to x-axis. (f) $m_{LM} = 2$ (g) $m_{NP} = -1$
(h) m_{QR} not defined; *QR* parallel to *y*-axis. (i) $m_{ST} = 0$; *ST* parallel to *x*-axis.

P **1** 5 **2** 11.66 **3** 7.62 **4** 6.40 **5** 12.81 **6** 13. **7** 6.40 **8** 8.60 **9** 4.47
10 13. **11** 1.41 **12** 3.16 **13** 3 **14** 7.81 **15** 6.40 **16** 8 **17** 7.62
18 8.49 **19** 11.66 **20** 9.49.

Q

	Gradient	Cuts *y*-axis at
1	3	(0, 5)
2	6	(0, −1)
3	5	(0, 0)
4	1	(0, 7)

	Gradient	Cuts *y*-axis at
5	−7	(0, −2)
6	$-\frac{3}{4}$	(0, 3)
7	$\frac{1}{2}$	$(0, -\frac{5}{2})$
8	0	(0, 8)

	Gradient	Cuts *y*-axis at
9	−1	(0, 1)
10	4	(0, −4)
11	0	(0, −5)
12	$\frac{1}{3}$	$(0, -\frac{2}{3})$

R

	$y = mx + c$	Gradient	Cuts y-axis at
1	$y = -\frac{2}{3}x + 2$	$-\frac{2}{3}$	(0, 2)
2	$y = -\frac{1}{4}x + 2$	$-\frac{1}{4}$	(0, 2)
3	$y = 7x - 14$	7	(0, −14)
4	$y = -x + 7$	−1	(0, 7)
5	$y = 2x + 4$	2	(0, 4)
6	$y = -2x + \frac{1}{2}$	−2	$(0, \frac{1}{2})$
7	$y = \frac{4}{5}x - 4$	$\frac{4}{5}$	(0, −4)
8	$y = \frac{1}{2}x + 3$	$\frac{1}{2}$	(0, 3)
9	$y = -\frac{2}{5}x - 2$	$-\frac{2}{5}$	(0, −2)
10	$y = \frac{2}{3}x - 2$	$\frac{2}{3}$	(0, −2)
11	$y = -\frac{1}{8}x - 2$	$-\frac{1}{8}$	(0, −2)
12	$y = \frac{5}{4}x - \frac{1}{2}$	$\frac{5}{4}$	$(0, -\frac{1}{2})$
13	$y = \frac{1}{5}x + \frac{3}{2}$	$\frac{1}{5}$	$(0, \frac{3}{2})$
14	$y = x - 1$	1	(0, −1)
15	$y = \frac{7}{2}x + 7$	$\frac{7}{2}$	(0, 7)
16	$y = -6x + 2$	−6	(0, 2)

UNIT M8 Quadratic Functions and their Graphs

B **2** (a) $x \geq 1, x \in Q$ (b) $x < 2, x \in Q$ (c) $x < 4, x \in Q$ (d) $x \geq -2, x \in Q$
4 (a) $-3 \leq x \leq 1, x \in Q$ (b) $0 < x < 4, x \in Q$ (c) $-1 \leq 2, x \in Q$
(d) $-20 \leq x < 30, x \in Q$

C **1** {1, 3, 5, 7, 9} **2** $1 \leq f(x) \leq 9, x \in Q$ **3** $f(0) = 1$; $f(1.4) = 3.8$; $f(3.6) = 8.2$

D **1**

x	−3	−2	−1	0	1	2
$3x$	−9	−6	−3	0	3	6
+2	+2	+2	+2	+2	+2	+2
$y = 3x + 2$	−7	−4	−1	2	5	8

2

x	−2	−1	0	1
$-4x$	8	4	0	−4
−3	−3	−3	−3	−3
$y = -4x - 3$	5	1	−3	−7

F **1** and **2** (a) $y = x^2$ (b) $y = x^2 + 1$ (c) $y = x^2 + 2$ (d) $y = x^2 - 1$ (e) $y = x^2 - 2$

G **1** {(−3, 13), (−2, 8), (−1, 5), (0, 4), (1, 5), (2, 8), (3, 13)}; $x = 0$
2 {(−3, 12), (−2, 7), (−1, 4), (0, 3), (1, 4), (2, 7), (3, 12)}; $x = 0$
3 {(−3, 6), (−2, 1), (−1, −2), (0, −3), (1, −2), (2, 1), (3, 6)}; $x = 0$

H **1** {(−3, −9), (−2, −4), (−1, −1), (0, 0), (1, −1), (2, −4), (3, −9)} **2** and **3**
(a) $y = -x^2$ (b) $y = -x^2 + 1$ (c) $y = -x^2 + 2$ (d) $y = -x^2 - 1$ (e) $y = -x^2 - 2$
(f) $y - -x^2 - 2.5$ **4** (a) $y = x^2 - 1$ (b) $y = x^2$ (c) $y = x^2 + 1$
5 (a) $y = -x^2$ (b) $y = -x^2 + 2$ (c) $y = -x^2 + 1$ **6** to **10** $x = 0$

I **1** {(−3, −6), (−2, −1), (−1, 2), (0, 3), (1, 2), (2, −1), (3, −6)}; $x = 0$
2 {(−3, −11), (−2, −6), (−1, −3), (0, −2), (1, −3), (2, −6), (3, −11)}; $x = 0$
3 (a) axis of symmetry $x = 0$, (b) axis of symmetry $x = 0$.

J **1** Maximum (0, 3) **2** Minimum (0, 1) **3** Maximum (0, −1) **4** Minimum (0, −4)
5 Minimum (0, 0) **6** Maximum (0, 6)

K **1** {(−3, 18), (−2, 8), (−1, 2), (0, 0), (1, 2), (2, 8), (3, 9)}
2 {(−3, 27), (−2, 12), (−1, 3), (0, 0), (1, 3), (2, 12), (3, 27)}
3 {(−3, −18), (−2, −8), (−1, −2), (0, 0), (1, −2), (2, −8), (3, −18)}
4 {(−3, −27), (−2, −12), (−1, −3), (0, 0), (1, −3), (2, −12), (3, −27)}

L **1** $\{(-2, 6), (-1, 1), (0, -2), (1, -3), (2, -2), (3, 1), (4, 6)\}$; axis of symmetry: $x = 1$; minimum $(1, -3)$ **2** $\{(-1, 7), (0, 2), (1, -1), (2, -2), (3, -1), (4, 2), (5, 7)\}$; axis of symmetry: $x = 2$; minimum $(2, -2)$, **3** $\{(-3, 12), (-2, 5), (-1, 0), (0, -3), (1, -4), (2, -3), (3, 0), (4, 5), (5, 12)\}$; minimum $(1, -4)$; axis of symmetry: $x = 1$

M Progress check

O **1**, **2**, **4**, **5** are quadratic functions

P **1** (a) $x = 1$; $x = 5$ (b) $x = 0$; $x = 3$ (c) $x = -2$; $x = 2.5$ (d) $x = -1$; $x = 3$
2 (a) $x = -1$; $x = 4$ (b) $x = -2$; $x = -1$ (c) $x = 1$; $x = 4$

Q **1** (a) $x = 3.3$; $x = -0.3$ (b) $x = 1.3$; $x = -3.8$ **2** (a) $x = 4.3$; $x = 0.7$ (b) $x = -1.8$; $x = 2.8$

R **1** Area $= x(8 - x)$ (a) 14 m^2 (b) 1.4 m × 6.6 m (c) 16 m^2; a square **2** 50 m^2
3 (a) 20 m (b) 2 s (c) 2.8 s (approx.)

S Progress check

UNIT M9 Transformations

B **1** (a) $\begin{pmatrix}4\\1\end{pmatrix}$ (b) $\begin{pmatrix}4\\-3\end{pmatrix}$ (c) $\begin{pmatrix}3\\-5\end{pmatrix}$ (d) $\begin{pmatrix}0\\5\end{pmatrix}$ (e) $\begin{pmatrix}6\\0\end{pmatrix}$

G **1** (a) *HOG; HOF; EOD; FOE; DOE;* (b) *AE; BF; HD; AE*

J **1** *DEF; KLM; QRP; VUT* **2** 45° clockwise; 90° anticlockwise; 135° anticlockwise; 180°

Q **1** A' (4, 5); B' (3, 4); C' (2, 2); D' (5, −2); E' (2, −3); F' (3, 1)
2 (a) (5, 5) (b) (9, 1) (c) (100, 100) (d) (23.4) (e) (−3, 3) (f) (0, 12) (g) (5, 1) (h) (−1, −2) **3** (a) (5, 2); (6, 3); (7, 4); (8, 5) (b) (5, 4); (6, 6); (7, 8); (8, 10)

R **1**

(−1, −2)	(1, 2)	(2, 4)	(3, 6)
(1, −2)	(3, 2)	(4, 4)	(5, 6)

2 Graph passes through (0, 0) and (3, 3)

S **1** (a) $A' = G(3, -6)$; $B' = K(-2, -5)$; $C' = E(-3, -6)$; $D' = L(2, 1)$; $E' = C(-3, 6)$; $F' = N(4, 2)$ (b) $A' = C(-3, 6)$; $B' = H(2, 5)$ $C' = A(3, 6)$; $D' = M(-2, -1)$; $E' = G(3, -6)$; $F' = P(-4, -2)$ (c) (3, −8); (6, −2); (−3, −2); (49, 7); $(a, -b)$ (d) (−6, 2); (−21, 4); (15, 81); (−7, 7); $(-a, b)$
2 $A'(2, -1)$; $B'(5, 0)$; $C'(3, -3)$ **3** $PQRS: y = 2x + 1$; $P'Q'R'S': y = -2x + 1$

U **1** $A'(3, 3)$; $B'(-2, 4)$; $C'(5, 2)$; $D'(7, -2)$; $E'(-2, 93)$
2 P' (3, −7); Q' (2, −1); R' (0, 3); S' (0, −2); T' (87, −4)
3 (−3, 1); (−4, 3); (−5, 5); (−6, 7); (1, 55)

V **1** $A'(1, 4)$; $B'(-1, 2)$; $C'(-1, -4)$; $D'(2, 0)$; $E'(1, -3)$
2 (0, 0); (−2, 1); (−4, 2); (−6, 3); (−8, 4)
3 (1, 7) → (−7, 1); (−2, −6) → (6, −2); (25, 3) → (−3, 25); $(a, b) \rightarrow (-b, a)$
4 A' (2, 0); B' (6, 0); C' (4, −4) **5** $P'(-2, 4)$; $Q'(-2, 6)$; $R'(-6, 6)$; $S'(-6, 4)$
6 $A'(-2, 1)$; $B'(-2, 5)$; $C'(-4, 5)$; $D'(-4, 1)$

W **1** $A'(-2, -1)$; $B'(-4, -1)$; $C'(-4, -4)$; $D'(-3, -5)$; $E'(-2, -4)$
2 (3, 9) → (−3, −9); (−6, 2) → (6, −2); $(a, b) \rightarrow (-a, -b)$
3 $X'(-3, -3)$; $Y'(-5, -3)$; $Z'(-4, -6)$ **4** $C \rightarrow G$; $H \rightarrow D$; $AB \rightarrow EF$; $ABCDE \rightarrow EFGHA$ **5** $P'(-1, -1)$; $Q'(-4, -1)$; $R'(-5, -3)$ $S'(-2, -3)$

X **1** $A'(6, 2)$; $B'(2, 4)$ **2** $P'(3, 0)$; $Q'(-3, -2)$ **3** $A'(4, -1)$; $B'(2, -1)$; $C'(2, 0)$
4 $A'(6, -3)$ **5** $A'(-2, -2)$; $B'(-8, -2)$; $C'(-6, -4)$ **6** $P'(11, 5)$; $Q'(17, 2)$
7 $P'(2, 1)$ **8** $T'(-8, 0)$; $R'(4, -3)$; $S'(-2, -6)$ **9** $A'(-4, 4)$; $B'(-10, 7)$

Y Progress check

UNIT M10 Simultaneous Equations and Inequations

A **1** (0, 3); (7, 0) **2** (0, −2); (5, 0) **3** (0, −3); (−2, 0) **4** (0, 3); (9, 0) **5** (0, 4), (5, 0)
6 (0, −4); (6, 0) **7** (0, −5); (6, 0)

B **1** (a) Yes (b) No (c) No **2** (a) No (b) Yes (c) No **3** (a) No (b) Yes (c) No
4 (a) $x - 2y = 2$ (b) neither (c) $2x - y = 7$ (d) both (e) neither (f) $2x - y = 7$

C **1** $x = 2; y = 5$ **2** $x = 2; y = 1$ **3** $x = 2; y = -1$ **4** $x = 4; y = -3$
5 $x = 2; y = 3$ **6** $x = 6; y = -2$ **7** $x = 7; y = 2$ **8** $x = -4; y = 4$

D **1** $x = 7; y = 4$ **2** $x = 2; y = 5$ **3** $x = 5; y = 4$ **4** $x = -2; y = 3$

E **1** $x = 2; y = 3$ **2** $x = 1; y = -1$ **3** $x = 5; y = 1$ **4** $x = 3; y = -2$

F **2** (a) $x = 4; y = 2$ (b) $x = -3; y = 2$ (c) $x = -1; y = -2$ (d) $x = 3; y = 3$
(e) $x = 2; y = 1$ (f) $x = 3; y = -1$

G **1** $x = 1; y = 2$ **2** $x = 3; y = -1$ **3** $x = 2; y = 2$ **4** $x = 5; y = -2$
5 $x = 2; y = -1$ **6** $x = -1; y = -2$

H **1** $x = 3; y = -3$ **2** $x = 1; y = 3$ **3** $x = 2; y = -1$ **4** $x = 4; y = 3$
5 $x = 2; y = 1$ **6** $x = 5; y = 1$

I Progress check

K **2** (1, 4), (−2, −2), (2, 5) (1.5, 4.5) **3** (2.6), (1, −1), (4.9, 0.7), (1.0001, 4),
(3, 100), (4, −1000)

L **1** (−2, 6), value 18; (1, 5), value 23; (4, 2), value 20; (7, 5), value 41; (8, −1) value 20
(b) (4, 0), value 12; (8, −3), value 12; (−4, 6), value 12 (c) (−2, 3), value 6;
(−1, −3), value −15;
(2, 1), value 10; (4, −2), value 4 **2** (a) (0, 4); (4, 0) (b) (−1, 6), value 5; (4, 2), value 6
(5, 5), value 10; (7, −2), value 5; ABOVE the line $x + y > 4$ (c) (−3, 1), value −2;
(−1, −4), value −5; (1, 2), value 3; (3, −2), value 1; BELOW the line $x + y < 4$
3 (a) (0, −3); (4, 0) (b) (−3, −2), value −1; (−2, 2), value −14; (2, −1), value 10;
(3, 4), value −7; ABOVE the line $3x - 4y < 12$ (c) (−1, −6), value 21; (1, −3), value
15; (6, 1), value 14; (6, −5), value 38; BELOW the line $3x - 4y > 12$

O **1** Solution region (0, 3), (0, 2), (1, 2), (0, 1), (1, 1), (2, 1), (0, 0), (1, 0), (2, 0), (3, 0)
2 Solution region (0, 2), (1, 2), (2, 2), (0, 1), (1, 1), (2, 1), (3, 1), (0, 0), (1, 0), (2, 0), (3, 0)
3 Solution region (2, 4), (3, 4), (4, 4), (5, 4), (6, 4), (4, 3), (5, 3), (6, 3), (6, 2)
4 Solution region (3, 1), (2, 0), (3, 0), (4, 0), **5** Solution region (3, 1), (4, 0), (5, 0), (6, 0)
6 Solution region (0, 0), (1, 1), (2, 1), (1, 2), (2, 2)

P Progress check

UNIT M11 Circles

A **1** (a) 74° (b) 32° (c) 148° **2** (a) 62°, 56°, 124° (b) 80°, 50°, 50° (c) 40°, 100°, 80°
(d) 45°, 90°, 90°

B **1** (a) $x = 50, y = 60$ (b) 110° **2** (a) $x = 44, y = 100$ (b) 144° **3** 162 **4** 62 **5** 90 **6** 180 **7** 35 **8** 89 **9** 61 **10** 90 **11** 200 **12** 280 **13** 95 **14** 130

C **1** 50 **2** 34 **3** 60 **4** 10 **5** 50 **6** 66 **7** 90 **8** 56 **9** 42

D **1** $x = 32, y = 32$ **2** $p = 50, q = 40$ **3** (a) $x = 52, y = 35, z = 20$ **3** (b) 52° (c) 35° **4** (a) $a = 51, b = 32, c = 97, d = 97$ (b) 51° **5** $x = 60, y = 20, z = 40$ **6** $x = 22, y = 75, z = 48$

E **1** *DA* **2** (a) $\hat{Q} = 90°$ (b) $\hat{P} = 20°$ **3** (a) rectangle (b) $p = 40, q = 40, r = 50, s = 80$ **4** $a = 60, b = 30$ **5** $S\hat{P}R = 60°$, so $P\hat{S}R = 90°$, so *PR* is a diameter

F **1** (a) 140 (b) 220 (c) 110 **2** (a) 250 (b) 110 (c) 55 **3** (a) 200 (b) 160 (c) 80 **4** (a) 120 (b) 240 (c) 120 **5** $p = 50, q = 135$ **6** $p = 90, q = 122$ **7** $p = 80, q = 112$ **8** $p = 70, q = 88$

G **1** $d = \sqrt{20} \simeq 4.47$ cm **2** radius $= \sqrt{13} \simeq 3.61$ cm **3** chord $= 2 \times 6 = 12$ cm **4** chord = 6 cm **5** 24 cm

I **1** 8.94 cm **2** 4.12 cm **3** 8 cm

L **1** $x = 55, y = 35$ **2** $x = 38, y = 52$ **3** $x = 17, y = 73$ **4** $x = 9, y = 81$ **5** $x = 60, y = 30, z = 30$ **6** $x = 45, y = 45, z = 45$ **7** $x = 20, y = 70, z = 70$ **8** $x = 51, y = 39, z = 39$ **9** (a) 38° (b) 25° (c) 128° **10** (a) 45° (b) 45° **11** (a) 40° (b) 49° (c) 94° (d) 71°

M **1** (a) $a = 4, b = 30, c = 90, d = 60$ (b) $a = 25, b = 90, c = 65, d = 90$ (c) $a = 90, b = 90, c = 120, d = 60$ (d) $a = 70, b = 70, c = 20, d = 140$ (e) $a = 5, b = 5, c = 4, d = 3$
2 (a) $AP = BP = 11.3$ cm (b) $AP = BP = 4.58$ cm (c) $AP = BP = 2.6$ cm
3 (a) 12.2 cm (b) 14.1 (c) 10.8 cm **4** 12.6 cm

O **1** (a) 18.8 cm (b) 28.3 cm (c) 37.7 cm (d) 47.1 cm (e) 84.8 cm **2** (a) 78.5 cm² (b) 62.8 cm² (c) 188.4 cm² (d) 282.6 cm²

P **1** (a) $x^2 + y^2 = 9$ (b) $x^2 + y^2 = 49$ (c) $x^2 + y^2 = 13$ **2** (a) 3 (b) 10 (c) 8 **3** $(0, -5), (3, 4), (3, -4), (\sqrt{8}, -\sqrt{17}), (2\sqrt{3}, \sqrt{13})$ lie on the circle **4** (a) on (b) outside (c) inside (d) outside **5** (a) $x^2 + y^2 = 34$ (b) $x^2 + y^2 = 20$ (c) $x^2 + y^2 = 74$

UNIT M12 The Cosine and Tangent Functions

A **1** (a) 50° (b) 80° (c) 35° (d) 70° (e) 80° (f) 20° (g) 60°
2 (a) 0.985 (b) −0.866 (c) 0.174 (d) −0.669 (e) 0.940 (f) 0.0 (g) 0.999 (h) −1.0 (i) 0.0 (j) −0.999 (k) 1.0 (l) −0.342. **3** (a) $a = 128°$; $b = 308°$ (b) $a = 70°$; $b = 250°$ **4** (a) 60 and 120 (b) 65 and 115 (c) 20 and 160 (d) 225 and 315 (e) 226 and 314 (f) 73 and 107 (g) 215 and 325 (h) 15 and 165 (i) 231 and 309

B **1** −cos 55° = −0.574 **2** −cos 20° = −0.940 **3** −cos 71° = −0.326 **4** −cos 39° = −0.777 **5** −cos 8° = −0.990 **6** −cos 70° = −0.342 **7** −cos 62° = −0.469 **8** −cos 18° = −0.951 **9** cos 60° = 0.5 **10** cos 48° = 0.669 **11** cos 12° = 0.978 **12** −cos 49° = −0.656 **13** −cos 17° = −0.956 **14** cos 66° = 0.407.

C **1** −cos 55° = −0.574 **2** −cos 10° = −0.985 **3** cos 10° = 0.985 **4** −cos 50° = −0.643 **5** −cos 25° = −0.906 **6** cos 55° = 0.574 **7** −cos 21° = −0.934 **8** −cos 63° = − 0.454 **9** cos 18° = 0.951.

D **1** 115 and 245 **2** 20 and 340 **3** 150 and 210 **4** 39 and 321
5 58 and 302 **6** 112 and 248 **7** 55 and 305 **8** 15 and 345
9 146 and 214 **10** 50.5 and 309.5.

E **1** $-\cos 40° = -0.766$ **2** $\cos 70° = 0.342$ **3** $\cos 40° = 0.766$
4 $\cos 30° = 0.866$ **5** $-\cos 75° = -0.259$ **6** 1.00 **7** −1.00

F **1** $-\tan 60° = -1.732$ **2** $-\tan 70° = -2.747$ **3** $-\tan 46° = -1.036$
4 $\tan 21° = 0.384$ **5** $-\tan 70° = -2.747$ **6** $-\tan 10° = -0.176$
7 $-\tan 6° = -0.105$ **8** $\tan 3.5° = 0.061$ **9** $-\tan 32.6° = -0.640$.

G **1** 145 and 325 **2** 130 and 310 **3** 76 and 256 **4** 11 and 191
5 163.5 and 343.5 **6** 124.6 and 304.6 **7** 78.7 and 258.7.

H **1** $\tan 50° = 1.192$ **2** $-\tan 40° = -0.839$ **3** $\tan 24° = 0.445$
4 $-\tan 48° = -1.111$ **5** $-\tan 55° = -1.428$ **6** $\tan 80° = 5.671$
7 $\tan 60° = 1.732$ **8** $-\tan 40° = -0.839$ **9** $-\tan 20° = -0.364$.

I **1** (a) 0·423 (b) −0.574 (c) −0.344 (d) 0·810 (e) 0·545 (f) 1.00 (g) 0.766.
2 (a) 15 and 165 (b) 160 and 200 (c) 27 and 207

J Progress check

L **1**

x	30	40	50	60	70	80	90
$\sin x°$	0.5	0.64	0.77	0.87	0.94	0.98	1.0
$\cos 2x°$	0.5	0.17	−0.17	−0.5	−0.77	−0.94	−1.0
$\sin x° + \cos 2x°$	1.0	0.81	0.6	0.37	0.17	0.04	0.0

(a) $x = 30$ (b) (i) Maximum value about 1.12 (ii) $x = 50$
2 (a), (b) about 101 and 196 (c) about 122 and 180 (d) about 90 and 167
3 $x \simeq 53$ **4** (a) $x \simeq 26$ (b) $x \simeq 33$ (c) $x \simeq 25$ **5** $x = 60°$ **6** $x \simeq 24.6$

M Progress check

ANSWERS TO PROGRESS CHECKS

Teachers may want to cut these pages from the book.

Unit M1

H **1** Fig. 2 **2** $k = 5$; length = 29.5 cm; breadth = 18.0 cm **3** Length = 9.6 cm; width = 2.8 cm; height = 2.4 cm **5** (a) Reduction; $k = 0.5$; $PQ = 8$; $RP = 3.5$ (b) Enlargement; $k = 2$; $XY = 10$; $ZX = 8$

M **1** $k = 0.8$ **2** $PQ = 4.5$ cm **3** $OB = 7.2$ cm; $OD = 10$ cm **4** 1.28 m^2 **5** $k = 2$; 4 litres **6** 2.4 m

Unit M2

Q **1** $\underline{v} = \begin{pmatrix} 7 \\ 2 \end{pmatrix}$; $\underline{u} = \begin{pmatrix} -4 \\ 2 \end{pmatrix}$; $\underline{w} = \begin{pmatrix} 2 \\ -4 \end{pmatrix}$; $\underline{s} = \begin{pmatrix} 3 \\ 0 \end{pmatrix}$; $\underline{t} = \begin{pmatrix} -3 \\ -2 \end{pmatrix}$

Length of $\underline{a}$ is 5.83 units; $\underline{b}$ is 3.61 units; $\underline{c}$ is 4 units; $\underline{d}$ is 3 units; $\underline{e}$ is 3.61 units.

4 (a) $\begin{pmatrix} 6 \\ 6 \end{pmatrix}$ (b) $\begin{pmatrix} 3 \\ 5 \end{pmatrix}$ (c) $\begin{pmatrix} 6 \\ 2 \end{pmatrix}$ (d) $\begin{pmatrix} 5 \\ 0 \end{pmatrix}$ **5** $-\underline{x} = \begin{pmatrix} -2 \\ -7 \end{pmatrix}$; $-\underline{y} = \begin{pmatrix} -3 \\ 1 \end{pmatrix}$; $-\underline{v} = \begin{pmatrix} 4 \\ 3 \end{pmatrix}$

6 $2\underline{u} = \begin{pmatrix} 6 \\ 8 \end{pmatrix}$; $-3\underline{a} = \begin{pmatrix} -6 \\ -12 \end{pmatrix}$

Z **1** (a) $\overrightarrow{QS} = \underline{a} + \underline{d}$; $\overrightarrow{XD} = \frac{1}{2}\underline{a} + \frac{1}{2}\underline{d}$ (b) $\overrightarrow{QS} = \underline{b} + \underline{c}$; $\overrightarrow{YZ} = \frac{1}{2}\underline{b} + \frac{1}{2}\underline{c}$ (c) XW is equal and parallel to YZ. **2** (a) $\overrightarrow{DQ} = \frac{1}{2}\underline{u}$ (b) $\overrightarrow{AQ} = \underline{v} + \frac{1}{2}\underline{u}$; $\frac{2}{3}\overrightarrow{AQ} = \frac{2}{3}\underline{v}$; $\overrightarrow{AP} = \frac{1}{3}\underline{u} + \frac{2}{3}\underline{v}$ (d) A, P, and Q lie on a straight line.

Unit M3

I **1** (a) 1 (b) 0 (c) 2 (d) 4 **2** (a) 18 (b) -8 (c) 4 (d) -28 **3** (a) $20 - a$ (b) $p + q$ (c) $\frac{8}{t}$ (d) rs **4** (a) 4 (b) 2.5 **5** (a) $3x - 12$ (b) $-2y + 6$ (c) $-15 + 6p$ **6** (a) 5 (b) 3 **7** (a) $(d - c)/c$ (b) $(q + cp)/c$

R **1** (a) $x \geq 2$ (b) $x \geq -2$ (c) $x > -5$ **2** (a) $y \leq -8$ (b) $x > 3$ (c) $x > -8.4$ (d) $x < 2$ **3** (a) $x = 13$ (b) $x < \frac{11}{14}$ **4** $3x - 2(x + 5) = 8$; 18, 23 **5** A pencil costs less than 9p.

6 (a) $R = \dfrac{100I}{PT}$ (b) $r = \sqrt{\dfrac{A}{4\pi}}$ (c) (i) $c = \dfrac{b^2 - D^2}{4a}$ (ii) $b = \sqrt{D^2 + 4ac}$

Unit M4

R **1** (a) 0.602 (b) 0.812 (c) 0.423 (d) 0.692 (e) 0.625 (f) 0.719 (g) 1.376 (h) 2.032 **2** (a) 51.0 (b) 62.5 or 62.6 (c) 24.0 (d) 65.5 (e) 59.5 (f) 63.6 (g) 59.0 (h) 67.8 **3** 21.8 **4** 48.2 **5** 9.06 **6** 32.0 **7** 15.3 **8** 9.19

W **1** 10.0 m **2**, 8.77 m **3** 6.53 m **4** 7.16 m **5** 7.71 m **6** 10.8 m **7** 18.7 cm **8** 20.4 cm **9** 2.80 m **10** 739 m **11** 4.79 m **12** 8.09 m **13** 10.2 m **14** KL = 13.8 m, alt = 5.79 m, area = 39.9 m^2 **15** 16.3 km **166** 15.7 km.

Unit M5

F **1** (a) $\{(0, 0), (2, 4), (4, 8), (6, 12)\}$ (b) $\{(0, 3), (1, 6), (2, 9), (3, 12)\}$
2 $f(1) = 2; f(3) = 3; f(5) = 4; f(7) = 5$ **3** $f(-2) = 2; f(-1) = 3; f(0) = 4;$ $f(1) = 5; f(2) = 6$ **4** $f(2) = 7; f(4) = 15; f(6) = 23$ **5** $f(-2) = -3;$ $f(-1) = -1; f(0) = 1; f(1) = 3; f(2) = 5; \{(-2, -3), (-1, -1), (0, 1), (1, 3), (2, 5)\}$
6 (a) $f(x) = 3x + 5$; domain: $\{-2, -1, 0, 1\}$; range: $\{-1, 2, 5, 8\}$ (b) $f(x) = x - 3$; domain: $\{-1, 0, 1, 2\}$; range: $\{-4, -3, -2, -1\}$

N **1** (a) $-1 < x < 4$ (b) $-6 \leq x \leq -1$ (c) $12 < x \leq 16$ **2** $p = 3$ **3** $a = 7$
4 (a) $f(-2) = -8; f(2) = 0$ (b) $-8 \leq f(x) \leq 0$ **5** $k = 3; h(2) = 1; h(-1) = -8$

Unit M6

I **1** (a) 0500 h; 1700 h (b) 1100 h; 2300 h (c) 3.3 m (d) 3.3 m (e) about 0300 h; about 0700 h; 1500 h; 1900 h (f) 0200 h; 0800 h; 1400 h; 2000 h (g) 12 h
2 (a) 140° (b) 220° (c) 320° (d) 25° (e) 205° (f) 335° **3** (a) sin 145° = sin 35° = 0.574 (b) sin 214° = −sin 34° = −0.559 (c) sin 105° = sin 75° = 0.966
(d) sin 317° = −sin 43° = −0.682

N **1**

sin pos	sin pos
sin neg	sin neg

2 (a) 0.208 (b) −0.719 (c) 0.0 (d) 0.985 (e) −0.766 (f) 1.0 (g) 0.0 **3** (a) 35.7 and 144.3 (b) 239 and 301 (c) 222 and 318 (d) 69.9 and 110.1 **4** (a) 0.407 (b) −0.407 (c) 0.829 (d) −0.866 **5** (a) −0.643 (b) −0.766 (c) 0.342 (d) 0.342 **6** (a) 7 and −7 (b) $\frac{3}{4}$ and $-\frac{3}{4}$ **7**(a) 120° (b) 240°

Unit M7

M **1** (a) $\frac{5}{2}$ (b) -6 (c) $\frac{3}{2}$ (d) -1 (e) $-\frac{1}{2}$ (f) $\frac{2}{3}$
4 (a) 2; (0, 3) (b) $\frac{1}{5}$; (0, 0) (c) $-\frac{1}{2}$; (0, 1) (d) 1; (0, −5)
5 (a) $y = 2x$ (b) $y = -\frac{3}{2}x$ (c) $y = \frac{1}{2}x + 2$ (d) $y = -\frac{1}{4}x + 3$ (e) $y = x - 4$
6 (a) line (a) represents fastest speed; line (c) represents slowest speed.
(b) line (a) represents 160 km per h; line (b) represents 68 km per h; line (c) represents 32 km per h
(c) (i) line (b) (ii) line (a) (iii) line (c)
7 (a) 30 minutes (b) 4 km per h (c) 12 km per h (d) 12.30.

U **1** (a) $\frac{3}{4}$ (b) 5 (c) $-\frac{7}{8}$
2 (i) (d) (ii) (g) (iii) (e) (iv) (b) (v) (f) (vi) (h) (vii) (a)
gradient of line (c) is not defined.
3 (a) 4.47 (b) 12.37 (c) 6.40
4 (a) (i) $\frac{4}{3}$ (ii) (0, −2) (b) (i) $-\frac{5}{2}$ (ii) (0, 2) (c) (i) $\frac{1}{4}$ (ii) (0, 3)

Unit M8

M **2** (a) $-1 \leq x \leq 2, x \in Q$ (b) $0 \leq x < 4, x \in Q$ **3** (−4, 12), (−3, 5), (−2, 0), (−1, −3), (0, −4), (1, −3), (2, 0), (3, 5), (4, 12); $x = 0$ **4** (i) Minimum (2, −1); $x = 2$ (ii) Minimum (−3, −4); $x = -3$ (iii) Maximum (3, 0); $x = 3$ (iv) Maximum (2, 1); $x=2$ **5** Minimum (1, 4); $x=2$

S **1** (a) (i) $x = 2$; Minimum (2, −1) (b) $x = -1$; Maximum(−1, 4) (b) (i) $x = 1$; $x = 3$ (ii) $x = -3$; $x = 1$